Thousand Year Canon of Solar Eclipses

1501 to 2500

Fred Espenak

Edition 1.1
January 2015

Thousand Year Canon of Solar Eclipses 1501 to 2500

Astropixels Publishing
P.O. Box 16197
Portal, AZ 85632

www.astropixels.com/pubs

Printed in the United States of America

ISBN 978-1-941983-00-3

Astropixels Publication: AP001

First Edition (Version 1.1)

Front Cover Photo: The Sun's corona is revealed during the total solar eclipse of 2006 March 29 from Jalu, LIBYA. This composite image was produced from 22 separate exposures, which were combined in Adobe Photoshop in order to approximate the details and appearance of the corona visible to the naked eye. Photo copyright ©2006 by Fred Espenak. More images of this eclipse can be seen at: *www.mreclipse.com/main/photoindex.html#solar*

Back Cover Photo: Copyright ©2014 by Babak Tafreshi

Preface

With the publication of the *Five Millennium Canon of Solar Eclipses* (Espenak & Meeus, 2006) and its companion volume the *Five Millennium Catalog of Solar Eclipses* (Espenak & Meeus, 2009c), there was no plan to produce future canons. But in the years that followed, it became evident that the 1000–year period encompassing the present era of these two publications was being used far more often than the rest. For this reason, it would be convenient to have a subset of the *Canon* and *Catalog* in a single smaller volume.

As the design of the *Thousand Year Canon of Solar Eclipses* took shape, new features were developed to distinguish it from the *Five Millennium Canon*. Most importantly, the maps would be ~60% larger with 12 per page instead of 20. This increase in map size makes it easier to discern regions of eclipse visibility and, in addition, more *curves of constant eclipse magnitude* (25%, 50%, and 75%, instead of only 50%) can be included. Larger maps also allow the addition of more parameters including ΔT (Delta T) and the lunar node of the eclipse. The narrative and explanatory sections of the *Thousand Year Canon* are newly written and include detailed eclipse statistics for the 1000-year period containing 2,389 solar eclipses. In addition to the *standard edition* of the *Canon* (published in blank and white), there is a *color edition* that makes the 200 pages of eclipse maps easier to interpret since different parts of each eclipse path are color coded.

The *Thousand Year Canon of Solar Eclipses* uses the Jet Propulsion Lab's DE406 — the same ephemeris used in their online HORIZONS service for dates thousands of years in the past or future. The *Five Millennium* publications are based on the older VSOP87 and ELP-2000/82 ephemerides for the Sun and Moon. There is excellent agreement in the eclipse predictions between these publications in spite of using widely different methods of calculating the positions of the Sun and the Moon. In this respect, the new *Canon* serves as a robust consistency check with the earlier *Five Millennium* publications over the period 1501 through 2500.

To compliment the new canon of solar eclipses, the *Thousand Year Canon of Lunar Eclipses 1501 to 2500* (Espenak, 2014) is being published in parallel. It covers the same period and includes a catalog and larger maps than those in the *Five Millennium Canon of Lunar Eclipses* (Espenak & Meeus, 2009a).

The figures, maps and catalogs in the two *Thousand Year Canons* are the basis of a new website on solar and lunar eclipse predictions: *www.EclipseWise.com*. A plain text file containing the entire solar eclipse catalog appearing in *Appendix A* can be downloaded from this website at: *www.EclipseWise.com/solar/SEpubs/TYCSEcatalog.txt*.

The NASA *Five Millennium* publications had a single printing with a limited distribution. In contrast, the two *Thousand Year Canons* are being published via print-on-demand so they will be available to a wider audience for many years to come.

The lessons learned from print-on-demand publishing will assist in developing new and expanded replacements for the *Fifty Year Canon of Solar Eclipses* (Espenak, 1987) and *Fifty Year Canon of Lunar Eclipses* (Espenak, 1989), as well as specialized publications on individual eclipses similar to the NASA eclipse bulletin series.

— *Fred Espenak*
July 2014

Acknowledgments

I am profoundly grateful to my wife Patricia Totten Espenak, for tirelessly editing the manuscript at multiple stages of its development. Her insightful comments and suggestions have been a major asset in creating the final version of the *Canon*. Any remaining typographical, grammatical, or technical errors are solely my responsibility. I also want to thank Michael Zeiler and Xavier Jubier for productive discussions about the jungle of self publishing, print-on-demand, ISBN numbers, etc.. Finally, I want to thank my mentor, colleague, co-author and friend Jean Meeus for a lifetime of inspiration, technical expertise and fascination in the calculation of solar system phenomena. His 1966 *Canon of Solar Eclipses* started me down the road of eclipse predictions shortly after viewing my first total solar eclipse in 1970.

Dedication

To Patricia Totten Espenak, my wife and best friend. We first met in the shadow of the Moon nearly twenty years ago and half a world away, and we've been chasing eclipses together ever since.

To Valerie Anne and Maggie Marie Delos-Reyes, my granddaughters who might see their very first total solar eclipse from their back yard in 2017.

And in loving memory of my parents Fred and Asie Espenak who always encouraged me to follow my own path, and of my sister Nancy J. Davies. I miss you all.

Table of Contents

Photo 1–1 shows various phases of the total solar eclipse of 1999 Aug 11. ©1999 F. Espenak

Section 1: Solar Eclipse Fundamentals

1.1 Introduction

The Moon orbits Earth once every 29.5306 days with respect to the Sun. Over the course of its orbit, the Moon's changing position relative to the Sun results in its familiar phases: New Moon > New Crescent > First Quarter > Waxing Gibbous > Full Moon > Waning Gibbous > Last Quarter > Old Crescent > New Moon. The New Moon phase is not visible because the illuminated side of the Moon points away from Earth. The other phases are easily seen as the Moon cycles through them month after month.

The Moon's orbit is tilted about 5.1° to Earth's orbit around the Sun. The points where the two orbits appear to cross are called the nodes. When the New Moon occurs near one of these nodes, the Moon's shadow can sometimes fall on some portion of Earth and a solar eclipse takes place.

The Moon's shadow is composed of three cone-shaped components. The outer or penumbral shadow is a zone where the Sun's rays are partially blocked. Nested within the penumbra is the umbral shadow — a region where direct rays from the Sun are completely blocked. The conical umbra tapers to a point beyond which extends an expanding cone called the antumbra. From within this third shadow, the Moon appears smaller than the Sun and is seen in silhouette against the solar disk.

1.2 Classification of Solar Eclipses

There are four basic types of solar eclipses:

1. **Partial Solar Eclipse** — The Moon's penumbral shadow traverses Earth. The Moon's umbral and antumbral shadows completely miss Earth. A portion of the Sun's disk is obscured from within the penumbra.
2. **Annular Solar Eclipse** — The Moon's penumbral and antumbral shadows traverse Earth. The Moon's umbral shadow completely misses Earth. The Moon's disk appears smaller than the Sun so a bright ring surrounds the Moon when viewed from within the antumbral shadow. A partial eclipse is seen within the penumbral shadow (Figure 1–1).
3. **Total Solar Eclipse** — The Moon's penumbral and umbral shadows traverse Earth. The Moon's antumbral shadow extends beyond Earth's surface. The Moon's disk appears larger than the Sun and completely covers the solar disk when viewed from within the umbral shadow. A partial eclipse is seen within the penumbral shadow (Figure 1–2).

4. **Hybrid Solar Eclipse** — The Moon's penumbral, umbral and antumbral shadows all traverse different parts of Earth. The curvature of Earth's surface brings some regions into the umbra and others into the antumbra. The eclipse appears total within the umbra and annular within the antumbra. A partial eclipse is seen within the penumbral shadow. Hybrid eclipses are also known as annular-total eclipses.

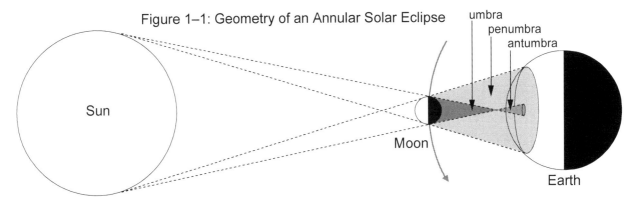

Figure 1–1: Geometry of an Annular Solar Eclipse

Figure 1–1 illustrates the geometry of an annular solar eclipse. A partial eclipse is visible from within the large penumbral shadow, while the annular eclipse is confined to the much smaller antumbral shadow.

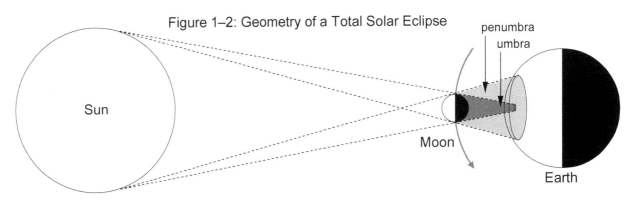

Figure 1–2: Geometry of a Total Solar Eclipse

Figure 1–2 illustrates the geometry of a total solar eclipse. A partial eclipse is visible from within the large penumbral shadow, while the total eclipse is only seen from the much smaller umbral shadow.

Annular, total and hybrid eclipses are sometimes referred to as *central* eclipses[1]. However, on rare occasions it is possible to have an annular or total eclipse that is non-central (Sect. 3.1).

1.3 Visual Appearance of Partial Solar Eclipses

When the Moon's penumbral shadow strikes Earth, a partial eclipse of the Sun is visible from that region. The Moon's apparent motion with respect to the Sun is relatively slow — the partial phases can last up to three hours or more. During this time, the Moon's dark limb slowly creeps across the Sun's disk.

---

[1] A central eclipse is one in which the central axis of the Moon's umbral/antumbral shadow intersects with Earth's surface.

Partial eclipses are dangerous to look at with the unprotected eye because the Sun is still extremely bright. Special techniques are needed to safely view the eclipse (Sect. 1.6). Even when a partial eclipse reaches its maximum phase, the sky and landscape remain bright. To the uninformed bystander, no sign of the eclipse is apparent. But careful inspection of dappled sunlight beneath a leafy tree will reveal multiple images of the eclipse. This effect occurs because gaps between the leaves act like the apertures of pinhole cameras and project images of the eclipse onto the ground below. If the eclipse occurs on a mostly cloudy day, brief views of the partial phases may be possible as the Sun passes though the more translucent clouds.

The Moon's penumbral shadow is 6700 to 7300 kilometers in diameter and can cover a significant fraction of the daytime hemisphere of Earth. Consequently, partial eclipses may be visible from large geographic areas as the penumbra sweeps across Earth's surface.

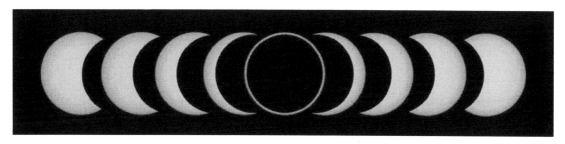

Photo 1–2 shows various phases of the Annular solar eclipse of 2005 Oct 03. ©2005 F. Espenak

1.4 Visual Appearance of Annular Solar Eclipses

During an annular eclipse, the Moon's penumbral and antumbral shadows sweep across Earth. While the penumbra is quite large, the antumbra is much smaller and has a maximum diameter of 374 kilometers. Because of this, the antumbra covers a much smaller fraction of Earth's surface.

The Moon's orbital motion typically carries the penumbral and antumbral shadows in a west to east direction. A partial eclipse is visible within the penumbral shadow, but only observers located in the much narrower track of the antumbra will see an annular eclipse. For this reason, the antumbra's trajectory across Earth is called the path of annularity.

All annular eclipses begin with a series of partial phases lasting about an hour. At the peak of the eclipse, the Moon's disk can be seen in complete silhouette against the Sun. The remaining solar photosphere appears as an intense ring of light surrounding the Moon. The annular phase lasts a maximum of 12 ½ minutes, but it is more typically 3 to 6 minutes in length. After annularity, another series of partial phases occurs as the Moon gradually uncovers the Sun.

Special precautions must be used to watch the eclipse (Sect. 1.6). Even during the annular phase, the Sun is dangerously bright and cannot be viewed without a solar filter. In this regard, annular eclipses are similar to partial eclipses. The landscape and sky remain bright throughout the eclipse, giving little indication of the celestial event in progress.

Figure 1–3: Path of Totality

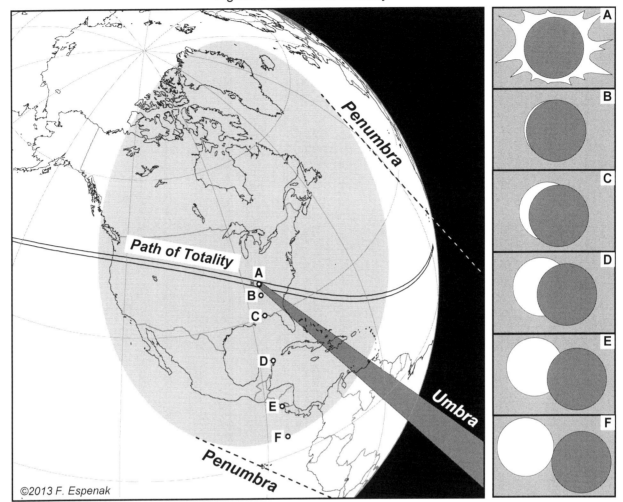

Figure 1–3 illustrates the path of totality for the total solar eclipse of 2017 Aug 21. The appearance of maximum eclipse from six different geographic locations on the map (labeled A through F) is shown in the side bar. The total eclipse is visible from position A because it lies in the path of totality.

1.5 Visual Appearance of Total Solar Eclipse

During a total eclipse, the Moon's penumbral and umbral shadows fall upon Earth. The umbra is much smaller than the penumbra and has a maximum diameter of 273 kilometers. The narrow track traced out by the umbra as it sweeps west to east across Earth's surface is called the path of totality. Anyone standing within this zone will see the Sun completely obscured by the Moon. The total phase can last up to 7 ½ minutes, but is more typically 2 to 3 minutes in length.

Total eclipses all begin and end with a series of partial phases lasting about an hour. But this is where the resemblance between partial and annular eclipses ends — the total phase is the most spectacular astronomical event visible to the naked eye. At this time, the Sun's outer atmosphere — the solar corona — appears as a gossamer halo surrounding the Moon, and bright stars and planets are visible.

The eclipse begins to take on a unique character about five minutes before the total phase commences. Sunlight takes on a foreboding quality and casts abnormally sharp shadows. The approaching lunar umbra darkens the western sky and the air temperature is noticeably cooler. A minute before totality, ghostly shadow bands[2] ripple across the ground. The ambient light grows feeble even though the crescent Sun is still too bright to see. In the final seconds, the Sun's corona emerges from the glare as the solar crescent shrinks to a single brilliant jewel. This celestial diamond ring[3] lingers for a moment before the last bead of sunlight is extinguished.

The Sun's glorious corona is now displayed to full advantage in the darkened sky of totality. The simple act of standing within the Moon's umbral shadow affords the rare and unprecedented opportunity to gaze directly at the glowing million-degree plasma surrounding our star. Twisted, tortured, and constrained by the Sun's enormous magnetic fields, the solar corona is revealed to the naked eye only during the brief seconds when the Moon completely blocks the brilliant disk of the Sun. An eerie twilight bathes the landscape and the colors of dusk surround the distant horizon.

Photo 1–3 The solar corona revealed during the total eclipse of 2006 Mar 29. ©2006 F. Espenak

Minutes race by like seconds. Suddenly, a sparkling bead of sunlight reappears along one edge of the Moon and quickly grows to blindingly bright proportions. Daylight returns as the corona fades and the total phase ends. Although another hour of partial phases remains before the eclipse ends, it is anticlimactic after the spectacle of totality.

---

[2] Shadow bands are caused by the thin slit-like solar crescent illuminating Earth's atmosphere moments before and after a total solar eclipse. They appear as thin parallel undulating lines of alternating light and dark that race across the ground. This motion is caused by atmospheric winds.
[3] This phenomenon is commonly known as the *diamond ring effect*.

While filters are required for viewing the partial phases, they must be removed for totality. The total phase is the only time it is completely safe to look directly at the Sun without protection. In fact, the total phase is not even visible through solar filters because the Sun's corona is a million times fainter than the photosphere[4].

1.6 Safely Observing Solar Eclipses

Partial eclipses, annular eclipses, and the partial phases of total eclipses are never safe to watch without special precautions. Even when 99% of the Sun's surface is obscured during the partial phases, the remaining photospheric crescent is intensely bright and cannot be viewed safely without eye protection (Chou, 1981; Marsh, 1982). Do not attempt to observe the partial or annular phases of any solar eclipse with the naked eye. Failure to use appropriate filtration may result in permanent eye damage or blindness. The only time it is safe to view the Sun directly with the naked eye is during the brief period of the total eclipse phase when the Sun's disk is completely covered by the Moon.

The same equipment, techniques and precautions used to observe the Sun outside of eclipse can be used for viewing partial phases and annular eclipses (Littmann, Espenak & Willcox, 2008, Reynolds & Sweetsir, 1995; Pasachoff & Covington, 1993). The safest and most inexpensive of these methods is by projection — a pinhole or small opening is used to project the Sun's image onto a screen placed two or more feet beyond the opening. Projected images of the Sun can even be seen on the ground by creating small openings between interlaced fingers, or in the dappled sunlight beneath a leafy tree. Binoculars can also be used to project a magnified image of the Sun on a white card, but avoid the temptation to use these instruments for direct viewing.

Observing the Sun directly is possible only when using filters specifically designed for this purpose. Such filters usually have a thin layer of aluminum, chromium or silver deposited on their surfaces that attenuates both visible and infrared energy. One of the most widely available filters for safe solar viewing is a number 14 welder's glass, available through welding supply outlets. More recently, black polymer has become a popular, inexpensive alternative. This material can be cut with scissors and adapted to any kind of viewing device. No filter is safe to use with an optical device (i.e., telescope, binoculars, etc.) unless it has been specifically designed for that purpose. Sources for filters can be found with a web search for *solar eclipse filters*.

UNSAFE filters include color film, some non-silver black and white film, smoked glass, photographic neutral density filters and polarizing filters. Solar filters designed to thread into telescope eyepieces are also dangerous. They should not be used for viewing the Sun since they often crack from overheating. Do not experiment with other filters unless certain they are safe. Damage to the eyes comes predominantly from invisible infrared wavelengths. The fact that the Sun appears dark in a filter or that there is no discomfort does not guarantee the filters are safe. Avoid all unnecessary risks. Local planetariums and amateur astronomy clubs are good sources for additional information. Remember, only the total phase of an eclipse can be safely viewed without a filter.

---

[4] The photosphere is the visible surface of the Sun's disk.

1.7 Central Line and Duration of Totality

The axis of the Moon's shadow determines the central line of the path of totality (and annularity). For the purposes of this discussion, it is assumed that the central line lies in the middle of the eclipse path.[5]

The duration of totality is longest on the central line, so great effort is made to get as close as possible to it. However, the duration actually drops off quite slowly with distance from the central line. For example, a location 20% from the center to the edge of the path still has a totality lasting 95% of the central line duration. Even if one travels half way to the path limit, the duration is still 71% of the central line value.

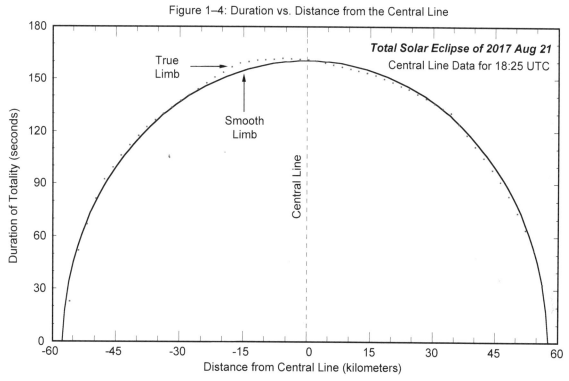

Just how gradually this occurs is depicted in figure 1–4. The solid curve plots the duration of totality as a function of distance from the central line. At a distance 67% of the way to the path limit, the duration drops to 50% of its central value. It is only in the final 25% of the way to the limit where the duration takes a precipitous drop. But even at a distance of 80%, the duration is still 31% of the central line value.

Although figure 1-4 plots data for the 2017 total solar eclipse, the same relationship holds for all total eclipse paths. The solid curve is calculated assuming a smooth lunar limb. In reality, the Moon's limb profile has mountains that extend the duration and valleys that shorten it. These topographic features typically change the duration by a second or two for most of the path — their effects become significantly larger near the umbral path limits. The dotted line in figure 1-4 has been calculated using the Moon's true profile.

---

[5] The position of the central line is actually offset from the center. The difference is greatest in cases where the Sun's altitude is low. Curvature of Earth's surface is responsible for this shift.

The following expression is useful for calculating the duration of totality for any location at a perpendicular distance of δ kilometers from the central line. It assumes a smooth profile for the Moon's limb.

$$d = D \times [\, 1 - (\, \delta/Z\,)^2\,]^{\frac{1}{2}} \text{ seconds} \tag{1.1}$$

Where: d = duration of totality at point of interest (seconds)
D = duration of totality on the central line (seconds)
δ = perpendicular distance from the central line to position of interest (kilometers)
Z = perpendicular distance from the central line to the path edge (kilometers)

The Moon's limb profile varies with the lunar libration, which changes from eclipse to eclipse. Consequently, the effects of the limb profile are different at each eclipse.

Photo 1–4 *The diamond ring effect is caught seconds after the end of totality during the total solar eclipse of 2008 August 01 from Jinta, China. ©2008 F. Espenak*

Section 2: Solar Eclipse Predictions

2.1 Solar Eclipse Contacts

During the course of a solar eclipse, the instants when the Moon's disk becomes tangent to the Sun's disk are known as eclipse contacts. They mark various stages or phases of a solar eclipse.

Partial solar eclipses have two primary contacts.

> **First Contact (C1)** — Instant of first exterior tangency of the Moon with the Sun
> (Partial Eclipse Begins)
> **Fourth Contact (C4)** — Instant of last exterior tangency of the Moon with the Sun
> (Partial Eclipse Ends)

Central solar eclipses (total, annular or hybrid) have four primary contacts. Contacts C2 and C3 mark the instants when the Moon's disk is first and last internally tangent to the Sun. These are the times when the annular or total phase of the eclipse begins and ends, respectively.

> **First Contact (C1)** — Instant of first exterior tangency of the Moon with the Sun
> (Partial Eclipse Begins)
> **Second Contact (C2)** — Instant of first interior tangency of the Moon with the Sun
> (Annular or Total Eclipse Begins)
> **Third Contact (C3)** — Instant of last interior tangency of the Moon with the Sun
> (Annular or Total Eclipse Ends)
> **Fourth Contact (C4)** — Instant of last exterior tangency of the Moon with the Sun
> (Partial Eclipse Ends)

Figure 2–1: Solar Eclipse Contacts

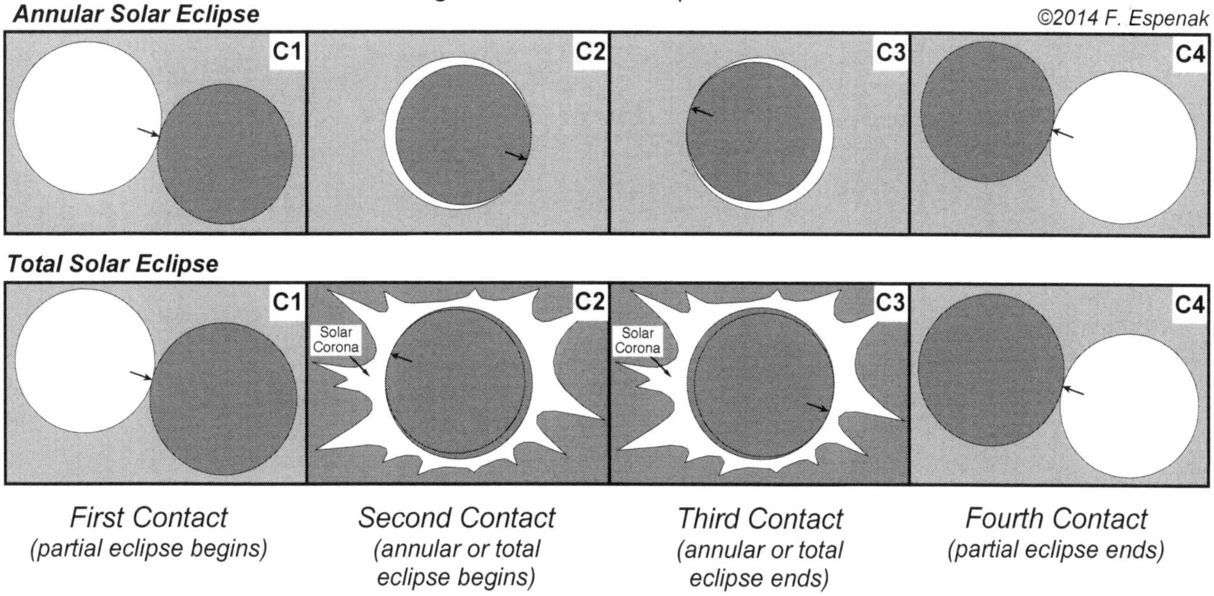

Figure 2–1 illustrates the four contacts for annular and total solar eclipses. The arrows indicate the contact point of the Sun's limb in each diagram.

15

2.2 Mean Lunar Radius

A fundamental parameter used in the prediction of solar eclipses is the Moon's mean radius k, expressed in units of Earth's equatorial radius. The actual radius of the Moon varies as a function of position angle and libration due to the irregularity of the lunar limb profile. From 1968 through 1980, the Nautical Almanac Office used two separate values for k in their eclipse predictions. The larger value (k=0.2724880), representing a mean over lunar topographic features, was used for all penumbral (i.e., exterior) contacts and for annular eclipses. A smaller value (k=0.272281), representing a mean minimum radius, was reserved exclusively for umbral (i.e., interior) contact calculations of total eclipses (Explanatory Supplement, 1974). Unfortunately, the use of two different values of k for central eclipses introduces a discontinuity in the case of hybrid or annular-total eclipses.

In August 1982, the IAU General Assembly adopted a value of k=0.2725076 for the mean lunar radius. This value is currently used by the Nautical Almanac Office for all solar eclipse predictions (Fiala and Lukac, 1983) and is believed to be the best mean radius, averaging mountain peaks and low valleys along the Moon's rugged limb. The adoption of one single value for k eliminates the discontinuity in the case of annular-total eclipses and ends confusion arising from the use of two different values. However, the use of even the best 'mean' value for the Moon's radius introduces a problem in predicting the character and duration of central eclipses, particularly total eclipses. A total eclipse can be defined as an eclipse in which the Sun's disk is completely occulted by the Moon. This cannot occur so long as any photospheric rays are visible through deep valleys along the Moon's limb (Meeus, Grosjean and Vanderleen, 1966). But the use of the IAU's mean k guarantees that some annular or annular-total eclipses will be misidentified as total. A case in point is the eclipse of 1986 Oct 03. The *Astronomical Almanac for 1986* identified this event as a total eclipse of 3 seconds duration when in it was in fact a beaded annular eclipse. Clearly, a smaller value of k is needed since it is more representative of the deepest lunar valley floors, hence the minimum solid disk radius, and ensures that an eclipse is truly total.

Of primary interest to most observers are the times when central eclipse begins and ends (second and third contacts, respectively) and the duration of the central phase. When the IAU's mean value for k is used to calculate these times, they must be corrected to accommodate low valleys (total) or high mountains (annular) along the Moon's limb. The calculation of these corrections is not trivial, but is essential, especially if one plans to observe near the path limits (Herald, 1983). For observers near the central line of a total eclipse, the limb corrections can be closely approximated by using a smaller value of k, which accounts for valleys along the profile.

This work uses the IAU's accepted value of k (k=0.2725076) for all penumbral (exterior) contacts. In order to avoid eclipse type misidentification and to predict central durations, which are closer to the actual durations observed at total eclipses, we depart from convention by adopting the smaller value for k (k=0.272281) for all central (interior) contacts. This is consistent with predictions published in *Five Millennium Canon of Solar Eclipses* (Espenak and Meeus, 2006). Consequently, the smaller k produces shorter central durations and narrower paths for total eclipses when compared with calculations using the IAU value for k. Similarly, the smaller k predicts longer central durations and wider paths for annular eclipses.

16

2.3 Solar and Lunar Coordinates

The coordinates of the Sun and the Moon used in the eclipse predictions presented here have been calculated with the JPL DE406 (Jet Propulsion Laboratory Developmental Ephemeris 406). The DE406 is based upon the International Celestial Reference Frame (ICRF), the adopted reference frame of the International Astronomical Union (IAU). The DE406 is often referred to as the "JPL long ephemeris" because it covers a 6000-year period from −3000 Feb 23 (JED 0625360.50) to +3000 May 06 (JED 02816912.50). While based on the DE405, the accuracy of the interpolating polynomials of the DE406 has been lessened in order to cover the much larger time span. The DE406 does not include nutation or libration.

The interpolating accuracy of the DE406 is within 25 meters for any planet and 1 meter for the Moon. Since the absolute accuracy of the DE405 is several kilometers for planetary positions, the difference between the DE405 and DE406 is of no consequence in the predictions presented in the *Canon*. The DE406 is used by JPL's online HORIZONS ephemeris service for dates in the distant past or future.

The Moon's center of figure does not coincide with its center of mass. To compensate for this property, an empirical correction is sometimes added to the Moon's center of mass position. Unfortunately, the large variation in lunar libration from one eclipse to the next minimizes the effectiveness of this empirical correction. Because of this, no correction has been made to the Moon's center of mass position in the *Thousand Year Canon*.

2.4 Secular Acceleration of the Moon

Ocean tides are caused by the gravitational pull of the Moon (and, to a lesser extent, the Sun). The resulting tidal bulge in Earth's oceans is dragged ahead of the Moon in its orbit because of the daily rotation of Earth. As a consequence, the ocean mass offset from the Earth–Moon line exerts a pull on the Moon and accelerates it in its orbit. Conversely, the Moon's gravitational tug on this mass exerts a torque that decelerates the rotation of Earth. The length of the day gradually increases as energy is transferred from Earth to the Moon and the lunar orbit and period of revolution about Earth increases.

The tides are not the only factor changing Earth's rotation rate. The melting of continental ice sheets at the end of the last glacial period result in the rise of land masses that were depressed by the enormous weight of the ice sheets. This "post-glacial rebound" of the land allows the return flow of mantle material back under the de-glaciated landmasses particularly in the polar regions. Through conservation of angular momentum, the resulting shift in mass from the equator to the poles will cause Earth's rotation to slow down. However, it will take many thousands of years for the land to reach an equilibrium level because of the extreme viscosity of the mantle.

The secular acceleration of the Moon is small, but it has a cumulative effect on the Moon's position when extrapolated over many centuries. Direct measurements of the acceleration have only been possible since 1969 using the Apollo retro-reflectors (LLR) left on the Moon. The results from LLR show that the Moon's mean distance from Earth is increasing by 3.8 centimeters per year (Dickey, et al., 1994). The corresponding acceleration in the Moon's ecliptic longitude is −25.858 arc-seconds/century[2] (Chapront, Chapront-Touzé, and Francou, 2002).

The value of the Moon's secular acceleration over long time spans is unknown. Careful records for its derivation only go back a century. Before then, spurious and incomplete eclipse and occultation observations from medieval and ancient manuscripts comprise the database. In any case, the current value implies an increase in the length of day (LOD) of ~ 2.3 milliseconds/century. Such a small amount may seem insignificant, but it has very measurable cumulative effects. For instance, time as measured with Earth's rotation during the 20th century lost 64 seconds when compared to atomic time.

2.5 Measurement of Time

The system of time measurement is crucial to the prediction of eclipses. Over the past several centuries, the way we measure time has changed significantly as our understanding of solar system dynamics and sub-atomic physics has developed.

The most natural form of time measurement is the solar day (usually measured from solar noon to solar noon). The length of the solar day varies during the year because of the eccentricity of Earth's orbit around the Sun. Mean solar time resolves this problem by using an average to define the mean solar day.

In 1884, Greenwich Mean Time (GMT) — the mean solar time on the Greenwich Meridian (0° longitude) — was adopted as the standard reference time for clocks around the world. A fundamental basis of GMT is the assumption that Earth's rotation on its axis is constant. It wasn't until the mid-twentieth century that astronomers realized the rotation period is gradually increasing. Earth is slowing down because of tidal friction with the Moon (Sect. 2.4).

For purposes of orbital calculations, time using Earth's rotation was abandoned for a more uniform time scale based on Earth's orbit about the Sun. In 1952, Ephemeris Time was introduced to address the problem. The ephemeris second was defined as a fraction of the tropical year[6] for 1900 Jan 01 as calculated from Newcomb's *Tables of the Sun* (1895). Ephemeris Time was used for Solar System ephemeris calculations until 1979.

Terrestrial Dynamical Time (TD) is the modern replacement for Ephemeris Time and is used in theories of planetary motion in the Solar System. TD is based on International Atomic Time (TAI), which is a high-precision standard using several hundred atomic clocks worldwide. To ensure continuity with Ephemeris Time, TD was defined to match ET for the date 1977 Jan 01. In 1991, the IAU refined the definition of TD to make it more precise. It was also renamed Terrestrial Time (TT) although the author prefers to use the older name Terrestrial Dynamical Time.

Civilian time used throughout the world is still based on mean solar time, although indirectly. While Greenwich Mean Time was determined though observations of the Sun, its modern day replacement, Universal Time (actually UT1) is based on Earth's rotation using observations of distant quasars. UT1 is a nonuniform time because Earth is gradually slowing down at an irregular rate (Sect. 2.4). At present (2014), the accumulated error in the rotation of Earth in the course of one year is ~0.3 seconds.

---

[6] The tropical year is the length of time that the Sun takes to return to the same position in the cycle of seasons, as seen from Earth (e.g., the time from vernal equinox to vernal equinox).

Coordinated Universal Time (UTC) is derived from International Atomic Time (TAI). The length of the UTC second is defined in terms of an atomic transition of cesium and is accurate to approximately one nanosecond (billionth of a second) per day. UTC was defined to closely parallel UT1. However, the two time systems are intrinsically incompatible since UTC is uniform while UT1 is based on Earth's rotation, which is gradually slowing. In order to keep the two times within 0.9 seconds of each other, a leap second is added to UTC as needed (currently once every few years).

Today, UTC is the time standard used to define time zones around the world. It is the time reference for GPS satellites and aviation, and is used to synchronize the clocks of computers across the Internet.

2.6 ΔT (Delta T)

The orbital positions of the Sun and the Moon, required by eclipse predictions, are calculated using Terrestrial Dynamical Time (TD) because it is a uniform time scale. However, world time zones and daily life are based on Universal Time[7] (UT1). In order to convert eclipse predictions from TD to UT1, the difference between these two time scales must be known. The parameter ΔT (Delta T) is the arithmetic difference, in seconds, between the two as:

$$\Delta T = TD - UT1 \qquad (2\text{-}1)$$

Past values of ΔT can be deduced from historical records. In spite of their relatively low precision, these data represent the only evidence for the value of ΔT prior to 1600. In the centuries following the introduction of the telescope (circa 1609), thousands of high quality observations have been made of lunar occultations of stars. The number and accuracy of these timings increase from the seventeenth through the twentieth century, affording valuable data in the determination of ΔT.

The estimated uncertainty in the value of ΔT is 20 seconds in the year 1500, but it drops to 1 second by 1800. A detailed analysis of historical measurements fitted with cubic splines for ΔT from 1500 to +1950 is presented in Table 2-1 and includes the standard error for each value (Morrison and Stephenson, 2004).

Table 2-1: Values of ΔT Derived from Historical Records

Year	ΔT (seconds)	Standard Error (seconds)
1500	200	20
1600	120	20
1700	9	5
1750	13	2
1800	14	1
1850	7	<1
1900	–3	<1
1950	29	<0.1

---

[7] World time zones are actually based on Coordinated Universal Time (UTC). It is an atomic time synchronized and adjusted to stay within a second of astronomically determined Universal Time (UT1) through the addition of an occasional "leap second" to compensate for the gradual slowing of Earth's rotation.

In modern times, the determination of ΔT is made using atomic clocks and radio observations of quasars. Table 2–2 gives the value of ΔT every five years from 1955 to 2010 (*Astronomical Almanac for 2011*, page K9) and the most recent value in 2014.

Table 2–2: Recent Values of ΔT from Direct Observations

Year	ΔT (seconds)	5–Year Change (seconds)	Average 1–Year Change (seconds)
1955.0	+31.1	—	—
1960.0	+33.2	2.1	0.42
1965.0	+35.7	2.5	0.50
1970.0	+40.2	4.5	0.90
1975.0	+45.5	5.3	1.06
1980.0	+50.5	5.0	1.00
1985.0	+54.3	3.8	0.76
1990.0	+56.9	2.6	0.52
1995.0	+60.8	3.9	0.78
2000.0	+63.8	3.0	0.60
2005.0	+64.7	0.9	0.18
2010.0	+66.1	1.4	0.28
2014.0	+67.3	1.5	0.30

As revealed in Table 2–2, the average 1–year change in ΔT ranges from 0.18 seconds to 1.06 seconds. Future changes in ΔT are unknown since theoretical models of the physical causes are imprecise. Extrapolations from the table weighted by the long period trend from tidal braking of the Moon offer estimates of ΔT of +70 seconds in 2020, +85 seconds in 2050, +127 seconds in 2100, and +271 seconds in the year 2200. It should be noted that extrapolations of future values of ΔT are little more than educated guesses due to the inherent uncertainties in the affects of tidal breaking and glacial rebound on Earth's rotation.

2.7 Polynomial Expressions for ΔT

Using the ΔT values obtained from the historical record and from direct observations (Tables 2–1 and 2–2, respectively), a series of polynomial expressions were created to simplify the evaluation of ΔT for any time during the interval 1501 to 2500. The decimal year "y" is defined as follows:

$$y = year + (month - 0.5)/12$$

This gives "y" for the middle of the month, which is accurate enough given the precision in the known values of ΔT. The following table of polynomial expressions can be used to calculate the value of ΔT (in seconds) over the interval of the *Canon*.

Table 2–3 lists twelve polynomial expression for ΔT, each one covering a specific range of dates. The time parameter in the third column is calculated from the decimal year as defined above. The first ten expressions covering the years 500 to 2005 are from the *Five Millennium Canon of Solar Eclipses* (Espenak & Meeus, 2006). The eleventh expression covering the period 2005 to 2015 was derived for this publication from the most recent values of ΔT. The last expression covering the years 2015 and beyond is an extrapolation based on recent values of ΔT combined with the long term trend obtained by fitting a quadratic function to the values of ΔT from the historic records. It is an updated expression based on van der Sluys (2010).

Table 2–3: Polynomial Expressions for ΔT

Date Range*	Polynomial Expression for Delta T (ΔT)	Time**
500 to 1600	ΔT = 1574.2 – 556.01 × u + 71.23472 × u^2 + 0.319781 × u^3 – 0.8503463 × u^4 – 0.005050998 × u^5 + 0.0083572073 × u^6	u = (y–1000)/100
1600 to 1700	ΔT = 120 – 0.9808 × t – 0.01532 × t^2 + t^3 / 7129	t = y – 1600
1700 to 1800	ΔT = 8.83 + 0.1603 × t – 0.0059285 × t^2 + 0.00013336 × t^3 – t^4 / 1174000	t = y – 1700
1800 to 1860	ΔT = 13.72 – 0.332447 × t + 0.0068612 × t^2 + 0.0041116 × t^3 – 0.00037436 × t^4 + 0.0000121272 × t^5 – 0.0000001699 × t^6 + 0.000000000875 × t^7	t = y – 1800
1860 to 1900	ΔT = 7.62 + 0.5737 × t – 0.251754 × t^2 + 0.01680668 × t^3 – 0.0004473624 × t^4 + t^5 / 233174	t = y – 1860
1900 to 1920	ΔT = –2.79 + 1.494119 × t – 0.0598939 × t^2 + 0.0061966 × t^3 – 0.000197 × t^4	t = y – 1900
1920 to 1941	ΔT = 21.20 + 0.84493×t – 0.076100 × t^2 + 0.0020936 × t^3	t = y – 1920
1941 to 1961	ΔT = 29.07 + 0.407 × t – t^2 / 233 + t^3 / 2547	t = y – 1950
1961 to 1986	ΔT = 45.45 + 1.067 × t – t^2 / 260 – t^3 / 718	t = y – 1975
1986 to 2005	ΔT = 63.86 + 0.3345 × t – 0.060374 × t^2 + 0.0017275 × t^3 + 0.000651814 × t^4 + 0.00002373599 × t^5	t = y – 2000
2005 to 2015	ΔT = 64.69 + 0.2930 × t	t = y – 2000
2015 to 2500	ΔT = 67.62 + 0.3645 × t + 0.0039755 × t^2	t = y – 2015

*The calendar date for each year in the *Date Range* corresponds to Jan 01 at 00:00:00.
** The variable *y* in the *Time* corresponds to the decimal year.

The largest deviation in the value of ΔT between the polynomial expressions in Table 2–3 and the historically derived values in Table 2–1 occurs in the period 500 to 1600 and is less than 4 seconds. This accuracy is acceptable so the polynomial expressions have been used in evaluating ΔT for all eclipses in the *Thousand Year Canon*.

2.8 Date Format

There are a number of ways to write the calendar date through variations in the order of day, month, and year. The International Organization for Standardization's (ISO) 8601 advises a numeric date representation, which organizes the elements from the largest to the smallest. The exact format is YYYY–MM–DD where YYYY is the calendar year, MM is the month of the year between 01 (January) and 12 (December), and DD is the day of the month between 01 and 31. For example, the 27th day of April in the year 1943 would then be expressed as 1943-04-27. The ISO convention is adopted here, but the month number has been replaced with the three-letter English abbreviation of the month name for additional clarity. From the previous example, the date then is expressed as 1943 Apr 27.

2.9 Calendar Date

The Gregorian calendar is the civil calendar currently used throughout most of the world. The older Julian calendar was used until 1582 Oct 04. As a consequence of the Gregorian Calendar Reform, the day following 1582 Oct 04 (Julian calendar) is 1582 Oct 15 (Gregorian calendar).

Pope Gregory XIII decreed the use of the Gregorian calendar in 1582 in order to correct a problem in a drift of the seasons. It adopts the convention of a year containing 365 days. Every fourth year is a leap year of 366 days if it is divisible by 4 (e.g., 2004, 2008, etc.). However, whole century years (e.g., 1700, 1800, 1900) are excluded from the leap year rule unless they are also divisible by 400 (e.g., 2000). This dating scheme was designed to keep the vernal equinox on or within a day of March 21. Precession of the equinoxes will eventually produce an error of one day in the Gregorian calendar in about 7700 years.

Prior to the Gregorian Calendar Reform of 1582, the Julian calendar was in wide use. It was less complicated in that all years divisible by 4 were counted as 366-day leap years, but this simplicity came at a cost. After more than 16 centuries of use, the Julian calendar date of the vernal equinox had drifted 11 days from March 21. It was this failure in the Julian calendar that prompted the Gregorian Calendar Reform.

2.10 Statistical Comparison with Five Millennium Canon of Solar Eclipses

As discussed in section 2.3, the *Thousand Year Canon* uses the JPL DE406, a numerically integrated ephemeris for the Sun and the Moon. In comparison, the *Five Millennium Canon of Solar Eclipses* (Espenak & Meeus, 2006) uses the older analytical ephemerides VSOP87 (Bretagnon & Francou, 1988) and ELP-2000/82 (Chapront-Touze and Chapront, 1983) for the Sun and the Moon, respectively.

Table 2–3: Statistical Comparison with the *Five Millennium Canon of Solar Eclipses*

Years	Greatest Eclipse (seconds)	Gamma (meters)	Eclipse Magnitude (x 10⁶)	X (meters)	Y (meters)
1501–1551	−1.56 [0.019]	±194.1 [2.4]	14.3 [1.6]	±52.1 [0.0]	±184.2 [2.2]
1601–1651	−0.97 [0.011]	±158.0 [0.3]	14.7 [1.2]	±41.4 [2.8]	±151.2 [0.6]
1701–1751	−0.47 [0.008]	±116.8 [4.5]	13.0 [0.3]	±33.9 [1.3]	±111.0 [4.2]
1801–1851	−0.21 [0.007]	±80.3 [1.0]	12.3 [1.3]	±22.0 [0.7]	±76.4 [0.7]
1901–1951	−0.05 [0.002]	±38.9 [0.2]	9.9 [0.9]	±9.8 [0.7]	±37.2 [0.5]
2001–2051	0.02 [0.001]	±22.2 [0.3]	8.4 [0.3]	±5.8 [0.4]	±21.2 [0.5]
2101–2151	−0.02 [0.000]	±52.4 [0.4]	8.9 [0.4]	±14.6 [0.8]	±50.1 [0.6]
2201–2251	−0.19 [0.007]	±102.6 [2.8]	11.2 [5.9]	±29.2 [3.4]	±97.6 [1.7]
2301–2351	−0.63 [0.009]	±157.2 [4.1]	12.7 [0.7]	±42.8 [1.6]	±149.4 [4.0]
2401–2451	−0.88 [0.009]	±202.4 [3.4]	15.4 [1.0]	±49.7 [4.4]	±194.0 [2.2]

Table 2–3 presents a statistical comparison between the "Five Millennium Canon of Solar Eclipses" and the "Thousand Year Canon of Solar Eclipses" for several parameters over a range of years. The tabulated values are averages of the differences between the "Thousand Year Canon" minus the "Five Millennium Canon" for ten 50-year periods. The values in square brackets are the standard deviations of the average differences.

A statistical comparison between the two canons for several parameters over a range of years is presented in Table 2–3. The tabulated values are averages of the differences between the *Thousand Year Canon* minus the *Five Millennium Canon* for ten 50-year periods.

The average difference in the instant of *Greatest Eclipse* ranges from 0.02 to –1.56 seconds. The average difference in *Gamma*[8] ranges from 22.2 to 202.4 meters while the *Eclipse Magnitude* spans 8.4×10^6 to 15.4×10^6. The average differences for Besselian elements *X* and *Y* range from 5.8 to 52.1 meters and 21.2 to 194.0 meters, respectively.

In all cases, the best agreement between the two canons occurs during the present era (2001–2051), while the largest differences arise 500 years in the past or future. This is remarkably good agreement, considering the computational differences between the numerically integrated and analytical ephemerides.

2.11 Map Accuracy

The accuracy of the eclipse maps depends principally on two factors. The first is the rigorousness of the solar and lunar ephemerides used in the calculations (Sect. 2.3). These ephemerides are accurate to approximately 1 arc-second over the entire span of the *Canon*. The agreement with predictions in the *Five Millennium Canon* using different ephemerides illustrates the level of accuracy (Sect. 2.10).

The second and greater source of error in the path of solar eclipses is due to the uncertainty in ΔT (Sect. 2.6). This parameter is the arithmetic difference between Terrestrial Dynamical Time (TD) and Universal Time (UT1). TD can be thought of as time measured with an idealized or perfect clock. In contrast, UT1 is based on Earth's rotation, which is gradually slowing down. TD is used to calculate solar system ephemerides and eclipse predictions, but UT1 is used for defining world time and longitudes.

Earth rotated faster in the past so eclipse predictions generated in TD must first be converted to UT1 (UT1 = TD – ΔT) before the geographic path of the Moon's shadow can be determined. In other words, the physical impact of ΔT on eclipse predictions is to shift an eclipse path east relative to the position calculated from TD. Because 1° in longitude corresponds to 4 minutes of time, a ΔT value of 240 seconds would shift a path 1° east of its TD position. The maps in the *Canon* already include the ΔT translation of eclipse paths from TD to UT1; thus, they depict the actual geographic regions of visibility of each eclipse.

The largest uncertainty in ΔT is 20 seconds in the year 1501. This corresponds to an error in the east-west longitudes of an eclipse path of 0.08 degrees.

---

[8] Gamma is the minimum distance of the Moon's shadow cone axis from Earth's center, in Earth equatorial radii.

Photo 2–1 Pat and Fred Espenak gaze at the Sun's corona during the total solar eclipse of 2008 August 01 from Jinta, China. ©2008 F. Espenak

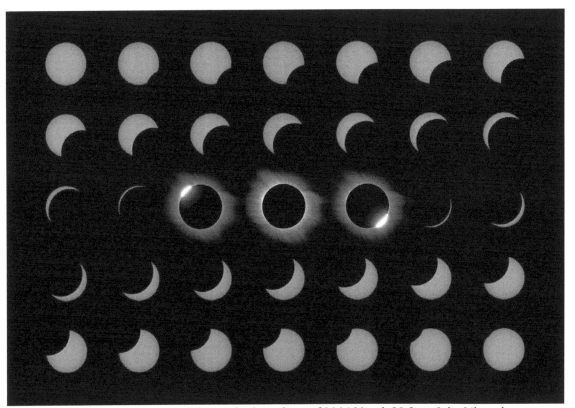

Photo 2–2 This image sequence of the total solar eclipse of 2006 March 29 from Jalu, Libya shows the entire eclipse from start to finish. . ©2006 F. Espenak

Section 3: Solar Eclipse Statistics

3.1 Statistical Distribution of Eclipse Types

Eclipses of the Sun can only occur during the New Moon phase. It is then possible for the Moon's penumbral, umbral and/or antumbral shadows to sweep across Earth's surface thereby producing an eclipse. There are four types of solar eclipses:

1. **Partial** — Moon's penumbral shadow traverses Earth (umbral and antumbral shadows completely miss Earth)
2. **Annular** — Moon's penumbral and antumbral shadows traverse Earth (Moon is too far from Earth to completely cover the Sun)
3. **Total** — Moon's penumbral and umbral shadows traverse Earth (Moon is close enough to Earth to completely cover the Sun)
4. **Hybrid** — Moon's penumbral, umbral and antumbral shadows traverse Earth (eclipse appears either annular or total along different sections of its path). Hybrid eclipses are also known as annular-total eclipses.

During the 1000-year period from 1501 to 2500, Earth experiences 2,389 eclipses of the Sun. The statistical distribution of the four eclipse types over this interval is shown in Table 3–1.

Table 3–1: Distribution of Basic Eclipse Types

Eclipse Type	Abbreviation	Number	Percent
All Eclipses	—	2389	100.0%
Partial	P	838	35.1%
Annular	A	794	33.2%
Total	T	651	27.2%
Hybrid	H	106	4.4%

All partial eclipses are events in which some portion of the Moon's penumbral shadow passes across Earth's surface. In comparison all annular, total and hybrid eclipses can be characterized as events in which some portion of the Moon's umbral and/or antumbral shadow crosses Earth.

In the case of umbral or antumbral eclipses (annular, total or hybrid), they can be further categorized as:

1. **Central (two limits)** — The central axis of the Moon's umbral or antumbral shadow traverses Earth thereby producing a central line in the eclipse track. The umbra or antumbra falls entirely upon Earth producing a ground track with both a northern and southern limit.
2. **Central (one limit)** — The central axis of the Moon's umbral or antumbral shadow traverses Earth. However, a portion of the umbra or antumbra misses Earth throughout the eclipse thereby producing a ground track with just one limit.
3. **Non-Central** — The central axis of the Moon's umbral or antumbral shadow misses Earth. However, one edge of the umbra or antumbra grazes Earth thereby producing a ground track with one limit and no central line.

Using these categories, the distribution of the 794 annular eclipses appears in Table 3–2.

Table 3–2: Statistics of Annular Eclipses

Annular Eclipses	Number	Percent
All Annular Eclipses	794	100.0%
Central (two limits)	768	96.7%
Central (one limit)	12	1.5%
Non-Central (one limit)	14	1.8%

Examples of central annular eclipses with one limit include: 1874 Oct 10, 2003 May 31, 2044 Feb 28, and 2101 Feb 28. Some examples of non-central annular eclipses are: 1950 Mar 18, 1957 Apr 30, 2014 Apr 29, and 2043 Oct 03.

Similarly, the distribution of the 651 total eclipses is shown in Table 3–3.

Table 3–3: Statistics of Total Eclipses

Total Eclipses	Number	Percent
All Total Eclipses	651	100.0%
Central (two limits)	641	98.5%
Central (one limit)	4	0.6%
Non-Central (one limit)	6	0.9%

Examples of central total eclipses with one limit include: 1494 Mar 07, 1523 Aug 11, 2185 Jul 26, and 2195 Aug 05. Several examples of non-central total eclipses are: 1957 Oct 23, 1967 Nov 02, 2043 Apr 09, and 2459 Jun 01.

All 106 hybrid eclipses are central with two limits. Hybrid eclipses with a single limit (both central and non-central) are exceedingly rare. An estimate of the mean frequency of non-central hybrid eclipses is one out of every 600 million eclipses or once every 250 million years (Meeus, 2002).

The central path of most hybrid eclipses begins annular, changes to total and finally reverts back to annular. This combination (ATA) occurs in 99 out of the 106 hybrid eclipses in the *Canon*. However, there are two other possibilities. If the vertex of the Moon's umbral shadow passes through Earth's fundamental plane during the eclipse, then the hybrid eclipse can begin as total and end as annular (TA) or it can begin as annular and end as total (AT). Table 3–4 shows the distribution of the three different classes of hybrid eclipses.

Table 3–4: Statistics of Hybrid Eclipses

Hybrid Eclipses	Number	Percent
All Hybrid Eclipses	106	100.0%
Hybrid (ATA)	99	93.3%
Hybrid (TA)	4	3.8%
Hybrid (AT)	3	2.8%

Examples of ATA hybrid eclipses include: 1986 Oct 03, 1987 Mar 29, 2005 Apr 08, and 2023 Apr 20. Examples of the relatively rare TA hybrid eclipse are: 1564 Jun 08, 1703 Jan 17, 1825 Dec 09, and 2386 Apr 29. Finally, examples of the rare AT hybrid eclipse include: 1854 Nov 20, 2013 Nov 03, and 2172 Oct 17.

3.2 Distribution of Eclipse Types by Century

Table 3–5 summarizes 1000 years of eclipses by eclipse type in 100-year intervals. The number of central and non-central (in square brackets) events is given for annular and total eclipses. The number of eclipses in any one century ranges from 224 to 251 with an average of 238.9.

Some remarkable patterns are present in this table. There is a cyclical variation in the number of eclipses per century with a period just under six centuries, giving alternating "rich" and "poor" periods (Meeus, 1997). The 20th and 21st centuries (1901 to 2100) are poor periods, with only 228 and 224 eclipses. This cycle is also present when only central eclipses are considered.

The cycle appears to have a period of approximately 600 years with an amplitude of ~30 eclipses. This is close to a known lunar eclipse period called the tetradia, which has a period of 586.02 years. The tetradia governs the recurrence of tetrads or groups of four successive total lunar eclipses each separated by six lunations. The tetradia cycle for lunar eclipse tetrads appears to be 180 degrees out of phase with the cycle for solar eclipses. When there are many tetrads, there are fewer solar eclipses. We are currently in a tetrad rich period with contemporary tetrads in 2003–2004, 2014–2015 and 2032–2033.

The number of hybrid solar eclipses per century also varies cyclically with a period of approximately 17 centuries.

Table 3–5: Eclipse Types by Century: 1501 to 2500

Century Interval	Number of Eclipses	Number of Partial Eclipses	Number of Annular Eclipses*	Number of Total Eclipses*	Number of Hybrid Eclipses
1501 to 1600	228	75	69 [3]	62 [0]	19
1601 to 1700	248	89	74 [0]	60 [1]	24
1701 to 1800	251	92	78 [0]	62 [0]	19
1801 to 1900	242	87	77 [0]	63 [0]	15
1901 to 2000	228	78	71 [2]	68 [3]	6
2001 to 2100	224	77	70 [2]	67 [1]	7
2101 to 2200	235	79	82 [5]	65 [0]	4
2201 to 2300	248	92	86 [0]	67 [0]	3
2301 to 2400	248	88	86 [0]	66 [0]	8
2401 to 2500	237	81	87 [2]	65 [1]	1

* The first quantity is the number of central eclipses, while the second quantity in square brackets is the number of non-central eclipses.

3.3 Distribution of Eclipse Types by Month

Table 3–6 summarizes 1000 years of eclipses by eclipse type in each month of the year. The first value in each column is the number of eclipses of a given type for the corresponding month. The second number in square brackets is the number of eclipses divided by the number of days in that month. This normalization allows direct comparison of eclipse frequencies in different months.

A brief examination of the values in the column Number of All Eclipses shows that eclipses are equally distributed throughout the year. The same holds true for partial eclipses. However, the columns for annular and total eclipses reveal something interesting. Annular eclipses are 4/3 times more likely during the period November–December–January compared to the months May–June–July. This effect is attributed to Earth's elliptical orbit. Earth currently reaches perihelion in early January and aphelion in early July. Consequently the Sun's apparent diameter varies from 1952 to 1887 arc-seconds between perihelion and aphelion. The Sun's larger apparent diameter at perihelion makes annular eclipses more frequent at that time.

The opposite argument holds true for total eclipses, which are nearly 3/2 times more likely during the period May–June–July compared to the months November–December–January. In this case the Sun's smaller apparent size around aphelion increases the frequency of total eclipses at that time. Total eclipses actually outnumber annular eclipses during the season May–June–July (Meeus, 2002).

Table 3–6: Eclipse Types by Month: 1501 to 2500

Month	Number of All Eclipses	Number of Partial Eclipses	Number of Annular Eclipses	Number of Total Eclipses	Number of Hybrid Eclipses
January	204 [6.58]	72 [2.32]	80 [2.58]	44 [1.42]	8 [0.26]
February	185 [6.61]	60 [2.14]	83 [2.96]	38 [1.36]	4 [0.14]
March	202 [6.52]	70 [2.26]	73 [2.35]	48 [1.55]	11 [0.35]
April	202 [6.73]	69 [2.30]	62 [2.07]	55 [1.83]	16 [0.53]
May	204 [6.58]	73 [2.35]	55 [1.77]	65 [2.10]	11 [0.35]
June	188 [6.27]	67 [2.23]	50 [1.67]	64 [2.13]	7 [0.23]
July	195 [6.29]	68 [2.19]	57 [1.84]	63 [2.03]	7 [0.23]
August	199 [6.42]	70 [2.26]	57 [1.84]	70 [2.26]	2 [0.06]
September	200 [6.67]	73 [2.43]	62 [2.07]	62 [2.07]	3 [0.10]
October	205 [6.61]	72 [2.32]	69 [2.23]	54 [1.74]	10 [0.32]
November	200 [6.67]	73 [2.43]	69 [2.30]	42 [1.40]	16 [0.53]
December	205 [6.61]	71 [2.29]	77 [2.48]	46 [1.48]	11 [0.35]

3.4 Eclipse Frequency and the Calendar Year

There are 2 to 5 solar eclipses in every calendar year. Table 3–7 shows the distribution in the number of eclipses per year for the 1000 years covered in the *Canon*.

Table 3–7: Number of Eclipses per Year

Number of Eclipses per Year	Number of Years	Percent
2	721	72.1%
3	172	17.2%
4	104	10.4%
5	3	0.3%

When two eclipses occur in one calendar year, they can be any combination of P, A, T or H (partial, annular, total or hybrid) with the one exception — they can not both be T. Table 3–8 lists the frequency of each eclipse combination along with the five examples nearest to the present when the combination occurs. The table makes no distinction in the order of any two eclipses. For example, the eclipse combination PA includes all years where the order is either PA or AP.

Table 3–8: Two Eclipses in One Year

Eclipse Combinations*	Number of Years	Percent	Examples (Years) **
PP	29	4.0%	..., 2004, 2007, 2022, 2025, 2040, ...
PA	14	1.9%	..., 2014, 2032, 2101, 2102, 2119, ...
PH	3	0.4%	..., 0227, 0245, 1909, 1986, 2050]
PT	36	5.0%	..., 2015, 2033, 2037, 2055, 2068, ...
AA	49	6.8%	..., 1951, 1969, 2056, 2074, 2085, ...
AH	50	6.9%	..., 2005, 2013, 2023, 2031, 2049, ...
AT	515	71.4%	..., 2006, 2008, 2009, 2010, 2012, ...
HH	14	1.9%	..., 1753, 1771, 1789, 1807, 1825]
HT	11	1.5%	..., 1843, 1894, 1912, 1930, 2910, ...

* P = Partial, A = Annular, T = Total and H = Hybrid.
** The square bracket indicates there are no other examples beyond the last year.

When three eclipses occur in one calendar year, there are 14 possible combinations of P, A, T or H. Table 3–9 lists the frequency of each eclipse combination along with the five examples nearest to the present when each combination occurs. The table makes no distinction in the order of eclipses in any combination. For example, the eclipse combination PAT includes all years where the order is PAT, PTA, APT, ATP, TAP and TPA. The rarest combinations PAH and AAH do not occur in the 1000-year span of the Canon.

Table 3–9: Three Eclipses in One Year

Eclipse Combinations*	Number of Years	Percent	Examples (Years)**
PPP	83	48.3%	..., 1971, 2018, 2036, 2054, 2058, ...
PPA	8	4.7%	..., 1722, 1740, 1899, 2224, 2242, ...
PPH	3	1.7%	[1544, 1609, 1703]
PPT	12	7.0%	..., 1834, 1852, 1928, 2130, 2271, ...
PAA	3	1.7%	[1704, 2419, 2437]
PAH	0	0.0%	—
PAT	28	16.3%	..., 1992, 2019, 2084, 2149, 2225, ...
PHH	1	0.6%	[1768]
PHT	1	0.6%	[1786]
AAH	0	0.0%	—
AAT	23	13.4%	..., 1954, 1973, 2038, 2103, 2122, ...
AHH	1	0.6%	[1666]
AHT	2	1.2%	[1731, 1908]
ATT	7	4.1%	..., 1554, 1712, 1889, 2057, 2252, ...

* P = Partial, A = Annular, T = Total and H = Hybrid.
** The square brackets indicate all examples are included in 1000 years.

When four eclipses occur in one calendar year, there are seven possible combinations of eclipse types P, A, T and H. Table 3–10 lists the frequency of each eclipse combination along with the five most recent years when each combination occurs. The table makes no distinction in the order of eclipses in the seven combinations. The rarest combinations PPAA and PPAH do not occur in the 1000-year span of the *Canon*.

Table 3–10: Four Eclipses in One Year

Eclipse Combinations*	Number of Years	Percent	Recent Examples (Years) **
PPPP	77	74.0%	..., 2000, 2011, 2029, 2047, 2065, ...
PPPA	14	13.5%	..., 1758, 1917, 2141, 2159, 2177, ...
PPPH	4	3.8%	[1573, 1591, 1685, 1750]
PPPT	7	6.7%	..., 1693, 1870, 2076, 2094, 2112, ...
PPAA	0	0.0%	—
PPAH	0	0.0%	—
PPAT	2	1.9%	[1880, 2195]

* P = Partial, A = Annular, T = Total and H = Hybrid.
** The square brackets indicate all examples are included in 1000 years.

The maximum number of five solar eclipses in one calendar year is quite rare. The first eclipse of such a quintet always occurs in the first half of January and the last eclipse falls in the latter half of December. Over the 1000-year span of the *Canon* there are only three years containing five solar eclipses. Each of them consists of 4 partial and 1 annular eclipse in the years 1805, 1935, and 2206.

3.5 Extremes in Eclipse Magnitude: Partial Eclipses

Eclipse magnitude is defined as the fraction of the Sun's diameter covered by the Moon. It reaches a maximum value at the instant of greatest eclipse. A search through the 2,389 eclipses in the *Canon* reveals some interesting cases involving extreme values of the eclipse magnitude.

Nine partial eclipses having a maximum magnitude less than 0.01 are listed in Table 3–11. These events are all the first or last members in a Saros series. The smallest magnitude was the partial eclipse of 1512 Apr 16 with a magnitude of just 0.0003.

Table 3–11: Partial Eclipses with Magnitude 0.01 or Less

Date (Dynamical Time)	Saros	Gamma	Eclipse Magnitude
1512 Apr 16	140	-1.5289	0.0003
1624 Oct 12	147	1.5466	0.0089
1639 Jan 04	145	1.5651	0.0009
1729 Aug 24	150	-1.5430	0.0067
1848 Aug 28	113	-1.5475	0.0091
1859 Feb 03	109	-1.5659	0.0077
1935 Jan 05	111	-1.5381	0.0013
2098 Oct 24	164	-1.5407	0.0057
2203 Sep 06	167	1.5374	0.0068

Seven partial eclipses having a maximum magnitude greater than 0.970. are listed in Table 3–12.

Table 3–12: Partial Eclipses with Magnitude 0.970 or More

Date (Dynamical Time)	Saros	Gamma	Eclipse Magnitude
1693 Jul 03	112	1.0058	0.9718
1750 Jul 03	142	-0.9985	0.9956
1920 May 18	146	-1.0239	0.9734
2051 Apr 11	120	1.0169	0.9849
2054 Sep 02	155	1.0215	0.9793
2062 Sep 03	126	1.0192	0.9749
2326 Jun 30	132	1.0107	0.9931

3.6 Extremes in Eclipse Magnitude: Annular Eclipses

Six annular eclipses have a maximum magnitude at greatest eclipse less than or equal to 0.910 (Table 3–13). Most of these events are central, but the last one is non-central with one limit.

Table 3–13: Annular Eclipses with Magnitude 0.910 or Less

Date (Dynamical Time)	Saros	Gamma	Eclipse Magnitude	Central Duration
1565 Nov 22	135	0.9564	0.9092	09m 37s
1583 Dec 14	135	0.9471	0.9083	10m 03s
1601 Dec 24	135	0.9402	0.9078	10m 14s
1620 Jan 04	135	0.9322	0.9081	10m 13s
1638 Jan 15	135	0.9242	0.9090	10m 00s
2485 Dec 07*	140	1.0243	0.9099	—

* Non-central annular eclipse with one limit.

Five annular eclipses have a maximum magnitude at greatest eclipse greater than or equal to 0.9995 (Table 3–14). All of these events have central durations lasting 2 seconds or less.

Table 3–14: Annular Eclipses with Magnitude 0.9995 or More

Date (Dynamical Time)	Saros	Gamma	Eclipse Magnitude	Central Duration
1704 Nov 27	118	0.6716	0.9999	00m 01s
1822 Feb 21	137	0.6914	0.9996	00m 02s
1858 Mar 15	137	0.6461	0.9996	00m 02s
1876 Mar 25	137	0.6142	0.9999	00m 01s
1948 May 09	137	0.4133	0.9999	00m 00s

3.7 Extremes in Eclipse Magnitude: Hybrid Eclipses

Six hybrid eclipses have a maximum magnitude at greatest eclipse less than or equal to 1.0002. All of these events are central with a central duration of totality of 1 second or less.

Table 3–15: Hybrid Eclipses with Magnitude 1.0002 or Less

Date (Dynamical Time)	Saros	Gamma	Eclipse Magnitude	Central Duration
1612 Nov 22	136	–0.7692	1.0002	00m 01s
1627 Aug 11	139	0.9401	1.0001	00m 00s
1702 Jul 24	131	0.3160	1.0002	00m 01s
1804 Feb 11	137	0.7053	1.0001	00m 00s
1894 Apr 06	137	0.5740	1.0001	00m 01s
1986 Oct 03	124	0.9931	1.0000	00m 00s

Eight hybrid eclipses have a maximum magnitude at greatest eclipse greater than or equal to 1.014. Six events have a duration of totality of 1 minute 30 seconds or more.

Table 3–16: Hybrid Eclipses with Magnitude 1.014 or More

Date (Dynamical Time)	Saros	Gamma	Eclipse Magnitude	Central Duration
1564 Jun 08	120	0.1252	1.0174	01m44s
1705 May 22	123	–0.1525	1.0147	01m32s
1825 Dec 09	139	0.5296	1.0148	01m34s
1854 Nov 20	140	–0.5179	1.0144	01m07s
1864 May 06	126	0.2622	1.0146	01m25s
2013 Nov 03	143	0.3272	1.0159	01m40s
2172 Oct 17	146	–0.1484	1.0174	01m34s
2386 Apr 29	154	–0.5483	1.0147	01m30s

3.8 Extremes in Eclipse Magnitude: Total Eclipses

Eight total eclipses have a maximum magnitude less than or equal to 1.01 (Table 3–17). Three of them are non-central eclipses.

Table 3–17: Total Eclipses with Magnitude 1.01 or Less

Date (Dynamical Time)	Saros	Gamma	Eclipse Magnitude	Central Duration
1522 Mar 27	131	0.9947	1.0076	00m26s
1536 Dec 13	134	–0.9343	1.0098	00m33s
1554 Dec 24	134	–0.9341	1.0075	00m25s
1562 Feb 03	133	0.9373	1.0091	00m41s
1957 Oct 23	123	–1.0022	1.0013	–
1968 Sep 22	124	0.9451	1.0099	00m40s
2043 Apr 09	149	1.0031	1.0096	–
2459 Jun 01	164	–1.0096	1.0038	–

Eleven total eclipses have a maximum magnitude of 1.079 or more. The central durations of all except one exceed six minutes. They take place when Earth is near aphelion (June–August), resulting in a small solar disk.

Table 3–18: Total Eclipses with Magnitude 1.079 or More

Date (Dynamical Time)	Saros	Gamma	Eclipse Magnitude	Central Duration
1973 Jun 30	136	–0.0785	1.0792	07m04s
1991 Jul 11	136	–0.0041	1.0800	06m53s
2009 Jul 22	136	0.0698	1.0799	06m39s
2027 Aug 02	136	0.1421	1.0790	06m23s
2150 Jun 25	139	–0.0911	1.0802	07m14s
2168 Jul 05	139	–0.1660	1.0807	07m26s
2186 Jul 16	139	–0.2396	1.0805	07m29s
2204 Jul 27	139	–0.3129	1.0793	07m22s
2327 Jun 20	142	0.2542	1.0795	06m21s
2345 Jun 30	142	0.3267	1.0797	06m07s
2363 Jul 12	142	0.4012	1.0792	05m51s

3.9 Greatest Central Duration: Annular Eclipses

Nine annular eclipses have a central duration at greatest eclipse of 11 1/2 minutes or more. These eclipses all take place when Earth is near the perihelion (Dec–Jan), resulting in a large solar disk. In all cases the eclipse magnitude is greater than 0.915.

Table 3–19: Annular Eclipses with Central Duration* of 11½ Minutes or More

Date (Dynamical Time)	Saros	Gamma	Eclipse Magnitude	Central Line Duration
1592 Dec 03	116	0.6102	0.9159	11m36s
1610 Dec 15	116	0.6195	0.9153	11m56s
1628 Dec 25	116	0.6264	0.9153	12m02s
1647 Jan 05	116	0.6336	0.9161	11m50s
1919 Nov 22	141	0.4549	0.9198	11m37s
1937 Dec 02	141	0.4389	0.9184	12m00s
1955 Dec 14	141	0.4266	0.9176	12m09s
1973 Dec 24	141	0.4171	0.9174	12m02s
1992 Jan 04	141	0.4091	0.9179	11m41s

*Central line duration at the instant of greatest eclipse

3.10 Greatest Central Duration: Total Eclipses

Eight total eclipses have a central duration at greatest eclipse of seven minutes or more. These eclipses all take place when Earth is near the aphelion (June–August), resulting in a small solar disk. The total eclipse with the longest duration of totality occurs on 2186 Jul 16. Its central duration of 7 minutes 29 seconds is very close to the theoretical maximum of 7 minutes 32.1 seconds during that epoch (Meeus, 2004). The eight eclipses are members of just two Saros series. The eclipses of 1937, 1955 and 1973 all belong to Saros 136. This is the same Saros producing the 6+ minute eclipses in 1991, 2009 and 2027. In all cases the eclipse magnitude is greater than 1.07.

Table 3–20: Total Eclipses with Central Duration* of 7 Minutes or More

Date (Dynamical Time)	Saros	Gamma	Eclipse Magnitude	Central Duration
1937 Jun 08	136	−0.225	1.075	07m 04s
1955 Jun 20	136	−0.153	1.078	07m 08s
1973 Jun 30	136	−0.079	1.079	07m 04s
2150 Jun 25	139	−0.091	1.080	07m 14s
2168 Jul 05	139	−0.166	1.081	07m 26s
2186 Jul 16	139	−0.240	1.080	07m 29s
2204 Jul 27	139	−0.313	1.079	07m 22s
2222 Aug 08	139	−0.384	1.077	07m 06s

*Central line duration at the instant of greatest eclipse

3.11 Greatest Central Duration: Hybrid Eclipses

Six hybrid eclipses have a central duration at greatest eclipse greater than or equal to 1 minute 30 seconds. . In all cases the eclipse magnitude is greater than 1.014

Table 3–21: Hybrid Eclipses with Central Duration* of 1m 30s or More

Date (Dynamical Time)	Saros	Gamma	Eclipse Magnitude	Central Duration*
1564 Jun 08	120	0.1252	1.0174	01m44s
1705 May 22	123	−0.1525	1.0147	01m32s
1825 Dec 09	139	0.5296	1.0148	01m34s
2013 Nov 03	143	0.3272	1.0159	01m40s
2172 Oct 17	146	−0.1484	1.0174	01m34s
2386 Apr 29	154	−0.5483	1.0147	01m30s

*Central line duration at the instant of greatest eclipse

3.12 Theoretical Maximum Duration of Annularity

The theoretical maximum duration of an annular solar eclipse slowly varies due to long term secular changes in the eccentricity of Earth's orbit and the longitude of its perihelion. Although the maximum theoretical duration differs between the ascending and descending nodes, the durations are equal in the year 1246 because the Sun's perihelion then coincides with longitude 270°.

Table 3–22 lists the maximum duration theoretically possible over the period -2000 to +7000 (Meeus, 2007). The values here are 0.2 seconds smaller than those in Meeus due to the use of a slightly larger value for the Moon's radius k (Sect. 2.2).

Table 3–22: Theoretical Maximum Duration of Annularity

Year	Duration at Ascending Node	Duration at Descending Node
−2000	12m 16.8s	11m 40.9s
−1000	12m 30.2s	12m 04.8s
0000	12m 35.5s	12m 21.3s
+1000	12m 32.3s	12m 29.5s
+2000	12m 20.7s	12m 29.2s
+3000	12m 01.4s	12m 20.6s
+4000	11m 35.6s	12m 04.6s
+5000	11m 04.9s	11m 42.4s
+6000	10m 31.0s	11m 15.9s
+7000	10m 33.1s	11m 15.7s

The absolute maximum of 12 minutes 35.6 seconds occurred at the Moon's ascending node about the year +125. An inflexion point occurs between the years +6000 and +7000, when the maximum possible durations increase once again.

All calculations in the *Canon* use the same mean lunar radius k for both annular and total eclipses (Sect. 2.2). Consequently, the annular durations are extended several seconds since they include the appearance of Baily's beads[9] at the start and end of the antumbral phase.

3.13 Theoretical Maximum Duration of Totality

The theoretical maximum duration of a total solar eclipse for a point on Earth's surface slowly varies with time. This effect is due to long term secular changes in the eccentricity of Earth's orbit and the longitude of its perihelion. That eccentricity is now 0.01671, but at some epochs in the distant past or future the orbit was or will be almost exactly circular, and at other times the eccentricity can be as large as 0.06.

Table 3–23 lists the maximum duration theoretically possible over the period −2000 to +7000 (Meeus 2003). The values here are 0.1 to 0.2 seconds larger than those in Meeus due to the use of a slightly larger value for the Moon's radius k (Sect. 2.2).

---

[9] Baily's beads are caused by the appearance of small points of sunlight shining through deep valleys along the Moon's limb at the beginning and end of the annular or total phase.

Table 3-23: Theoretical Maximum Duration of Totality

Year	Duration at Ascending Node	Duration at Descending Node
−2000	7m 07.4s	7m 29.8s
−1000	7m 19.1s	7m 34.6s
0000	7m 27.4s	7m 36.0s
+1000	7m 31.9s	7m 33.6s
+2000	7m 32.3s	7m 27.1s
+3000	7m 28.8s	7m 17.1s
+4000	7m 22.1s	7m 04.0s
+5000	7m 12.9s	6m 48.7s
+6000	7m 03.3s	6m 32.5s
+7000	7m 01.9s	6m 32.8s

The absolute maximum of 7 minutes 36.1 seconds occurred at the Moon's descending node about the year −120. Prior to −2000 there must have been epochs when the maximum possible duration was even larger due to an even greater value of the eccentricity of Earth's orbit.

3.14 Eclipse Duos

A duo is a pair of eclipses separated by one lunation (synodic month). Of the 2,389 eclipses in the *Canon*, 282 eclipses (11.8%) belong to a duo. In most cases, both eclipses in a duo are partial eclipses. However there are three instances in the *Canon* where one eclipse is partial and the other is total. The dates and eclipse combinations are listed in Table 3-24.

Table 3-24: Eclipse Duos of Two Types

Dates (Dynamical Time)	Eclipse Combinations
1928 May–Jun	TP
2195 Jul–Aug	PT
2459 May–Jun	PT

3.15 Eclipses Duos in One Calendar Month

There are ten instances where both members of an eclipse duo occur in the same calendar month. In all cases, both eclipses in the duos are partial. The year and month of each occurrence appears in Table 3-25.

Table 3-25: Two Eclipses in One Calendar Month

1631 May	2000 Jul	2304 Sep
1696 May	2206 Dec	2380 Aug
1805 Jan	2261 Jan	
1880 Dec	2282 Nov	

3.16 Eclipse Seasons

The ~5.1° inclination of the lunar orbit around Earth means that the Moon's orbit crosses the ecliptic at two points or nodes. If New Moon takes place within approximately 17° of a node[10], then a solar eclipse will be visible from some location on Earth.

The Sun makes one complete circuit of the ecliptic in 365.24 days, so its average angular velocity is 0.99° per day. At this rate, it takes 34.5 days for the Sun to cross the 34° wide eclipse zone centered on each node. Because the Moon's orbit with respect to the Sun has a mean duration of 29.53 days, there will always be one and possibly two solar eclipses during each 34.5-day interval when the Sun passes through the nodal eclipse zones. These time periods are called eclipse seasons.

The mid-point of each eclipse season is separated by 173.3 days because this is the mean time for the Sun to travel from one node to the next. The period is a little less that half a calendar year because the lunar nodes slowly regress westward by 19.3° per year.

Figure 3–1: Eclipse Seasons and Orbital Nodes

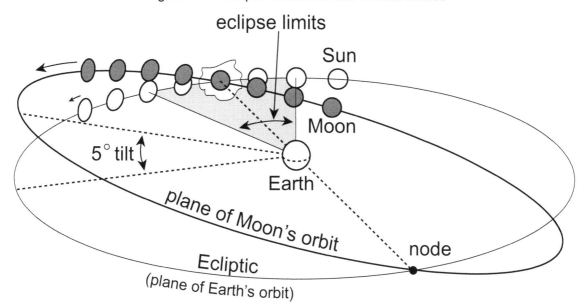

Figure 3–1 The paths of the Sun and Moon through the sky illustrate why eclipses occur only when the Sun is near the intersection or node where the Moon crosses the ecliptic. The plane of the Moon's orbit is inclined approximately 5° to the ecliptic plane.

---

[10] The exact angular distance from the node depends on the distances of the Sun and the Moon from Earth, which determine their angular diameters.

3.17 Quincena

The mean time interval between New Moon and Full Moon is 14.77 days. This is less than half the duration of a 34.5-day eclipse season. As a consequence, the same Sun–node alignment geometry responsible for producing a solar eclipse always results in a complementary lunar eclipse within a fortnight. The lunar eclipse may precede or succeed the solar eclipse. In either case, the pair of eclipses is referred to here as a quincena[11]. The QLE (Quincena Lunar Eclipse parameter) identifies the type of the lunar eclipse and whether it precedes or succeeds a particular solar eclipse. There are three basic types of lunar eclipses:

1. penumbral lunar eclipse (n) — Moon passes partly or completely within Earth's penumbral shadow
2. partial lunar eclipse (p) — Moon passes partly within Earth's umbral shadow
3. total lunar eclipse (t) — Moon passes completely within Earth's umbral shadow

The QLE is a two character string consisting of one or more of the above lunar eclipse types. The first character in the QLE identifies the type of lunar eclipse preceding a solar eclipse. The second character identifies the type of lunar eclipse succeeding a solar eclipse. In most instances, one of the two characters is "–" indicating no lunar eclipse occurs. For example, a QLE of "-p" means that no lunar eclipse precedes a solar eclipse, but a partial lunar eclipse follows the solar eclipse 15 days later.

On rare occasions, a double quincena occurs in which a solar eclipse is both preceded and succeeded by a lunar eclipse.

3.18 Quincena Combinations with Partial Solar Eclipses

A partial solar eclipse is almost always preceded or succeeded by a total lunar eclipse (99.6 %). On extremely rare occasions (0.3%), a partial lunar eclipse occurs before a partial solar eclipse. However, there are no instances of a partial lunar eclipse following a partial solar eclipse in the *Canon*. No double quincenas occur with partial solar eclipses. A list of partial solar eclipse and quincena lunar eclipse combinations is found in Table 3–26.

Table 3–26. Quincena Combinations with Partial Solar Eclipses

Quincena Lunar Eclipse	QLE	Number	Percent	Examples (Years)
– total	-t	426	50.8%	..., 2000, 2004, 2015, 2018, 2019,...
total –	t–	411	49.0%	..., 2000, 2007, 2011, 2014, 2018,...
partial –	p–	1	0.1%	2086

---

[11] Quincena is a Spanish word meaning *a period of fifteen days*. This also happens to be the time interval, rounded to the nearest day, between New Moon and Full Moon, or Full Moon and New Moon. So *quincena* is a convenient and appropriate term for describing a pair of eclipses (one solar and one lunar) separated by this period.

3.19 Quincena Combinations with Annular Solar Eclipses

An annular solar eclipse can be preceded or succeeded by a total lunar eclipse (9.0%), a partial lunar eclipse (57.4%), or a penumbral lunar eclipse (8.5%). Double quincenas for annular solar eclipses consisting of two penumbral lunar eclipses (23.8%) are common, but penumbral–partial combinations are rare (1.3%). A list of quincena lunar eclipse combinations with annular solar eclipses is found in Table 3–27.

Table 3–27. Quincena Combinations with Annular Solar Eclipses

Quincena Lunar Eclipse	QLE	Number	Percent	Examples (Years)
– total	–t	34	4.3%	..., 1990, 2008, 2026, 2044, 2102,...
total –	t–	37	4.7%	..., 1891, 2003, 2014, 2021, 2032,...
– partial	–p	227	28.6%	..., 1994, 2005, 2012, 2023, 2030,...
partial –	p–	195	24.6%	..., 2006, 2010, 2024, 2028, 2039,...
– penumbral	–n	36	4.5%	..., 2001, 2009, 2016, 2019, 2027,...
penumbral –	n–	35	4.4%	..., 1999, 2017, 2035, 2042, 2053,...
partial–penumbral	pn	7	0.9%	..., 1608, 1749, 2013, 2147, 2288,...
penumbral–partial	np	4	0.5%	1553, 1694, 1835, 1958
penumbral–penumbral	nn	219	27.6%	..., 1998, 2002, 2020, 2031, 2038, 2049,...

3.20 Quincena Combinations with Total Solar Eclipses

A total solar eclipse can be preceded or succeeded by a total lunar eclipse (7.9%), a partial lunar eclipse (53.8%), or a penumbral lunar eclipse (27.4%). Double quincenas for total solar eclipses (the solar eclipse is both preceded and succeeded by a lunar eclipse) occur with a frequency of 14.0% and always consist of two penumbral lunar eclipses. A detailed list of total solar eclipse and quincena lunar eclipse combinations appears in Table 3–28.

Table 3–28 Quincena Combinations with Total Solar Eclipses

Quincena Lunar Eclipse	QLE	Number	Percent	Examples (Years)
– total	–t	27	4.1%	..., 1968, 2015, 2033, 2044, 2073,...
total –	t–	25	3.8%	..., 2003, 2043, 2061, 2072, 2090,...
– partial	–p	179	27.5%	..., 2008, 2019, 2026, 2037, 2041,...
partial –	p–	171	26.3%	..., 1999, 2010, 2017, 2021, 2028,...
– penumbral	–n	87	13.4%	..., 1998, 2012, 2016, 2030, 2034,...
penumbral –	n–	91	14.0%	..., 2006, 2020, 2024, 2038, 2042,...
penumbral–penumbral	nn	71	10.9%	..., 1991, 2009, 2027, 2096, 2114,...

3.21 Quincena Combinations with Hybrid Solar Eclipses

A hybrid solar eclipse can be preceded or succeeded by a total lunar eclipse (3.0%), a partial lunar eclipse (51.1%), or a penumbral lunar eclipse (24.9%). Double quincenas consisting of two penumbral lunar eclipses (20.9%) are also fairly common. A complete list of quincena lunar eclipse combinations with hybrid solar eclipses appears in Table 3–29.

Table 3–29. Quincena Combinations with Hybrid Solar Eclipses

Quincena Lunar Eclipse	QLE	Number	Percent	Examples (Years)
– total	–t	1	0.9%	1986
total –	t–	6	5.7%	1544, 1627, 1645, 1768, 1909, 2050
– partial	–p	18	17.0%	..., 1827, 1845, 2164, 2182, 2323,...
partial –	p–	54	50.9%	..., 1912, 1930, 2209, 2350, 2368,...
– penumbral	–n	5	4.7%	1864, 1987, 2005, 2023, 2385
penumbral –	n–	6	5.7%	1702, 1908, 2013, 2031, 2049, 2067
penumbral–penumbral	nn	16	15.1%	..., 1843, 1846, 2172, 2190, 2208,...

Photo 3–1 A few minutes after the annular phase, the crescent Sun sets behind a field of wind turbines from Elida, New Mexico. ©2012 F. Espenak

Section 4: Explanation of Solar Eclipse Catalog in Appendix A

4.1 Introduction

Earth experiences 2,389 eclipses of the Sun during the 1000-year period from 1501 to 2500. The catalog in *Appendix A* consists of a series of tables that summarize the principal characteristics of each eclipse over this time interval. The tables compliment the eclipse maps in *Appendix B*.

Each line in the catalog corresponds to a single eclipse and provides concise parameters to characterize the eclipse. The calendar date and Dynamical Time of the instant of greatest eclipse (when the Moon's shadow axis passes closest to Earth's center) are given, along with the adopted value of Delta T (ΔT). The lunation number (since 2000 Jan 06) and the Saros series are listed along with the eclipse type (P=Partial, A=Annular, T=Total, or H=Hybrid). Gamma is the distance of the shadow axis from Earth's center at greatest eclipse, while the eclipse magnitude is defined as the fraction of the Sun's diameter obscured at that instant. The geographic latitude and longitude of the umbral or antumbral axis are given for greatest eclipse, along with the Sun's altitude and azimuth, the width of the path (kilometers), and the central line duration of totality or annularity. For both partial and non-central total or annular eclipses, the latitude and longitude correspond to the point closest to the shadow cone axis at greatest eclipse. The Sun's altitude is always 0° at this location. Detailed descriptions of each field in the catalog appear in the following sections.

4.2 Cat Num (Catalog Number)

The catalog number is the sequential number assigned to each eclipse from 1 to 2,389.

4.3 Canon Plate

Appendix B consists of 200 plates with 12 eclipse maps per plate. The canon plate identifies the plate number where each eclipse map appears.

4.4 Calendar Date

The Julian calendar is used prior to 1582 Oct 15. All eclipse dates from 1582 Oct 15 onwards use the modern Gregorian calendar currently found throughout most of the world. Because of the Gregorian Calendar Reform, the day following 1582 Oct 04 (Julian calendar) is 1582 Oct 15 (Gregorian calendar).

4.5 TD of Greatest Eclipse (Terrestrial Dynamical Time of Greatest Eclipse)

The instant of greatest eclipse occurs when the distance between the axis of the Moon's shadow cone and the center of Earth reaches a minimum. For partial eclipses, the instant of greatest eclipse differs slightly from the instant of greatest magnitude due to Earth's flattening. For total eclipses, the instant of greatest eclipse differs slightly from the instant of greatest duration, although the differences are relatively small.

Greatest eclipse is given in Terrestrial Dynamical Time or TD (Sect. 2.5), which is a time system based on International Atomic Time. As such, TD is the modern equivalent to its predecessor Ephemeris Time and is used in theories of planetary motion in the Solar System. To determine the geographic visibility of an eclipse, TD is converted to Universal Time (UT1) using the parameter Delta T (Sect. 2.6).

4.6 ΔT (Delta T)

ΔT (Delta T) is the arithmetic difference, in seconds, between Terrestrial Dynamical Time (TD) and Universal Time (UT1). For more information on ΔT, see Section 2.6.

4.7 Luna Num (Lunation Number)

The lunation number is the number of synodic months or lunations since New Moon on 2000 Jan 06. It can be converted to the Brown Lunation Number[12] by adding 953.

4.8 Saros Num (Saros Series Number)

Each eclipse belongs to a Saros series using a numbering system first introduced by van den Bergh (1955). The eclipses with an odd Saros number take place at the ascending node of the Moon's orbit; those with an even Saros number take place at the descending node. This relationship is reversed for *lunar* eclipses.

The Saros is a period of 223 synodic months (~ 18 years, 11 days, and 8 hours). Eclipses separated by this period belong to the same Saros series and share similar geometry and characteristics.

4.9 Ecl Type (Solar Eclipse Type)

The first character in this 2-character parameter gives the eclipse type. The four basic types of solar eclipses are:

1. Partial Solar Eclipse (P) — The Moon's penumbral shadow traverses Earth; the Moon's umbral and antumbral shadows completely miss Earth
2. Annular Solar Eclipse (A) — The Moon's penumbral and antumbral shadows traverse Earth; the Moon is too far from Earth to completely cover the Sun
3. Total Solar Eclipse (T) — The Moon's penumbral and umbral shadow traverse Earth; the Moon is close enough to Earth to completely cover the Sun
4. Hybrid Solar Eclipse (H) — The Moon's penumbral, umbral and antumbral shadows traverse different parts of Earth; eclipse appears either total or annular along different sections of its path; hybrid eclipses are also known as annular-total eclipses

---

[12] The *Brown Lunation Number* defines lunation 1 as beginning at the first New Moon of 1923, the year when Ernest W. Brown's lunar theory was introduced in the major national astronomical almanacs.

The second character of the eclipse type is a qualifier defined as follows.

1. m = Middle eclipse of Saros series
2. n = Central eclipse with no northern limit
3. s = Central eclipse with no southern limit
4. + = Non-central eclipse with no northern limit
5. – = Non-central eclipse with no southern limit
6. 2 = Hybrid eclipse path begins total and ends annular
7. 3 = Hybrid eclipse path begins annular and ends total
8. b = Saros series begins (first eclipse in a Saros series)
9. e = Saros series ends (last eclipse in a Saros series)

Qualifiers 1 through 5 are used with annular, total or hybrid eclipses but not partial eclipses. Qualifiers 6 and 7 apply only to special classes of hybrid eclipses while qualifiers 8 and 9 are used exclusively with partial eclipses.

4.10 QLE (Quincena Lunar Eclipse Parameter)

A lunar eclipse always occurs within 15 days of a solar eclipse. The Quincena Lunar Eclipse parameter (QLE) identifies the type of the lunar eclipse and whether it precedes or succeeds a particular solar eclipse. There are three basic types of lunar eclipses:

1. Penumbral Lunar Eclipse (n) — The Moon passes partly or completely through Earth's penumbra
2. Partial Lunar Eclipse (p) — The Moon passes partly through Earth's umbra
3. Total Lunar Eclipse (t) — The Moon passes completely through Earth's umbra

The QLE consists of a two-character string. The characters identify the type of lunar eclipse preceding and succeeding a solar eclipse, respectively. In most instances, one of the two characters in the QLE is "–" indicating no lunar eclipse occurs. On some occasions, a double quincena occurs in which a solar eclipse is both preceded and succeeded by a lunar eclipse. The QLE then consists of two characters identifying the types of the two lunar eclipses. (Section 3.17).

4.11 Gamma

Gamma is the minimum distance from the axis of the lunar shadow cone to the center of Earth, in units of Earth's equatorial radius. This distance is positive or negative, depending on whether the axis of the shadow cone passes north or south of Earth's center. If gamma is between +0.997 and – 0.997, the eclipse is a central one (either total, annular, or hybrid). The limiting value 0.997 differs from unity because of the flattening of Earth.

4.12 Ecl Mag (Eclipse Magnitude)

The eclipse magnitude is defined as the fraction of the Sun's diameter occulted by the Moon. For partial eclipses, the eclipse magnitude at the instant of greatest eclipse is given for the geographic position closest to the axis of the Moon's shadow cone. For central eclipses (total, annular, and hybrid), the eclipse magnitude listed is actually the ratio of the topocentric apparent diameters of the Moon and the Sun at greatest eclipse. The eclipse magnitude is always less than 1.0 for partial and annular eclipses, but equal to, or greater than, 1.0 for total and hybrid eclipses.

4.13 Lat Long (Latitude and Longitude)

The latitude and longitude corresponds to the geographic position intersected by the axis of the lunar shadow cone at greatest eclipse.

4.14 Sun Alt (Altitude of Sun)

The Sun's altitude at the geographic position intersected by the axis of the lunar shadow cone is given at the instant of greatest eclipse. For partial eclipses, the Sun's altitude is always 0° because the shadow axis misses Earth. In this case, the geographic position corresponds to the point closest to the shadow axis.

4.15 Sun Azm (Azimuth of Sun)

The Sun's azimuth at the geographic position intersected by the axis of the lunar shadow cone is given at the instant of greatest eclipse. The values 0°, 90°, 180°, and 270° correspond to the cardinal directions north, east, south and west, respectively.

4.16 Path Width

For central eclipses (total, annular, or hybrid), the width of the path of totality or annularity (kilometers) is given at the geographic position intersected by the axis of the lunar shadow cone at the instant of greatest eclipse.

4.17 Central Line Dur (Central Line Duration)

For central eclipses (total, annular, or hybrid), the central line duration of the total or annular phase (in minutes and seconds) is given at the geographic position intersected by the axis of the lunar shadow cone at the instant of greatest eclipse.

In the case of total and hybrid eclipses, this duration is very close to the maximum duration (ignoring limb profile effects) of the total phase along the entire umbral path. For annular eclipses, the duration at greatest eclipse may be near either the minimum or maximum duration of the annular phase along the path. If the annular phase duration exceeds approximately 2.3 min, then it is very close to the maximum duration along the central line track. If the annular phase duration is less, however, then it corresponds to a minimum and the annular duration increases towards the ends of the central path.

4.18 EclipseWise.com and Solar Eclipse Catalog

The maps and catalog in the *Thousand Year Canon* form the basis of a new website on solar and lunar eclipse predictions: *www.EclipseWise.com*. A plain text file containing the entire solar eclipse catalog in *Appendix A* can be downloaded at: *www.EclipseWise.com/solar/SEpubs/TYCSEcatalog.txt*. This catalog may not be distributed, published, posted or used in any other fashion without written permission from the author.

Section 5: Explanation of Solar Eclipse Maps in Appendix B

5.1 Introduction

Earth experiences 2,389 eclipses of the Sun during the 1000-year period from 1501 to 2500. An individual global map for each eclipse appears in *Appendix B*.

The geographic visibility of each eclipse is illustrated with an orthographic projection map of Earth showing the path of the Moon's penumbral (partial) and umbral/antumbral (total, hybrid, or annular) shadows with respect to the continental coastlines, political boundaries (circa 2000) and the Equator. North is to the top and the daylight terminator is drawn for the instant of greatest eclipse. An x symbol marks the sub-solar point where the Sun appears directly overhead at that time. The salient features of the eclipse maps are identified in Figure 5–1, which serves as a key.

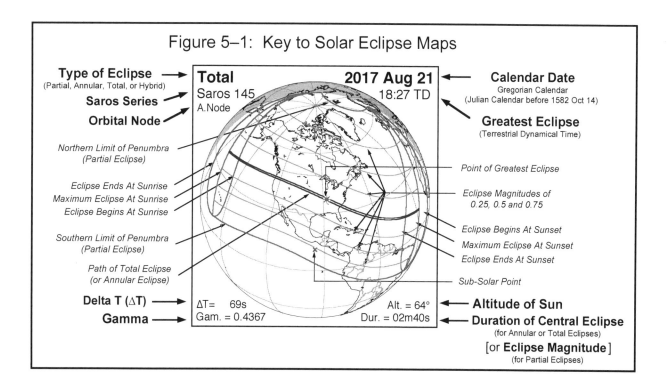

The limits of the Moon's penumbral shadow delineate the region of visibility of a partial solar eclipse. This irregular or saddle shaped region often covers more than half the daylight hemisphere of Earth and consists of several distinct zones or limits. At the northern and/or southern boundaries lie the limits of the penumbra's path. Partial eclipses have only one of these limits, as do central eclipses when the Moon's shadow axis falls no closer than about 0.45 radii from Earth's center. Great loops at the western and eastern extremes of the penumbra's path identify the areas where the eclipse begins/ends at sunrise and sunset, respectively. If the penumbra has both a northern and southern limit, the rising and setting curves form two separate, closed loops (e.g., 2017 Aug 21). Otherwise, the curves are connected in a distorted figure eight (e.g., 2019 Jul 02). Bisecting the *eclipse begins/ends at sunrise and sunset* loops is the curve of maximum eclipse at sunrise (western loop) and sunset (eastern loop).

The eclipse magnitude is defined as the fraction of the Sun's diameter occulted by the Moon. A curve of constant eclipse magnitude delineates the locus of all points where the local magnitude at maximum eclipse is equal to a constant value. The maps include *curves of constant eclipse magnitude* for values of 0.25, 0.5 and 0.75. These curves run exclusively between the curves of maximum eclipse at sunrise and sunset. They are approximately parallel to the northern/southern penumbral limits and the umbral/antumbral paths of central eclipses. The northern and southern limits of the penumbra may be thought of as curves of eclipse magnitude of 0.0. For total eclipses, the northern and southern limits of the umbra are curves of eclipse magnitude of 1.0.

Greatest eclipse is the instant when the axis of the Moon's shadow cone passes closest to Earth's center. Although greatest eclipse differs slightly from the instants of greatest magnitude and greatest duration (for total eclipses), the differences are relatively small. The point on Earth's surface intersected by the axis of the Moon's shadow cone at greatest eclipse is marked by an asterisk symbol "*". For partial eclipses, the shadow axis misses Earth entirely, so the point of greatest eclipse lies on the day/night terminator and the Sun appears on the horizon.

Data relevant to an eclipse appear in the corners of each map. In the top left corner are the eclipse type (total, hybrid, annular, or partial), the Saros series of the eclipse, and the node of the Moon's orbit where the eclipse occurs. To the top right are the Gregorian calendar date (Julian calendar prior to 1582 Oct 14), the time of greatest eclipse (Terrestrial Dynamical Time), and the value of Delta T (ΔT).

The bottom left corner lists gamma (the minimum distance of the Moon's shadow cone axis from Earth's center, in Earth equatorial radii). The Sun's altitude at the geographic position of greatest eclipse is found to the lower right. The content of the final datum in the bottom right corner depends on the type of eclipse. If the eclipse is partial then the eclipse magnitude is given. If the eclipse is total, hybrid or annular, then the duration of the total or annular phase is given at the instant of greatest eclipse. A detailed explanation of each of these items appears in the following sections.

5.2 Solar Eclipse Type

There are four basic types of solar eclipses:

1. Partial Solar Eclipse — Moon's penumbral shadow traverses Earth; Moon's umbral and antumbral shadows completely miss Earth
2. Annular Solar Eclipse — Moon's penumbral and antumbral shadows traverse Earth; Moon is too far from Earth to completely cover the Sun from within the antumbral path.
3. Total Solar Eclipse — Moon's penumbral and umbral shadow traverse Earth; Moon is close enough to Earth to completely cover the Sun from within the umbral path.
4. Hybrid Solar Eclipse — Moon's penumbral, umbral and antumbral shadows traverse different parts of Earth; eclipse appears either total or annular along different sections of the central path; hybrid eclipses are also known as annular-total eclipses.

5.3 Saros Series Number

Each eclipse belongs to a Saros series using a numbering system first introduced by van den Bergh (1955). The eclipses with an odd Saros number take place at the ascending node of the Moon's orbit; those with an even Saros number take place at the descending node. This relationship is reversed for *lunar* eclipses.

The Saros is a period of 223 synodic months (~ 18 years, 11 days, and 8 hours). Eclipses separated by this period belong to the same Saros series and share similar geometry and characteristics.

5.4 Node

A solar eclipse is only possible when New Moon occurs near one of the Moon's two orbital nodes. The ascending node (A. Node) is the point where the Moon travels from south to north through Earth's orbital plane. Similarly, the descending node (D. Node) is the point where the Moon travels from north to south through Earth's orbital plane.

5.5 Calendar Date

The Julian calendar is used prior to 1582 Oct 15. All eclipse dates from 1582 Oct 15 onwards use the modern Gregorian calendar currently found throughout most of the world. Because of the Gregorian Calendar Reform, the day following 1582 Oct 04 (Julian calendar) is 1582 Oct 15 (Gregorian calendar).

5.6 Greatest Eclipse

The instant of greatest eclipse occurs when the distance between the axis of the Moon's shadow cone and the center of Earth reaches a minimum. For partial eclipses, the instant of greatest eclipse differs slightly from the instant of greatest magnitude due to Earth's flattening. For total eclipses, the instant of greatest eclipse differs slightly from the instant of greatest duration, although the differences are relatively small.

Greatest eclipse is given in Terrestrial Dynamical Time or TD (Sect. 2.5), which is a time system based on International Atomic Time. As such, TD is the modern equivalent to its predecessor Ephemeris Time and is used in theories of planetary motion in the Solar System. To determine the geographic visibility of an eclipse, TD is converted to Universal Time (UT1) using the parameter Delta T (Sect. 2.6).

5.7 ΔT (Delta T)

ΔT (Delta T) is the arithmetic difference, in seconds, between Terrestrial Dynamical Time (TD) and Universal Time (UT1). For more information on ΔT, see Section 2.6.

5.8 Gamma

The quantity gamma is the minimum distance from the axis of the lunar shadow cone to the center of Earth, in units of Earth's equatorial radius. This distance is positive or negative, depending on whether the axis of the shadow cone passes north or south of Earth's center. If gamma is between +0.997 and –0.997, the eclipse is a central one (either total, annular or hybrid). The limiting value 0.997 differs from unity due of the flattening of Earth.

5.9 Altitude of Sun

The Sun's altitude at the geographic position intersected by the axis of the lunar shadow cone is given at the instant of greatest eclipse. For partial eclipses, the Sun's altitude is always 0° because the shadow axis misses Earth. In this case, the geographic position corresponds to the point closest to the shadow axis.

5.10 Duration of Central Eclipse

For central eclipses (total, annular, or hybrid), the central line duration of the total or annular phase (in minutes and seconds) is given at the geographic position intersected by the axis of the lunar shadow cone at the instant of greatest eclipse.

5.11 Eclipse Magnitude

The eclipse magnitude is defined as the fraction of the Sun's diameter occulted by the Moon. For partial eclipses, the eclipse magnitude at the instant of greatest eclipse is given for the geographic position closest to the axis of the Moon's shadow cone. For central eclipses (total, annular, and hybrid), the eclipse magnitude listed is actually the ratio of the topocentric apparent diameters of the Moon and the Sun at greatest eclipse. The eclipse magnitude is always less than 1.0 for partial and annular eclipses, but equal to, or greater than, 1.0 for total and hybrid eclipses.

References

Astronomical Almanac for 1986, Washington: US Government Printing Office; London: HM Stationery Office (1985).

Astronomical Almanac for 2011, Washington: US Government Printing Office; London: HM Stationery Office (2010).

Bretagnon, P., and Francou G., "Planetary theories in rectangular and spherical variables: VSOP87 solution," *Astron. Astrophys.,* **202**(309) (1988).

Chapront-Touzé, M., and Chapront, J., "The Lunar Ephemeris ELP 2000," *Astron. Astrophys.,* vol. 124, no. 1, pp. 50–62 (1983).

Chapront, J., Chapront-Touzé, M., and Francou, G., "A new determination of lunar orbital parameters, precession constant and tidal acceleration from LLR measurements," *Astron. Astrophys.,* vol. 387, pp. 700–709 (2002).

Dickey, J.O., Bender, P.L., Faller, J.E., Newhall, X.X., Ricklefs, R.L., Ries,, J.G., Shelus, P.J., Veillet, C., Whipple, A.L., Wiant, J.R., Williams, J.G., and Yoder, C.F., "Lunar Laser Ranging: a Continuing Legacy of the Apollo Program," *Science,* 265, pp. 482–490 (1994).

Espenak, F., *Fifty Year Canon of Solar Eclipses: 1986–2035,* Sky Publishing Corp., Cambridge, Massuchusetts (1987).

Espenak, F., *Fifty Year Canon of Lunar Eclipses: 1986–2035,* Sky Publishing Corp., Cambridge, Massuchusetts (1989).

Espenak, F., *Thousand Year Canon of Lunar Eclipses: 1501 to 2500,* Astropixels Publishing, Portal, Arizona (2014).

Espenak, F., and Meeus, J., *Five Millennium Canon of Solar Eclipses: –1999 to +3000 (2000 BCE to 3000 CE),* NASA Tech. Pub. 2006-214141, NASA Goddard Space Flight Center, Greenbelt, Maryland (2006).

Espenak, F., and Meeus, J., *Five Millennium Canon of Lunar Eclipses: –1999 to +3000 (2000 BCE to 3000 CE),* NASA Tech. Pub. 2006-214172, NASA Goddard Space Flight Center, Greenbelt, Maryland (2009a).

Espenak, F., and Meeus, J., *Five Millennium Catalog of Lunar Eclipses: –1999 to +3000 (2000 BCE to 3000 CE),* NASA Tech. Pub. 2006-214173, NASA Goddard Space Flight Center, Greenbelt, Maryland (2009b).

Espenak, F., and Meeus, J., *Five Millennium Catalog of Solar Eclipses: –1999 to +3000 (2000 BCE to 3000 CE),* NASA Tech. Pub. 2006-214174, NASA Goddard Space Flight Center, Greenbelt, Maryland (2009c).

Espenak, F., *Thousand Year Catalog of Lunar Eclipses 1501 to 2500,* Astropixels Publishing, Portal, Arizona (2014).

49

Explanatory Supplement to the Ephemeris, H.M. Almanac Office, London (1974).

Littmann, M., Espenak, F., and Willcox, K., *Totality—Eclipses of the Sun*, 3rd Ed., Oxford University Press, New York (2008).

Meeus, J., *Mathematical Astronomy Morsels*, Willmann-Bell, pp. 56–62 (1997).

——, *More Mathematical Astronomy Morsels*, Willmann-Bell, pp. 120–126 (2002a).

——, *More Mathematical Astronomy Morsels*, Willmann-Bell, pp. 70–72 (2002b).

——, "The maximum possible duration of a total solar eclipse," *J. Br. Astron. Assoc.,* **113**(6) (2003).

——, *Mathematical Astronomy Morsels III*, Willmann-Bell, pp. 109–111, (2004).

——, *Mathematical Astronomy Morsels IV*, Willmann-Bell, pp. 44–45, (2007).

——, Grosjean, C.C., and Vanderleen, W., *Canon of Solar Eclipses*, Pergamon Press, Oxford, United Kingdom (1966).

Morrison, L., and Stephenson, F.R., "Historical Values of the Earth's Clock Error DT and the Calculation of Eclipses," *J. Hist. Astron.,* Vol. 35 Part 3, August 2004, No. 120, pp, 327–336 (2004).

Mucke, H., and Meeus, J., *Canon of Solar Eclipses: –2003 to +2526*, Astronomisches Büro, Vienna (1983).

Newcomb, S., "Tables of the Motion of the Earth on its Axis Around the Sun," *Astron. Papers Amer. Eph.,* Vol. 6, Part I (1895).

Stephenson, F.R., *Historical Eclipses and Earth's Rotation*, Cambridge University Press, Cambridge (1997).

van den Bergh, *Periodicity and Variation of Solar (and Lunar) Eclipses*, Tjeenk Willink, and Haarlem, Netherlands (1955).

van der Sluys, M. , *http://hemel.waarnemen.com/Computing/deltat.html* (2010).

von Oppolzer, T.R., *Canon der Finsternisse*, Wien, (1887); Gingerich, O., (Translator) *Canon of Eclipses*, Dover Publications, New York (1962).

Appendix A

Solar Eclipse Catalog: 1501 to 2500

Key to Solar Eclipse Catalog

Cat Num — sequential Catalog Number assigned to each eclipse from 1 to 2,389

Canon Plate — plate number assigned to each eclipse map

Calendar Date — Gregorian date of Greatest Eclipse (Julian date prior to 1582 Oct 04)

TD of Greatest Eclipse — Terrestrial Dynamical Time of Greatest Eclipse

ΔT — arithmetic difference between Terrestrial Dynamical Time Universal Time (seconds)

Luna Num — number of synodic months, or lunations, since New Moon on 2000 Jan 06

Saros Num — Saros Series Number of eclipse

Ecl Type — Solar Eclipse Type

    P = Partial Solar Eclipse
    A = Annular Solar Eclipse
    T = Total Solar Eclipse
    H = Hybrid Solar Eclipse
    m = Middle eclipse of Saros series
    n = Central eclipse of with no northern limit
    s = Central eclipse of with no southern limit
    + = Non-central eclipse of with no northern limit
    – = Non-central eclipse of with no southern limit
    2 = Hybrid eclipse path begins total and ends annular
    3 = Hybrid eclipse path begins annular and ends total
    b = Saros series begins (first eclipse in a Saros series)
    e = Saros series ends (last eclipse in a Saros series)

QLE — Quincena Lunar Eclipse Parameter

    n = Penumbral Lunar Eclipse
    p = Partial Lunar Eclipse
    t = Total Lunar Eclipse

Gamma — minimum distance from the axis of the lunar shadow to the center of Earth

Ecl Mag — Eclipse Magnitude; fraction of the Sun's diameter obscured by the Moon

Lat & Lng — latitude and longitude where the Sun appears in zenith at greatest eclipse

Sun Alt & **Sun Azm** — altitude and azimuth of the Sun at greatest eclipse

Path Width — width of the central path (km) at greatest eclipse (total, annular & hybrid eclipses)

Central Line Dur — Central Line Duration (minutes. seconds) at greatest eclipse

Cat Num	Canon Plate	Calendar Date	TD of Greatest Eclipse	ΔT s	Luna Num	Saros Num	Ecl Type	QLE	Gamma	Ecl Mag	Lat °	Long °	Sun Alt °	Sun Azm °	Path Width km	Central Line Dur
0001	001	1501 Apr 17	16:15:50	194	-6168	101	P	-t	-1.2070	0.6156	61.9S	1.1W	0	300		
0002	001	1501 May 17	03:27:42	194	-6167	139	Pb	t-	1.5002	0.0905	63.7N	13.6W	0	35		
0003	001	1501 Oct 12	07:30:03	193	-6162	106	P	-t	1.1783	0.6585	61.4N	133.9E	0	247		
0004	001	1502 Apr 07	05:49:57	193	-6156	111	T	-n	-0.4275	1.0567	12.6S	104.7E	65	333	205	04m49s
0005	001	1502 Oct 01	08:36:15	192	-6150	116	A	-p	0.4913	0.9277	19.3N	62.8E	60	210	306	08m16s
0006	001	1503 Mar 27	22:28:19	192	-6144	121	T	n-	0.2904	1.0640	21.1N	164.1W	73	150	218	05m04s
0007	001	1503 Sep 20	08:52:36	191	-6138	126	A	n-	-0.2315	0.9494	14.1S	38.6E	77	30	190	05m27s
0008	001	1504 Mar 16	13:30:08	191	-6132	131	P	t-	1.0345	0.9348	61.0N	114.0W	0	86		
0009	001	1504 Sep 08	15:12:13	190	-6126	136	A	t-	-0.9486	0.9924	55.3S	102.6W	18	58	83	00m32s
0010	001	1505 Feb 04	06:29:06	190	-6121	103	P	-t	-1.0774	0.8255	61.7S	156.9W	0	241		
0011	001	1505 Jul 30	20:51:54	189	-6115	108	T	-t	0.9352	1.0635	67.9N	55.6W	20	263	593	03m25s
0012	001	1506 Jan 24	05:58:05	189	-6109	113	A	-p	-0.3978	0.9209	38.3S	106.1E	66	332	325	08m26s
0013	002	1506 Jul 20	13:46:56	188	-6103	118	T	-n	0.2112	1.0623	30.4N	19.8W	78	202	209	05m08s
0014	002	1507 Jan 13	07:20:08	188	-6097	123	A	n-	0.3024	0.9526	3.0S	68.3E	72	162	181	05m42s
0015	002	1507 Jul 10	03:06:32	187	-6091	128	H	p-	-0.5680	1.0095	12.4S	126.0E	55	16	40	01m01s
0016	002	1508 Jan 02	15:45:07	187	-6085	133	A	t-	0.9732	0.9941	52.8N	77.0W	13	157	92	00m28s
0017	002	1508 May 29	19:09:01	187	-6080	100	P	-t	1.4443	0.2020	67.1N	72.8E	0	360		
0018	002	1508 Jun 28	09:28:42	186	-6079	138	P	t-	-1.3860	0.2993	64.5S	10.4E	0	27		
0019	002	1508 Nov 22	19:24:21	186	-6074	105	P	-t	-1.0850	0.8490	67.8S	74.6E	0	173		
0020	002	1509 May 18	19:49:34	186	-6068	110	A	-p	0.6865	0.9539	64.9N	124.3W	46	171	233	03m56s
0021	002	1509 Nov 12	10:00:13	185	-6062	115	H	-p	-0.4338	1.0131	45.8S	23.2E	64	9	50	01m06s
0022	002	1510 May 08	01:16:14	185	-6056	120	H	nn	-0.1030	1.0033	13.5N	161.4E	84	352	12	00m22s
0023	002	1510 Nov 01	19:13:49	184	-6050	125	A	n-	0.2782	0.9607	1.5S	108.7W	74	190	148	04m54s
0024	002	1511 Apr 27	13:47:22	184	-6044	130	T	p-	-0.8425	1.0463	40.0S	14.7W	32	346	286	03m50s
0025	003	1511 Oct 21	21:19:48	183	-6038	135	A+	t-	1.0059	0.9416	70.7N	98.6W	0	223	-	-
0026	003	1512 Mar 17	22:14:34	183	-6033	102	P	-t	1.0321	0.9517	72.0N	110.2E	0	81		
0027	003	1512 Apr 16	06:22:23	183	-6032	140	Pb	t-	-1.5289	0.0003	70.6S	131.9E	0	314		
0028	003	1512 Sep 10	05:03:24	182	-6027	107	P	-t	-1.2304	0.5689	72.0S	17.4E	0	86		
0029	003	1513 Mar 07	11:54:02	182	-6021	112	H	-p	0.3421	1.0040	17.6N	1.8W	70	161	15	00m24s
0030	003	1513 Aug 30	13:35:50	181	-6015	117	T	-n	-0.4392	1.0211	19.5S	31.9W	64	18	80	02m03s
0031	003	1514 Feb 24	18:45:29	181	-6009	122	A	n-	-0.3974	0.9479	28.2S	90.0W	66	341	208	05m51s
0032	003	1514 Aug 20	04:25:14	180	-6003	127	T	n-	0.3032	1.0667	26.5N	119.9E	72	197	228	05m38s
0033	003	1515 Feb 13	19:08:18	180	-5997	132	P	t-	-1.1153	0.7580	71.5S	18.9E	0	237		
0034	003	1515 Jul 11	13:36:50	180	-5992	99	Pe	-t	-1.5262	0.0154	68.5S	38.2W	0	15		
0035	003	1515 Aug 09	21:21:23	180	-5991	137	P	t-	1.0259	0.9686	70.8N	7.1W	0	313		
0036	003	1516 Jan 04	03:38:39	179	-5986	104	P	-t	1.1652	0.6830	68.1N	117.7E	0	170		
0037	004	1516 Jun 30	01:15:14	179	-5980	109	A	-t	-0.8291	0.9899	33.8S	161.3E	34	2	64	01m03s
0038	004	1516 Dec 23	14:00:49	178	-5974	114	T	-n	0.4256	1.0199	2.2N	27.9W	65	181	75	02m05s
0039	004	1517 Jun 19	05:41:29	178	-5968	119	A	nn	-0.0683	0.9552	19.5N	96.1E	86	357	164	05m50s
0040	004	1517 Dec 13	05:04:11	177	-5962	124	T	n-	-0.2520	1.0468	38.2S	103.0E	75	6	161	03m52s
0041	004	1518 Jun 08	06:15:22	177	-5956	129	A	p-	0.6956	0.9496	67.0N	73.4E	46	162	259	04m13s
0042	004	1518 Dec 02	20:14:56	176	-5950	134	T	p-	-0.9365	1.0124	80.4S	128.7E	20	111	125	00m41s
0043	004	1519 Apr 28	23:35:42	176	-5945	101	P	-t	-1.2666	0.5071	62.5S	120.2W	0	309		
0044	004	1519 May 28	10:20:07	176	-5944	139	P	t-	1.4188	0.2342	64.6N	126.3W	0	26		
0045	004	1519 Oct 23	15:20:32	176	-5939	106	P	-t	1.2064	0.6096	61.9N	7.4E	0	238		
0046	004	1520 Apr 17	13:36:44	175	-5933	111	T	-p	-0.4825	1.0609	12.6S	12.2W	61	335	226	05m15s
0047	004	1520 Oct 11	16:03:18	175	-5927	116	A	-p	0.5277	0.9244	17.8N	49.4W	58	208	329	08m57s
0048	004	1521 Apr 07	06:26:04	174	-5921	121	T	n-	0.2414	1.0662	22.8N	77.3E	76	151	222	05m15s
0049	005	1521 Sep 30	16:21:41	174	-5915	126	A	nn	-0.1893	0.9489	16.3S	73.3W	79	29	191	05m30s
0050	005	1522 Mar 27	21:22:57	173	-5909	131	T	t-	0.9947	1.0076	62.0N	127.7E	4	84	349	00m26s
0051	005	1522 Sep 19	22:57:31	173	-5903	136	A	t-	-0.9012	0.9946	53.9S	146.1E	25	55	42	00m23s
0052	005	1523 Feb 15	14:16:42	172	-5898	103	P	-t	-1.1030	0.7827	61.2S	77.4E	0	250		
0053	005	1523 Aug 11	04:33:15	172	-5892	108	Tn	-t	0.9968	1.0559	62.7N	135.9W	2	294	-	02m44s
0054	005	1524 Feb 04	13:45:34	172	-5886	113	A	-p	-0.4176	0.9235	35.4S	9.3W	65	330	315	08m05s
0055	005	1524 Jul 30	21:17:37	171	-5880	118	T	-n	0.2797	1.0577	30.8N	130.2W	74	206	198	04m40s
0056	005	1525 Jan 23	15:31:19	171	-5874	123	A	n-	0.2898	0.9569	1.2S	54.8W	73	159	163	04m58s
0057	005	1525 Jul 20	10:11:02	170	-5868	128	H	p-	-0.4947	1.0054	9.3S	19.4E	60	19	22	00m35s
0058	005	1526 Jan 13	00:22:29	170	-5862	133	A	t-	0.9644	0.9985	51.0N	148.8E	15	151	19	00m07s
0059	005	1526 Jun 10	01:34:31	169	-5857	100	Pe	-t	1.5297	0.0558	66.1N	34.1W	0	350		
0060	005	1526 Jul 09	16:02:40	169	-5856	138	P	t-	-1.3063	0.4379	63.6S	97.8W	0	36		

Cat Num	Canon Plate	Calendar Date	TD of Greatest Eclipse	ΔT s	Luna Num	Saros Num	Ecl Type	QLE	Gamma	Ecl Mag	Lat °	Long °	Sun Alt °	Sun Azm °	Path Width km	Central Line Dur
0061	006	1526 Dec 04	04:14:38	169	-5851	105	P	-t	-1.0905	0.8382	66.7S	68.9W	0	184		
0062	006	1527 May 30	02:22:59	169	-5845	110	A	-p	0.7688	0.9556	73.4N	144.6E	39	180	255	03m28s
0063	006	1527 Nov 23	18:36:36	168	-5839	115	H	-p	-0.4422	1.0089	48.6S	102.5W	64	3	34	00m45s
0064	006	1528 May 18	08:21:04	168	-5833	120	H	nn	-0.0290	1.0085	19.9N	54.6E	88	356	29	00m56s
0065	006	1528 Nov 12	03:22:57	167	-5827	125	A	n-	-0.2653	0.9562	4.9S	128.4E	75	186	166	05m36s
0066	006	1529 May 07	21:19:48	167	-5821	130	T	p-	-0.7760	1.0526	31.3S	133.1W	39	351	276	04m38s
0067	006	1529 Nov 01	05:04:10	166	-5815	135	An	t-	0.9846	0.9119	61.7N	122.8E	9	201	-	08m09s
0068	006	1530 Mar 29	06:16:35	166	-5810	102	P	-t	1.0769	0.8672	71.7N	24.4W	0	67		
0069	006	1530 Apr 27	14:07:18	166	-5809	140	P	t-	-1.4726	0.1082	69.9S	2.9E	0	327		
0070	006	1530 Sep 21	12:31:36	166	-5804	107	P	-t	-1.2718	0.4970	72.0S	108.9W	0	100		
0071	006	1531 Mar 18	19:47:20	165	-5798	112	H	-p	0.3817	1.0036	24.3N	122.1W	67	161	13	00m21s
0072	006	1531 Sep 10	21:21:50	165	-5792	117	T	-p	-0.4856	1.0208	26.4S	151.0W	61	20	81	01m56s
0073	007	1532 Mar 07	02:21:38	164	-5786	122	A	n-	-0.3625	0.9488	21.8S	154.3E	69	341	201	05m59s
0074	007	1532 Aug 30	12:17:43	164	-5780	127	T	n-	0.2500	1.0654	19.3N	0.0E	75	198	221	05m40s
0075	007	1533 Feb 24	02:42:08	163	-5774	132	P	t-	-1.0860	0.8077	71.9S	108.5W	0	251		
0076	007	1533 Aug 20	05:03:59	163	-5768	137	T	t-	0.9693	1.0479	73.7N	178.3E	13	257	678	02m40s
0077	007	1534 Jan 14	12:01:17	163	-5763	104	P	-t	1.1685	0.6779	69.1N	19.7W	0	158		
0078	007	1534 Jul 11	08:08:45	162	-5757	109	A	-t	-0.9103	0.9833	44.9S	52.5E	24	8	144	01m35s
0079	007	1535 Jan 03	22:45:48	162	-5751	114	T	-n	0.4285	1.0228	3.8N	160.1W	65	176	86	02m22s
0080	007	1535 Jun 30	12:08:18	161	-5745	119	A	nn	-0.1565	0.9533	13.5N	0.6W	81	1	173	06m19s
0081	007	1535 Dec 24	13:56:56	161	-5739	124	T	n-	-0.2483	1.0469	37.5S	27.4W	75	1	161	03m55s
0082	007	1536 Jun 18	12:43:20	161	-5733	129	A	p-	0.6080	0.9523	61.0N	13.4W	52	174	220	04m17s
0083	007	1536 Dec 13	04:59:19	160	-5727	134	T	p-	-0.9343	1.0098	84.5S	17.2W	20	125	97	00m33s
0084	007	1537 May 09	06:52:55	160	-5722	101	P	-t	-1.3289	0.3923	63.2S	121.2E	0	318		
0085	008	1537 Jun 07	17:14:04	160	-5721	139	P	t-	1.3373	0.3795	65.5N	120.2E	0	17		
0086	008	1537 Nov 02	23:17:00	159	-5716	106	P	-t	1.2286	0.5713	62.6N	120.7W	0	228		
0087	008	1538 Apr 28	21:17:29	159	-5710	111	T	-p	-0.5431	1.0645	13.7S	127.6W	57	338	249	05m38s
0088	008	1538 Oct 22	23:38:40	159	-5704	116	A	-p	0.5572	0.9214	16.6N	164.1W	56	205	351	09m41s
0089	008	1539 Apr 18	14:15:06	158	-5698	121	T	n-	0.1854	1.0680	23.7N	38.7W	79	154	225	05m28s
0090	008	1539 Oct 12	00:01:44	158	-5692	126	A	nn	-0.1551	0.9484	18.7S	172.2E	81	28	192	05m35s
0091	008	1540 Apr 07	05:04:29	157	-5686	131	T	p-	0.9462	1.0115	63.1N	34.7E	18	104	123	00m42s
0092	008	1540 Sep 30	06:54:10	157	-5680	136	A	p-	-0.8621	0.9960	54.6S	29.2E	30	54	27	00m17s
0093	008	1541 Feb 25	21:54:41	157	-5675	103	P	-t	-1.1360	0.7273	61.0S	45.8W	0	259		
0094	008	1541 Aug 21	12:20:05	156	-5669	108	P	-t	1.0541	0.9172	61.3N	102.0E	0	289		
0095	008	1541 Sep 19	20:34:00	156	-5668	146	Pb	t-	-1.5141	0.0378	61.1S	135.3E	0	95		
0096	008	1542 Feb 14	21:27:22	156	-5663	113	A	-p	-0.4423	0.9265	32.5S	123.8W	64	328	305	07m44s
0097	009	1542 Aug 11	04:51:04	155	-5657	118	T	-n	0.3454	1.0525	30.6N	118.6E	70	209	184	04m12s
0098	009	1543 Feb 03	23:38:50	155	-5651	123	A	n-	0.2736	0.9617	1.0N	177.0W	74	156	143	04m14s
0099	009	1543 Jul 31	17:16:22	155	-5645	128	H	p-	-0.4229	1.0007	7.3S	87.0W	65	22	3	00m05s
0100	009	1544 Jan 24	08:57:44	154	-5639	133	H	t-	0.9533	1.0035	49.7N	16.0E	17	146	40	00m16s
0101	009	1544 Jul 19	22:38:20	154	-5633	138	P	t-	-1.2282	0.5730	62.8S	153.9E	0	45		
0102	009	1544 Dec 14	13:06:27	153	-5628	105	P	-t	-1.0948	0.8298	65.6S	147.6E	0	195		
0103	009	1545 Jun 09	08:57:26	153	-5622	110	A	-p	0.8506	0.9567	81.2N	72.0E	31	208	303	03m06s
0104	009	1545 Dec 04	03:15:40	153	-5616	115	H	-p	-0.4480	1.0051	50.1S	132.1E	63	357	20	00m25s
0105	009	1546 May 29	15:24:38	152	-5610	120	H	nn	0.0470	1.0133	25.7N	51.0W	87	180	46	01m24s
0106	009	1546 Nov 23	11:35:40	152	-5604	125	A	n-	0.2562	0.9521	7.3S	5.0E	75	182	181	06m13s
0107	009	1547 May 19	04:48:57	151	-5598	130	T	p-	-0.7060	1.0581	23.5S	110.7E	45	356	270	05m22s
0108	009	1547 Nov 12	12:54:22	151	-5592	135	A	p-	0.9684	0.9106	55.5N	4.7W	14	191	1420	08m59s
0109	010	1548 Apr 08	14:10:06	151	-5587	102	P	-t	1.1282	0.7699	71.2N	156.5W	0	54		
0110	010	1548 May 07	21:46:51	151	-5586	140	P	t-	-1.4121	0.2250	69.0S	124.2W	0	338		
0111	010	1548 Oct 01	20:10:49	150	-5581	107	P	-t	-1.3049	0.4395	71.7S	122.3E	0	113		
0112	010	1549 Mar 29	03:30:53	150	-5575	112	H	-p	0.4285	1.0029	31.4N	120.1E	64	161	11	00m16s
0113	010	1549 Sep 21	05:16:22	150	-5569	117	T	-p	-0.5257	1.0205	33.2S	88.0E	58	21	82	01m49s
0114	010	1550 Mar 18	09:47:47	149	-5563	122	A	nn	-0.0300	0.9497	15.1S	40.8E	71	342	194	06m05s
0115	010	1550 Sep 10	20:17:36	149	-5557	127	T	n-	0.2029	1.0636	12.4N	121.8W	78	198	212	05m37s
0116	010	1551 Mar 07	10:05:17	148	-5551	132	P	t-	-1.0477	0.8730	72.2S	126.5E	0	265		
0117	010	1551 Aug 31	12:52:59	148	-5545	137	T	p-	0.9185	1.0460	65.8N	28.4E	23	226	391	02m52s
0118	010	1552 Jan 25	20:19:42	148	-5540	104	P	-t	1.1760	0.6656	70.0N	156.6W	0	146		
0119	010	1552 Jul 21	15:03:46	147	-5534	109	As	-t	-0.9892	0.9742	62.9S	64.5W	7	20	-	02m05s
0120	010	1553 Jan 14	07:28:07	147	-5528	114	T	-n	0.4339	1.0263	6.3N	68.3E	64	172	99	02m41s

Cat Num	Canon Plate	Calendar Date	TD of Greatest Eclipse	ΔT s	Luna Num	Saros Num	Ecl Type	QLE	Gamma	Ecl Mag	Lat °	Long °	Sun Alt °	Sun Azm °	Path Width km	Central Line Dur
0121	011	1553 Jul 10	18:36:33	147	-5522	119	A	np	-0.2430	0.9509	6.8N	98.5W	76	5	185	06m46s
0122	011	1554 Jan 03	22:49:37	146	-5516	124	T	n-	-0.2447	1.0474	35.8S	158.1W	76	355	163	04m00s
0123	011	1554 Jun 29	19:10:38	146	-5510	129	A	p-	0.5192	0.9546	54.0N	104.8W	58	182	195	04m22s
0124	011	1554 Dec 24	13:45:20	146	-5504	134	T	p-	-0.9341	1.0075	87.5S	159.2E	20	176	75	00m25s
0125	011	1555 May 20	14:06:05	145	-5499	101	P	-t	-1.3947	0.2697	64.0S	3.3E	0	328		
0126	011	1555 Jun 19	00:07:15	145	-5498	139	P	t-	1.2542	0.5289	66.5N	6.6E	0	7		
0127	011	1555 Nov 14	07:19:25	145	-5493	106	P	-t	1.2454	0.5424	63.3N	109.4E	0	219		
0128	011	1556 May 09	04:53:34	145	-5487	111	T	-p	-0.6079	1.0673	16.0S	117.8E	52	342	274	05m58s
0129	011	1556 Nov 02	07:22:12	144	-5481	116	A	-p	0.5798	0.9190	15.5N	78.9E	54	201	370	10m24s
0130	011	1557 Apr 28	21:59:03	144	-5475	121	T	nn	0.1251	1.0692	24.0N	153.1W	83	157	227	05m42s
0131	011	1557 Oct 22	07:49:26	143	-5469	126	A	nn	-0.1267	0.9482	21.1S	56.0E	83	25	192	05m40s
0132	011	1558 Apr 18	12:39:26	143	-5463	131	T	p-	0.8930	1.0132	64.1N	67.8W	26	114	100	00m50s
0133	012	1558 Oct 11	14:58:54	143	-5457	136	A	p-	-0.8290	0.9971	56.5S	90.3W	34	53	18	00m12s
0134	012	1559 Mar 09	05:22:59	142	-5452	103	P	-t	-1.1760	0.6599	60.8S	166.6W	0	268		
0135	012	1559 Sep 01	20:13:57	142	-5446	108	P	-t	1.1055	0.8172	61.1N	25.3W	0	280		
0136	012	1559 Oct 01	04:46:45	142	-5445	146	P	t-	-1.4772	0.1083	61.3S	3.4E	0	104		
0137	012	1560 Feb 26	05:00:43	142	-5440	113	A	-p	-0.4741	0.9299	29.9S	123.5E	62	327	294	07m22s
0138	012	1560 Aug 21	12:30:54	141	-5434	118	T	-p	0.4050	1.0469	29.7N	5.3E	66	212	170	03m44s
0139	012	1561 Feb 14	07:39:20	141	-5428	123	A	n-	-0.2507	0.9670	3.4N	62.6E	75	153	122	03m30s
0140	012	1561 Aug 11	00:27:06	141	-5422	128	A	n-	-0.3564	0.9956	6.5S	165.5E	69	25	16	00m27s
0141	012	1562 Feb 03	17:27:32	140	-5416	133	T	t-	0.9373	1.0091	48.6N	114.5W	20	142	89	00m41s
0142	012	1562 Jul 31	05:16:44	140	-5410	138	P	t-	-1.1522	0.7033	62.2S	45.1E	0	54		
0143	012	1562 Dec 25	21:58:38	140	-5405	105	P	-t	-1.0990	0.8218	64.6S	4.6E	0	205		
0144	012	1563 Jun 20	15:30:53	139	-5399	110	A	-t	0.9338	0.9565	81.3N	55.3E	20	290	454	02m49s
0145	013	1563 Dec 15	11:55:48	139	-5393	115	H	-p	-0.4524	1.0020	50.3S	6.8E	63	350	8	00m10s
0146	013	1564 Jun 08	22:26:47	139	-5387	120	H2	nn	0.1252	1.0174	30.8N	155.4W	83	185	60	01m44s
0147	013	1564 Dec 03	19:52:05	138	-5381	125	A	nn	0.2504	0.9487	8.8S	119.2W	76	178	195	06m42s
0148	013	1565 May 29	12:14:58	138	-5375	130	T	p-	-0.6329	1.0629	16.5S	3.7W	51	0	266	05m57s
0149	013	1565 Nov 22	20:49:54	138	-5369	135	A	p-	0.9564	0.9092	51.4N	130.4W	16	184	1220	09m37s
0150	013	1566 Apr 19	21:55:59	137	-5364	102	P	-t	1.1855	0.6611	70.5N	73.9E	0	41		
0151	013	1566 May 19	05:20:58	137	-5363	140	P	t-	-1.3472	0.3507	68.1S	110.7E	0	350		
0152	013	1566 Oct 13	03:59:22	137	-5358	107	P	-t	-1.3311	0.3940	71.1S	8.6W	0	127		
0153	013	1567 Apr 09	11:04:07	137	-5352	112	H	-p	0.4830	1.0020	38.9N	4.9E	61	161	8	00m11s
0154	013	1567 Oct 02	13:20:26	136	-5346	117	T	-p	-0.5584	1.0200	39.7S	34.9W	56	22	82	01m42s
0155	013	1568 Mar 28	17:04:20	136	-5340	122	A	nn	-0.2701	0.9507	8.1S	70.5W	74	343	187	06m10s
0156	013	1568 Sep 21	04:25:00	136	-5334	127	T	n-	0.1619	1.0615	5.8N	114.6E	81	198	204	05m32s
0157	014	1569 Mar 17	17:21:17	135	-5328	132	A-	t-	-1.0034	0.9489	72.1S	3.1E	0	279	-	-
0158	014	1569 Sep 10	20:48:15	135	-5322	137	T	p-	0.8733	1.0428	57.4N	103.4W	29	215	293	02m55s
0159	014	1570 Feb 05	04:34:48	135	-5317	104	P	-t	1.1866	0.6475	70.9N	66.7E	0	133		
0160	014	1570 Aug 01	22:00:20	134	-5311	109	P	-t	-1.0655	0.8624	70.4S	171.9E	0	38		
0161	014	1571 Jan 25	16:07:35	134	-5305	114	T	-n	0.4421	1.0302	9.5N	62.8W	64	169	113	02m59s
0162	014	1571 Jul 22	01:07:17	134	-5299	119	A	-p	-0.3266	0.9481	0.5S	162.1E	71	9	201	07m08s
0163	014	1572 Jan 15	07:38:11	133	-5293	124	T	n-	-0.2381	1.0485	33.0S	71.6E	76	351	166	04m07s
0164	014	1572 Jul 10	01:42:41	133	-5287	129	A	p-	0.4339	0.9562	46.6N	159.7E	64	187	177	04m30s
0165	014	1573 Jan 03	22:28:34	133	-5281	134	H	p-	-0.9328	1.0058	85.9S	54.0W	21	258	57	00m20s
0166	014	1573 May 30	21:18:23	133	-5276	101	P	-t	-1.4618	0.1437	64.9S	114.6W	0	337		
0167	014	1573 Jun 29	07:03:34	133	-5275	139	P	t-	1.1724	0.6769	67.5N	108.2W	0	356		
0168	014	1573 Nov 24	15:24:44	132	-5270	106	P	-t	1.2590	0.5192	64.3N	21.4W	0	209		
0169	015	1574 May 20	12:25:41	132	-5264	111	T	-p	-0.6762	1.0694	19.7S	3.8E	47	346	305	06m09s
0170	015	1574 Nov 13	15:12:15	132	-5258	116	A	-p	0.5970	0.9171	14.8N	40.0W	53	197	387	11m03s
0171	015	1575 May 10	05:34:43	131	-5252	121	Tm	nn	0.0584	1.0697	23.1N	94.6E	87	162	227	05m56s
0172	015	1575 Nov 02	15:47:26	131	-5246	126	A	nn	-0.1061	0.9483	23.5S	62.6W	84	22	191	05m44s
0173	015	1576 Apr 28	20:04:43	131	-5240	131	T	p-	0.8329	1.0140	64.8N	168.0W	33	124	86	00m55s
0174	015	1576 Oct 21	23:13:04	130	-5234	136	A	p-	-0.8031	0.9981	59.2S	147.9E	36	51	11	00m08s
0175	015	1577 Mar 19	12:41:14	130	-5229	103	P	-t	-1.2234	0.5799	60.9S	75.2E	0	277		
0176	015	1577 Sep 12	04:15:21	130	-5223	108	P	-t	1.1507	0.7298	61.0N	154.4W	0	271		
0177	015	1577 Oct 11	13:08:01	130	-5222	146	P	t-	-1.4473	0.1654	61.6S	130.8W	0	113		
0178	015	1578 Mar 08	12:26:50	130	-5217	113	A	-p	-0.5120	0.9336	27.7S	12.3E	59	327	283	07m01s
0179	015	1578 Sep 01	20:15:07	129	-5211	118	T	-p	0.4602	1.0408	28.4N	109.6W	62	213	152	03m17s
0180	015	1579 Feb 25	15:34:46	129	-5205	123	A	n-	0.2229	0.9728	6.0N	56.4W	77	151	100	02m48s

Cat Num	Canon Plate	Calendar Date	TD of Greatest Eclipse	ΔT s	Luna Num	Saros Num	Ecl Type	QLE	Gamma	Ecl Mag	Lat °	Long °	Sun Alt °	Sun Azm °	Path Width km	Central Line Dur
0181	016	1579 Aug 22	07:41:31	129	-5199	128	A	n-	-0.2938	0.9901	6.6S	57.2E	73	27	36	01m00s
0182	016	1580 Feb 15	01:52:11	128	-5193	133	T	t-	0.9164	1.0151	47.9N	117.3E	23	138	127	01m07s
0183	016	1580 Aug 10	12:00:04	128	-5187	138	P	t-	-1.0803	0.8257	61.6S	64.6W	0	63		
0184	016	1581 Jan 05	06:49:57	128	-5182	105	P	-t	-1.1041	0.8121	63.7S	137.9W	0	216		
0185	016	1581 Jun 30	22:06:52	128	-5176	110	P	-t	1.0151	0.9455	64.2N	2.2W	0	331		
0186	016	1581 Dec 25	20:35:19	127	-5170	115	A	-p	-0.4567	0.9993	49.4S	118.5W	63	343	3	00m04s
0187	016	1582 Jun 20	05:30:26	127	-5164	120	T	nn	0.2032	1.0210	35.0N	100.8E	78	190	73	01m59s
0188	016	1582 Dec 25	04:08:38	127	-5158	125	A	nn	0.2457	0.9459	9.4S	116.8E	76	173	206	07m02s
0189	016	1583 Jun 19	19:39:31	127	-5152	130	T	p-	-0.5581	1.0667	10.4S	116.9W	56	4	262	06m23s
0190	016	1583 Dec 14	04:48:37	126	-5146	135	A	p-	0.9471	0.9083	48.5N	104.1E	18	177	1116	10m03s
0191	016	1584 May 10	05:35:05	126	-5141	102	P	-t	1.2478	0.5425	69.7N	53.5W	0	29		
0192	016	1584 Jun 08	12:52:24	126	-5140	140	P	t-	-1.2802	0.4805	67.1S	13.3W	0	0		
0193	017	1584 Nov 02	11:56:43	126	-5135	107	P	-t	-1.3510	0.3596	70.4S	141.1W	0	140		
0194	017	1585 Apr 29	18:28:57	125	-5129	112	H	-p	0.5436	1.0005	46.6N	107.7W	57	162	2	00m03s
0195	017	1585 Oct 22	21:33:24	125	-5123	117	T	-p	-0.5845	1.0196	45.7S	159.2W	54	21	82	01m35s
0196	017	1586 Apr 19	00:10:07	125	-5117	122	A	nn	-0.2120	0.9517	0.9S	179.1W	78	345	181	06m12s
0197	017	1586 Oct 12	12:40:31	125	-5111	127	T	n-	0.1278	1.0591	0.3S	10.8W	83	197	196	05m23s
0198	017	1587 Apr 08	00:27:04	124	-5105	132	A	t-	-0.9502	0.9271	60.5S	151.9W	18	325	889	06m26s
0199	017	1587 Oct 02	04:51:23	124	-5099	137	T	p-	0.8352	1.0387	50.0N	128.3E	33	208	235	02m51s
0200	017	1588 Feb 26	12:42:30	124	-5094	104	P	-t	1.2038	0.6178	71.5N	68.8W	0	119		
0201	017	1588 Aug 22	05:01:46	124	-5088	109	P	-t	-1.1364	0.7355	71.1S	53.5E	0	51		
0202	017	1589 Feb 15	00:42:19	123	-5082	114	T	-n	0.4544	1.0344	13.6N	167.1E	63	166	129	03m17s
0203	017	1589 Aug 11	07:41:03	123	-5076	119	A	-p	-0.4072	0.9450	8.2S	61.4E	66	12	221	07m24s
0204	017	1590 Feb 04	16:24:04	123	-5070	124	T	n-	-0.2293	1.0498	29.3S	58.8W	77	347	170	04m17s
0205	018	1590 Jul 31	08:17:38	123	-5064	129	A	p-	0.3503	0.9574	38.8N	61.6E	69	191	166	04m38s
0206	018	1591 Jan 25	07:09:21	122	-5058	134	H	p-	-0.9298	1.0047	81.9S	150.6E	21	283	45	00m16s
0207	018	1591 Jun 21	04:28:42	122	-5053	101	Pe	-t	-1.5311	0.0130	65.8S	127.7E	0	347		
0208	018	1591 Jul 20	14:02:06	122	-5052	139	P	t-	1.0911	0.8249	68.5N	136.0E	0	346		
0209	018	1591 Dec 15	23:33:55	122	-5047	106	P	-t	1.2689	0.5024	65.3N	153.5W	0	199		
0210	018	1592 Jun 09	19:55:48	122	-5041	111	T	-p	-0.7465	1.0705	24.7S	110.3W	42	350	344	06m11s
0211	018	1592 Dec 03	23:07:15	122	-5035	116	A	-p	0.6102	0.9159	14.5N	160.2W	52	193	401	11m36s
0212	018	1593 May 30	13:07:29	121	-5029	121	T	nn	-0.0106	1.0696	21.4N	17.0W	90	342	227	06m08s
0213	018	1593 Nov 22	23:52:05	121	-5023	126	A	nn	-0.0906	0.9488	25.4S	177.5E	85	18	189	05m46s
0214	018	1594 May 20	03:23:16	121	-5017	131	T	p-	0.7678	1.0141	64.9N	94.1E	40	136	76	00m58s
0215	018	1594 Nov 12	07:34:48	121	-5011	136	A	p-	-0.7829	0.9991	62.4S	25.1E	38	48	5	00m04s
0216	018	1595 Apr 09	19:50:04	120	-5006	103	P	-t	-1.2776	0.4880	61.1S	40.7W	0	286		
0217	019	1595 Oct 03	12:24:35	120	-5000	108	P	-t	1.1896	0.6546	61.1N	74.6E	0	262		
0218	019	1595 Nov 01	21:36:52	120	-4999	146	P	t-	-1.4234	0.2111	62.1S	93.1E	0	122		
0219	019	1596 Mar 28	19:43:17	120	-4994	113	A	-p	-0.5583	0.9373	26.3S	96.5W	56	328	275	06m41s
0220	019	1596 Sep 22	04:07:01	120	-4988	118	T	-p	0.5084	1.0346	26.8N	133.0E	59	213	134	02m50s
0221	019	1597 Mar 17	23:22:38	119	-4982	123	A	n-	0.1879	0.9788	8.4N	173.3W	79	151	77	02m08s
0222	019	1597 Sep 11	15:01:20	119	-4976	128	A	nn	-0.2363	0.9843	7.6S	52.4W	76	29	57	01m35s
0223	019	1598 Mar 07	10:10:00	119	-4970	133	T	p-	0.8894	1.0214	47.7N	8.2W	27	135	156	01m33s
0224	019	1598 Aug 31	18:48:46	119	-4964	138	A-	t-	-1.0126	0.9397	61.2S	175.6W	0	72	-	-
0225	019	1599 Jan 26	15:37:09	119	-4959	105	P	-t	-1.1125	0.7965	62.9S	80.9E	0	225		
0226	019	1599 Jul 22	04:45:14	118	-4953	110	P	-t	1.0949	0.8068	63.4N	111.2W	0	321		
0227	019	1600 Jan 16	05:12:45	118	-4947	115	A	-p	-0.4622	0.9972	47.4S	115.9E	62	337	11	00m14s
0228	019	1600 Jul 10	12:35:57	117	-4941	120	T	-n	0.2803	1.0238	38.2N	2.6W	74	196	84	02m08s
0229	020	1601 Jan 04	12:24:37	117	-4935	125	A	nn	0.2410	0.9437	9.1S	7.0W	76	169	214	07m13s
0230	020	1601 Jun 30	03:03:58	117	-4929	130	T	p-	-0.4826	1.0697	5.3S	130.7E	61	8	259	06m37s
0231	020	1601 Dec 24	12:50:30	116	-4923	135	A	p-	0.9402	0.9078	46.6N	21.5W	19	171	1051	10m14s
0232	020	1602 May 21	13:06:43	116	-4918	102	P	-t	1.3157	0.4133	68.8N	178.3W	0	18		
0233	020	1602 Jun 19	20:19:20	116	-4917	140	P	t-	-1.2097	0.6173	66.1S	135.7W	0	10		
0234	020	1602 Nov 13	20:03:04	115	-4912	107	P	-t	-1.3643	0.3364	69.5S	84.8E	0	153		
0235	020	1603 May 11	01:44:58	115	-4906	112	A	-p	0.6107	0.9987	54.7N	142.6E	52	163	6	00m07s
0236	020	1603 Nov 03	05:54:54	114	-4900	117	T	-p	-0.6041	1.0193	51.1S	75.6E	53	20	83	01m31s
0237	020	1604 Apr 29	07:07:20	114	-4894	122	A	nn	-0.1474	0.9525	6.3N	74.8E	82	347	176	06m12s
0238	020	1604 Oct 22	21:03:47	113	-4888	127	T	n-	0.1000	1.0567	5.9S	137.8W	84	195	188	05m12s
0239	020	1605 Apr 18	07:26:43	112	-4882	132	A	p-	-0.8918	0.9327	49.8S	89.9E	26	337	553	06m43s
0240	020	1605 Oct 12	12:59:57	112	-4876	137	T	p-	0.8023	1.0344	43.4N	0.6E	36	203	193	02m43s

Cat Num	Canon Plate	Calendar Date	TD of Greatest Eclipse	ΔT s	Luna Num	Saros Num	Ecl Type	QLE	Gamma	Ecl Mag	Lat °	Long °	Sun Alt °	Sun Azm °	Path Width km	Central Line Dur
0241	021	1606 Mar 08	20:45:38	111	-4871	104	P	-t	1.2253	0.5801	71.9N	156.4E	0	105		
0242	021	1606 Sep 02	12:07:22	111	-4865	109	P	-t	-1.2026	0.6183	71.7S	66.5W	0	64		
0243	021	1607 Feb 26	09:10:37	110	-4859	114	T	-n	0.4727	1.0388	18.4N	38.2E	62	163	147	03m34s
0244	021	1607 Aug 22	14:20:47	110	-4853	119	A	-p	-0.4824	0.9416	16.1S	41.4W	61	15	245	07m34s
0245	021	1608 Feb 16	01:03:27	109	-4847	124	T	n-	-0.2154	1.0515	24.8S	171.7E	77	345	175	04m29s
0246	021	1608 Aug 10	15:00:05	109	-4841	129	A	pn	0.2722	0.9581	31.0N	39.6W	74	194	158	04m46s
0247	021	1609 Feb 04	15:43:42	108	-4835	134	H	p-	-0.9224	1.0041	77.3S	7.2E	22	297	37	00m15s
0248	021	1609 Jul 30	21:07:07	107	-4829	139	P	t-	1.0140	0.9656	69.5N	17.9E	0	334		
0249	021	1609 Dec 26	07:43:33	107	-4824	106	P	-t	1.2776	0.4878	66.3N	73.9E	0	188		
0250	021	1610 Jun 21	03:22:59	106	-4818	111	T	-p	-0.8193	1.0705	31.5S	135.5E	35	354	400	05m59s
0251	021	1610 Dec 15	07:06:47	106	-4812	116	A	-p	0.6195	0.9153	14.7N	78.3E	52	188	409	11m56s
0252	021	1611 Jun 10	20:34:24	105	-4806	121	T	nn	-0.0836	1.0686	18.4N	127.6W	85	350	224	06m16s
0253	022	1611 Dec 04	08:03:42	104	-4800	126	A	nn	-0.0803	0.9498	26.9S	56.0E	85	13	185	05m44s
0254	022	1612 May 30	10:34:28	104	-4794	131	T	p-	0.6976	1.0135	63.6N	1.9W	45	149	65	00m58s
0255	022	1612 Nov 22	16:04:34	103	-4788	136	H	p-	-0.7692	1.0002	65.7S	98.4W	39	43	1	00m01s
0256	022	1613 Apr 20	02:49:28	103	-4783	103	P	-t	-1.3388	0.3839	61.5S	154.4W	0	295		
0257	022	1613 May 19	17:43:35	103	-4782	141	Pb	t-	1.5171	0.0712	63.3N	137.6E	0	41		
0258	022	1613 Oct 13	20:40:23	102	-4777	108	P	-t	1.2231	0.5902	61.3N	58.2W	0	253		
0259	022	1613 Nov 12	06:12:14	102	-4776	146	P	t-	-1.4048	0.2464	62.7S	44.8W	0	132		
0260	022	1614 Apr 09	02:52:56	101	-4771	113	A	-p	-0.6103	0.9411	25.7S	156.2E	52	329	268	06m22s
0261	022	1614 Oct 03	12:04:50	101	-4765	118	T	-p	0.5511	1.0282	25.2N	13.5E	56	212	113	02m23s
0262	022	1615 Mar 29	07:03:23	100	-4759	123	A	nn	0.1461	0.9851	10.7N	71.7E	82	151	53	01m28s
0263	022	1615 Sep 22	22:27:20	100	-4753	128	A	nn	-0.1850	0.9784	9.1S	163.5W	79	29	78	02m11s
0264	022	1616 Mar 17	18:21:44	99	-4747	133	T	p-	0.8568	1.0280	48.0N	131.4W	31	134	180	01m58s
0265	023	1616 Sep 11	01:44:04	98	-4741	138	A	t-	-0.9506	0.9319	54.1S	102.3E	18	55	808	05m42s
0266	023	1617 Feb 06	00:20:22	98	-4736	105	P	-t	-1.1240	0.7751	62.2S	59.0W	0	235		
0267	023	1617 Mar 07	10:05:35	98	-4735	143	Pb	t-	1.5110	0.0419	61.2N	48.6W	0	101		
0268	023	1617 Aug 01	11:29:43	97	-4730	110	P	-t	1.1701	0.6756	62.7N	138.3E	0	312		
0269	023	1618 Jan 26	13:46:43	96	-4724	115	A	-p	-0.4700	0.9955	44.7S	9.7W	62	333	18	00m23s
0270	023	1618 Jul 21	19:44:29	96	-4718	120	T	-n	0.3558	1.0260	40.4N	106.3W	69	201	94	02m13s
0271	023	1619 Jan 15	20:38:06	95	-4712	125	A	nn	0.2349	0.9422	8.1S	130.4W	76	165	220	07m16s
0272	023	1619 Jul 11	10:29:58	94	-4706	130	T	p-	-0.4078	1.0718	1.3S	18.6E	66	12	255	06m41s
0273	023	1620 Jan 04	20:51:03	94	-4700	135	A	-p	0.9322	0.9081	45.0N	146.4W	21	165	976	10m13s
0274	023	1620 May 31	20:33:44	93	-4695	102	P	-t	1.3868	0.2783	67.8N	58.5E	0	7		
0275	023	1620 Jun 30	03:46:24	93	-4694	140	P	t-	-1.1393	0.7535	65.1S	102.3E	0	20		
0276	023	1620 Nov 24	04:16:34	92	-4689	107	P	-t	-1.3729	0.3213	68.5S	50.6W	0	165		
0277	024	1621 May 21	08:53:43	92	-4683	112	A	-p	0.6827	0.9962	63.1N	36.1E	47	167	18	00m18s
0278	024	1621 Nov 13	14:23:12	91	-4677	117	T	-p	-0.6187	1.0194	55.8S	49.7W	52	16	84	01m28s
0279	024	1622 May 10	13:55:34	90	-4671	122	Am	nn	-0.0758	0.9531	13.5N	28.8W	86	350	172	06m07s
0280	024	1622 Nov 03	05:34:47	90	-4665	127	T	n-	-0.0789	1.0544	10.7S	93.7E	86	193	180	05m01s
0281	024	1623 Apr 29	14:15:59	89	-4659	132	A	p-	-0.8244	0.9378	39.8S	20.4W	34	344	405	06m54s
0282	024	1623 Oct 23	21:17:09	88	-4653	137	T	p-	0.7770	1.0298	37.8N	128.0W	39	199	159	02m31s
0283	024	1624 Mar 19	04:40:35	88	-4648	104	P	-t	1.2540	0.5288	72.0N	23.5E	0	91		
0284	024	1624 Apr 17	17:16:17	87	-4647	142	Pb	t-	-1.5208	0.0582	71.2S	23.1W	0	306		
0285	024	1624 Sep 12	19:19:25	87	-4642	109	P	-t	-1.2624	0.5133	72.0S	171.5E	0	77		
0286	024	1624 Oct 12	08:53:54	87	-4641	147	Pb	t-	1.5466	0.0089	71.5N	109.9E	0	245		
0287	024	1625 Mar 08	17:32:38	86	-4636	114	T	-p	0.4965	1.0434	23.9N	89.4W	60	161	166	03m50s
0288	024	1625 Sep 01	21:06:57	85	-4630	119	A	-p	-0.5520	0.9380	24.2S	146.4W	56	18	274	07m37s
0289	025	1626 Feb 26	09:37:26	85	-4624	124	T	n-	-0.1971	1.0535	19.7S	42.7E	79	343	180	04m42s
0290	025	1626 Aug 21	21:47:41	84	-4618	129	A	nn	0.1976	0.9584	23.1N	142.8W	78	195	154	04m54s
0291	025	1627 Feb 16	00:13:30	83	-4612	134	H	p-	-0.9119	1.0040	72.3S	130.9W	24	307	34	00m15s
0292	025	1627 Aug 11	04:17:13	82	-4606	139	H	t-	0.9401	1.0001	77.7N	173.2W	19	253	1	00m00s
0293	025	1628 Jan 06	15:52:51	82	-4601	106	P	-t	1.2858	0.4740	67.4N	59.2W	0	177		
0294	025	1628 Jul 01	10:50:38	81	-4595	111	T	-t	-0.8917	1.0692	40.3S	20.0E	27	358	501	05m32s
0295	025	1628 Dec 25	15:08:46	80	-4589	116	A	-p	0.6264	0.9153	15.4N	44.0W	51	184	413	12m02s
0296	025	1629 Jun 21	03:59:23	80	-4583	121	T	-n	-0.1580	1.0670	14.5N	121.6E	81	354	221	06m20s
0297	025	1629 Dec 14	16:19:06	79	-4577	126	A	nn	-0.0726	0.9513	27.6S	66.2W	86	9	179	05m38s
0298	025	1630 Jun 10	17:41:06	78	-4571	131	H	p-	0.6245	1.0122	60.9N	98.3W	51	161	54	00m55s
0299	025	1630 Dec 04	00:38:58	78	-4565	136	H	p-	-0.7585	1.0017	68.7S	139.6E	40	36	9	00m07s
0300	025	1631 May 01	09:39:22	77	-4560	103	P	-t	-1.4069	0.2678	62.0S	94.2E	0	304		

Cat Num	Canon Plate	Calendar Date	TD of Greatest Eclipse	ΔT s	Luna Num	Saros Num	Ecl Type	QLE	Gamma	Ecl Mag	Lat °	Long °	Sun Alt °	Sun Azm °	Path Width km	Central Line Dur
0301	026	1631 May 31	00:25:37	77	-4559	141	P	t-	1.4433	0.1996	64.1N	27.6E	0	32		
0302	026	1631 Oct 25	05:04:14	76	-4554	108	P	-t	1.2502	0.5385	61.7N	167.0E	0	244		
0303	026	1631 Nov 23	14:53:43	76	-4553	146	P	t-	-1.3912	0.2723	63.5S	175.4E	0	141		
0304	026	1632 Apr 19	09:54:29	75	-4548	113	A	-p	-0.6694	0.9447	26.4S	50.8E	48	331	267	06m03s
0305	026	1632 Oct 13	20:09:38	75	-4542	118	T	-p	0.5872	1.0220	23.7N	108.2W	54	210	91	01m55s
0306	026	1633 Apr 08	14:37:05	74	-4536	123	A	nn	0.0976	0.9913	12.4N	41.2W	84	152	31	00m51s
0307	026	1633 Oct 03	06:00:37	73	-4530	128	Am	nn	-0.1405	0.9726	11.2S	83.4E	82	29	99	02m48s
0308	026	1634 Mar 29	02:25:10	72	-4524	133	T	p-	0.8169	1.0346	48.7N	108.6E	35	133	198	02m24s
0309	026	1634 Sep 22	08:47:03	72	-4518	138	A	p-	-0.8947	0.9300	51.5S	2.3E	26	51	572	06m03s
0310	026	1635 Feb 17	08:57:23	71	-4513	105	P	-t	-1.1407	0.7441	61.6S	162.7E	0	244		
0311	026	1635 Mar 18	18:24:52	71	-4512	143	P	t-	1.4813	0.0973	61.1N	177.7E	0	92		
0312	026	1635 Aug 12	18:20:09	70	-4507	110	P	-t	1.2411	0.5514	62.1N	26.6E	0	303		
0313	027	1636 Feb 06	22:14:32	70	-4501	115	A	-p	-0.4825	0.9943	41.6S	134.7W	61	329	23	00m29s
0314	027	1636 Aug 01	02:58:15	69	-4495	120	T	-p	0.4279	1.0275	41.5N	148.9E	64	207	103	02m15s
0315	027	1637 Jan 26	04:48:31	68	-4489	125	A	nn	0.2265	0.9412	6.4S	107.0E	77	161	223	07m12s
0316	027	1637 Jul 21	17:57:08	67	-4483	130	T	n-	-0.3335	1.0731	1.8N	93.4W	71	16	251	06m37s
0317	027	1638 Jan 15	04:51:53	67	-4477	135	A	p-	0.9242	0.9090	44.0N	88.9E	22	159	907	10m00s
0318	027	1638 Jun 12	03:55:43	66	-4472	102	Pe	-t	1.4614	0.1371	66.8N	62.9W	0	356		
0319	027	1638 Jul 11	11:11:51	66	-4471	140	P	t-	-1.0676	0.8916	64.2S	19.0W	0	30		
0320	027	1638 Dec 05	12:36:34	65	-4466	107	P	-t	-1.3768	0.3144	67.5S	173.0E	0	176		
0321	027	1639 Jan 04	04:56:18	65	-4465	145	Pb	t-	1.5651	0.0009	64.6N	80.0E	0	155		
0322	027	1639 Jun 01	15:55:15	65	-4460	112	A	-p	0.7597	0.9930	71.7N	65.3W	40	173	38	00m31s
0323	027	1639 Nov 24	22:58:54	64	-4454	117	T	-p	-0.6278	1.0197	59.6S	174.7W	51	10	87	01m27s
0324	027	1640 May 20	20:37:51	63	-4448	122	A	nn	0.0002	0.9533	20.4N	130.2W	90	180	171	06m00s
0325	028	1640 Nov 13	14:11:19	62	-4442	127	T	n-	0.0623	1.0522	14.8S	35.8W	87	189	173	04m50s
0326	028	1641 May 09	21:01:18	62	-4436	132	A	p-	-0.7533	0.9425	30.8S	127.3W	41	349	321	06m56s
0327	028	1641 Nov 03	05:40:08	61	-4430	137	T	p-	0.7570	1.0252	33.0N	102.5E	41	194	130	02m15s
0328	028	1642 Mar 30	12:29:28	60	-4425	104	P	-t	1.2883	0.4669	71.9N	108.0W	0	77		
0329	028	1642 Apr 29	00:29:42	60	-4424	142	P	t-	-1.4586	0.1660	70.6S	144.7W	0	318		
0330	028	1642 Sep 24	02:37:36	60	-4419	109	P	-t	-1.3163	0.4200	72.1S	47.6E	0	91		
0331	028	1642 Oct 23	16:48:35	59	-4418	147	P	t-	1.5221	0.0551	71.0N	22.5W	0	232		
0332	028	1643 Mar 20	01:47:18	59	-4413	114	T	-p	0.5271	1.0479	30.0N	144.6E	58	159	186	04m02s
0333	028	1643 Sep 13	04:01:20	58	-4407	119	A	-p	-0.6144	0.9343	32.3S	106.3E	52	21	307	07m35s
0334	028	1644 Mar 08	18:02:42	57	-4401	124	T	n-	-0.1717	1.0555	14.0S	84.7W	80	342	186	04m57s
0335	028	1644 Sep 01	04:45:27	57	-4395	129	A	nn	0.1307	0.9584	15.4N	110.9E	82	197	152	05m00s
0336	028	1645 Feb 26	08:35:06	56	-4389	134	H	p-	-0.8956	1.0043	66.7S	94.3E	26	316	34	00m17s
0337	029	1645 Aug 21	11:34:17	55	-4383	139	H	t-	0.8710	1.0040	68.2N	43.7E	29	222	28	00m16s
0338	029	1646 Jan 16	23:59:17	55	-4378	106	P	-t	1.2956	0.4574	68.5N	167.8E	0	166		
0339	029	1646 Jul 12	18:18:18	54	-4372	111	T	-t	-0.9640	1.0658	53.1S	98.0W	15	5	834	04m44s
0340	029	1647 Jan 05	23:10:59	53	-4366	116	A	-p	0.6336	0.9161	16.9N	166.5W	51	179	413	11m50s
0341	029	1647 Jul 02	11:21:20	52	-4360	121	T	-n	-0.2344	1.0643	9.6N	11.0E	77	359	217	06m15s
0342	029	1647 Dec 26	00:38:34	52	-4354	126	A	nn	-0.0675	0.9535	27.4S	170.6E	86	4	170	05m25s
0343	029	1648 Jun 21	00:43:21	51	-4348	131	H	p-	0.5483	1.0102	56.7N	164.0E	56	171	42	00m49s
0344	029	1648 Dec 14	09:17:54	50	-4342	136	H	p-	-0.7510	1.0035	70.9S	19.6E	41	25	18	00m14s
0345	029	1649 May 11	16:22:04	50	-4337	103	P	-t	-1.4800	0.1428	62.7S	15.7W	0	313		
0346	029	1649 Jun 10	07:02:36	50	-4336	141	P	t-	1.3658	0.3345	65.0N	81.5W	0	22		
0347	029	1649 Nov 04	13:35:07	49	-4331	108	P	-t	1.2716	0.4978	62.2N	30.2E	0	235		
0348	029	1649 Dec 03	23:40:37	49	-4330	146	P	t-	-1.3820	0.2896	64.4S	34.1E	0	151		
0349	030	1650 Apr 30	16:48:48	48	4325	113	A	-p	-0.7347	0.9481	28.5S	52.9W	43	334	274	05m43s
0350	030	1650 Oct 25	04:21:25	48	-4319	118	T	-p	0.6170	1.0159	22.3N	127.9E	52	207	68	01m26s
0351	030	1651 Apr 19	22:04:36	47	-4313	123	A	nn	0.0433	0.9976	13.7N	152.4W	87	154	8	00m14s
0352	030	1651 Oct 14	13:40:55	46	-4307	128	A	nn	-0.1025	0.9668	13.5S	31.3W	84	28	120	03m27s
0353	030	1652 Apr 08	10:22:27	45	-4301	133	T	p-	0.7713	1.0412	49.6N	8.9W	39	135	213	02m49s
0354	030	1652 Oct 02	15:58:29	45	-4295	138	A	p-	-0.8459	0.9275	51.2S	102.7W	32	50	497	06m19s
0355	030	1653 Feb 27	17:28:49	44	-4290	105	P	-t	-1.1619	0.7043	61.3S	26.0E	0	253		
0356	030	1653 Mar 29	02:38:06	44	-4289	143	P	t-	1.4469	0.1621	61.2N	45.6E	0	83		
0357	030	1653 Aug 23	01:17:26	44	-4284	110	P	-t	1.3072	0.4357	61.6N	86.7W	0	295		
0358	030	1653 Sep 21	15:55:43	43	-4283	148	Pb	t-	-1.5450	0.0324	61.0S	149.7W	0	89		
0359	030	1654 Feb 17	06:36:37	43	-4278	115	A	-p	-0.4991	0.9933	38.3S	100.9E	60	327	27	00m34s
0360	030	1654 Aug 12	10:17:42	42	-4272	120	T	-p	0.4962	1.0285	41.7N	42.5E	60	211	110	02m16s

THOUSAND YEAR CANON OF SOLAR ECLIPSES: 1501 TO 2500

Cat Num	Canon Plate	Calendar Date	TD of Greatest Eclipse	ΔT s	Luna Num	Saros Num	Ecl Type	QLE	Gamma	Ecl Mag	Lat °	Long °	Sun Alt °	Sun Azm °	Path Width km	Central Line Dur
0361	031	1655 Feb 06	12:51:54	41	-4266	125	A	nn	0.2130	0.9408	4.2S	14.0W	78	157	224	07m03s
0362	031	1655 Aug 02	01:28:36	41	-4260	130	T	n-	-0.2625	1.0735	3.7N	154.0E	75	20	247	06m28s
0363	031	1656 Jan 26	12:48:09	40	-4254	135	A	p-	0.9122	0.9106	43.2N	34.1W	24	154	820	09m38s
0364	031	1656 Jul 21	18:39:47	39	-4248	140	T-	t-	-0.9983	1.0244	63.4S	140.6W	0	39	-	-
0365	031	1656 Dec 15	20:59:51	39	-4243	107	P	-t	-1.3790	0.3102	66.4S	36.3E	0	187		
0366	031	1657 Jan 14	13:08:11	39	-4242	145	P	t-	1.5547	0.0171	63.7N	52.7W	0	145		
0367	031	1657 Jun 11	22:52:09	38	-4237	112	A	-t	0.8394	0.9888	80.5N	153.7W	33	190	73	00m45s
0368	031	1657 Dec 05	07:39:36	38	-4231	117	T	-p	-0.6335	1.0205	62.1S	61.3E	50	3	91	01m29s
0369	031	1658 Jun 01	03:11:37	37	-4225	122	A	nn	0.0828	0.9532	27.0N	131.3E	85	178	172	05m49s
0370	031	1658 Nov 24	22:54:41	36	-4219	127	T	nn	0.0514	1.0502	18.0S	166.3W	87	186	167	04m40s
0371	031	1659 May 21	03:38:52	36	-4213	132	A	p-	-0.6747	0.9469	22.2S	129.2E	47	353	264	06m50s
0372	031	1659 Nov 14	14:10:07	35	-4207	137	T	p-	0.7432	1.0208	29.2N	28.2W	42	190	106	01m56s
0373	032	1660 Apr 09	20:10:11	35	-4202	104	P	-t	1.3301	0.3907	71.5N	122.9E	0	64		
0374	032	1660 May 09	07:36:44	34	-4201	142	P	t-	-1.3898	0.2868	69.7S	95.9E	0	331		
0375	032	1660 Oct 04	10:03:43	34	-4196	109	P	-t	-1.3629	0.3402	72.0S	78.2W	0	105		
0376	032	1660 Nov 03	00:50:38	34	-4195	147	P	t-	1.5039	0.0898	70.3N	156.2W	0	219		
0377	032	1661 Mar 30	09:55:23	33	-4190	114	T	-p	0.5634	1.0524	36.7N	20.2E	55	158	209	04m12s
0378	032	1661 Sep 23	11:02:33	33	-4184	119	A	-p	-0.6711	0.9306	40.3S	3.0W	48	23	347	07m29s
0379	032	1662 Mar 20	02:21:48	32	-4178	124	T	n-	-0.1414	1.0576	7.9S	149.1E	82	342	192	05m11s
0380	032	1662 Sep 12	11:50:44	32	-4172	129	A	nn	0.0694	0.9582	7.9N	2.6E	86	197	153	05m05s
0381	032	1663 Mar 09	16:48:41	31	-4166	134	H	p-	-0.8735	1.0049	60.5S	37.1W	29	323	35	00m21s
0382	032	1663 Sep 01	18:59:08	30	-4160	139	H	p-	0.8073	1.0065	58.6N	78.9W	36	212	38	00m29s
0383	032	1664 Jan 28	08:02:30	30	-4155	106	P	-t	1.3074	0.4377	69.6N	35.0E	0	154		
0384	032	1664 Jul 23	01:48:45	29	-4149	111	P	-t	-1.0342	0.9581	68.8S	134.7E	0	18		
0385	033	1664 Aug 21	08:58:23	29	-4148	149	Pb	t-	1.4871	0.0844	71.0N	173.8E	0	309		
0386	033	1665 Jan 16	07:11:51	29	-4143	116	A	-p	0.6419	0.9174	19.1N	71.2E	50	175	409	11m24s
0387	033	1665 Jul 12	18:44:05	28	-4137	121	T	-n	-0.3095	1.0611	3.9N	100.6W	72	3	211	06m02s
0388	033	1666 Jan 05	08:58:50	28	-4131	126	A	nn	-0.0624	0.9562	26.3S	47.1E	86	359	160	05m07s
0389	033	1666 Jul 02	07:42:29	27	-4125	131	H	p-	0.4705	1.0075	51.4N	64.4E	62	178	29	00m39s
0390	033	1666 Dec 25	17:59:15	26	-4119	136	H	p-	-0.7452	1.0058	71.6S	98.3W	42	11	30	00m24s
0391	033	1667 May 22	22:57:59	26	-4114	103	Pe	-t	-1.5574	0.0103	63.5S	124.0W	0	322		
0392	033	1667 Jun 21	13:36:07	26	-4113	141	P	t-	1.2858	0.4732	65.9N	170.1E	0	13		
0393	033	1667 Nov 15	22:12:05	25	-4108	108	P	-t	1.2880	0.4667	62.9N	108.2W	0	225		
0394	033	1667 Dec 15	08:29:58	25	-4107	146	P	t-	-1.3752	0.3024	65.3S	108.2W	0	162		
0395	033	1668 May 10	23:37:24	25	-4102	113	A	-p	-0.8048	0.9510	32.3S	155.4W	36	336	296	05m21s
0396	033	1668 Nov 04	12:40:05	24	-4096	118	H	-p	0.6401	1.0102	21.1N	1.8E	50	204	45	00m57s
0397	034	1669 Apr 30	05:26:06	24	-4090	123	H	nn	-0.0170	1.0036	14.1N	98.2E	89	334	13	00m22s
0398	034	1669 Oct 24	21:28:04	23	-4084	128	A	nn	-0.0710	0.9613	15.9S	147.7W	86	26	141	04m07s
0399	034	1670 Apr 19	18:12:20	23	-4078	133	T	p-	0.7191	1.0476	50.6N	123.3W	44	137	225	03m15s
0400	034	1670 Oct 13	23:19:00	22	-4072	138	A	p-	-0.8043	0.9247	52.4S	149.1E	36	49	467	06m34s
0401	034	1671 Mar 11	01:50:57	22	-4067	105	P	-t	-1.1906	0.6505	61.0S	108.3W	0	262		
0402	034	1671 Apr 09	10:41:24	22	-4066	143	P	t-	1.4047	0.2423	61.4N	84.1W	0	74		
0403	034	1671 Sep 03	08:23:56	21	-4061	110	P	-t	1.3664	0.3319	61.3N	157.8E	0	286		
0404	034	1671 Oct 02	23:13:21	21	-4060	148	P	t-	-1.4952	0.1177	61.0S	92.1E	0	98		
0405	034	1672 Feb 28	14:50:42	21	-4055	115	A	-p	-0.5218	0.9926	35.2S	22.0W	58	326	30	00m38s
0406	034	1672 Aug 22	17:44:06	20	-4049	120	T	-p	0.5593	1.0288	41.2N	66.2W	56	215	117	02m15s
0407	034	1673 Feb 16	20:49:18	20	-4043	125	A	nn	0.1951	0.9409	1.8S	133.5W	79	154	223	06m52s
0408	034	1673 Aug 12	09:04:05	19	-4037	130	T	n-	-0.1946	1.0731	4.6N	40.6E	79	23	242	06m15s
0409	035	1674 Feb 05	20:41:35	19	-4031	135	A	p-	0.8979	0.9129	42.8N	155.7W	26	149	736	09m09s
0410	035	1674 Aug 02	02:07:57	19	-4025	140	T	t-	-0.9295	1.0560	45.9S	120.8E	21	29	498	04m08s
0411	035	1674 Dec 27	05:27:32	18	-4020	107	P	-t	-1.3784	0.3109	65.4S	100.9W	0	198		
0412	035	1675 Jan 25	21:19:47	18	-4019	145	P	t-	1.5434	0.0346	62.9N	175.1E	0	135		
0413	035	1675 Jun 23	05:44:38	18	-4014	112	A	-t	0.9219	0.9835	84.1N	166.1W	22	282	154	01m01s
0414	035	1675 Dec 16	16:24:03	17	-4008	117	T	-p	-0.6367	1.0218	63.1S	62.0W	50	353	97	01m33s
0415	035	1676 Jun 11	09:42:36	17	-4002	122	A	nn	0.1672	0.9527	33.0N	34.6E	80	182	176	05m38s
0416	035	1676 Dec 05	07:42:07	17	-3996	127	T	nn	0.0435	1.0486	20.2S	62.5E	88	181	162	04m30s
0417	035	1677 May 31	10:13:52	16	-3990	132	A	p-	-0.5935	0.9510	14.4S	27.5E	53	358	223	06m35s
0418	035	1677 Nov 24	22:44:02	16	-3984	137	T	p-	0.7332	1.0166	26.3N	159.6W	43	186	84	01m36s
0419	035	1678 Apr 21	03:45:49	15	-3979	104	P	-t	1.3765	0.3050	71.0N	4.5W	0	51		
0420	035	1678 May 20	14:40:42	15	-3978	142	P	t-	-1.3172	0.4158	68.8S	22.1W	0	342		

Cat Num	Canon Plate	Calendar Date	TD of Greatest Eclipse	ΔT s	Luna Num	Saros Num	Ecl Type	QLE	Gamma	Ecl Mag	Lat °	Long °	Sun Alt °	Sun Azm °	Path Width km	Central Line Dur
0421	036	1678 Oct 15	17:36:58	15	-3973	109	P	-t	-1.4026	0.2731	71.6S	154.5E	0	119		
0422	036	1678 Nov 14	08:58:13	15	-3972	147	P	t-	1.4908	0.1148	69.4N	69.4E	0	206		
0423	036	1679 Apr 10	17:55:12	15	-3967	114	T	-p	0.6070	1.0565	43.8N	102.2W	52	157	233	04m17s
0424	036	1679 Oct 04	18:13:56	14	-3961	119	A	-p	-0.7191	0.9270	48.0S	114.9W	44	26	391	07m21s
0425	036	1680 Mar 30	10:32:00	14	-3955	124	T	nn	-0.1039	1.0595	1.5S	24.9E	84	343	197	05m25s
0426	036	1680 Sep 22	19:06:23	14	-3949	129	A	nn	0.0160	0.9578	0.7N	108.2W	89	198	153	05m08s
0427	036	1681 Mar 20	00:52:58	13	-3943	134	H	p-	-0.8445	1.0057	53.8S	165.3W	32	329	37	00m26s
0428	036	1681 Sep 12	02:33:12	13	-3937	139	H	p-	0.7504	1.0083	49.8N	161.1E	41	207	43	00m40s
0429	036	1682 Feb 07	15:59:21	13	-3932	106	P	-t	1.3238	0.4101	70.5N	96.8W	0	141		
0430	036	1682 Aug 03	09:21:10	12	-3926	111	P	-t	-1.1028	0.8246	69.7S	9.5E	0	30		
0431	036	1682 Sep 01	16:42:24	12	-3925	149	P	t-	1.4280	0.1978	71.5N	44.3E	0	296		
0432	036	1683 Jan 27	15:10:08	12	-3920	116	A	-p	0.6525	0.9195	22.1N	50.6W	49	171	401	10m44s
0433	037	1683 Jul 24	02:06:59	12	-3914	121	T	-p	-0.3838	1.0569	2.5S	147.1E	67	7	203	05m38s
0434	037	1684 Jan 16	17:18:52	11	-3908	126	A	nn	-0.0565	0.9597	24.2S	76.7W	87	355	147	04m43s
0435	037	1684 Jul 12	14:40:34	11	-3902	131	H	p-	0.3927	1.0041	45.2N	37.1W	67	184	16	00m23s
0436	037	1685 Jan 05	02:42:50	11	-3896	136	H	p-	-0.7409	1.0086	70.7S	143.1E	42	357	44	00m35s
0437	037	1685 Jul 01	20:06:06	11	-3890	141	P	t-	1.2030	0.6163	66.9N	62.2E	0	3		
0438	037	1685 Nov 26	06:54:43	10	-3885	108	P	-t	1.3000	0.4443	63.7N	111.8E	0	215		
0439	037	1685 Dec 25	17:22:34	10	-3884	146	P	t-	-1.3710	0.3102	66.4S	108.3E	0	172		
0440	037	1686 May 22	06:21:19	10	-3879	113	A	-p	-0.8791	0.9533	38.6S	103.3E	28	339	353	04m56s
0441	037	1686 Nov 15	21:04:59	10	-3873	118	H	-p	0.6578	1.0048	20.2N	126.0W	49	200	22	00m28s
0442	037	1687 May 11	12:42:28	10	-3867	123	H	nn	-0.0827	1.0094	13.6N	9.9W	85	339	33	00m57s
0443	037	1687 Nov 05	05:22:24	10	-3861	128	A	nn	-0.0460	0.9561	18.3S	94.3E	87	23	160	04m49s
0444	037	1688 Apr 30	01:57:33	9	-3855	133	T	p-	0.6621	1.0535	51.4N	124.4E	48	141	234	03m40s
0445	038	1688 Oct 24	06:46:41	9	-3849	138	A	p-	-0.7686	0.9221	54.4S	39.2E	39	47	453	06m49s
0446	038	1689 Mar 21	10:06:41	9	-3844	105	P	-t	-1.2245	0.5868	61.0S	119.0E	0	271		
0447	038	1689 Apr 19	18:39:22	9	-3843	143	P	t-	1.3581	0.3313	61.7N	147.5E	0	65		
0448	038	1689 Sep 13	15:39:21	9	-3838	110	P	-t	1.4190	0.2395	61.1N	40.2E	0	277		
0449	038	1689 Oct 13	06:40:02	9	-3837	148	P	t-	-1.4517	0.1920	61.2S	28.3W	0	107		
0450	038	1690 Mar 10	22:56:00	9	-3832	115	A	-p	-0.5511	0.9920	32.5S	143.0W	56	325	33	00m42s
0451	038	1690 Sep 03	01:17:46	9	-3826	120	T	-p	0.6173	1.0287	40.3N	177.4W	52	217	122	02m13s
0452	038	1691 Feb 28	04:37:41	8	-3820	125	A	nn	0.1701	0.9414	0.8N	109.3E	80	152	220	06m40s
0453	038	1691 Aug 23	16:45:56	8	-3814	130	T	n-	-0.1317	1.0720	4.5N	74.3W	82	26	236	06m01s
0454	038	1692 Feb 17	04:26:55	8	-3808	135	A	p-	0.8765	0.9159	42.4N	85.6E	28	145	644	08m36s
0455	038	1692 Aug 12	09:41:05	8	-3802	140	T	p-	-0.8649	1.0546	39.8S	8.6E	30	31	353	04m10s
0456	038	1693 Jan 06	13:55:33	8	-3797	107	P	-t	-1.3788	0.3097	64.4S	122.2E	0	208		
0457	039	1693 Feb 05	05:27:09	8	-3796	145	P	t-	1.5276	0.0597	62.2N	44.2E	0	125		
0458	039	1693 Jul 03	12:33:51	8	-3791	112	P	-t	1.0058	0.9718	64.8N	146.3E	0	336		
0459	039	1693 Dec 27	01:10:50	8	-3785	117	T	-p	-0.6387	1.0236	62.5S	174.3E	50	343	105	01m39s
0460	039	1694 Jun 22	16:08:45	8	-3779	122	A	np	0.2556	0.9517	38.4N	59.7W	75	187	183	05m27s
0461	039	1694 Dec 16	16:33:11	8	-3773	127	T	nn	0.0388	1.0475	21.3S	69.2W	88	176	158	04m22s
0462	039	1695 Jun 11	16:44:23	8	-3767	132	A	p-	-0.5077	0.9545	7.4S	72.2W	59	2	193	06m13s
0463	039	1695 Dec 06	07:23:18	8	-3761	137	T	p-	0.7280	1.0128	24.3N	67.9E	43	181	64	01m16s
0464	039	1696 May 01	11:15:19	8	-3756	104	P	-t	1.4286	0.2079	70.2N	129.8W	0	38		
0465	039	1696 May 30	21:41:22	8	-3755	142	P	t-	-1.2406	0.5534	67.8S	138.7W	0	353		
0466	039	1696 Oct 26	01:17:06	8	-3750	109	P	-t	-1.4361	0.2173	70.9S	25.9E	0	133		
0467	039	1696 Nov 24	17:10:40	8	-3749	147	P	t-	1.4822	0.1318	68.4N	65.6W	0	194		
0468	039	1697 Apr 21	01:49:21	8	-3744	114	T	-p	0.6559	1.0602	51.4N	136.9E	49	157	262	04m18s
0469	040	1697 Oct 15	01:33.41	8	-3738	119	A	-p	-0.7603	0.9236	55.4S	131.2E	40	29	441	07m12s
0470	040	1698 Apr 10	18:34:25	8	-3732	124	Tm	nn	-0.0600	1.0613	5.1N	97.3W	87	344	201	05m36s
0471	040	1698 Oct 04	02:31:24	8	-3726	129	A	nn	-0.0305	0.9573	6.2S	138.8E	88	17	155	05m10s
0472	040	1699 Mar 31	08:48:44	8	-3720	134	H	p-	-0.8089	1.0065	46.8S	69.7E	36	334	38	00m32s
0473	040	1699 Sep 23	10:16:12	8	-3714	139	H	p-	0.6999	1.0095	41.8N	40.7E	45	204	46	00m49s
0474	040	1700 Feb 18	23:49:34	8	-3709	106	P	-t	1.3450	0.3744	71.2N	132.4E	0	128		
0475	040	1700 Aug 14	16:59:05	8	-3703	111	P	-t	-1.1668	0.7001	70.6S	117.5W	0	42		
0476	040	1700 Sep 13	00:34:18	8	-3702	149	P	t-	1.3749	0.2996	71.9N	87.6W	0	283		
0477	040	1701 Feb 07	23:04:53	8	-3697	116	A	-p	0.6662	0.9219	25.9N	171.7W	48	167	393	09m55s
0478	040	1701 Aug 04	09:31:44	8	-3691	121	T	-p	-0.4558	1.0521	9.4S	33.7E	63	10	193	05m06s
0479	040	1702 Jan 28	01:37:09	8	-3685	126	A	nn	-0.0485	0.9636	21.2S	159.6E	87	351	132	04m14s
0480	040	1702 Jul 24	21:38:51	8	-3679	131	H	n-	0.3160	1.0002	38.4N	140.4W	71	188	1	00m01s

60

Cat Num	Canon Plate	Calendar Date	TD of Greatest Eclipse	ΔT s	Luna Num	Saros Num	Ecl Type	QLE	Gamma	Ecl Mag	Lat °	Long °	Sun Alt °	Sun Azm °	Path Width km	Central Line Dur
0481	041	1703 Jan 17	11:24:25	8	-3673	136	H2	p-	-0.7345	1.0120	67.9S	22.2E	42	347	61	00m50s
0482	041	1703 Jul 14	02:36:33	8	-3667	141	P	t-	1.1207	0.7580	67.9N	46.3W	0	352		
0483	041	1703 Dec 08	15:41:29	8	-3662	108	P	-t	1.3086	0.4282	64.6N	29.5W	0	205		
0484	041	1704 Jan 07	02:14:50	8	-3661	146	P	t-	-1.3669	0.3177	67.4S	35.5W	0	183		
0485	041	1704 Jun 02	13:02:36	8	-3656	113	A	-t	-0.9561	0.9542	49.1S	3.4E	16	341	578	04m26s
0486	041	1704 Nov 27	05:33:52	8	-3650	118	A	-p	0.6716	0.9999	19.7N	104.9E	48	196	1	00m01s
0487	041	1705 May 22	19:55:05	9	-3644	123	Hm	nn	-0.1525	1.0147	12.2N	117.0W	81	343	51	01m32s
0488	041	1705 Nov 16	13:23:05	9	-3638	128	A	nn	-0.0271	0.9514	20.4S	25.0W	88	19	178	05m31s
0489	041	1706 May 12	09:35:08	9	-3632	133	T	p-	0.5984	1.0591	51.5N	15.2E	53	147	242	04m06s
0490	041	1706 Nov 05	14:23:56	9	-3626	138	A	p-	-0.7407	0.9196	57.0S	72.6W	42	44	449	07m02s
0491	041	1707 Apr 02	18:12:24	9	-3621	105	P	-t	-1.2661	0.5083	61.1S	11.1W	0	280		
0492	041	1707 May 02	02:28:16	9	-3620	143	P	t-	1.3047	0.4339	62.2N	21.4E	0	56		
0493	042	1707 Sep 25	23:05:05	9	-3615	110	P	-t	1.4641	0.1604	61.1N	80.0W	0	268		
0494	042	1707 Oct 25	14:17:22	9	-3614	148	P	t-	-1.4161	0.2528	61.6S	151.3W	0	116		
0495	042	1708 Mar 22	06:51:36	9	-3609	115	A	-p	-0.5878	0.9913	30.4S	98.3E	54	326	37	00m46s
0496	042	1708 Sep 14	09:00:22	9	-3603	120	T	-p	0.6685	1.0281	39.2N	68.3E	48	218	126	02m10s
0497	042	1709 Mar 11	12:18:34	9	-3597	125	Am	nn	0.1395	0.9422	3.4N	5.9W	82	151	216	06m29s
0498	042	1709 Sep 04	00:32:26	9	-3591	130	T	nn	-0.0725	1.0703	3.7N	169.7E	86	28	229	05m47s
0499	042	1710 Feb 28	12:07:28	9	-3585	135	A	p-	0.8509	0.9194	42.5N	31.2W	31	141	562	08m00s
0500	042	1710 Aug 24	17:17:15	9	-3579	140	T	p-	-0.8031	1.0519	36.5S	105.1W	36	33	282	04m00s
0501	042	1711 Jan 18	22:23:37	9	-3574	107	P	-t	-1.3796	0.3076	63.5S	14.4W	0	218		
0502	042	1711 Feb 17	13:30:14	9	-3573	145	P	t-	1.5077	0.0919	61.6N	85.4W	0	116		
0503	042	1711 Jul 15	19:22:11	9	-3568	112	P	-t	1.0894	0.8217	63.9N	34.6E	0	327		
0504	042	1712 Jan 08	09:58:39	9	-3562	117	T	-p	-0.6406	1.0258	60.6S	49.2E	50	335	114	01m48s
0505	043	1712 Jul 03	22:34:57	9	-3556	122	A	-p	0.3433	0.9503	42.8N	152.7W	70	194	194	05m18s
0506	043	1712 Dec 28	01:24:54	9	-3550	127	T	nn	0.0347	1.0466	21.5S	159.0E	88	171	155	04m15s
0507	043	1713 Jun 22	23:15:38	9	-3544	132	A	p-	-0.4217	0.9576	1.3S	171.2W	65	6	170	05m45s
0508	043	1713 Dec 17	16:04:20	9	-3538	137	H	p-	0.7249	1.0094	23.1N	64.8W	43	176	47	00m56s
0509	043	1714 May 13	18:39:34	9	-3533	104	Pe	-t	1.4855	0.1008	69.4N	106.9E	0	26		
0510	043	1714 Jun 12	04:40:01	9	-3532	142	P	t-	-1.1610	0.6976	66.8S	105.8E	0	4		
0511	043	1714 Nov 07	09:04:34	9	-3527	109	P	-t	-1.4630	0.1731	70.1S	103.9W	0	145		
0512	043	1714 Dec 07	01:27:09	9	-3526	147	P	t-	1.4772	0.1420	67.4N	159.0E	0	183		
0513	043	1715 May 03	09:36:29	9	-3521	114	T	-p	0.7112	1.0632	59.4N	17.9E	44	157	295	04m14s
0514	043	1715 Oct 27	09:02:48	9	-3515	119	A	-p	-0.7939	0.9206	62.5S	15.5E	37	31	494	07m02s
0515	043	1716 Apr 22	02:28:32	9	-3509	124	T	nn	-0.0091	1.0625	11.8N	142.6E	90	343	205	05m43s
0516	043	1716 Oct 15	10:07:38	10	-3503	129	A	nn	-0.0687	0.9570	12.5S	23.5E	86	16	157	05m10s
0517	044	1717 Apr 11	16:34:40	10	-3497	134	H	p-	-0.7660	1.0072	39.5S	52.1W	40	339	39	00m39s
0518	044	1717 Oct 04	18:08:27	10	-3491	139	H	p-	0.6563	1.0104	34.6N	81.1W	49	201	47	00m56s
0519	044	1718 Mar 02	07:31:36	10	-3486	106	P	-t	1.3723	0.3285	71.8N	3.2E	0	114		
0520	044	1718 Aug 26	00:41:45	10	-3480	111	P	-t	-1.2267	0.5838	71.2S	113.7E	0	55		
0521	044	1718 Sep 24	08:34:19	10	-3479	149	P	t-	1.3283	0.3888	72.0N	138.3E	0	269		
0522	044	1719 Feb 19	06:52:57	10	-3474	116	A	-p	0.6855	0.9250	30.5N	68.6E	47	163	384	09m01s
0523	044	1719 Aug 15	16:59:51	10	-3468	121	T	-p	-0.5243	1.0466	16.8S	81.1W	58	13	181	04m27s
0524	044	1720 Feb 08	09:52:30	10	-3462	126	A	nn	-0.0375	0.9681	17.4S	36.1E	88	348	115	03m40s
0525	044	1720 Aug 04	04:38:14	10	-3456	131	A	nn	0.2410	0.9957	31.1N	114.8E	76	192	16	00m27s
0526	044	1721 Jan 27	20:05:11	10	-3450	136	T	p-	-0.7269	1.0158	64.0S	102.4W	43	340	79	01m07s
0527	044	1721 Jul 24	09:06:55	10	-3444	141	P	t-	1.0383	0.8990	68.9N	155.2W	0	341		
0528	044	1721 Dec 19	00:31:50	10	-3439	108	P	-t	1.3144	0.4172	65.7N	172.0W	0	195		
0529	045	1722 Jan 17	11:07:09	10	-3438	146	P	t-	-1.3629	0.3251	68.5S	179.9W	0	195		
0530	045	1722 Jun 13	19:40:18	10	-3433	113	P	-t	-1.0364	0.9084	65.2S	93.5W	0	340		
0531	045	1722 Dec 08	14:07:34	10	-3427	118	A	-p	0.6808	0.9955	19.5N	25.4W	47	191	21	00m28s
0532	045	1723 Jun 03	03:05:13	10	-3421	123	T	nn	-0.2251	1.0196	9.6N	136.1E	77	347	69	02m05s
0533	045	1723 Nov 27	21:28:15	10	-3415	128	A	nn	-0.0125	0.9471	22.0S	145.2W	89	14	195	06m12s
0534	045	1724 May 22	17:10:08	10	-3409	133	T	p-	0.5319	1.0640	50.8N	92.9W	58	154	247	04m33s
0535	045	1724 Nov 15	22:07:37	10	-3403	138	A	p-	-0.7183	0.9174	59.9S	175.0E	44	40	448	07m15s
0536	045	1725 Apr 13	02:11:22	10	-3398	105	P	-t	-1.3132	0.4193	61.4S	139.6W	0	289		
0537	045	1725 May 12	10:12:19	10	-3397	143	P	t-	1.2472	0.5447	62.8N	103.7W	0	47		
0538	045	1725 Oct 06	06:39:42	10	-3392	110	P	-t	1.5028	0.0924	61.2N	157.7E	0	259		
0539	045	1725 Nov 04	22:02:51	10	-3391	148	P	t-	-1.3861	0.3038	62.1S	83.5E	0	125		
0540	045	1726 Apr 02	14:38:16	10	-3386	115	A	-p	-0.6312	0.9906	29.2S	18.3W	51	327	42	00m52s

61

Cat Num	Canon Plate	Calendar Date	TD of Greatest Eclipse	ΔT s	Luna Num	Saros Num	Ecl Type	QLE	Gamma	Ecl Mag	Lat °	Long °	Sun Alt °	Sun Azm °	Path Width km	Central Line Dur
0541	046	1726 Sep 25	16:51:44	10	-3380	120	T	-p	0.7133	1.0273	38.0N	49.0W	44	218	129	02m07s
0542	046	1727 Mar 22	19:47:55	10	-3374	125	A	nn	0.0996	0.9432	5.7N	118.0W	84	151	211	06m20s
0543	046	1727 Sep 15	08:27:30	10	-3368	130	T	nn	-0.0202	1.0681	2.2N	51.4E	89	29	222	05m33s
0544	046	1728 Mar 10	19:38:55	10	-3362	135	A	p-	0.8172	0.9233	42.8N	144.6W	35	139	485	07m25s
0545	046	1728 Sep 04	00:59:22	10	-3356	140	T	p-	-0.7466	1.0484	35.0S	139.6E	41	34	236	03m44s
0546	046	1729 Jan 29	06:48:43	10	-3351	107	P	-t	-1.3838	0.2994	62.8S	149.9W	0	228		
0547	046	1729 Feb 27	21:27:02	10	-3350	145	P	t-	1.4817	0.1347	61.2N	146.6E	0	107		
0548	046	1729 Jul 26	02:10:39	10	-3345	112	P	-t	1.1717	0.6747	63.1N	76.9W	0	318		
0549	046	1729 Aug 24	13:48:31	10	-3344	150	Pb	t-	-1.5430	0.0067	61.7S	95.2W	0	66		
0550	046	1730 Jan 18	18:45:15	10	-3339	117	T	-p	-0.6439	1.0286	57.8S	77.4W	50	329	126	01m59s
0551	046	1730 Jul 15	04:59:08	10	-3333	122	A	-p	0.4325	0.9484	46.3N	115.9E	64	200	210	05m13s
0552	046	1731 Jan 08	10:17:44	10	-3327	127	Tm	nn	0.0313	1.0464	20.7S	27.0E	88	166	155	04m10s
0553	047	1731 Jul 04	05:46:25	11	-3321	132	A	p-	-0.3341	0.9602	3.8N	90.8E	71	10	153	05m15s
0554	047	1731 Dec 29	00:46:52	11	-3315	137	H	p-	0.7234	1.0065	22.7N	162.2E	44	171	32	00m39s
0555	047	1732 Jun 22	11:38:47	11	-3309	142	P	t-	-1.0800	0.8457	65.8S	9.3W	0	14		
0556	047	1732 Nov 17	16:58:50	11	-3304	109	P	-t	-1.4841	0.1390	69.2S	125.3E	0	158		
0557	047	1732 Dec 17	09:46:56	11	-3303	147	P	t-	1.4752	0.1470	66.3N	23.4E	0	172		
0558	047	1733 May 13	17:18:28	11	-3298	114	T	-p	0.7712	1.0656	67.9N	99.5W	39	157	339	04m06s
0559	047	1733 Nov 06	16:40:14	11	-3292	119	A	-p	-0.8208	0.9179	69.0S	101.2W	34	32	548	06m53s
0560	047	1734 May 03	10:15:56	11	-3286	124	T	nn	0.0472	1.0635	18.4N	24.6E	87	168	208	05m46s
0561	047	1734 Oct 26	17:53:27	11	-3280	129	A	nn	-0.0996	0.9567	18.2S	93.8W	84	14	159	05m08s
0562	047	1735 Apr 23	00:11:35	11	-3274	134	H	p-	-0.7164	1.0077	32.2S	171.0W	44	343	38	00m44s
0563	047	1735 Oct 16	02:10:33	11	-3268	139	H	p-	0.6202	1.0110	28.3N	155.2E	51	198	48	01m02s
0564	047	1736 Mar 12	15:05:55	11	-3263	106	P	-t	1.4049	0.2733	72.1N	124.5W	0	100		
0565	048	1736 Apr 11	07:18:06	11	-3262	144	Pb	t-	-1.5166	0.0748	71.5S	134.3E	0	298		
0566	048	1736 Sep 05	08:30:25	11	-3257	111	P	-t	-1.2817	0.4776	71.7S	17.1W	0	68		
0567	048	1736 Oct 04	16:41:33	11	-3256	149	P	t-	1.2874	0.4670	71.9N	2.4E	0	255		
0568	048	1737 Mar 01	14:35:17	11	-3251	116	A	-p	0.7098	0.9283	36.0N	50.1W	45	160	378	08m04s
0569	048	1737 Aug 26	00:32:08	11	-3245	121	T	-p	-0.5885	1.0407	24.4S	162.5E	54	17	167	03m44s
0570	048	1738 Feb 18	18:02:31	11	-3239	126	A	nn	-0.0211	0.9732	12.8S	86.7W	89	346	96	03m03s
0571	048	1738 Aug 15	11:40:12	11	-3233	131	A	nn	0.1688	0.9907	23.7N	8.4E	80	194	33	01m00s
0572	048	1739 Feb 08	04:41:13	11	-3227	136	T	p-	-0.7150	1.0203	59.2S	131.0E	44	336	99	01m27s
0573	048	1739 Aug 04	15:40:56	11	-3221	141	A	t-	0.9588	0.9408	79.9N	42.9E	16	280	801	03m59s
0574	048	1739 Dec 30	09:22:03	11	-3216	108	P	-t	1.3203	0.4062	66.7N	45.1E	0	184		
0575	048	1740 Jan 28	19:54:59	11	-3215	146	P	t-	-1.3556	0.3387	69.5S	36.2E	0	207		
0576	048	1740 Jun 24	02:18:53	11	-3210	113	P	-t	-1.1163	0.7697	66.2S	156.7E	0	350		
0577	049	1740 Dec 18	22:43:17	11	-3204	118	A	-p	0.6876	0.9917	19.9N	156.4W	46	187	40	00m53s
0578	049	1741 Jun 13	10:12:47	12	-3198	123	T	-n	-0.3007	1.0239	6.0N	29.4E	73	352	85	02m35s
0579	049	1741 Dec 08	05:37:59	12	-3192	128	A	nn	-0.0024	0.9434	23.0S	93.6W	90	6	209	06m51s
0580	049	1742 Jun 03	00:39:56	12	-3186	133	T	-p	0.4607	1.0683	49.0N	160.2E	62	161	251	05m00s
0581	049	1742 Nov 27	05:58:59	12	-3180	138	A	p-	-0.7019	0.9156	62.6S	62.2E	45	34	450	07m26s
0582	049	1743 Apr 24	10:00:09	12	-3175	105	P	-t	-1.3682	0.3153	61.8S	94.4E	0	298		
0583	049	1743 May 23	17:48:55	12	-3174	143	P	t-	1.1838	0.6671	63.5N	132.9E	0	38		
0584	049	1743 Oct 17	14:25:41	12	-3169	110	Pe	-t	1.5334	0.0388	61.5N	32.5E	0	250		
0585	049	1743 Nov 16	05:58:24	12	-3168	148	P	t-	-1.3634	0.3424	62.8S	44.4W	0	135		
0586	049	1744 Apr 12	22:15:24	12	-3163	115	A	-p	-0.6819	0.9895	29.0S	132.6W	47	329	49	00m59s
0587	049	1744 Oct 06	00:51:23	12	-3157	120	T	-p	0.7521	1.0263	37.0N	169.1W	41	216	132	02m04s
0588	049	1745 Apr 02	03:09:18	12	-3151	125	A	nn	0.0536	0.9444	7.7N	132.2E	87	152	205	06m13s
0589	050	1745 Sep 25	16:28:55	12	-3145	130	Tm	nn	0.0269	1.0655	0.3N	68.6W	88	209	214	05m21s
0590	050	1746 Mar 22	03:02:48	12	-3139	135	A	p-	0.7771	0.9277	43.5N	104.7E	39	138	419	06m51s
0591	050	1746 Sep 15	08:46:36	12	-3133	140	T	p-	-0.6948	1.0441	34.9S	23.0E	46	36	201	03m23s
0592	050	1747 Feb 09	15:11:17	12	-3128	107	P	-t	-1.3908	0.2861	62.1S	75.5E	0	237		
0593	050	1747 Mar 11	05:18:08	12	-3127	145	P	t-	1.4504	0.1872	61.0N	20.2E	0	98		
0594	050	1747 Aug 06	09:01:21	12	-3122	112	P	-t	1.2512	0.5340	62.4N	171.3E	0	309		
0595	050	1747 Sep 04	21:07:56	12	-3121	150	P	t-	-1.4881	0.1086	61.4S	146.1E	0	75		
0596	050	1748 Jan 30	03:29:13	12	-3116	117	T	-p	-0.6501	1.0317	54.4S	154.8E	49	324	140	02m12s
0597	050	1748 Jul 25	11:27:02	12	-3110	122	A	-p	0.5183	0.9461	48.7N	24.5E	59	207	231	05m12s
0598	050	1749 Jan 18	19:08:56	13	-3104	127	T	nn	0.0265	1.0465	19.1S	104.9W	89	161	155	04m07s
0599	050	1749 Jul 14	12:19:20	13	-3098	132	A	pn	-0.2476	0.9623	7.8N	7.2W	76	14	141	04m46s
0600	050	1750 Jan 08	09:28:42	13	-3092	137	H	p-	0.7217	1.0041	23.0N	29.3E	44	167	20	00m24s

Cat Num	Canon Plate	Calendar Date	TD of Greatest Eclipse	ΔT s	Luna Num	Saros Num	Ecl Type	QLE	Gamma	Ecl Mag	Lat °	Long °	Sun Alt °	Sun Azm °	Path Width km	Central Line Dur
0601	051	1750 Jul 03	18:38:51	13	-3086	142	P	t-	-0.9985	0.9956	64.8S	124.3W	0	23		
0602	051	1750 Nov 29	00:58:14	13	-3081	109	P	-t	-1.5004	0.1130	68.2S	6.2W	0	170		
0603	051	1750 Dec 28	18:06:51	13	-3080	147	P	t-	1.4737	0.1506	65.3N	111.8W	0	161		
0604	051	1751 May 25	00:55:15	13	-3075	114	T	-p	0.8359	1.0670	77.0N	144.7E	33	157	402	03m53s
0605	051	1751 Nov 18	00:26:00	13	-3069	119	A	-p	-0.8411	0.9159	74.9S	142.8E	32	31	597	06m45s
0606	051	1752 May 13	17:56:28	13	-3063	124	T	nn	0.1090	1.0637	24.9N	91.1W	84	171	210	05m42s
0607	051	1752 Nov 06	01:48:14	13	-3057	129	A	nn	-0.1239	0.9567	23.2S	147.4E	83	12	159	05m03s
0608	051	1753 May 03	07:39:39	13	-3051	134	H	p-	-0.6601	1.0079	24.9S	73.0E	49	347	36	00m48s
0609	051	1753 Oct 26	10:22:00	13	-3045	139	H	p-	0.5911	1.0115	22.7N	29.7E	54	195	49	01m08s
0610	051	1754 Mar 23	22:28:58	13	-3040	106	P	-t	1.4463	0.2032	72.1N	110.6E	0	86		
0611	051	1754 Apr 22	14:25:56	13	-3039	144	P	t-	-1.4631	0.1669	71.0S	14.0E	0	311		
0612	051	1754 Sep 16	16:25:41	13	-3034	111	P	-t	-1.3314	0.3822	71.9S	149.9W	0	82		
0613	052	1754 Oct 16	00:57:45	13	-3033	149	P	t-	1.2535	0.5314	71.5N	135.5W	0	241		
0614	052	1755 Mar 12	22:09:32	14	-3028	116	A	-p	0.7413	0.9319	42.2N	167.4W	42	156	375	07m07s
0615	052	1755 Sep 06	08:09:45	14	-3022	121	T	-p	-0.6478	1.0342	32.1S	44.3E	49	20	150	03m00s
0616	052	1756 Mar 01	02:07:09	14	-3016	126	A	nn	0.0006	0.9787	7.5S	151.4E	90	29	76	02m24s
0617	052	1756 Aug 25	18:46:17	14	-3010	131	Am	nn	0.1009	0.9853	16.1N	99.5W	84	196	52	01m38s
0618	052	1757 Feb 18	13:14:12	14	-3004	136	T	p-	-0.6999	1.0251	53.8S	2.9E	45	335	119	01m51s
0619	052	1757 Aug 14	22:16:45	14	-2998	141	A	p-	0.8807	0.9407	71.6N	113.4W	28	224	467	04m36s
0620	052	1758 Jan 09	18:13:42	14	-2993	108	P	-t	1.3251	0.3972	67.8N	98.7W	0	173		
0621	052	1758 Feb 08	04:40:51	14	-2992	146	P	t-	-1.3468	0.3549	70.4S	107.8W	0	220		
0622	052	1758 Jul 05	08:57:44	14	-2987	113	P	-t	-1.1961	0.6303	67.2S	46.4E	0	0		
0623	052	1758 Dec 30	07:20:12	14	-2981	118	A	-p	0.6929	0.9885	20.8N	72.2E	46	182	56	01m15s
0624	052	1759 Jun 24	17:20:59	14	-2975	123	T	-n	-0.3768	1.0275	1.4N	78.1W	68	356	101	02m59s
0625	053	1759 Dec 19	13:50:05	14	-2969	128	A	nn	0.0051	0.9404	23.3S	28.0W	90	193	221	07m25s
0626	053	1760 Jun 13	08:09:15	14	-2963	133	T	p-	0.3883	1.0719	46.0N	52.7E	67	168	254	05m27s
0627	053	1760 Dec 07	13:53:44	14	-2957	138	A	p-	-0.6882	0.9144	64.7S	49.4W	46	26	451	07m36s
0628	053	1761 May 04	17:43:11	14	-2952	105	P	-t	-1.4274	0.2032	62.4S	30.3W	0	307		
0629	053	1761 Jun 03	01:22:37	14	-2951	143	P	t-	1.1182	0.7939	64.4N	9.9E	0	29		
0630	053	1761 Nov 26	14:00:27	15	-2945	148	P	t-	-1.3451	0.3732	63.7S	174.2W	0	144		
0631	053	1762 Apr 24	05:42:10	15	-2940	115	A	-p	-0.7402	0.9881	30.3S	115.6E	42	331	61	01m08s
0632	053	1762 Oct 17	09:00:34	15	-2934	120	T	-p	0.7836	1.0253	36.2N	67.6E	38	214	135	02m02s
0633	053	1763 Apr 13	10:19:31	15	-2928	125	A	nn	-0.0010	0.9455	9.0N	25.3E	90	250	201	06m11s
0634	053	1763 Oct 07	00:39:04	15	-2922	130	T	nn	0.0666	1.0627	2.0S	169.1E	86	209	206	05m09s
0635	053	1764 Apr 01	10:17:14	15	-2916	135	A	p-	0.7289	0.9323	44.2N	2.5W	43	138	361	06m20s
0636	053	1764 Sep 25	16:41:43	15	-2910	140	T	p-	-0.6502	1.0394	36.0S	95.5W	49	37	171	03m01s
0637	054	1765 Feb 19	23:28:38	15	-2905	107	P	-t	-1.4028	0.2635	61.6S	57.7W	0	247		
0638	054	1765 Mar 21	13:01:44	15	-2904	145	P	t-	1.4120	0.2525	61.0N	104.3W	0	89		
0639	054	1765 Aug 16	15:54:01	15	-2899	112	P	-t	1.3278	0.3995	61.8N	59.2E	0	300		
0640	054	1765 Sep 15	04:32:34	15	-2898	150	P	t-	-1.4378	0.2009	61.1S	26.2E	0	84		
0641	054	1766 Feb 09	12:09:44	15	-2893	117	T	-p	-0.6597	1.0352	50.7S	26.6E	48	321	156	02m27s
0642	054	1766 Aug 05	17:56:57	15	-2887	122	A	-p	0.6023	0.9433	50.2N	67.0W	53	214	260	05m15s
0643	054	1767 Jan 30	03:56:55	15	-2881	127	T	nn	0.0190	1.0471	16.8S	123.9E	89	157	157	04m06s
0644	054	1767 Jul 25	18:55:47	15	-2875	132	A	nn	-0.1630	0.9638	10.8N	105.5W	81	18	132	04m21s
0645	054	1768 Jan 19	18:09:29	15	-2869	137	H	p-	0.7195	1.0022	23.9N	103.2W	44	162	11	00m13s
0646	054	1768 Jul 14	01:40:57	16	-2863	142	H	t-	-0.9176	1.0055	43.0S	137.4E	23	19	48	00m29s
0647	054	1768 Dec 09	09:01:38	16	-2858	109	P	-t	-1.5129	0.0933	67.1S	138.1W	0	181		
0648	054	1769 Jan 08	02:26:41	16	-2857	147	P	t-	1.4728	0.1531	64.3N	113.5E	0	151		
0649	055	1769 Jun 04	08:28:34	16	-2852	114	T	-t	0.9037	1.0671	87.3N	26.2E	25	153	521	03m36s
0650	055	1769 Nov 28	08:18:39	16	-2846	119	A	-p	-0.8559	0.9144	80.0S	32.0E	31	22	638	06m38s
0651	055	1770 May 25	01:30:11	16	-2840	124	T	-n	0.1760	1.0634	31.2N	155.6E	80	174	211	05m31s
0652	055	1770 Nov 17	09:51:53	16	-2834	129	A	nn	-0.1416	0.9571	27.3S	27.1E	82	9	158	04m56s
0653	055	1771 May 14	15:00:02	16	-2828	134	H	p-	-0.5981	1.0076	17.8S	40.4W	53	351	33	00m49s
0654	055	1771 Nov 06	18:41:02	16	-2822	139	H	p-	0.5676	1.0120	17.9N	97.3W	55	192	50	01m13s
0655	055	1772 Apr 03	05:43:52	16	-2817	106	P	-t	1.4935	0.1229	71.9N	12.3W	0	72		
0656	055	1772 May 02	21:26:41	16	-2816	144	P	t-	-1.4044	0.2683	70.2S	104.1W	0	323		
0657	055	1772 Sep 27	00:28:19	16	-2811	111	P	-t	-1.3751	0.2988	72.0S	75.4E	0	96		
0658	055	1772 Oct 26	09:21:17	16	-2810	149	P	t-	1.2255	0.5846	70.9N	85.1E	0	228		
0659	055	1773 Mar 23	05:36:57	16	-2805	116	A	-p	0.7785	0.9357	49.2N	76.2E	39	152	378	06m13s
0660	055	1773 Sep 16	15:52:23	16	-2799	121	T	-p	-0.7020	1.0275	39.9S	75.5W	45	23	130	02m18s

Cat Num	Canon Plate	Calendar Date	TD of Greatest Eclipse	ΔT s	Luna Num	Saros Num	Ecl Type	QLE	Gamma	Ecl Mag	Lat °	Long °	Sun Alt °	Sun Azm °	Path Width km	Central Line Dur
0661	056	1774 Mar 12	10:05:14	16	-2793	126	A	nn	0.0284	0.9845	1.7S	30.8E	88	162	55	01m43s
0662	056	1774 Sep 06	01:57:40	16	-2787	131	A	nn	0.0385	0.9797	8.7N	150.9E	88	197	72	02m20s
0663	056	1775 Mar 01	21:39:20	16	-2781	136	T	p-	-0.6783	1.0304	47.9S	124.8W	47	335	139	02m20s
0664	056	1775 Aug 26	04:59:40	16	-2775	141	A	p-	0.8088	0.9391	61.3N	132.0E	36	213	383	05m16s
0665	056	1776 Jan 21	03:02:27	16	-2770	108	P	-t	1.3318	0.3848	68.8N	117.6E	0	161		
0666	056	1776 Feb 19	13:20:10	16	-2769	146	P	t-	-1.3334	0.3800	71.1S	109.2E	0	233		
0667	056	1776 Jul 15	15:39:29	16	-2764	113	P	-t	-1.2739	0.4935	68.2S	65.1W	0	11		
0668	056	1776 Aug 14	05:22:56	16	-2763	151	Pb	t-	1.5357	0.0435	70.6N	123.5W	0	318		
0669	056	1777 Jan 09	15:55:35	16	-2758	118	A	-p	0.6987	0.9859	22.4N	58.9W	46	177	70	01m32s
0670	056	1777 Jul 05	00:29:29	16	-2752	123	T	-p	-0.4531	1.0305	4.2S	173.7E	63	0	115	03m17s
0671	056	1777 Dec 29	22:03:28	17	-2746	128	A	nn	0.0109	0.9380	22.7S	150.0W	90	183	231	07m53s
0672	056	1778 Jun 24	15:34:55	17	-2740	133	T	n-	0.3127	1.0746	41.8N	55.0W	72	175	255	05m52s
0673	057	1778 Dec 18	21:53:53	17	-2734	138	A	p-	-0.6788	0.9137	65.8S	160.6W	47	16	450	07m44s
0674	057	1779 May 16	01:17:39	17	-2729	105	Pe	-t	-1.4928	0.0796	63.0S	153.1W	0	316		
0675	057	1779 Jun 14	08:51:28	17	-2728	143	P	t-	1.0489	0.9275	65.3N	112.1W	0	19		
0676	057	1779 Dec 07	22:08:56	17	-2722	148	P	t-	-1.3315	0.3962	64.6S	54.2E	0	154		
0677	057	1780 May 04	13:00:41	17	-2717	115	A	-p	-0.8043	0.9861	33.3S	5.9E	36	334	81	01m21s
0678	057	1780 Oct 27	17:18:27	17	-2711	120	T	-p	0.8083	1.0244	35.6N	58.6W	36	210	138	02m00s
0679	057	1781 Apr 23	17:21:25	17	-2705	125	A	nn	-0.0620	0.9467	9.7N	79.2W	87	334	197	06m13s
0680	057	1781 Oct 17	08:55:58	17	-2699	130	T	-n	0.1007	1.0596	4.3S	45.1E	84	207	197	04m59s
0681	057	1782 Apr 12	17:24:47	17	-2693	135	A	p-	0.6745	0.9370	45.1N	107.1W	47	140	311	05m51s
0682	057	1782 Oct 07	00:43:19	17	-2687	140	T	p-	-0.6113	1.0344	37.9S	144.6E	52	37	144	02m37s
0683	057	1783 Mar 03	07:40:30	17	-2682	107	P	-t	-1.4200	0.2313	61.3S	170.6E	0	256		
0684	057	1783 Apr 01	20:38:38	17	-2681	145	P	t-	1.3671	0.3300	61.0N	132.8E	0	80		
0685	058	1783 Aug 27	22:52:05	17	-2676	112	P	-t	1.3991	0.2758	61.4N	54.1W	0	291		
0686	058	1783 Sep 26	12:04:17	17	-2675	150	P	t-	-1.3935	0.2814	61.1S	95.4W	0	93		
0687	058	1784 Feb 20	20:45:38	17	-2670	117	T	-p	-0.6739	1.0389	47.2S	101.5W	47	320	174	02m44s
0688	058	1784 Aug 16	00:31:53	17	-2664	122	A	-p	0.6819	0.9402	50.9N	159.8W	47	220	299	05m23s
0689	058	1785 Feb 09	12:40:41	17	-2658	127	T	nn	0.0080	1.0480	14.1S	6.6W	90	150	159	04m07s
0690	058	1785 Aug 05	01:37:22	17	-2652	132	A	nn	-0.0817	0.9650	12.7N	155.3E	85	22	127	04m01s
0691	058	1786 Jan 30	02:45:26	17	-2646	137	H	p-	0.7141	1.0009	25.1N	125.5E	44	158	5	00m05s
0692	058	1786 Jul 25	08:46:33	17	-2640	142	T	t-	-0.8384	1.0106	34.6S	30.8E	33	21	66	00m59s
0693	058	1786 Dec 20	17:07:24	16	-2635	109	P	-t	-1.5232	0.0773	66.0S	89.9E	0	192		
0694	058	1787 Jan 19	10:43:13	16	-2634	147	P	t-	1.4697	0.1591	63.4N	20.1W	0	141		
0695	058	1787 Jun 15	15:59:25	16	-2629	114	T	-t	0.9738	1.0648	78.7N	104.8E	12	346	997	03m09s
0696	058	1787 Dec 09	16:15:38	16	-2623	119	A	-p	-0.8674	0.9136	83.4S	62.7W	29	357	672	06m32s
0697	059	1788 Jun 04	08:59:30	16	-2617	124	T	-n	0.2465	1.0623	37.0N	44.4E	76	179	211	05m15s
0698	059	1788 Nov 27	18:02:53	16	-2611	129	A	nn	-0.1542	0.9579	30.4S	94.3W	81	4	155	04m46s
0699	059	1789 May 24	22:11:58	16	-2605	134	H	p-	-0.5297	1.0068	11.0S	151.0W	58	355	28	00m46s
0700	059	1789 Nov 17	03:08:34	16	-2599	139	H	p-	0.5505	1.0126	14.1N	133.9E	57	188	52	01m19s
0701	059	1790 Apr 14	12:48:14	16	-2594	106	Pe	-t	1.5487	0.0287	71.4N	132.1W	0	58		
0702	059	1790 May 14	04:17:21	16	-2593	144	P	t-	-1.3374	0.3840	69.4S	140.9E	0	335		
0703	059	1790 Oct 08	08:38:51	16	-2588	111	P	-t	-1.4122	0.2287	71.7S	61.3W	0	110		
0704	059	1790 Nov 06	17:53:11	16	-2587	149	P	t-	1.2044	0.6245	70.1N	55.8W	0	215		
0705	059	1791 Apr 03	12:55:13	16	-2582	116	A	-p	0.8236	0.9394	57.1N	39.5W	34	147	394	05m21s
0706	059	1791 Sep 27	23:42:29	16	-2576	121	T	-p	-0.7492	1.0206	47.6S	162.4E	41	27	106	01m38s
0707	059	1792 Mar 22	17:57:34	16	-2570	126	A	nn	0.0618	0.9906	4.5N	88.7W	86	162	33	01m02s
0708	059	1792 Sep 16	09:13:51	16	-2564	131	A	nn	-0.0191	0.9739	1.3N	39.9E	89	18	93	03m02s
0709	060	1793 Mar 12	06:00:07	16	-2558	136	T	p-	-0.6524	1.0359	41.7S	107.8E	49	336	158	02m51s
0710	060	1793 Sep 05	11:47:24	15	-2552	141	A	p-	0.7408	0.9370	51.7N	23.0E	42	207	346	06m02s
0711	060	1794 Jan 31	11:48:45	15	-2547	108	P	-t	1.3407	0.3681	69.8N	26.0W	0	149		
0712	060	1794 Mar 01	21:53:59	15	-2546	146	P	t-	-1.3155	0.4136	71.6S	32.9W	0	246		
0713	060	1794 Jul 26	22:24:27	15	-2541	113	P	-t	-1.3496	0.3599	69.1S	178.0W	0	22		
0714	060	1794 Aug 25	12:08:56	15	-2540	151	P	t-	1.4616	0.1709	71.3N	121.9E	0	305		
0715	060	1795 Jan 21	00:29:13	15	-2535	118	A	-p	0.7055	0.9837	24.8N	170.3E	45	173	81	01m44s
0716	060	1795 Jul 16	07:41:36	15	-2529	123	T	-p	-0.5274	1.0327	10.4S	63.8E	58	4	130	03m26s
0717	060	1796 Jan 10	06:14:52	15	-2523	128	A	nn	0.0179	0.9362	21.1S	88.3E	89	177	238	08m15s
0718	060	1796 Jul 04	23:02:54	15	-2517	133	T	n-	0.2385	1.0764	36.8N	164.6W	76	180	255	06m15s
0719	060	1796 Dec 29	05:54:58	15	-2511	138	A	p-	-0.6703	0.9136	65.5S	88.6E	48	5	446	07m51s
0720	060	1797 Jun 24	16:18:13	14	-2505	143	T	t-	0.9780	1.0570	77.2N	133.9E	11	17	975	02m47s

64

Cat Num	Canon Plate	Calendar Date	TD of Greatest Eclipse	ΔT s	Luna Num	Saros Num	Ecl Type	QLE	Gamma	Ecl Mag	Lat °	Long °	Sun Alt °	Sun Azm °	Path Width km	Central Line Dur
0721	061	1797 Dec 18	06:21:51	14	-2499	148	P	t-	-1.3208	0.4142	65.6S	79.0W	0	164		
0722	061	1798 May 15	20:10:32	14	-2494	115	A	-t	-0.8744	0.9832	38.6S	101.6W	29	336	121	01m36s
0723	061	1798 Nov 08	01:44:38	14	-2488	120	T	-p	0.8270	1.0237	35.1N	172.5E	34	206	141	01m59s
0724	061	1799 May 05	00:13:07	14	-2482	125	A	nn	-0.1310	0.9476	9.3N	178.9E	83	338	194	06m20s
0725	061	1799 Oct 28	17:21:46	13	-2476	130	T	-n	0.1274	1.0566	6.7S	81.3W	83	205	188	04m50s
0726	061	1800 Apr 24	00:23:59	13	-2470	135	A	p-	0.6125	0.9417	45.7N	151.3E	52	143	269	05m27s
0727	061	1800 Oct 18	08:51:52	13	-2464	140	T	p-	-0.5788	1.0293	40.3S	23.2E	54	36	120	02m14s
0728	061	1801 Mar 14	15:45:34	13	-2459	107	P	-t	-1.4434	0.1874	61.2S	40.6E	0	265		
0729	061	1801 Apr 13	04:08:06	13	-2458	145	P	t-	1.3152	0.4208	61.3N	11.7E	0	71		
0730	061	1801 Sep 08	05:54:39	13	-2453	112	P	-t	1.4657	0.1615	61.1N	168.5W	0	282		
0731	061	1801 Oct 07	19:42:34	13	-2452	150	P	t-	-1.3552	0.3505	61.2S	141.3E	0	102		
0732	061	1802 Mar 04	05:14:29	13	-2447	117	T	-p	-0.6942	1.0428	44.0S	131.5E	46	320	196	03m02s
0733	062	1802 Aug 28	07:12:00	13	-2441	122	A	-p	0.7569	0.9367	51.3N	105.7E	41	225	354	05m35s
0734	062	1803 Feb 21	21:18:46	12	-2435	127	T	nn	-0.0075	1.0492	11.1S	135.9W	90	337	163	04m09s
0735	062	1803 Aug 17	08:25:03	12	-2429	132	A	nn	-0.0048	0.9657	13.6N	54.7E	90	35	124	03m47s
0736	062	1804 Feb 11	11:16:32	12	-2423	137	H	p-	0.7053	1.0001	26.7N	4.5W	45	153	0	00m00s
0737	062	1804 Aug 05	15:57:13	12	-2417	142	T	p-	-0.7622	1.0144	29.3S	77.1W	40	24	75	01m20s
0738	062	1805 Jan 01	01:14:56	12	-2412	109	P	-t	-1.5315	0.0642	65.0S	42.1W	0	202		
0739	062	1805 Jan 30	18:57:01	12	-2411	147	P	t-	1.4651	0.1675	62.7N	152.8W	0	131		
0740	062	1805 Jun 26	23:27:40	12	-2406	114	P	-t	1.0462	0.9358	65.5N	9.9W	0	343		
0741	062	1805 Jul 26	06:14:18	12	-2405	152	Pb	t-	-1.4571	0.1405	63.2S	42.8E	0	42		
0742	062	1805 Dec 21	00:17:37	12	-2400	119	A	-p	-0.8751	0.9134	83.1S	143.8W	29	317	692	06m26s
0743	062	1806 Jun 16	16:24:26	12	-2394	124	T	-n	0.3203	1.0604	42.2N	64.6W	71	184	210	04m55s
0744	062	1806 Dec 10	02:19:39	12	-2388	129	A	nn	-0.1627	0.9591	32.4S	143.4E	80	360	151	04m32s
0745	063	1807 Jun 06	05:18:31	12	-2382	134	H	p-	-0.4577	1.0055	4.7S	100.4E	63	359	21	00m38s
0746	063	1807 Nov 29	11:42:09	12	-2376	139	H	p-	0.5377	1.0135	11.1N	3.9E	57	184	55	01m26s
0747	063	1808 May 25	11:02:35	12	-2370	144	P	t-	-1.2665	0.5064	68.4S	27.8E	0	347		
0748	063	1808 Oct 19	16:55:30	12	-2365	111	P	-t	-1.4443	0.1688	71.3S	160.8E	0	123		
0749	063	1808 Nov 18	02:30:03	12	-2364	149	P	t-	1.1874	0.6564	69.2N	162.6E	0	202		
0750	063	1809 Apr 14	20:07:11	12	-2359	116	A	-p	0.8742	0.9429	65.8N	157.3W	29	139	435	04m35s
0751	063	1809 Oct 09	07:38:41	12	-2353	121	T	-p	-0.7904	1.0137	55.1S	38.4E	37	30	77	01m02s
0752	063	1810 Apr 04	01:41:19	12	-2347	126	A	nn	0.1031	0.9967	11.1N	153.8E	84	163	12	00m21s
0753	063	1810 Sep 28	16:37:25	12	-2341	131	A	nn	-0.0696	0.9681	5.8S	72.8W	86	18	115	03m45s
0754	063	1811 Mar 24	14:12:13	12	-2335	136	T	p-	-0.6190	1.0416	35.2S	18.0W	52	338	176	03m27s
0755	063	1811 Sep 17	18:43:45	12	-2329	141	A	p-	0.6798	0.9345	43.0N	85.9W	47	204	330	06m51s
0756	063	1812 Feb 12	20:28:40	12	-2324	108	P	-t	1.3545	0.3422	70.7N	168.8W	0	136		
0757	064	1812 Mar 13	06:19:30	12	-2323	146	P	t-	-1.2913	0.4594	71.9S	173.3W	0	260		
0758	064	1812 Aug 07	05:15:50	12	-2318	113	P	-t	-1.4205	0.2344	70.0S	67.0E	0	34		
0759	064	1812 Sep 05	19:04:10	12	-2317	151	P	t-	1.3939	0.2874	71.8N	4.5E	0	292		
0760	064	1813 Feb 01	08:58:26	12	-2312	118	A	-p	0.7151	0.9820	27.9N	40.4E	44	169	91	01m52s
0761	064	1813 Jul 27	14:55:35	12	-2306	123	T	-p	-0.6006	1.0341	17.4S	47.4W	53	8	144	03m27s
0762	064	1814 Jan 21	14:24:46	12	-2300	128	A	nn	0.0253	0.9350	18.6S	33.4W	89	173	242	08m28s
0763	064	1814 Jul 17	06:30:29	12	-2294	133	T	n-	0.1641	1.0774	30.9N	84.7E	80	185	254	06m33s
0764	064	1815 Jan 10	13:57:06	12	-2288	138	A	p-	-0.6626	0.9143	63.7S	23.6W	48	355	438	07m55s
0765	064	1815 Jul 06	23:43:07	12	-2282	143	T	t-	0.9062	1.0593	88.1N	162.7W	25	192	470	03m13s
0766	064	1815 Dec 30	14:38:39	12	-2276	148	P	t-	-1.3129	0.4273	66.7S	146.4E	0	175		
0767	064	1816 May 27	03:13:24	12	-2271	115	A	-t	-0.9492	0.9791	48.0S	153.5E	18	338	238	01m54s
0768	064	1816 Nov 19	10:17:22	12	-2265	120	T	-p	0.8407	1.0233	35.0N	41.5E	33	202	144	02m00s
0769	065	1817 May 16	06:58:14	12	-2259	125	A	nn	-0.2049	0.9483	7.9N	78.5E	78	341	194	06m30s
0770	065	1817 Nov 09	01:53:52	12	-2253	130	T	-n	0.1487	1.0536	8.9S	150.9E	82	202	179	04m42s
0771	065	1818 May 05	07:15:49	12	-2247	135	A	p-	0.5440	0.9464	45.8N	52.5E	57	148	233	05m05s
0772	065	1818 Oct 29	17:07:09	12	-2241	140	T	p-	-0.5524	1.0241	43.1S	99.4W	56	34	98	01m51s
0773	065	1819 Mar 25	23:44:29	12	-2236	107	P	-t	-1.4722	0.1330	61.2S	87.9W	0	274		
0774	065	1819 Apr 24	11:31:59	12	-2235	145	P	t-	1.2579	0.5225	61.7N	108.0W	0	62		
0775	065	1819 Sep 19	13:03:47	12	-2230	112	Pe	-t	1.5258	0.0595	61.0N	75.6E	0	274		
0776	065	1819 Oct 19	03:27:17	12	-2229	150	P	t-	-1.3227	0.4085	61.5S	16.4E	0	111		
0777	065	1820 Mar 14	13:37:15	12	-2224	117	T	-p	-0.7199	1.0467	41.5S	5.7E	44	320	220	03m20s
0778	065	1820 Sep 07	13:59:58	11	-2218	122	A	-p	0.8251	0.9330	51.6N	8.7E	34	229	432	05m49s
0779	065	1821 Mar 04	05:50:13	11	-2212	127	T	nn	-0.0284	1.0506	8.0S	96.3E	88	333	168	04m14s
0780	065	1821 Aug 27	15:19:42	11	-2206	132	A	nn	0.0671	0.9661	13.6N	47.8W	86	207	123	03m38s

Cat Num	Canon Plate	Calendar Date	TD of Greatest Eclipse	ΔT s	Luna Num	Saros Num	Ecl Type	QLE	Gamma	Ecl Mag	Lat °	Long °	Sun Alt °	Sun Azm °	Path Width km	Central Line Dur
0781	066	1822 Feb 21	19:40:40	11	-2200	137	A	p-	0.6914	0.9996	28.6N	132.3W	46	150	2	00m02s
0782	066	1822 Aug 16	23:14:34	11	-2194	142	T	p-	-0.6904	1.0173	26.1S	173.5E	46	27	80	01m35s
0783	066	1823 Jan 12	09:20:12	11	-2189	109	P	-t	-1.5413	0.0484	64.0S	173.0W	0	212		
0784	066	1823 Feb 11	03:03:02	11	-2188	147	P	t-	1.4546	0.1856	62.0N	76.7E	0	122		
0785	066	1823 Jul 08	06:56:27	10	-2183	114	P	-t	1.1182	0.7958	64.6N	132.0W	0	333		
0786	066	1823 Aug 06	13:45:41	10	-2182	152	P	t-	-1.3871	0.2753	62.5S	79.3W	0	51		
0787	066	1824 Jan 01	08:21:09	10	-2177	119	A	-p	-0.8821	0.9139	79.9S	116.2E	28	295	705	06m21s
0788	066	1824 Jun 26	23:46:33	10	-2171	124	T	-p	0.3960	1.0578	46.6N	171.4W	66	190	207	04m31s
0789	066	1824 Dec 20	10:40:35	10	-2165	129	Am	nn	-0.1685	0.9610	33.3S	20.4E	80	354	144	04m15s
0790	066	1825 Jun 16	12:19:03	10	-2159	134	H	p-	-0.3813	1.0036	1.0N	6.0W	68	3	13	00m25s
0791	066	1825 Dec 09	20:21:45	9	-2153	139	H2	p-	0.5296	1.0148	9.2N	127.4W	58	180	60	01m34s
0792	066	1826 Jun 05	17:39:04	9	-2147	144	P	t-	-1.1887	0.6407	67.4S	82.5W	0	357		
0793	067	1826 Oct 31	01:20:38	9	-2142	111	P	-t	-1.4696	0.1222	70.6S	21.2E	0	136		
0794	067	1826 Nov 29	11:14:08	9	-2141	149	P	t-	1.1764	0.6770	68.2N	19.9E	0	191		
0795	067	1827 Apr 26	03:11:14	9	-2136	116	A	-p	0.9316	0.9458	74.8N	73.4E	21	118	559	03m53s
0796	067	1827 Oct 20	15:42:05	8	-2130	121	H	-p	-0.8251	1.0070	62.3S	87.6W	34	34	43	00m30s
0797	067	1828 Apr 14	09:19:38	8	-2124	126	Hm	nn	0.1498	1.0029	17.9N	37.7E	81	164	10	00m18s
0798	067	1828 Oct 09	00:07:46	8	-2118	131	A	nn	-0.1139	0.9623	12.5S	173.0E	83	17	137	04m26s
0799	067	1829 Apr 03	22:18:36	8	-2112	136	T	p-	-0.5803	1.0474	28.5S	142.6W	54	341	192	04m05s
0800	067	1829 Sep 28	01:46:53	8	-2106	141	A	p-	0.6244	0.9318	34.9N	164.3E	51	202	323	07m43s
0801	067	1830 Feb 23	05:04:13	7	-2101	108	P	-t	1.3716	0.3101	71.3N	49.0E	0	123		
0802	067	1830 Mar 24	14:38:43	7	-2100	146	P	t-	-1.2622	0.5148	72.0S	47.7E	0	274		
0803	067	1830 Aug 18	12:13:35	7	-2095	113	P	-t	-1.4866	0.1172	70.7S	50.2W	0	46		
0804	067	1830 Sep 17	02:08:12	7	-2094	151	P	t-	1.3325	0.3930	72.1N	115.6W	0	278		
0805	068	1831 Feb 12	17:21:44	7	-2089	118	A	-p	0.7288	0.9807	31.9N	88.3W	43	165	100	01m57s
0806	068	1831 Aug 07	22:15:59	7	-2083	123	T	-p	-0.6691	1.0349	24.9S	160.9W	48	12	158	03m20s
0807	068	1832 Feb 01	22:30:14	7	-2077	128	A	nn	0.0354	0.9344	15.3S	154.4W	88	169	245	08m35s
0808	068	1832 Jul 27	14:01:06	6	-2071	133	T	nn	0.0919	1.0776	24.5N	27.9W	85	188	252	06m46s
0809	068	1833 Jan 20	21:56:55	6	-2065	138	A	p-	-0.6530	0.9155	60.6S	137.4W	49	347	426	07m59s
0810	068	1833 Jul 17	07:08:02	6	-2059	143	T	p-	0.8348	1.0591	77.5N	92.5E	33	200	357	03m29s
0811	068	1834 Jan 09	22:55:30	6	-2053	148	P	t-	-1.3043	0.4418	67.8S	11.3E	0	186		
0812	068	1834 Jun 07	10:08:38	6	-2048	115	P	-t	-1.0291	0.9295	64.6S	55.4E	0	334		
0813	068	1834 Nov 30	18:56:35	6	-2042	120	T	-p	0.8497	1.0233	34.9N	91.6W	32	197	150	02m02s
0814	068	1835 May 27	13:35:42	6	-2036	125	A	np	-0.2846	0.9486	5.3N	20.2W	74	345	196	06m44s
0815	068	1835 Nov 20	10:31:58	6	-2030	130	T	-n	0.1649	1.0510	10.7S	21.6E	81	198	171	04m35s
0816	068	1836 May 15	14:01:39	5	-2024	135	A	p-	0.4700	0.9509	45.1N	44.4W	62	153	203	04m47s
0817	069	1836 Nov 09	01:29:25	5	-2018	140	T	p-	-0.5327	1.0191	46.1S	136.8E	58	31	77	01m28s
0818	069	1837 Apr 05	07:35:29	5	-2013	107	Pe	-t	-1.5080	0.0651	61.3S	145.6E	0	283		
0819	069	1837 May 04	18:48:28	5	-2012	145	P	t-	1.1934	0.6381	62.3N	133.9E	0	54		
0820	069	1837 Oct 29	11:19:24	5	-2006	150	P	t-	-1.2967	0.4542	61.9S	110.5W	0	120		
0821	069	1838 Mar 25	21:52:16	5	-2001	117	T	-p	-0.7524	1.0505	39.7S	118.3W	41	321	249	03m39s
0822	069	1838 Sep 18	20:55:56	5	-1995	122	A	-p	0.8868	0.9289	52.4N	90.6W	27	232	562	06m06s
0823	069	1839 Mar 15	14:13:42	5	-1989	127	T	nn	-0.0557	1.0520	5.1S	29.5W	87	331	172	04m20s
0824	069	1839 Sep 07	22:23:26	5	-1983	132	Am	nn	0.1324	0.9661	12.8N	152.7W	82	209	123	03m34s
0825	069	1840 Mar 04	03:58:22	5	-1977	137	A	p-	0.6728	0.9995	30.6N	101.7E	48	147	2	00m03s
0826	069	1840 Aug 27	06:37:32	5	-1971	142	T	p-	-0.6224	1.0195	24.3S	62.9E	51	29	83	01m45s
0827	069	1841 Jan 22	17:24:15	5	-1966	109	P	-t	-1.5515	0.0317	63.1S	56.6E	0	222		
0828	069	1841 Feb 21	11:03:56	5	-1965	147	P	t-	1.4406	0.2096	61.5N	52.4W	0	113		
0829	070	1841 Jul 18	14:25:14	5	-1960	114	P	-t	1.1903	0.6556	63.7N	106.2E	0	324		
0830	070	1841 Aug 16	21:20:24	5	-1959	152	P	t-	-1.3193	0.4059	61.9S	158.0E	0	60		
0831	070	1842 Jan 11	16:25:41	5	-1954	119	A	-p	-0.8882	0.9151	75.8S	1.4E	27	288	710	06m15s
0832	070	1842 Jul 08	07:06:27	6	-1948	124	T	-p	0.4727	1.0543	50.1N	83.6E	62	198	204	04m05s
0833	070	1842 Dec 31	19:04:24	6	-1942	129	A	nn	-0.1727	0.9634	33.1S	103.2W	80	349	135	03m54s
0834	070	1843 Jun 27	19:17:03	6	-1936	134	H	nn	-0.3037	1.0011	5.9N	111.0W	72	7	4	00m07s
0835	070	1843 Dec 21	05:03:26	6	-1930	139	T	p-	0.5227	1.0165	8.0N	101.0E	58	175	66	01m43s
0836	070	1844 Jun 16	00:13:21	6	-1924	144	P	t-	-1.1092	0.7777	66.4S	168.3E	0	8		
0837	070	1844 Nov 10	09:51:45	6	-1919	111	P	-t	-1.4901	0.0848	69.8S	119.3W	0	149		
0838	070	1844 Dec 09	20:01:39	6	-1918	149	P	t-	1.1682	0.6924	67.1N	123.0W	0	179		
0839	070	1845 May 06	10:09:00	6	-1913	116	An	-t	0.9945	0.9462	73.4N	110.6W	4	41	-	03m15s
0840	070	1845 Oct 30	23:51:57	6	-1907	121	H	-p	-0.8537	1.0005	69.1S	144.5E	31	39	3	00m02s

66

Cat Num	Canon Plate	Calendar Date	TD of Greatest Eclipse	ΔT s	Luna Num	Saros Num	Ecl Type	QLE	Gamma	Ecl Mag	Lat °	Long °	Sun Alt °	Sun Azm °	Path Width km	Central Line Dur
0841	071	1846 Apr 25	16:50:30	6	-1901	126	H	nn	0.2038	1.0088	24.8N	76.2W	78	165	31	00m53s
0842	071	1846 Oct 20	07:46:11	6	-1895	131	A	nn	-0.1506	0.9567	18.7S	57.3E	81	16	159	05m05s
0843	071	1847 Apr 15	06:16:13	6	-1889	136	T	p-	-0.5339	1.0530	21.6S	95.0E	58	343	206	04m44s
0844	071	1847 Oct 09	09:00:22	7	-1883	141	A	p-	0.5774	0.9290	27.7N	52.8E	55	199	323	08m35s
0845	071	1848 Mar 05	13:31:35	7	-1878	108	P	-t	1.3950	0.2662	71.8N	91.7W	0	109		
0846	071	1848 Apr 03	22:49:06	7	-1877	146	P	t-	-1.2264	0.5834	71.8S	89.0W	0	288		
0847	071	1848 Aug 28	19:18:22	7	-1872	113	Pe	-t	-1.5475	0.0091	71.3S	169.6W	0	59		
0848	071	1848 Sep 27	09:21:19	7	-1871	151	P	t-	1.2774	0.4875	72.2N	121.9E	0	264		
0849	071	1849 Feb 23	01:38:09	7	-1866	118	A	-p	0.7474	0.9796	36.7N	144.3E	41	161	108	01m58s
0850	071	1849 Aug 18	05:40:49	7	-1860	123	T	-p	-0.7343	1.0349	32.9S	83.5E	43	16	172	03m07s
0851	071	1850 Feb 12	06:29:37	7	-1854	128	A	nn	0.0503	0.9345	11.0S	85.6E	87	166	245	08m35s
0852	071	1850 Aug 07	21:33:54	7	-1848	133	T	nn	0.0215	1.0769	17.7N	141.8W	89	191	249	06m50s
0853	072	1851 Feb 01	05:54:27	7	-1842	138	A	p-	-0.6413	0.9175	56.4S	106.9E	50	342	409	08m01s
0854	072	1851 Jul 28	14:33:42	7	-1836	143	T	p-	0.7644	1.0577	68.0N	19.6W	40	201	296	03m41s
0855	072	1852 Jan 21	07:12:16	7	-1830	148	P	t-	-1.2948	0.4577	68.9S	124.3W	0	198		
0856	072	1852 Jun 17	16:59:50	7	-1825	115	P	-t	-1.1111	0.7828	65.6S	57.3W	0	344		
0857	072	1852 Dec 11	03:40:44	7	-1819	120	T	-p	0.8551	1.0237	35.2N	133.9E	31	191	156	02m05s
0858	072	1853 Jun 06	20:07:21	7	-1813	125	A	-p	-0.3685	0.9486	1.5N	117.9W	68	349	203	06m59s
0859	072	1853 Nov 30	19:15:39	7	-1807	130	T	-n	0.1763	1.0485	12.0S	109.0W	80	194	164	04m28s
0860	072	1854 May 26	20:42:53	7	-1801	135	A	p-	0.3918	0.9551	43.3N	140.1W	67	159	178	04m32s
0861	072	1854 Nov 20	09:56:58	7	-1795	140	H3	p-	-0.5179	1.0144	48.9S	12.7E	59	27	57	01m07s
0862	072	1855 May 16	02:01:12	7	-1789	145	P	t-	1.1249	0.7624	62.9N	16.6E	0	45		
0863	072	1855 Nov 09	19:17:51	7	-1783	150	P	t-	-1.2767	0.4892	62.5S	121.0E	0	129		
0864	072	1856 Apr 05	06:01:01	7	-1778	117	T	-p	-0.7906	1.0539	39.1S	119.2E	38	323	285	03m56s
0865	073	1856 Sep 29	03:59:44	7	-1772	122	A	-p	0.9420	0.9246	54.3N	169.1E	19	236	831	06m21s
0866	073	1857 Mar 25	22:29:38	7	-1766	127	T	-n	-0.0892	1.0534	2.4S	153.4W	85	331	177	04m28s
0867	073	1857 Sep 18	05:36:05	7	-1760	132	A	nn	0.1912	0.9659	11.6N	100.0E	79	210	125	03m34s
0868	073	1858 Mar 15	12:05:28	7	-1754	137	A	p-	0.6461	0.9996	32.7N	20.9W	50	145	2	00m02s
0869	073	1858 Sep 07	14:09:29	7	-1748	142	T	p-	-0.5609	1.0210	23.9S	49.8W	56	31	85	01m50s
0870	073	1859 Feb 03	01:22:42	7	-1743	109	Pe	-t	-1.5659	0.0077	62.4S	72.1W	0	232		
0871	073	1859 Mar 04	18:54:49	7	-1742	147	P	t-	1.4192	0.2461	61.2N	178.8W	0	103		
0872	073	1859 Jul 29	21:56:57	7	-1737	114	P	-t	1.2598	0.5205	63.0N	16.0W	0	315		
0873	073	1859 Aug 28	05:02:00	7	-1736	152	P	t-	-1.2569	0.5261	61.5S	33.7E	0	69		
0874	073	1860 Jan 23	00:27:31	8	-1731	119	A	-p	-0.8969	0.9168	71.8S	117.2W	26	286	719	06m07s
0875	073	1860 Jul 18	14:26:24	8	-1725	124	T	-p	0.5487	1.0500	52.5N	20.3W	56	205	198	03m39s
0876	073	1861 Jan 11	03:29:23	8	-1719	129	A	nn	-0.1766	0.9664	31.8S	132.7E	80	344	123	03m30s
0877	074	1861 Jul 08	02:10:26	8	-1713	134	A	nn	-0.2231	0.9979	10.0N	145.8E	77	12	7	00m14s
0878	074	1861 Dec 31	13:49:06	8	-1707	139	T	p-	0.5187	1.0186	7.8N	31.6W	59	171	74	01m55s
0879	074	1862 Jun 27	06:42:21	8	-1701	144	P	t-	-1.0252	0.9221	65.4S	60.8E	0	18		
0880	074	1862 Nov 21	18:29:48	7	-1696	111	P	-t	-1.5052	0.0580	68.8S	99.1E	0	161		
0881	074	1862 Dec 21	04:53:02	7	-1695	149	P	t-	1.1633	0.7016	66.0N	93.6E	0	168		
0882	074	1863 May 17	17:00:45	7	-1690	116	P	-t	1.0627	0.8607	69.2N	126.8E	0	22		
0883	074	1863 Nov 11	08:09:03	7	-1684	121	A	-p	-0.8759	0.9943	75.4S	15.1E	28	43	42	00m22s
0884	074	1864 May 06	00:16:48	6	-1678	126	H	-n	0.2622	1.0146	31.6N	171.5E	75	168	52	01m25s
0885	074	1864 Oct 30	15:30:31	6	-1672	131	A	nn	-0.1816	0.9514	24.3S	59.3W	79	14	181	05m41s
0886	074	1865 Apr 25	14:08:34	6	-1666	136	T	p-	-0.4826	1.0584	14.8S	25.8W	61	346	219	05m23s
0887	074	1865 Oct 19	16:21:13	5	-1660	141	A	p-	0.5366	0.9263	21.3N	60.2W	57	196	326	09m27s
0888	074	1866 Mar 16	21:51:25	5	-1655	108	P	-t	1.4241	0.2114	72.0N	129.2E	0	95		
0889	075	1866 Apr 15	06:51:40	5	-1654	146	P	t-	-1.1846	0.6637	71.4S	136.6E	0	302		
0890	075	1866 Oct 08	16:44:22	4	-1648	151	P	t-	1.2296	0.5693	71.9N	3.0W	0	250		
0891	075	1867 Mar 06	09:46:47	4	-1643	118	A	-p	0.7716	0.9787	42.3N	18.4E	39	157	118	01m57s
0892	075	1867 Aug 29	13:13:07	3	-1637	123	T	-p	-0.7940	1.0344	41.1S	34.9W	37	21	189	02m51s
0893	075	1868 Feb 23	14:21:31	3	-1631	128	A	nn	0.0706	0.9348	6.1S	33.0W	86	164	243	08m30s
0894	075	1868 Aug 18	05:12:10	2	-1625	133	Tm	nn	-0.0443	1.0756	10.6N	102.2E	88	14	245	06m47s
0895	075	1869 Feb 11	13:46:39	2	-1619	138	A	p-	-0.6251	0.9201	51.3S	9.7W	51	339	387	08m02s
0896	075	1869 Aug 07	22:01:05	1	-1613	143	T	p-	0.6960	1.0551	59.1N	133.2W	46	202	254	03m48s
0897	075	1870 Jan 31	15:26:25	1	-1607	148	P	t-	-1.2829	0.4781	69.9S	100.0E	0	210		
0898	075	1870 Jun 28	23:46:43	0	-1602	115	P	-t	-1.1949	0.6335	66.6S	169.4W	0	354		
0899	075	1870 Jul 28	11:02:31	0	-1601	153	Pb	t-	1.5044	0.0742	69.2N	170.9E	0	336		
0900	075	1870 Dec 22	12:27:33	-0	-1596	120	T	-p	0.8585	1.0248	35.7N	1.5W	31	186	165	02m11s

Cat Num	Canon Plate	Calendar Date	TD of Greatest Eclipse	ΔT s	Luna Num	Saros Num	Ecl Type	QLE	Gamma	Ecl Mag	Lat °	Long °	Sun Alt °	Sun Azm °	Path Width km	Central Line Dur
0901	076	1871 Jun 18	02:35:01	-1	-1590	125	A	-p	-0.4550	0.9481	3.5S	144.7E	63	353	214	07m14s
0902	076	1871 Dec 12	04:03:38	-1	-1584	130	T	-n	0.1836	1.0465	12.7S	119.4E	80	190	157	04m23s
0903	076	1872 Jun 06	03:20:03	-1	-1578	135	A	p-	0.3095	0.9590	40.5N	124.8E	72	166	157	04m20s
0904	076	1872 Nov 30	18:29:33	-2	-1572	140	H	p-	-0.5081	1.0099	51.2S	111.8W	59	22	40	00m47s
0905	076	1873 May 26	09:08:56	-2	-1566	145	P	t-	1.0513	0.8971	63.7N	99.6W	0	35		
0906	076	1873 Nov 20	03:22:52	-2	-1560	150	P	t-	-1.2625	0.5138	63.2S	9.5W	0	138		
0907	076	1874 Apr 16	14:00:53	-3	-1555	117	T	-p	-0.8364	1.0569	39.9S	0.9W	33	325	335	04m11s
0908	076	1874 Oct 10	11:13:33	-3	-1549	122	An	-t	0.9889	0.9193	58.6N	72.0E	7	244	–	06m28s
0909	076	1875 Apr 06	06:37:26	-3	-1543	127	T	-n	-0.1291	1.0547	0.2S	84.8E	83	332	182	04m37s
0910	076	1875 Sep 29	12:58:09	-4	-1537	132	A	nn	0.2427	0.9656	10.0N	10.1W	76	209	127	03m36s
0911	076	1876 Mar 25	20:05:06	-4	-1531	137	A	p-	0.6142	0.9999	34.8N	141.1W	52	144	1	00m01s
0912	076	1876 Sep 17	21:49:15	-4	-1525	142	T	p-	-0.5054	1.0220	24.6S	164.5W	60	32	86	01m53s
0913	077	1877 Mar 15	02:38:09	-4	-1519	147	P	t-	1.3924	0.2917	61.0N	56.7E	0	94		
0914	077	1877 Aug 09	05:30:24	-4	-1514	114	P	-t	1.3277	0.3889	62.3N	138.6W	0	306		
0915	077	1877 Sep 07	12:48:42	-4	-1513	152	P	t-	-1.1985	0.6382	61.2S	91.8W	0	78		
0916	077	1878 Feb 02	08:27:52	-5	-1508	119	A	-p	-0.9071	0.9191	67.9S	122.4E	24	286	729	05m59s
0917	077	1878 Jul 29	21:47:18	-5	-1502	124	T	-p	0.6232	1.0450	53.8N	124.0W	51	213	191	03m11s
0918	077	1879 Jan 22	11:53:08	-5	-1496	129	A	nn	-0.1824	0.9700	29.8S	8.5E	79	340	109	03m03s
0919	077	1879 Jul 19	09:04:32	-5	-1490	134	Am	nn	-0.1439	0.9942	13.0N	42.9E	82	16	20	00m39s
0920	077	1880 Jan 11	22:34:25	-5	-1484	139	T	p-	0.5136	1.0212	8.3N	164.1W	59	166	84	02m07s
0921	077	1880 Jul 07	13:10:28	-5	-1478	144	A	t-	-0.9406	0.9441	46.4S	33.4W	19	17	611	05m47s
0922	077	1880 Dec 02	03:11:33	-5	-1473	111	P	-t	-1.5172	0.0370	67.8S	42.9W	0	173		
0923	077	1880 Dec 31	13:45:01	-5	-1472	149	P	t-	1.1591	0.7096	65.0N	49.5W	0	158		
0924	077	1881 May 27	23:48:40	-5	-1467	116	P	-t	1.1345	0.7370	68.2N	13.3E	0	10		
0925	078	1881 Nov 21	16:31:10	-5	-1461	121	A	-p	-0.8930	0.9887	81.2S	114.5W	26	46	90	00m43s
0926	078	1882 May 17	07:36:27	-5	-1455	126	T	-n	0.3269	1.0200	38.4N	61.6E	71	171	72	01m50s
0927	078	1882 Nov 10	23:22:21	-6	-1449	131	A	-n	-0.2056	0.9466	29.2S	177.0W	78	11	201	06m14s
0928	078	1883 May 06	21:53:49	-6	-1443	136	T	p-	-0.4250	1.0634	8.1S	144.6W	65	349	229	05m58s
0929	078	1883 Oct 30	23:50:54	-6	-1437	141	A	p-	0.5030	0.9238	15.6N	174.9W	60	193	331	10m17s
0930	078	1884 Mar 27	06:02:10	-6	-1432	108	P	-t	1.4602	0.1436	72.0N	7.7W	0	81		
0931	078	1884 Apr 25	14:46:17	-6	-1431	146	P	t-	-1.1365	0.7563	70.7S	4.6E	0	315		
0932	078	1884 Oct 19	00:17:42	-6	-1425	151	P	t-	1.1892	0.6385	71.5N	130.2W	0	237		
0933	078	1885 Mar 16	17:45:42	-6	-1420	118	A	-p	0.8030	0.9778	48.9N	106.1W	36	153	132	01m55s
0934	078	1885 Sep 08	20:51:52	-6	-1414	123	T	-p	-0.8489	1.0332	49.6S	156.5W	32	27	211	02m31s
0935	078	1886 Mar 05	22:05:25	-6	-1408	128	A	nn	0.0970	0.9357	0.5S	150.1W	84	163	240	08m20s
0936	078	1886 Aug 29	12:55:23	-6	-1402	133	T	nn	-0.1059	1.0735	3.5N	15.3W	84	16	240	06m36s
0937	079	1887 Feb 22	21:33:03	-6	-1396	138	A	p-	-0.6040	0.9232	45.7S	126.5W	53	338	362	08m01s
0938	079	1887 Aug 19	05:32:05	-6	-1390	143	T	p-	0.6312	1.0518	50.6N	111.9E	51	202	221	03m50s
0939	079	1888 Feb 11	23:38:15	-6	-1384	148	P	t-	-1.2684	0.5029	70.7S	35.7W	0	223		
0940	079	1888 Jul 09	06:30:52	-6	-1379	115	P	-t	-1.2797	0.4833	67.6S	78.8E	0	4		
0941	079	1888 Aug 07	18:05:46	-6	-1378	153	P	t-	1.4369	0.1983	70.1N	53.0E	0	325		
0942	079	1889 Jan 01	21:16:50	-6	-1373	120	T	-p	0.8603	1.0262	36.7N	137.6W	30	181	175	02m17s
0943	079	1889 Jun 28	09:00:00	-6	-1367	125	A	-p	-0.5431	0.9471	9.6S	47.3E	57	357	232	07m22s
0944	079	1889 Dec 22	12:54:14	-6	-1361	130	T	-n	0.1888	1.0449	12.7S	12.8W	79	185	152	04m18s
0945	079	1890 Jun 17	09:55:05	-6	-1355	135	A	nn	0.2247	0.9625	36.5N	29.3E	77	172	140	04m09s
0946	079	1890 Dec 12	03:05:28	-6	-1349	140	H	p-	-0.5016	1.0059	52.8S	123.9E	60	15	24	00m28s
0947	079	1891 Jun 06	16:15:36	-6	-1343	145	A	t-	0.9755	0.9981	74.5N	163.8E	12	45	33	00m06s
0948	079	1891 Dec 01	11:31:08	-6	-1337	150	P	t-	-1.2515	0.5326	64.1S	140.9W	0	148		
0949	080	1892 Apr 26	21:55:20	-6	-1332	117	T	-p	-0.8870	1.0591	42.5S	119.4W	27	327	414	04m19s
0950	080	1892 Oct 20	18:36:06	-6	-1326	122	P	-t	1.0286	0.9054	61.4N	33.3W	0	247		
0951	080	1893 Apr 16	14:36:11	-6	-1320	127	T	-n	-0.1763	1.0556	1.3N	34.6W	80	334	186	04m47s
0952	080	1893 Oct 09	20:30:22	-6	-1314	132	A	nn	0.2866	0.9652	8.1N	123.0W	73	208	130	03m41s
0953	080	1894 Apr 06	03:53:41	-6	-1308	137	H	p-	0.5740	1.0001	36.7N	102.4E	55	144	1	00m01s
0954	080	1894 Sep 29	05:39:02	-6	-1302	142	T	p-	-0.4574	1.0226	26.1S	78.5E	63	32	86	01m55s
0955	080	1895 Mar 26	10:09:33	-6	-1296	147	P	t-	1.3565	0.3531	61.0N	64.8W	0	85		
0956	080	1895 Aug 20	13:09:16	-6	-1291	114	P	-t	1.3911	0.2665	61.8N	97.7E	0	297		
0957	080	1895 Sep 18	20:44:01	-6	-1290	152	P	t-	-1.1469	0.7369	61.0S	140.7E	0	86		
0958	080	1896 Feb 13	16:23:13	-6	-1285	119	A	-p	-0.9220	0.9218	64.6S	3.4E	22	287	761	05m48s
0959	080	1896 Aug 09	05:09:00	-6	-1279	124	T	-p	0.6963	1.0392	54.4N	132.2E	46	220	182	02m43s
0960	080	1897 Feb 01	20:15:15	-6	-1273	129	A	nn	-0.1903	0.9742	27.1S	115.7W	79	336	94	02m34s

Cat Num	Canon Plate	Calendar Date	TD of Greatest Eclipse	ΔT s	Luna Num	Saros Num	Ecl Type	QLE	Gamma	Ecl Mag	Lat °	Long °	Sun Alt °	Sun Azm °	Path Width km	Central Line Dur
0961	081	1897 Jul 29	15:56:58	-5	-1267	134	A	nn	-0.0640	0.9899	15.3N	59.0W	86	20	35	01m05s
0962	081	1898 Jan 22	07:19:12	-5	-1261	139	T	p-	0.5079	1.0244	9.5N	63.6E	59	162	96	02m21s
0963	081	1898 Jul 18	19:36:54	-4	-1255	144	A	p-	-0.8547	0.9450	35.7S	130.1W	31	19	385	06m11s
0964	081	1898 Dec 13	11:58:13	-4	-1250	111	P	-t	-1.5252	0.0232	66.8S	174.5E	0	184		
0965	081	1899 Jan 11	22:38:02	-4	-1249	149	P	t-	1.1558	0.7158	64.0N	167.5E	0	148		
0966	081	1899 Jun 08	06:33:43	-4	-1244	116	P	-t	1.2089	0.6077	67.2N	98.9W	0	360		
0967	081	1899 Dec 03	00:57:28	-3	-1238	121	A	-p	-0.9061	0.9836	86.6S	121.5E	25	43	140	01m01s
0968	081	1900 May 28	14:53:56	-2	-1232	126	T	-n	0.3943	1.0249	44.8N	46.5W	67	175	92	02m10s
0969	081	1900 Nov 22	07:19:43	-2	-1226	131	A	-n	-0.2245	0.9421	33.1S	64.8E	77	7	220	06m42s
0970	081	1901 May 18	05:33:48	-1	-1220	136	T	n-	-0.3626	1.0680	1.7S	98.4E	69	353	238	06m29s
0971	081	1901 Nov 11	07:28:21	-0	-1214	141	A	p-	0.4758	0.9216	10.8N	68.9E	62	190	336	11m01s
0972	081	1902 Apr 08	14:05:06	0	-1209	108	Pe	-t	1.5024	0.0643	71.7N	142.4W	0	67		
0973	082	1902 May 07	22:34:16	0	-1208	146	P	t-	-1.0831	0.8594	70.0S	125.1W	0	327		
0974	082	1902 Oct 31	08:00:17	1	-1202	151	P	t-	1.1556	0.6960	70.8N	100.8E	0	223		
0975	082	1903 Mar 29	01:35:23	2	-1197	118	A	-p	0.8413	0.9767	56.2N	130.3E	32	147	153	01m53s
0976	082	1903 Sep 21	04:39:52	2	-1191	123	T	-p	-0.8967	1.0316	58.0S	77.2E	26	35	241	02m12s
0977	082	1904 Mar 17	05:40:44	3	-1185	128	A	nn	0.1299	0.9368	5.6N	94.7E	82	162	237	08m07s
0978	082	1904 Sep 09	20:44:21	3	-1179	133	T	-n	-0.1625	1.0709	3.7S	134.5W	81	17	234	06m20s
0979	082	1905 Mar 06	05:12:26	4	-1173	138	A	p-	-0.5768	0.9269	39.5S	117.4E	55	338	334	07m58s
0980	082	1905 Aug 30	13:07:26	5	-1167	143	T	p-	0.5708	1.0477	42.5N	4.3W	55	202	192	03m46s
0981	082	1906 Feb 23	07:43:20	5	-1161	148	P	t-	-1.2479	0.5386	71.4S	170.3W	0	237		
0982	082	1906 Jul 21	13:14:19	6	-1156	115	P	-t	-1.3637	0.3355	68.6S	33.3W	0	15		
0983	082	1906 Aug 20	01:12:50	6	-1155	153	P	t-	1.3731	0.3147	70.8N	66.4W	0	313		
0984	082	1907 Jan 14	06:05:43	6	-1150	120	T	-p	0.8628	1.0281	38.3N	86.4E	30	175	189	02m25s
0985	083	1907 Jul 10	15:24:32	7	-1144	125	A	-p	-0.6313	0.9456	16.9S	50.9W	51	2	258	07m23s
0986	083	1908 Jan 03	21:45:21	8	-1138	130	T	-n	0.1933	1.0437	11.8S	145.1W	79	180	149	04m14s
0987	083	1908 Jun 28	16:29:51	8	-1132	135	A	nn	0.1390	0.9655	31.4N	67.2W	82	177	126	04m00s
0988	083	1908 Dec 23	11:44:28	9	-1126	140	H	n-	-0.4985	1.0024	53.4S	0.5W	60	8	10	00m12s
0989	083	1909 Jun 17	23:18:38	10	-1120	145	H	t-	0.8957	1.0065	82.9N	123.6E	26	110	51	00m24s
0990	083	1909 Dec 12	19:44:48	10	-1114	150	P	t-	-1.2456	0.5424	65.0S	86.0E	0	158		
0991	083	1910 May 09	05:42:13	11	-1109	117	T	-t	-0.9437	1.0600	48.2S	125.2E	19	328	595	04m15s
0992	083	1910 Nov 02	02:08:32	12	-1103	122	P	-t	1.0603	0.8515	61.9N	155.1W	0	238		
0993	083	1911 Apr 28	22:27:22	12	-1097	127	T	-n	-0.2294	1.0562	1.9N	151.9W	77	336	190	04m57s
0994	083	1911 Oct 22	04:13:02	13	-1091	132	A	-n	0.3224	0.9650	6.3N	121.4E	71	206	133	03m47s
0995	083	1912 Apr 17	11:34:22	14	-1085	137	H	p-	0.5280	1.0003	38.4N	11.3W	58	146	1	00m02s
0996	083	1912 Oct 10	13:36:14	14	-1079	142	T	p-	-0.4149	1.0229	28.1S	40.1W	65	32	85	01m55s
0997	084	1913 Apr 06	17:33:07	15	-1073	147	P	t-	1.3147	0.4244	61.2N	175.7E	0	77		
0998	084	1913 Aug 31	20:52:12	15	-1068	114	P	-t	1.4512	0.1513	61.5N	26.8W	0	288		
0999	084	1913 Sep 30	04:45:49	15	-1067	152	P	t-	-1.1005	0.8252	61.0S	11.6E	0	95		
1000	084	1914 Feb 25	00:13:01	16	-1062	119	A	-p	-0.9416	0.9248	62.1S	113.3W	19	287	839	05m35s
1001	084	1914 Aug 21	12:34:27	17	-1056	124	A	-p	0.7655	1.0328	54.5N	27.1E	40	227	170	02m14s
1002	084	1915 Feb 14	04:33:20	17	-1050	129	A	nn	-0.2024	0.9789	24.0S	120.7E	78	333	77	02m04s
1003	084	1915 Aug 10	22:52:25	18	-1044	134	A	nn	0.0124	0.9853	16.4N	161.4W	89	200	52	01m33s
1004	084	1916 Feb 03	16:00:21	18	-1038	139	T	p-	0.4987	1.0280	11.1N	67.7W	60	158	108	02m36s
1005	084	1916 Jul 30	02:06:10	19	-1032	144	A	p-	-0.7710	0.9447	29.0S	132.4E	39	22	313	06m24s
1006	084	1916 Dec 24	20:46:22	19	-1027	111	P	-t	-1.5321	0.0115	65.7S	32.1E	0	195		
1007	084	1917 Jan 23	07:28:31	19	-1026	149	P	t-	1.1508	0.7254	63.2N	25.6E	0	138		
1008	084	1917 Jun 19	13:16:20	20	-1021	116	P	-t	1.2857	0.4730	66.2N	150.1E	0	350		
1009	085	1917 Jul 19	02:42:42	20	-1020	154	Pb	t-	-1.5101	0.0863	63.7S	101.8E	0	36		
1010	085	1917 Dec 14	09:27:20	20	-1015	121	A	-t	-0.9157	0.9791	88.0S	124.7E	23	271	189	01m17s
1011	085	1918 Jun 08	22:07:43	20	-1009	126	T	-p	0.4658	1.0292	50.9N	152.0W	62	180	112	02m23s
1012	085	1918 Dec 03	15:22:01	21	-1003	131	A	-n	-0.2387	0.9383	36.1S	53.7W	76	3	236	07m06s
1013	085	1919 May 29	13:08:55	21	-997	136	T	n-	-0.2955	1.0719	4.4N	16.7W	73	356	244	06m51s
1014	085	1919 Nov 22	15:14:11	21	-991	141	A	p-	0.4549	0.9198	6.9N	48.9W	63	186	341	11m37s
1015	085	1920 May 18	06:14:55	21	-985	146	P	t-	-1.0239	0.9734	69.1S	107.7E	0	339		
1016	085	1920 Nov 10	15:52:15	22	-979	151	P	t-	1.1287	0.7420	69.9N	29.8W	0	211		
1017	085	1921 Apr 08	09:15:01	22	-974	118	A	-t	0.8869	0.9753	64.5N	5.6E	27	139	191	01m50s
1018	085	1921 Oct 01	12:35:58	22	-968	123	T	-p	-0.9383	1.0293	66.1S	56.1W	20	48	291	01m52s
1019	085	1922 Mar 28	13:05:26	23	-962	128	A	nn	0.1711	0.9381	12.3N	18.0W	80	162	233	07m50s
1020	085	1922 Sep 21	04:40:31	23	-956	133	T	-n	-0.2130	1.0678	10.7S	104.5E	78	18	226	05m59s

Cat Num	Canon Plate	Calendar Date	TD of Greatest Eclipse	ΔT s	Luna Num	Saros Num	Ecl Type	QLE	Gamma	Ecl Mag	Lat °	Long °	Sun Alt °	Sun Azm °	Path Width km	Central Line Dur
1021	086	1923 Mar 17	12:44:58	23	-950	138	A	p-	-0.5438	0.9310	33.0S	2.4E	57	339	305	07m51s
1022	086	1923 Sep 10	20:47:29	23	-944	143	T	p-	0.5149	1.0430	34.7N	121.8W	59	201	167	03m37s
1023	086	1924 Mar 05	15:44:20	24	-938	148	P	t-	-1.2232	0.5820	71.9S	55.6E	0	250		
1024	086	1924 Jul 31	19:58:20	24	-933	115	P	-t	-1.4459	0.1920	69.6S	146.0W	0	27		
1025	086	1924 Aug 30	08:23:00	24	-932	153	P	t-	1.3123	0.4245	71.5N	172.9E	0	300		
1026	086	1925 Jan 24	14:54:03	24	-927	120	T	-p	0.8661	1.0304	40.5N	49.6W	30	170	206	02m32s
1027	086	1925 Jul 20	21:48:42	24	-921	125	A	-p	-0.7193	0.9436	25.3S	150.0W	44	6	300	07m15s
1028	086	1926 Jan 14	06:36:58	24	-915	130	T	-n	0.1973	1.0430	10.1S	82.3E	79	176	147	04m11s
1029	086	1926 Jul 09	23:06:02	24	-909	135	A	nn	0.0538	0.9680	25.6N	165.1W	87	181	115	03m51s
1030	086	1927 Jan 03	20:22:53	24	-903	140	A	n-	-0.4956	0.9995	52.8S	124.8W	60	0	2	00m03s
1031	086	1927 Jun 29	06:23:27	24	-897	145	T	t-	0.8163	1.0128	78.1N	73.8E	35	167	77	00m50s
1032	086	1927 Dec 24	03:59:41	24	-891	150	P	t-	-1.2416	0.5490	66.1S	47.7W	0	169		
1033	087	1928 May 19	13:24:20	24	-886	117	T-	-t	-1.0048	1.0140	63.3S	22.5E	0	319	-	-
1034	087	1928 Jun 17	20:27:28	24	-885	155	Pb	t-	1.5107	0.0376	65.6N	70.6E	0	16		
1035	087	1928 Nov 12	09:48:24	24	-880	122	P	-t	1.0861	0.8078	62.6N	81.1E	0	229		
1036	087	1929 May 09	06:10:34	24	-874	127	T	-n	-0.2887	1.0562	1.6N	92.7E	73	339	193	05m07s
1037	087	1929 Nov 01	12:05:10	24	-868	132	A	-n	0.3514	0.9649	4.5N	3.1E	69	204	134	03m54s
1038	087	1930 Apr 28	19:03:34	24	-862	137	H	p-	0.4731	1.0003	39.4N	121.2W	62	149	1	00m01s
1039	087	1930 Oct 21	21:43:53	24	-856	142	T	p-	-0.3804	1.0230	30.5S	161.1W	67	31	84	01m55s
1040	087	1931 Apr 18	00:45:35	24	-850	147	P	t-	1.2643	0.5107	61.5N	58.9E	0	68		
1041	087	1931 Sep 12	04:41:25	24	-845	114	Pe	-t	1.5060	0.0471	61.2N	152.8W	0	280		
1042	087	1931 Oct 11	12:55:40	24	-844	152	P	t-	-1.0607	0.9005	61.2S	119.5W	0	104		
1043	087	1932 Mar 07	07:55:50	24	-839	119	A	-p	-0.9673	0.9277	60.7S	134.4E	14	285	1083	05m19s
1044	087	1932 Aug 31	20:03:41	24	-833	124	T	-p	0.8307	1.0257	54.5N	79.5W	34	232	155	01m45s
1045	088	1933 Feb 24	12:46:39	24	-827	129	A	nn	-0.2191	0.9841	20.8S	2.1W	77	331	58	01m32s
1046	088	1933 Aug 21	05:49:11	24	-821	134	A	nn	0.0869	0.9801	16.9N	95.9E	85	206	71	02m04s
1047	088	1934 Feb 14	00:38:41	24	-815	139	T	-t	0.4868	1.0321	13.2N	161.7E	61	155	123	02m53s
1048	088	1934 Aug 10	08:37:48	24	-809	144	A	p-	-0.6890	0.9436	24.5S	34.6E	46	25	280	06m33s
1049	088	1935 Jan 05	05:35:46	24	-804	111	Pe	-t	-1.5381	0.0013	64.7S	110.2W	0	205		
1050	088	1935 Feb 03	16:16:20	24	-803	149	P	t-	1.1438	0.7390	62.5N	115.4W	0	128		
1051	088	1935 Jun 30	19:59:46	24	-798	116	P	-t	1.3623	0.3375	65.2N	39.1E	0	340		
1052	088	1935 Jul 30	09:16:28	24	-797	154	P	t-	-1.4259	0.2315	62.9S	5.9W	0	45		
1053	088	1935 Dec 25	17:59:52	24	-792	121	A	-t	-0.9228	0.9753	83.5S	9.4E	22	258	234	01m30s
1054	088	1936 Jun 19	05:20:31	24	-786	126	T	-p	0.5389	1.0329	56.1N	104.7E	57	188	132	02m31s
1055	088	1936 Dec 13	23:28:12	24	-780	131	A	-n	-0.2493	0.9349	37.8S	172.6W	75	357	251	07m25s
1056	088	1937 Jun 08	20:41:02	24	-774	136	T	n-	-0.2253	1.0751	9.9N	130.5W	77	0	250	07m04s
1057	089	1937 Dec 02	23:05:45	24	-768	141	A	p-	0.4389	0.9184	4.0N	167.8W	64	182	344	12m00s
1058	089	1938 May 29	13:50:18	24	-762	146	T	t-	-0.9607	1.0552	52.7S	22.0W	16	354	675	04m05s
1059	089	1938 Nov 21	23:52:25	24	-756	151	P	t-	1.1077	0.7781	68.9N	162.0W	0	198		
1060	089	1939 Apr 19	16:45:53	24	-751	118	A	-t	0.9388	0.9731	73.1N	129.1W	20	118	285	01m49s
1061	089	1939 Oct 12	20:40:23	24	-745	123	T	-p	-0.9737	1.0266	72.8S	155.1E	12	74	418	01m32s
1062	089	1940 Apr 07	20:21:21	24	-739	128	A	nn	0.2190	0.9394	19.2N	128.5W	77	163	230	07m30s
1063	089	1940 Oct 01	12:44:06	25	-733	133	T	-n	-0.2573	1.0645	17.5S	18.2W	75	18	218	05m35s
1064	089	1941 Mar 27	20:08:08	25	-727	138	A	p-	-0.5025	0.9355	26.2S	110.9W	60	341	276	07m41s
1065	089	1941 Sep 21	04:34:03	25	-721	143	T	p-	0.4649	1.0379	27.3N	119.1E	62	200	143	03m22s
1066	089	1942 Mar 16	23:37:07	25	-715	148	P	t-	-1.1908	0.6394	72.2S	76.8W	0	264		
1067	089	1942 Aug 12	02:45:12	26	-710	115	Pe	-t	-1.5244	0.0562	70.4S	99.9E	0	39		
1068	089	1942 Sep 10	15:39:32	26	-709	153	P	t-	1.2571	0.5231	71.9N	50.0E	0	286		
1069	090	1943 Feb 04	23:38:10	26	-704	120	T	-p	0.8731	1.0331	43.6N	175.1E	29	165	229	02m39s
1070	090	1943 Aug 01	04:16:13	26	-698	125	A	-p	-0.8041	0.9409	34.8S	108.6E	36	11	367	06m59s
1071	090	1944 Jan 25	15:26:42	26	-692	130	T	-n	0.2025	1.0428	7.6S	50.2W	78	172	146	04m09s
1072	090	1944 Jul 20	05:43:13	27	-686	135	A	nn	-0.0314	0.9700	19.0N	95.7E	88	6	108	03m42s
1073	090	1945 Jan 14	05:01:43	27	-680	140	A	n-	-0.4937	0.9970	51.1S	110.3E	60	354	12	00m15s
1074	090	1945 Jul 09	13:27:45	27	-674	145	T	p-	0.7356	1.0180	70.0N	17.2W	42	184	92	01m15s
1075	090	1946 Jan 03	12:16:11	27	-668	150	P	t-	-1.2392	0.5529	67.1S	177.6E	0	180		
1076	090	1946 May 30	21:00:24	28	-663	117	P	-t	-1.0710	0.8865	64.1S	101.0W	0	328		
1077	090	1946 Jun 29	03:51:58	28	-662	155	P	t-	1.4361	0.1802	66.6N	50.8W	0	6		
1078	090	1946 Nov 23	17:37:12	28	-657	122	P	-t	1.1050	0.7759	63.4N	45.3W	0	219		
1079	090	1947 May 20	13:47:47	28	-651	127	T	-p	-0.3528	1.0557	0.2N	21.4W	69	343	196	05m13s
1080	090	1947 Nov 12	20:05:37	28	-645	132	A	-n	0.3743	0.9650	3.0N	117.4W	68	200	135	03m59s

Cat Num	Canon Plate	Calendar Date	TD of Greatest Eclipse	ΔT s	Luna Num	Saros Num	Ecl Type	QLE	Gamma	Ecl Mag	Lat °	Long °	Sun Alt °	Sun Azm °	Path Width km	Central Line Dur
1081	091	1948 May 09	02:26:04	28	-639	137	A	p-	0.4133	0.9999	39.8N	131.2E	65	153	0	00m00s
1082	091	1948 Nov 01	05:59:18	29	-633	142	T	n-	-0.3517	1.0231	33.1S	76.2E	69	28	84	01m56s
1083	091	1949 Apr 28	07:48:53	29	-627	147	P	t-	1.2068	0.6092	61.9N	55.7W	0	59		
1084	091	1949 Oct 21	21:13:01	29	-621	152	P	t-	-1.0270	0.9638	61.5S	107.5E	0	113		
1085	091	1950 Mar 18	15:32:01	29	-616	119	A-	-t	-0.9988	0.9620	60.9S	40.9E	0	268	-	-
1086	091	1950 Sep 12	03:38:47	29	-610	124	T	-t	0.8903	1.0182	54.8N	172.3E	27	236	134	01m14s
1087	091	1951 Mar 07	20:53:40	30	-604	129	A	-n	-0.2420	0.9896	17.7S	123.5W	76	330	38	00m59s
1088	091	1951 Sep 01	12:51:51	30	-598	134	A	nn	0.1557	0.9747	16.5N	8.5W	81	208	91	02m36s
1089	091	1952 Feb 25	09:11:35	30	-592	139	T	p-	0.4697	1.0366	15.6N	32.7E	62	152	138	03m09s
1090	091	1952 Aug 20	15:13:35	30	-586	144	A	p-	-0.6102	0.9420	21.7S	64.1W	52	27	264	06m40s
1091	091	1953 Feb 14	00:59:30	30	-580	149	P	t-	1.1331	0.7596	61.9N	104.9E	0	119		
1092	091	1953 Jul 11	02:44:14	30	-575	116	P	-t	1.4388	0.2015	64.3N	71.7W	0	331		
1093	092	1953 Aug 09	15:55:03	30	-574	154	P	t-	-1.3440	0.3729	62.2S	114.7W	0	54		
1094	092	1954 Jan 05	02:32:01	31	-569	121	A	-t	-0.9296	0.9720	79.1S	120.8W	21	260	278	01m42s
1095	092	1954 Jun 30	12:32:38	31	-563	126	T	-p	0.6134	1.0357	60.5N	4.2E	52	197	153	02m35s
1096	092	1954 Dec 25	07:36:42	31	-557	131	A	-n	-0.2576	0.9323	38.4S	68.2E	75	352	262	07m39s
1097	092	1955 Jun 20	04:10:42	31	-551	136	T	n-	-0.1528	1.0776	14.8N	117.0E	81	5	254	07m08s
1098	092	1955 Dec 14	07:02:25	31	-545	141	A	p-	0.4266	0.9176	2.1N	72.2E	65	178	346	12m09s
1099	092	1956 Jun 08	21:20:39	32	-539	146	T	p-	-0.8934	1.0581	40.8S	140.7W	26	0	429	04m45s
1100	092	1956 Dec 02	08:00:35	32	-533	151	P	t-	1.0923	0.8047	67.9N	64.6E	0	187		
1101	092	1957 Apr 30	00:05:28	32	-528	118	A+	-t	0.9992	0.9799	70.6N	40.3E	0	41	-	-
1102	092	1957 Oct 23	04:54:02	32	-522	123	T-	-t	-1.0022	1.0013	71.2S	23.1W	0	127	-	-
1103	092	1958 Apr 19	03:27:17	32	-516	128	A	np	0.2750	0.9408	26.5N	123.6E	74	164	228	07m07s
1104	092	1958 Oct 12	20:55:28	33	-510	133	T	-n	-0.2951	1.0608	24.0S	142.4W	73	18	209	05m11s
1105	093	1959 Apr 08	03:24:08	33	-504	138	A	p-	-0.4546	0.9401	19.1S	137.6E	63	343	247	07m26s
1106	093	1959 Oct 02	12:27:00	33	-498	143	T	n-	0.4207	1.0325	20.4N	1.4W	65	199	120	03m02s
1107	093	1960 Mar 27	07:25:07	33	-492	148	P	t-	-1.1537	0.7058	72.1S	151.9E	0	279		
1108	093	1960 Sep 20	22:59:56	33	-486	153	P	t-	1.2057	0.6139	72.1N	74.1W	0	273		
1109	093	1961 Feb 15	08:19:48	34	-481	120	T	-p	0.8830	1.0360	47.4N	40.0E	28	159	258	02m45s
1110	093	1961 Aug 11	10:46:47	34	-475	125	A	-p	-0.8859	0.9375	45.8S	4.0E	27	17	499	06m35s
1111	093	1962 Feb 05	00:12:38	34	-469	130	T	-n	0.2107	1.0430	4.2S	178.1E	78	169	147	04m08s
1112	093	1962 Jul 31	12:25:33	34	-463	135	Am	nn	-0.1130	0.9716	12.0N	5.7W	84	9	103	03m33s
1113	093	1963 Jan 25	13:37:12	35	-457	140	A	n-	-0.4898	0.9951	48.2S	15.0W	60	348	20	00m25s
1114	093	1963 Jul 20	20:36:13	35	-451	145	T	p-	0.6571	1.0224	61.7N	119.6W	49	191	101	01m40s
1115	093	1964 Jan 14	20:30:08	35	-445	150	P	t-	-1.2354	0.5592	68.2S	43.1E	0	191		
1116	093	1964 Jun 10	04:34:07	35	-440	117	P	-t	-1.1393	0.7545	65.0S	135.9E	0	338		
1117	094	1964 Jul 09	11:17:53	35	-439	155	P	t-	1.3623	0.3222	67.6N	172.9W	0	355		
1118	094	1964 Dec 04	01:31:54	36	-434	122	P	-t	1.1193	0.7518	64.3N	173.3W	0	209		
1119	094	1965 May 30	21:17:31	36	-428	127	T	-p	-0.4225	1.0544	2.5S	133.8W	65	347	198	05m15s
1120	094	1965 Nov 23	04:14:51	36	-422	132	A	-n	0.3906	0.9656	1.7N	119.8E	67	197	134	04m02s
1121	094	1966 May 20	09:39:02	37	-416	137	A	-n	-0.3467	0.9992	39.2N	26.4E	70	158	3	00m05s
1122	094	1966 Nov 12	14:23:28	37	-410	142	T	n-	-0.3300	1.0234	35.6S	48.2W	71	25	84	01m57s
1123	094	1967 May 09	14:42:48	38	-404	147	P	t-	1.1422	0.7201	62.5N	168.1W	0	50		
1124	094	1967 Nov 02	05:38:56	38	-398	152	T-	t-	-1.0007	1.0126	62.0S	27.8W	0	122	-	-
1125	094	1968 Mar 28	23:00:30	38	-393	119	P	-t	-1.0370	0.8990	61.0S	79.8W	0	277		
1126	094	1968 Sep 22	11:18:46	39	-387	124	T	-t	0.9451	1.0099	56.2N	64.0E	19	240	104	00m40s
1127	094	1969 Mar 18	04:54:57	39	-381	129	A	-n	-0.2704	0.9954	14.8S	116.3E	74	330	16	00m26s
1128	094	1969 Sep 11	19:58:59	40	-375	134	A	nn	0.2201	0.9690	15.6N	114.1W	77	210	114	03m11s
1129	095	1970 Mar 07	17:38:30	40	-369	139	T	p-	0.4473	1.0414	18.2N	94.7W	63	150	153	03m28s
1130	095	1970 Aug 31	21:55:30	41	-363	144	A	p-	-0.5364	0.9400	20.3S	164.0W	57	29	258	06m47s
1131	095	1971 Feb 25	09:38:07	41	-357	149	P	t-	1.1188	0.7872	61.4N	33.5W	0	110		
1132	095	1971 Jul 22	09:31:55	42	-352	116	Pe	-t	1.5130	0.0690	63.5N	177.0E	0	321		
1133	095	1971 Aug 20	22:39:31	42	-351	154	P	t-	-1.2659	0.5080	61.7S	135.4E	0	63		
1134	095	1972 Jan 16	11:03:22	42	-346	121	A	-t	-0.9365	0.9692	74.9S	107.7E	20	263	321	01m53s
1135	095	1972 Jul 10	19:46:38	43	-340	126	T	-p	0.6872	1.0379	63.5N	94.2W	46	209	175	02m36s
1136	095	1973 Jan 04	15:46:21	43	-334	131	A	-n	-0.2644	0.9303	37.9S	51.2W	74	346	271	07m49s
1137	095	1973 Jun 30	11:38:41	44	-328	136	T	nn	-0.0785	1.0792	18.8N	5.6E	86	9	256	07m04s
1138	095	1973 Dec 24	15:02:44	44	-322	141	A	p-	0.4171	0.9174	1.1N	48.5W	65	174	345	12m02s
1139	095	1974 Jun 20	04:48:04	45	-316	146	T	p-	-0.8239	1.0592	32.1S	103.7E	34	5	344	05m09s
1140	095	1974 Dec 13	16:13:13	45	-310	151	P	t-	1.0797	0.8266	66.8N	69.4W	0	176		

Cat Num	Canon Plate	Calendar Date	TD of Greatest Eclipse	ΔT s	Luna Num	Saros Num	Ecl Type	QLE	Gamma	Ecl Mag	Lat °	Long °	Sun Alt °	Sun Azm °	Path Width km	Central Line Dur
1141	096	1975 May 11	07:17:33	46	-305	118	P	-t	1.0647	0.8636	69.7N	80.2W	0	28		
1142	096	1975 Nov 03	13:15:54	46	-299	123	P	-t	-1.0248	0.9588	70.4S	161.7W	0	141		
1143	096	1976 Apr 29	10:24:18	47	-293	128	A	-p	0.3378	0.9421	34.0N	18.3E	70	165	227	06m41s
1144	096	1976 Oct 23	05:13:45	47	-287	133	T	-n	-0.3270	1.0572	30.0S	92.3E	71	17	199	04m46s
1145	096	1977 Apr 18	10:31:30	48	-281	138	A	p-	-0.3990	0.9449	11.9S	28.3E	66	345	220	07m04s
1146	096	1977 Oct 12	20:27:27	48	-275	143	T	n-	0.3836	1.0269	14.1N	123.6W	67	197	99	02m37s
1147	096	1978 Apr 07	15:03:47	49	-269	148	P	t-	-1.1081	0.7883	71.9S	23.3E	0	293		
1148	096	1978 Oct 02	06:28:43	49	-263	153	P	t-	1.1616	0.6905	72.0N	159.6E	0	259		
1149	096	1979 Feb 26	16:55:06	50	-258	120	T	-p	0.8981	1.0391	52.1N	94.5W	26	153	298	02m49s
1150	096	1979 Aug 22	17:22:38	50	-252	125	A	-t	-0.9632	0.9329	59.6S	108.5W	15	29	953	06m03s
1151	096	1980 Feb 16	08:54:01	51	-246	130	T	-n	0.2224	1.0434	0.1S	47.1E	77	166	149	04m08s
1152	096	1980 Aug 10	19:12:21	51	-240	135	A	nn	-0.1915	0.9727	4.6N	108.9W	79	12	100	03m23s
1153	097	1981 Feb 04	22:09:24	51	-234	140	A	n-	-0.4838	0.9938	44.4S	140.8W	61	344	25	00m33s
1154	097	1981 Jul 31	03:46:37	52	-228	145	T	p-	0.5792	1.0258	53.3N	134.1E	54	195	108	02m02s
1155	097	1982 Jan 25	04:42:53	52	-222	150	P	t-	-1.2311	0.5663	69.3S	91.7W	0	203		
1156	097	1982 Jun 21	12:04:33	53	-217	117	P	-t	-1.2102	0.6168	65.9S	13.2E	0	347		
1157	097	1982 Jul 20	18:44:44	53	-216	155	P	t-	1.2886	0.4643	68.6N	64.2E	0	345		
1158	097	1982 Dec 15	09:32:09	53	-211	122	P	-t	1.1293	0.7351	65.3N	56.9E	0	199		
1159	097	1983 Jun 11	04:43:34	53	-205	127	T	-p	-0.4947	1.0524	6.2S	114.2E	60	351	199	05m11s
1160	097	1983 Dec 04	12:31:15	54	-199	132	A	-n	0.4015	0.9666	0.9N	4.7W	66	192	131	04m01s
1161	097	1984 May 30	16:45:42	54	-193	137	A	nn	0.2755	0.9980	37.5N	76.7W	74	163	7	00m11s
1162	097	1984 Nov 22	22:54:17	54	-187	142	T	n-	-0.3132	1.0237	37.8S	173.6W	72	21	85	02m00s
1163	097	1985 May 19	21:29:38	55	-181	147	P	t-	1.0720	0.8406	63.2N	81.1E	0	41		
1164	097	1985 Nov 12	14:11:27	55	-175	152	T	t-	-0.9795	1.0388	68.6S	142.6W	11	111	690	01m59s
1165	098	1986 Apr 09	06:21:22	55	-170	119	P	-t	-1.0822	0.8236	61.2S	161.4E	0	286		
1166	098	1986 Oct 03	19:06:15	55	-164	124	H	-t	0.9931	1.0000	59.9N	37.1W	5	252	1	00m00s
1167	098	1987 Mar 29	12:49:47	55	-158	129	H	-n	-0.3053	1.0013	12.3S	2.3W	72	331	5	00m08s
1168	098	1987 Sep 23	03:12:22	56	-152	134	A	-n	0.2787	0.9634	14.3N	138.4E	74	210	137	03m49s
1169	098	1988 Mar 18	01:58:56	56	-146	139	T	n-	0.4188	1.0464	20.7N	140.0E	65	149	169	03m46s
1170	098	1988 Sep 11	04:44:29	56	-140	144	A	p-	-0.4681	0.9377	20.0S	94.4E	62	31	258	06m57s
1171	098	1989 Mar 07	18:08:41	56	-134	149	P	t-	1.0981	0.8268	61.2N	169.8W	0	101		
1172	098	1989 Aug 31	05:31:47	57	-128	154	P	t-	-1.1928	0.6344	61.3S	23.6E	0	72		
1173	098	1990 Jan 26	19:31:24	57	-123	121	A	-t	-0.9457	0.9670	71.0S	22.2W	18	266	373	02m03s
1174	098	1990 Jul 22	03:03:07	57	-117	126	T	-t	0.7597	1.0391	65.2N	168.9E	40	222	201	02m33s
1175	098	1991 Jan 15	23:53:51	58	-111	131	A	-n	-0.2727	0.9290	36.4S	170.4W	74	341	277	07m53s
1176	098	1991 Jul 11	19:07:01	58	-105	136	Tm	nn	-0.0041	1.0800	22.0N	105.2W	90	30	258	06m53s
1177	099	1992 Jan 04	23:05:37	58	-99	141	A	p-	0.4091	0.9179	1.0N	169.7W	66	169	340	11m41s
1178	099	1992 Jun 30	12:11:22	59	-93	146	T	p-	-0.7512	1.0592	25.2S	9.5W	41	10	294	05m21s
1179	099	1992 Dec 24	00:31:41	59	-87	151	P	t-	1.0711	0.8422	65.7N	155.7E	0	165		
1180	099	1993 May 21	14:20:15	59	-82	118	P	-t	1.1372	0.7352	68.8N	162.3E	0	17		
1181	099	1993 Nov 13	21:45:51	60	-76	123	P	-t	-1.0411	0.9280	69.6S	58.3E	0	153		
1182	099	1994 May 10	17:12:27	60	-70	128	A	-p	0.4077	0.9431	41.5N	84.1W	66	168	230	06m13s
1183	099	1994 Nov 03	13:40:06	61	-64	133	T	-n	-0.3522	1.0535	35.4S	34.2W	69	15	189	04m23s
1184	099	1995 Apr 29	17:33:21	61	-58	138	A	p-	-0.3382	0.9497	4.8S	79.4W	70	348	195	06m37s
1185	099	1995 Oct 24	04:33:31	61	-52	143	T	n-	0.3518	1.0213	8.4N	113.2E	69	195	78	02m10s
1186	099	1996 Apr 17	22:38:12	62	-46	148	P	t-	-1.0580	0.8799	71.3S	104.0W	0	306		
1187	099	1996 Oct 12	14:03:04	62	-40	153	P	t-	1.1227	0.7575	71.7N	32.1E	0	245		
1188	099	1997 Mar 09	01:24:51	62	-35	120	T	-p	0.9183	1.0420	57.8N	130.7E	23	146	356	02m50s
1189	100	1997 Sep 02	00:04:48	63	-29	125	P	-t	-1.0352	0.8988	71.8S	114.3E	0	64		
1190	100	1998 Feb 26	17:29:27	63	-23	130	T	-n	0.2391	1.0441	4.7N	82.7W	76	164	151	04m09s
1191	100	1998 Aug 22	02:07:11	63	-17	135	A	nn	-0.2644	0.9734	3.0S	145.4E	75	14	99	03m14s
1192	100	1999 Feb 16	06:34:38	63	-11	140	A	n-	-0.4726	0.9928	39.8S	93.9E	62	342	29	00m40s
1193	100	1999 Aug 11	11:04:09	64	-5	145	T	p-	0.5062	1.0286	45.1N	24.3E	59	197	112	02m23s
1194	100	2000 Feb 05	12:50:27	64	1	150	P	t-	-1.2233	0.5795	70.2S	134.1E	0	215		
1195	100	2000 Jul 01	19:33:34	64	6	117	P	-t	-1.2821	0.4768	66.9S	109.5W	0	358		
1196	100	2000 Jul 31	02:14:08	64	7	155	P	t-	1.2166	0.6034	69.5N	59.9W	0	333		
1197	100	2000 Dec 25	17:35:57	64	12	122	P	-t	1.1367	0.7228	66.3N	74.1W	0	189		
1198	100	2001 Jun 21	12:04:46	64	18	127	T	-p	-0.5701	1.0495	11.3S	2.7E	55	355	200	04m57s
1199	100	2001 Dec 14	20:53:01	64	24	132	A	-n	0.4089	0.9681	0.6N	130.7W	66	188	126	03m53s
1200	100	2002 Jun 10	23:45:22	64	30	137	A	nn	0.1993	0.9962	34.5N	178.6W	78	169	13	00m23s

Cat Num	Canon Plate	Calendar Date	TD of Greatest Eclipse	ΔT s	Luna Num	Saros Num	Ecl Type	QLE	Gamma	Ecl Mag	Lat °	Long °	Sun Alt °	Sun Azm °	Path Width km	Central Line Dur
1201	101	2002 Dec 04	07:32:16	64	36	142	T	n-	-0.3020	1.0244	39.5S	59.6E	72	16	87	02m04s
1202	101	2003 May 31	04:09:23	64	42	147	An	t-	0.9960	0.9384	66.6N	24.5W	3	35	–	03m37s
1203	101	2003 Nov 23	22:50:22	64	48	152	T	t-	-0.9638	1.0379	72.7S	88.4E	15	111	496	01m57s
1204	101	2004 Apr 19	13:35:05	65	53	119	P	-t	-1.1335	0.7367	61.6S	44.3E	0	295		
1205	101	2004 Oct 14	03:00:23	65	59	124	P	-t	1.0348	0.9283	61.2N	153.7W	0	253		
1206	101	2005 Apr 08	20:36:51	65	65	129	H	-n	-0.3473	1.0074	10.6S	119.0W	70	332	27	00m42s
1207	101	2005 Oct 03	10:32:47	65	71	134	A	-p	0.3306	0.9576	12.9N	28.7E	71	209	162	04m32s
1208	101	2006 Mar 29	10:12:23	65	77	139	T	n-	0.3843	1.0515	23.2N	16.7E	67	149	184	04m07s
1209	101	2006 Sep 22	11:41:16	65	83	144	A	p-	-0.4062	0.9352	20.6S	9.1W	66	31	261	07m09s
1210	101	2007 Mar 19	02:32:58	65	89	149	P	t-	1.0728	0.8756	61.0N	55.5E	0	92		
1211	101	2007 Sep 11	12:32:24	65	95	154	P	t-	-1.1255	0.7507	61.0S	90.2W	0	80		
1212	101	2008 Feb 07	03:56:10	66	100	121	A	-t	-0.9570	0.9650	67.6S	150.5W	16	269	444	02m12s
1213	102	2008 Aug 01	10:22:12	66	106	126	T	-p	0.8307	1.0394	65.7N	72.3E	34	235	237	02m27s
1214	102	2009 Jan 26	07:59:45	66	112	131	A	-n	-0.2820	0.9282	34.1S	70.2E	73	337	280	07m54s
1215	102	2009 Jul 22	02:36:25	66	118	136	T	nn	0.0698	1.0799	24.2N	144.1E	86	198	258	06m39s
1216	102	2010 Jan 15	07:07:39	66	124	141	A	p-	0.4002	0.9190	1.6N	69.3E	66	165	333	11m08s
1217	102	2010 Jul 11	19:34:38	66	130	146	T	p-	-0.6788	1.0580	19.7S	121.9W	47	14	259	05m20s
1218	102	2011 Jan 04	08:51:42	66	136	151	P	t-	1.0626	0.8576	64.7N	20.8E	0	155		
1219	102	2011 Jun 01	21:17:18	67	141	118	P	-t	1.2130	0.6011	67.8N	46.8E	0	6		
1220	102	2011 Jul 01	08:39:30	67	142	156	Pb	t-	-1.4917	0.0971	65.2S	28.6E	0	21		
1221	102	2011 Nov 25	06:21:25	67	147	123	P	-t	-1.0536	0.9047	68.6S	82.4W	0	165		
1222	102	2012 May 20	23:53:54	67	153	128	A	-p	0.4828	0.9439	49.1N	176.3E	61	171	237	05m46s
1223	102	2012 Nov 13	22:12:55	67	159	133	T	-n	-0.3719	1.0500	40.0S	161.3W	68	11	179	04m02s
1224	102	2013 May 10	00:26:20	67	165	138	A	pn	-0.2694	0.9544	2.2N	175.5E	74	350	173	06m03s
1225	103	2013 Nov 03	12:47:36	67	171	143	H3	n-	0.3272	1.0159	3.5N	11.7W	71	192	58	01m40s
1226	103	2014 Apr 29	06:04:33	67	177	148	A-	t-	-1.0000	0.9868	70.6S	131.3E	0	319	–	–
1227	103	2014 Oct 23	21:45:39	68	183	153	P	t-	1.0908	0.8114	71.2N	97.2W	0	231		
1228	103	2015 Mar 20	09:46:47	68	188	120	T	-t	0.9454	1.0446	64.4N	6.6W	18	135	463	02m47s
1229	103	2015 Sep 13	06:55:19	68	194	125	P	-t	-1.1004	0.7875	72.1S	2.3W	0	77		
1230	103	2016 Mar 09	01:58:19	68	200	130	T	-n	0.2609	1.0450	10.1N	148.8E	75	162	155	04m09s
1231	103	2016 Sep 01	09:08:02	68	206	135	A	-n	-0.3330	0.9736	10.7S	37.8E	70	16	100	03m06s
1232	103	2017 Feb 26	14:54:33	68	212	140	A	n-	-0.4578	0.9922	34.7S	31.2W	63	340	31	00m44s
1233	103	2017 Aug 21	18:26:40	69	218	145	T	p-	0.4367	1.0306	37.0N	87.7W	64	198	115	02m40s
1234	103	2018 Feb 15	20:52:33	69	224	150	P	t-	-1.2116	0.5991	71.0S	0.6E	0	228		
1235	103	2018 Jul 13	03:02:16	69	229	117	P	-t	-1.3542	0.3365	67.9S	127.4E	0	8		
1236	103	2018 Aug 11	09:47:28	69	230	155	P	t-	1.1476	0.7368	70.4N	174.5E	0	321		
1237	104	2019 Jan 06	01:42:38	69	235	122	P	-t	1.1417	0.7146	67.4N	153.6E	0	178		
1238	104	2019 Jul 02	19:24:07	69	241	127	T	-p	-0.6466	1.0459	17.4S	109.0W	50	359	201	04m33s
1239	104	2019 Dec 26	05:18:53	69	247	132	A	-n	0.4135	0.9701	1.0N	102.2E	66	184	118	03m39s
1240	104	2020 Jun 21	06:41:15	70	253	137	Am	nn	0.1209	0.9940	30.5N	79.7E	83	174	21	00m38s
1241	104	2020 Dec 14	16:14:39	70	259	142	T	n-	-0.2939	1.0254	40.3S	68.0W	73	10	90	02m10s
1242	104	2021 Jun 10	10:43:07	70	265	147	A	t-	0.9152	0.9435	80.8N	66.8W	23	90	527	03m51s
1243	104	2021 Dec 04	07:34:38	70	271	152	T	p-	-0.9526	1.0367	76.8S	46.2W	17	115	419	01m54s
1244	104	2022 Apr 30	20:42:37	70	276	119	P	-t	-1.1901	0.6396	62.1S	71.5W	0	304		
1245	104	2022 Oct 25	11:01:20	71	282	124	P	-t	1.0701	0.8619	61.6N	77.3E	0	244		
1246	104	2023 Apr 20	04:17:56	71	288	129	H	-n	-0.3952	1.0132	9.6S	125.8E	67	334	49	01m16s
1247	104	2023 Oct 14	18:00:41	71	294	134	A	-p	0.3753	0.9520	11.4N	83.1W	68	208	187	05m17s
1248	104	2024 Apr 08	18:18:29	71	300	139	T	n-	0.3431	1.0566	25.3N	104.1W	70	149	198	04m28s
1249	105	2024 Oct 02	18:46:13	71	306	144	A	p-	-0.3509	0.9326	22.0S	114.5W	69	31	266	07m25s
1250	105	2025 Mar 29	10:48:36	72	312	149	P	t-	1.0405	0.9376	61.1N	77.1W	0	83		
1251	105	2025 Sep 21	19:43:04	72	318	154	P	t-	-1.0651	0.8550	60.9S	153.5E	0	89		
1252	105	2026 Feb 17	12:13:06	72	323	121	A	-t	-0.9743	0.9630	64.7S	86.7E	12	268	616	02m20s
1253	105	2026 Aug 12	17:47:06	72	329	126	T	-p	0.8977	1.0386	65.2N	25.2W	26	248	294	02m18s
1254	105	2027 Feb 06	16:00:48	73	335	131	A	-n	-0.2952	0.9281	31.3S	48.5W	73	334	282	07m51s
1255	105	2027 Aug 02	10:07:50	73	341	136	T	nn	0.1421	1.0790	25.5N	33.2E	82	202	258	06m23s
1256	105	2028 Jan 26	15:08:59	73	347	141	A	p-	0.3901	0.9208	3.0N	51.6W	67	161	323	10m27s
1257	105	2028 Jul 22	02:56:40	73	353	146	T	p-	-0.6056	1.0560	15.6S	126.7E	53	17	230	05m10s
1258	105	2029 Jan 14	17:13:48	73	359	151	P	t-	1.0553	0.8714	63.7N	114.2W	0	145		
1259	105	2029 Jun 12	04:06:13	74	364	118	P	-t	1.2943	0.4576	66.8N	66.2W	0	355		
1260	105	2029 Jul 11	15:37:19	74	365	156	P	t-	-1.4191	0.2303	64.3S	85.6W	0	30		

Cat Num	Canon Plate	Calendar Date	TD of Greatest Eclipse	ΔT s	Luna Num	Saros Num	Ecl Type	QLE	Gamma	Ecl Mag	Lat °	Long °	Sun Alt °	Sun Azm °	Path Width km	Central Line Dur
1261	106	2029 Dec 05	15:03:58	74	370	123	P	-t	-1.0609	0.8911	67.5S	135.6E	0	177		
1262	106	2030 Jun 01	06:29:13	74	376	128	A	-p	0.5626	0.9443	56.5N	80.1E	55	176	250	05m21s
1263	106	2030 Nov 25	06:51:37	74	382	133	T	-n	-0.3867	1.0468	43.6S	71.2E	67	7	169	03m44s
1264	106	2031 May 21	07:16:04	75	388	138	A	nn	-0.1970	0.9589	8.9N	71.7E	79	354	152	05m26s
1265	106	2031 Nov 14	21:07:31	75	394	143	H	n-	0.3078	1.0106	0.6S	137.6W	72	189	38	01m08s
1266	106	2032 May 09	13:26:42	75	400	148	A	t-	-0.9375	0.9957	51.3S	7.1W	20	345	44	00m22s
1267	106	2032 Nov 03	05:34:13	75	406	153	P	t-	1.0643	0.8554	70.4N	132.6E	0	218		
1268	106	2033 Mar 30	18:02:36	75	411	120	T	-t	0.9778	1.0462	71.3N	155.8W	11	111	781	02m37s
1269	106	2033 Sep 23	13:54:31	76	417	125	P	-t	-1.1583	0.6890	72.2S	121.3W	0	91		
1270	106	2034 Mar 20	10:18:45	76	423	130	T	-n	0.2894	1.0458	16.1N	22.2E	73	162	159	04m09s
1271	106	2034 Sep 12	16:19:28	76	429	135	A	-p	-0.3936	0.9736	18.2S	72.6W	67	18	102	02m58s
1272	106	2035 Mar 09	23:05:54	76	435	140	A	n-	-0.4368	0.9919	29.0S	155.0W	64	340	31	00m48s
1273	107	2035 Sep 02	01:56:46	77	441	145	T	p-	0.3727	1.0320	29.1N	158.0E	68	199	116	02m54s
1274	107	2036 Feb 27	04:46:49	77	447	150	P	t-	-1.1942	0.6286	71.6S	131.5W	0	242		
1275	107	2036 Jul 23	10:32:06	77	452	117	P	-t	-1.4250	0.1992	68.9S	3.5E	0	19		
1276	107	2036 Aug 21	17:25:45	77	453	155	P	t-	1.0825	0.8622	71.1N	47.0E	0	309		
1277	107	2037 Jan 16	09:48:55	77	458	122	P	-t	1.1477	0.7049	68.5N	20.8E	0	166		
1278	107	2037 Jul 13	02:40:36	78	464	127	T	-p	-0.7246	1.0413	24.8S	139.1E	43	3	201	03m58s
1279	107	2038 Jan 05	13:47:11	78	470	132	A	-n	-0.4169	0.9728	2.1N	25.5W	65	179	107	03m18s
1280	107	2038 Jul 02	13:32:55	78	476	137	A	nn	0.0398	0.9911	25.4N	21.9W	88	179	31	01m00s
1281	107	2038 Dec 26	01:00:10	79	482	142	T	n-	-0.2881	1.0269	40.3S	163.9E	73	5	95	02m18s
1282	107	2039 Jun 21	17:12:54	79	488	147	A	p-	0.8312	0.9454	78.9N	102.1W	33	153	365	04m05s
1283	107	2039 Dec 15	16:23:46	79	494	152	T	p-	-0.9458	1.0356	80.9S	172.8E	18	123	380	01m51s
1284	107	2040 May 11	03:43:02	79	499	119	P	-t	-1.2529	0.5306	62.8S	174.4E	0	313		
1285	108	2040 Nov 04	19:09:02	80	505	124	P	-t	1.0993	0.8074	62.2N	53.4W	0	234		
1286	108	2041 Apr 30	11:52:21	80	511	129	T	-p	-0.4492	1.0189	9.6S	12.2E	63	337	72	01m51s
1287	108	2041 Oct 25	01:36:22	80	517	134	A	-p	0.4133	0.9467	9.9N	162.8E	66	206	213	06m07s
1288	108	2042 Apr 20	02:17:30	80	523	139	T	n-	0.2956	1.0614	27.0N	137.3E	73	151	210	04m51s
1289	108	2042 Oct 14	02:00:42	81	529	144	A	n-	-0.3030	0.9301	23.7S	137.8E	72	30	273	07m44s
1290	108	2043 Apr 09	18:57:49	81	535	149	T+	t-	1.0031	1.0096	61.3N	151.9E	0	74	-	-
1291	108	2043 Oct 03	03:01:49	81	541	154	A-	t-	-1.0102	0.9497	61.0S	35.2E	0	98	-	-
1292	108	2044 Feb 28	20:24:40	82	546	121	As	-t	-0.9954	0.9600	62.2S	25.6W	4	260	-	02m27s
1293	108	2044 Aug 23	01:17:02	82	552	126	T	-t	0.9613	1.0364	64.3N	120.5W	15	264	453	02m04s
1294	108	2045 Feb 16	23:56:07	82	558	131	A	-n	-0.3125	0.9285	28.3S	166.2W	72	331	281	07m47s
1295	108	2045 Aug 12	17:42:39	82	564	136	T	-n	0.2116	1.0774	25.9N	78.6W	78	206	256	06m06s
1296	108	2046 Feb 05	23:06:26	83	570	141	A	p-	0.3765	0.9232	4.8N	171.4W	68	157	310	09m42s
1297	109	2046 Aug 02	10:21:13	83	576	146	T	p-	-0.5350	1.0531	12.7S	15.1E	58	21	206	04m51s
1298	109	2047 Jan 26	01:33:18	83	582	151	P	t-	1.0450	0.8908	62.9N	111.7E	0	135		
1299	109	2047 Jun 23	10:52:31	84	587	118	P	-t	1.3766	0.3129	65.8N	178.0W	0	346		
1300	109	2047 Jul 22	22:36:17	84	588	156	P	t-	-1.3477	0.3605	63.4S	160.1E	0	40		
1301	109	2047 Dec 16	23:50:12	84	593	123	P	-t	-1.0661	0.8817	66.4S	6.6W	0	188		
1302	109	2048 Jun 11	12:58:53	84	599	128	A	-p	0.6468	0.9441	63.7N	11.5W	49	184	271	04m58s
1303	109	2048 Dec 05	15:35:27	84	605	133	T	-n	-0.3973	1.0440	46.1S	56.4W	66	1	160	03m28s
1304	109	2049 May 31	13:59:59	85	611	138	A	nn	-0.1187	0.9631	15.3N	29.9W	83	358	134	04m45s
1305	109	2049 Nov 25	05:33:48	85	617	143	H	n-	0.2943	1.0057	3.8S	95.2E	73	185	21	00m38s
1306	109	2050 May 20	20:42:50	85	623	148	H	t-	-0.8688	1.0038	40.1S	123.7W	29	352	27	00m21s
1307	109	2050 Nov 14	13:30:53	86	629	153	P	t-	1.0447	0.8874	69.5N	1.0E	0	206		
1308	109	2051 Apr 11	02:10:39	86	634	120	P	-t	1.0169	0.9849	71.6N	32.1E	0	63		
1309	110	2051 Oct 04	21:02:15	86	640	125	P	-t	-1.2094	0.6024	72.0S	117.7E	0	105		
1310	110	2052 Mar 30	18:31:53	87	646	130	T	-n	0.3239	1.0466	22.4N	102.6W	71	161	164	04m08s
1311	110	2052 Sep 22	23:39:10	87	652	135	A	-p	-0.4480	0.9734	25.7S	174.9E	63	20	106	02m51s
1312	110	2053 Mar 20	07:08:19	87	658	140	A	n-	-0.4089	0.9919	23.0S	82.9E	66	341	31	00m50s
1313	110	2053 Sep 12	09:34:09	88	664	145	T	n-	0.3140	1.0328	21.5N	41.7E	72	199	116	03m04s
1314	110	2054 Mar 09	12:33:40	88	670	150	P	t-	-1.1711	0.6678	72.0S	97.9E	0	259		
1315	110	2054 Aug 03	18:04:02	88	675	117	Pe	-t	-1.4941	0.0656	69.8S	121.4W	0	31		
1316	110	2054 Sep 02	01:09:34	88	676	155	P	t-	1.0215	0.9793	71.7N	82.4W	0	296		
1317	110	2055 Jan 27	17:54:05	88	681	122	P	-t	1.1550	0.6932	69.5N	112.3W	0	154		
1318	110	2055 Jul 24	09:57:50	89	687	127	T	-p	-0.8012	1.0359	33.3S	25.7E	37	8	202	03m17s
1319	110	2056 Jan 16	22:16:45	89	693	132	A	-n	0.4199	0.9760	3.9N	153.6W	65	175	95	02m52s
1320	110	2056 Jul 12	20:21:59	89	699	137	A	nn	-0.0426	0.9878	19.4N	123.8W	88	3	43	01m26s

Thousand Year Canon of Solar Eclipses: 1501 to 2500

Cat Num	Canon Plate	Calendar Date	TD of Greatest Eclipse	ΔT s	Luna Num	Saros Num	Ecl Type	QLE	Gamma	Ecl Mag	Lat °	Long °	Sun Alt °	Sun Azm °	Path Width km	Central Line Dur
1321	111	2057 Jan 05	09:47:52	90	705	142	T	n-	-0.2837	1.0287	39.2S	35.1E	73	359	102	02m29s
1322	111	2057 Jul 01	23:40:15	90	711	147	A	p-	0.7455	0.9464	71.5N	176.3W	41	177	298	04m22s
1323	111	2057 Dec 26	01:14:35	90	717	152	T	p-	-0.9405	1.0348	84.9S	21.7E	19	141	355	01m50s
1324	111	2058 May 22	10:39:26	91	722	119	P	-t	-1.3194	0.4141	63.5S	61.1E	0	322		
1325	111	2058 Jun 21	00:19:35	91	723	157	Pb	t-	1.4869	0.1261	65.9N	9.8E	0	13		
1326	111	2058 Nov 16	03:23:07	91	728	124	P	-t	1.1224	0.7644	62.9N	174.1E	0	225		
1327	111	2059 May 11	19:22:16	91	734	129	T	-p	-0.5080	1.0242	10.7S	100.5W	59	340	95	02m23s
1328	111	2059 Nov 05	09:18:15	92	740	134	A	-p	0.4454	0.9417	8.7N	47.0E	63	203	238	07m00s
1329	111	2060 Apr 30	10:10:00	92	746	139	T	n-	0.2422	1.0660	28.0N	20.8E	76	154	222	05m15s
1330	111	2060 Oct 24	09:24:10	92	752	144	A	nn	-0.2625	0.9277	25.8S	28.0E	75	28	281	08m06s
1331	111	2061 Apr 20	02:56:49	93	758	149	T	t-	0.9578	1.0476	64.5N	59.1E	16	97	559	02m37s
1332	111	2061 Oct 13	10:32:10	93	764	154	A	t-	-0.9639	0.9469	62.1S	54.5W	15	79	743	03m41s
1333	112	2062 Mar 11	04:26:16	93	769	121	P	-t	-1.0238	0.9331	61.0S	147.2W	0	263		
1334	112	2062 Sep 03	08:54:27	94	775	126	P	-t	1.0192	0.9749	61.3N	150.2E	0	286		
1335	112	2063 Feb 28	07:43:30	94	781	131	A	-p	-0.3360	0.9293	25.2S	77.6E	70	329	280	07m41s
1336	112	2063 Aug 24	01:22:11	95	787	136	T	-n	0.2771	1.0750	25.6N	168.3E	74	209	252	05m49s
1337	112	2064 Feb 17	07:00:23	95	793	141	A	p-	0.3597	0.9262	7.0N	69.6E	69	154	295	08m56s
1338	112	2064 Aug 12	17:46:06	95	799	146	T	p-	-0.4652	1.0495	10.9S	96.1W	62	24	184	04m28s
1339	112	2065 Feb 05	09:52:26	96	805	151	P	t-	1.0336	0.9123	62.2N	22.0W	0	125		
1340	112	2065 Jul 03	17:33:52	96	810	118	P	-t	1.4619	0.1639	64.8N	71.7E	0	336		
1341	112	2065 Aug 02	05:34:17	96	811	156	P	t-	-1.2758	0.4903	62.7S	46.4E	0	49		
1342	112	2065 Dec 27	08:39:56	96	816	123	P	-t	-1.0688	0.8769	65.4S	149.3W	0	198		
1343	112	2066 Jun 22	19:25:48	97	822	128	A	-p	0.7330	0.9435	70.1N	96.5W	43	198	309	04m40s
1344	112	2066 Dec 17	00:23:40	97	828	133	T	-n	-0.4043	1.0416	47.4S	175.6E	66	355	152	03m14s
1345	113	2067 Jun 11	20:42:26	97	834	138	A	nn	-0.0387	0.9670	21.0N	130.3W	88	2	119	04m05s
1346	113	2067 Dec 06	14:03:43	98	840	143	H	n-	0.2845	1.0011	6.0S	32.5W	74	181	4	00m08s
1347	113	2068 May 31	03:56:39	98	846	148	P	p-	-0.7970	1.0110	31.0S	123.1E	37	357	63	01m06s
1348	113	2068 Nov 24	21:32:30	99	852	153	P	t-	1.0299	0.9109	68.5N	131.2W	0	194		
1349	113	2069 Apr 21	10:11:09	99	857	120	P	-t	1.0624	0.8992	71.0N	101.4W	0	50		
1350	113	2069 May 20	17:53:18	99	858	158	Pb	t-	-1.4852	0.0879	68.8S	70.1W	0	342		
1351	113	2069 Oct 15	04:19:56	99	863	125	P	-t	-1.2524	0.5298	71.6S	5.6W	0	119		
1352	113	2070 Apr 11	02:36:09	100	869	130	T	-n	0.3652	1.0472	29.1N	134.9E	68	162	168	04m04s
1353	113	2070 Oct 04	07:08:57	100	875	135	A	-p	-0.4950	0.9731	32.8S	60.3E	60	21	110	02m44s
1354	113	2071 Mar 31	15:01:06	100	881	140	A	n-	-0.3739	0.9919	16.7S	37.2W	68	342	31	00m52s
1355	113	2071 Sep 23	17:20:28	101	887	145	T	n-	0.2620	1.0333	14.2N	76.9W	75	198	116	03m11s
1356	113	2072 Mar 19	20:10:31	101	893	150	P	t-	-1.1405	0.7199	72.2S	30.5W	0	270		
1357	114	2072 Sep 12	08:59:20	102	899	155	T	t-	0.9655	1.0558	69.8N	101.8E	14	240	732	03m13s
1358	114	2073 Feb 07	01:55:59	102	904	122	P	-t	1.1651	0.6768	70.5N	114.7E	0	141		
1359	114	2073 Aug 03	17:15:23	102	910	127	T	-t	-0.8763	1.0294	43.2S	89.6W	28	14	206	02m29s
1360	114	2074 Jan 27	06:44:15	103	916	132	A	-n	0.4251	0.9798	6.6N	78.6E	65	171	79	02m21s
1361	114	2074 Jul 24	03:10:32	103	922	137	A	nn	-0.1242	0.9838	12.8N	133.6E	83	7	58	01m57s
1362	114	2075 Jan 16	18:36:04	104	928	142	T	n-	-0.2799	1.0311	37.2S	94.3W	74	354	110	02m42s
1363	114	2075 Jul 13	06:05:44	104	934	147	A	p-	0.6583	0.9467	63.1N	95.0E	49	186	262	04m45s
1364	114	2076 Jan 06	10:07:28	104	940	152	T	p-	-0.9373	1.0342	87.2S	173.9W	20	203	340	01m49s
1365	114	2076 Jun 01	17:31:22	105	945	119	P	-t	-1.3897	0.2897	64.4S	51.4W	0	331		
1366	114	2076 Jul 01	06:50:43	105	946	157	P	t-	1.4005	0.2746	67.0N	98.3W	0	3		
1367	114	2076 Nov 26	11:43:01	105	951	124	P	-t	1.1401	0.7315	63.7N	39.9E	0	215		
1368	114	2077 May 22	02:46:05	106	957	129	T	-p	-0.5725	1.0290	13.1S	148.1E	55	343	119	02m54s
1369	115	2077 Nov 15	17:07:56	106	963	134	A	-p	0.4705	0.9371	7.8N	71.0W	62	199	262	07m54s
1370	115	2078 May 11	17:56:55	106	969	139	T	n-	0.1838	1.0701	28.1N	93.9W	79	158	232	05m40s
1371	115	2078 Nov 04	16:55:44	107	975	144	A	nn	-0.2285	0.9255	27.8S	83.5W	77	25	287	08m29s
1372	115	2079 May 01	10:50:13	107	981	149	T	p-	0.9081	1.0512	66.2N	46.5W	24	108	406	02m55s
1373	115	2079 Oct 24	18:11:21	108	987	154	A	t-	-0.9243	0.9484	63.4S	160.8W	22	72	495	03m39s
1374	115	2080 Mar 21	12:20:15	108	992	121	P	-t	-1.0578	0.8734	60.9S	85.7E	0	271		
1375	115	2080 Sep 13	16:38:09	108	998	126	P	-t	1.0724	0.8743	61.1N	25.6E	0	277		
1376	115	2081 Mar 10	15:23:31	109	1004	131	A	-p	-0.3653	0.9304	22.4S	36.9W	68	329	277	07m36s
1377	115	2081 Sep 03	09:07:31	109	1010	136	T	-n	0.3379	1.0720	24.6N	53.4E	70	211	247	05m33s
1378	115	2082 Feb 27	14:47:00	110	1016	141	A	p-	0.3361	0.9298	9.4N	47.3W	70	152	277	08m12s
1379	115	2082 Aug 24	01:16:21	110	1022	146	T	n-	-0.4004	1.0452	10.3S	151.6E	66	26	163	04m01s
1380	115	2083 Feb 16	18:06:36	111	1028	151	P	t-	1.0170	0.9433	61.6N	154.3W	0	116		

Cat Num	Canon Plate	Calendar Date	TD of Greatest Eclipse	ΔT s	Luna Num	Saros Num	Ecl Type	QLE	Gamma	Ecl Mag	Lat °	Long °	Sun Alt °	Sun Azm °	Path Width km	Central Line Dur
1381	116	2083 Jul 15	00:14:23	111	1033	118	Pe	-t	1.5464	0.0169	64.0N	37.9W	0	327		
1382	116	2083 Aug 13	12:34:41	111	1034	156	P	t-	-1.2064	0.6146	62.1S	67.7W	0	58		
1383	116	2084 Jan 07	17:30:24	111	1039	123	P	-t	-1.0715	0.8723	64.4S	68.3E	0	209		
1384	116	2084 Jul 03	01:50:26	112	1045	128	A	-p	0.8208	0.9421	75.0N	169.3W	35	222	377	04m25s
1385	116	2084 Dec 27	09:13:48	112	1051	133	T	-n	-0.4094	1.0396	47.3S	47.5W	66	349	146	03m04s
1386	116	2085 Jun 22	03:21:16	113	1057	138	A	nn	0.0453	0.9704	26.2N	131.0E	87	186	106	03m29s
1387	116	2085 Dec 16	22:37:48	113	1063	143	A	n-	0.2786	0.9971	7.3S	161.0W	74	176	10	00m19s
1388	116	2086 Jun 11	11:07:14	114	1069	148	T	p-	-0.7215	1.0174	23.2S	12.2E	44	2	86	01m48s
1389	116	2086 Dec 06	05:38:55	114	1075	153	P	p-	1.0194	0.9271	67.4N	96.0E	0	182		
1390	116	2087 May 02	18:04:42	115	1080	120	P	-t	1.1139	0.8011	70.3N	127.3E	0	37		
1391	116	2087 Jun 01	01:27:14	115	1081	158	P	t-	-1.4186	0.2146	67.8S	165.1E	0	354		
1392	116	2087 Oct 26	11:46:57	115	1086	125	P	-t	-1.2882	0.4696	71.0S	130.8W	0	132		
1393	117	2088 Apr 21	10:31:49	115	1092	130	T	-p	0.4135	1.0474	36.0N	14.8E	65	163	173	03m58s
1394	117	2088 Oct 14	14:48:05	116	1098	135	A	-p	-0.5349	0.9727	39.7S	56.3W	57	21	115	02m38s
1395	117	2089 Apr 10	22:44:42	116	1104	140	A	n-	-0.3319	0.9919	10.2S	155.0W	71	344	30	00m53s
1396	117	2089 Oct 04	01:15:23	117	1110	145	T	n-	0.2167	1.0333	7.4N	162.5E	77	197	115	03m14s
1397	117	2090 Mar 31	03:38:08	117	1116	150	P	t-	-1.1028	0.7843	72.1S	156.6W	0	284		
1398	117	2090 Sep 23	16:56:36	118	1122	155	T	t-	0.9157	1.0562	60.7N	40.7W	23	218	463	03m36s
1399	117	2091 Feb 18	09:54:40	118	1127	122	P	-t	1.1779	0.6558	71.2N	18.0W	0	128		
1400	117	2091 Aug 15	00:34:43	119	1133	127	T	-t	-0.9490	1.0216	55.6S	150.2E	18	23	237	01m38s
1401	117	2092 Feb 07	15:10:20	119	1139	132	A	-n	0.4322	0.9840	9.9N	49.0W	64	168	62	01m48s
1402	117	2092 Aug 03	09:59:33	120	1145	137	A	nn	-0.2044	0.9794	5.6N	30.0E	78	10	75	02m31s
1403	117	2093 Jan 27	03:22:16	120	1151	142	T	n-	-0.2737	1.0340	34.1S	136.1E	74	350	119	02m58s
1404	117	2093 Jul 23	12:32:04	120	1157	147	A	p-	0.5717	0.9463	54.6N	1.1E	55	191	241	05m11s
1405	118	2094 Jan 16	18:59:03	121	1163	152	T	p-	-0.9333	1.0342	84.8S	10.9W	21	267	329	01m52s
1406	118	2094 Jun 13	00:22:11	121	1168	119	P	-t	-1.4613	0.1618	65.3S	163.9W	0	341		
1407	118	2094 Jul 12	13:24:35	121	1169	157	P	t-	1.3149	0.4225	68.0N	152.5E	0	352		
1408	118	2094 Dec 07	20:05:56	122	1174	124	P	-t	1.1547	0.7046	64.7N	95.3W	0	205		
1409	118	2095 Jun 02	10:07:40	122	1180	129	T	-p	-0.6396	1.0332	16.7S	36.9E	50	347	145	03m18s
1410	118	2095 Nov 27	01:02:57	123	1186	134	A	-p	0.4903	0.9330	7.2N	169.5E	61	195	285	08m47s
1411	118	2096 May 22	01:37:14	123	1192	139	T	nn	0.1196	1.0737	27.3N	153.1E	83	162	241	06m06s
1412	118	2096 Nov 15	00:36:15	124	1198	144	A	nn	-0.2018	0.9237	29.7S	163.0E	78	22	294	08m53s
1413	118	2097 May 11	18:34:31	124	1204	149	T	p-	0.8516	1.0538	67.4N	149.8W	31	121	339	03m10s
1414	118	2097 Nov 04	02:01:25	125	1210	154	A	t-	-0.8926	0.9494	65.8S	86.5E	26	68	411	03m36s
1415	118	2098 Apr 01	20:02:31	125	1215	121	P	-t	-1.1005	0.7984	61.0S	38.4W	0	280		
1416	118	2098 Sep 25	00:31:16	126	1221	126	P	-t	1.1184	0.7871	61.1N	101.3W	0	268		
1417	119	2098 Oct 24	10:36:11	126	1222	164	Pb	t-	-1.5407	0.0057	61.8S	95.8W	0	116		
1418	119	2099 Mar 21	22:54:32	126	1227	131	A	-p	-0.4016	0.9318	20.0S	149.4W	66	329	275	07m32s
1419	119	2099 Sep 14	16:57:53	127	1233	136	T	-n	0.3942	1.0684	23.4N	63.1W	67	211	241	05m18s
1420	119	2100 Mar 10	22:28:11	127	1239	141	A	n-	0.3077	0.9338	12.0N	162.7W	72	151	257	07m29s
1421	119	2100 Sep 04	08:49:20	128	1245	146	T	n-	-0.3384	1.0402	10.5S	38.7E	70	28	142	03m32s
1422	119	2101 Feb 28	02:16:26	128	1251	151	An	t-	0.9964	0.9609	60.5N	79.7E	3	111	-	02m44s
1423	119	2101 Aug 24	19:37:03	129	1257	156	P	t-	-1.1392	0.7337	61.6S	177.9E	0	67		
1424	119	2102 Jan 19	02:21:30	129	1262	123	P	-t	-1.0741	0.8682	63.5S	73.9W	0	218		
1425	119	2102 Jul 15	08:15:14	130	1268	128	A	-t	0.9080	0.9398	75.9N	133.8E	24	261	539	04m14s
1426	119	2103 Jan 08	18:04:21	130	1274	133	T	-n	-0.4140	1.0381	46.1S	81.1W	65	342	140	02m57s
1427	119	2103 Jul 04	10:01:48	131	1280	138	Am	nn	0.1285	0.9734	30.3N	32.8E	82	191	96	02m57s
1428	119	2103 Dec 29	07:13:18	131	1286	143	A	n-	0.2747	0.9936	7.5S	70.2E	74	172	23	00m43s
1429	120	2104 Jun 22	18:16:21	132	1292	148	T	p-	-0.6437	1.0231	16.6S	97.2W	50	6	103	02m26s
1430	120	2104 Dec 17	13:48:27	132	1298	153	A+	p-	1.0120	0.9381	66.4N	37.0W	0	171	-	-
1431	120	2105 May 14	01:52:06	133	1303	120	P	-t	1.1708	0.6921	69.4N	1.7W	0	25		
1432	120	2105 Jun 12	08:58:11	133	1304	158	P	t-	-1.3489	0.3483	66.8S	41.6E	0	4		
1433	120	2105 Nov 06	19:23:02	133	1309	125	P	-t	-1.3168	0.4218	70.2S	102.4E	0	145		
1434	120	2106 May 03	18:19:20	134	1315	130	T	-p	0.4681	1.0472	43.1N	102.6W	62	164	178	03m47s
1435	120	2106 Oct 26	22:37:40	134	1321	135	A	-p	-0.5671	0.9725	45.9S	174.5W	55	20	119	02m32s
1436	120	2107 Apr 23	06:18:41	135	1327	140	A	nn	-0.2829	0.9918	3.6S	89.6E	74	346	30	00m56s
1437	120	2107 Oct 16	09:18:27	135	1333	145	T	n-	0.1778	1.0332	1.1N	40.2E	80	196	114	03m16s
1438	120	2108 Apr 11	10:55:37	136	1339	150	P	t-	-1.0573	0.8620	71.7S	80.2E	0	298		
1439	120	2108 Oct 05	01:01:20	136	1345	155	T	p-	0.8722	1.0551	52.5N	172.3W	29	209	371	03m50s
1440	120	2109 Mar 01	17:45:53	137	1350	122	P	-t	1.1972	0.6238	71.8N	149.5W	0	114		

Cat Num	Canon Plate	Calendar Date	TD of Greatest Eclipse	ΔT s	Luna Num	Saros Num	Ecl Type	QLE	Gamma	Ecl Mag	Lat °	Long °	Sun Alt °	Sun Azm °	Central Path Width km	Line Dur
1441	121	2109 Aug 26	07:57:26	137	1356	127	P	-t	-1.0178	0.9670	71.4S	4.8E	0	56		
1442	121	2110 Feb 18	23:31:35	138	1362	132	A	-n	0.4438	0.9888	14.1N	175.6W	64	165	44	01m12s
1443	121	2110 Aug 15	16:50:45	138	1368	137	A	-p	-0.2819	0.9746	2.0S	74.7W	74	13	94	03m07s
1444	121	2111 Feb 08	12:05:33	139	1374	142	T	n-	-0.2650	1.0374	30.2S	6.5E	74	346	130	03m17s
1445	121	2111 Aug 04	19:00:22	140	1380	147	A	p-	0.4867	0.9455	46.0N	95.7W	61	194	230	05m42s
1446	121	2112 Jan 29	03:49:52	140	1386	152	T	p-	-0.9292	1.0346	80.6S	164.2W	21	287	322	01m56s
1447	121	2112 Jun 24	07:09:53	141	1391	119	Pe	-t	-1.5356	0.0282	66.3S	84.0E	0	351		
1448	121	2112 Jul 23	19:58:32	141	1392	157	P	t-	1.2284	0.5725	69.0N	42.7E	0	341		
1449	121	2112 Dec 19	04:33:16	141	1397	124	P	-t	1.1648	0.6858	65.7N	128.1E	0	195		
1450	121	2113 Jun 13	17:26:00	142	1403	129	T	-p	-0.7097	1.0367	21.7S	74.2W	45	351	174	03m36s
1451	121	2113 Dec 08	09:03:27	142	1409	134	A	-p	0.5049	0.9296	7.1N	48.5E	60	191	304	09m35s
1452	121	2114 Jun 03	09:14:09	143	1415	139	T	nn	0.0525	1.0766	25.4N	40.9E	87	167	248	06m32s
1453	122	2114 Nov 27	08:24:15	143	1421	144	A	nn	-0.1815	0.9223	31.3S	48.0E	79	17	298	09m14s
1454	122	2115 May 24	02:13:56	144	1427	149	T	p-	0.7912	1.0557	67.8N	109.0E	37	134	301	03m24s
1455	122	2115 Nov 16	09:58:55	144	1433	154	A	p-	-0.8664	0.9503	68.7S	28.2W	30	63	365	03m32s
1456	122	2116 Apr 13	03:36:55	145	1438	121	P	-t	-1.1487	0.7138	61.3S	160.6W	0	289		
1457	122	2116 Oct 06	08:31:51	145	1444	126	P	-t	1.1589	0.7105	61.2N	130.0E	0	259		
1458	122	2116 Nov 04	18:50:09	146	1445	164	P	t-	-1.5102	0.0613	62.3S	131.9E	0	125		
1459	122	2117 Apr 02	06:15:20	146	1450	131	A	-p	-0.4459	0.9333	18.4S	100.7E	63	330	274	07m30s
1460	122	2117 Sep 26	00:55:42	147	1456	136	T	-p	0.4442	1.0645	21.9N	178.0E	64	211	233	05m03s
1461	122	2118 Mar 22	06:00:55	147	1462	141	A	n-	0.2719	0.9382	14.3N	84.3E	74	150	237	06m50s
1462	122	2118 Sep 15	16:28:26	148	1468	146	T	n-	-0.2823	1.0349	11.5S	75.7W	74	29	122	03m04s
1463	122	2119 Mar 11	10:19:19	148	1474	151	A	t-	0.9693	0.9694	56.7N	29.6W	14	120	451	02m13s
1464	122	2119 Sep 05	02:44:27	149	1480	156	P	t-	-1.0766	0.8431	61.2S	62.3E	0	75		
1465	123	2120 Jan 30	11:09:56	149	1485	123	P	-t	-1.0792	0.8594	62.7S	144.8E	0	228		
1466	123	2120 Jul 25	14:40:02	150	1491	128	An	-t	0.9948	0.9343	66.0N	90.0E	4	312	-	04m00s
1467	123	2121 Jan 19	02:54:15	151	1497	133	T	-n	-0.4190	1.0371	43.9S	149.7E	65	337	137	02m52s
1468	123	2121 Jul 14	16:42:38	151	1503	138	A	nn	0.2125	0.9758	33.6N	64.7W	78	197	88	02m32s
1469	123	2122 Jan 08	15:48:51	152	1509	143	A	n-	0.2713	0.9907	6.9S	58.6W	74	168	34	01m02s
1470	123	2122 Jul 04	01:25:31	152	1515	148	T	p-	-0.5649	1.0280	11.0S	154.2E	56	10	114	02m56s
1471	123	2122 Dec 28	22:00:56	153	1521	153	A+	p-	1.0072	0.9451	65.3N	170.2W	0	161	-	-
1472	123	2123 May 25	09:33:27	153	1526	120	P	-t	1.2325	0.5729	68.5N	128.7W	0	14		
1473	123	2123 Jun 23	16:26:12	153	1527	158	P	t-	-1.2763	0.4882	65.8S	80.8W	0	14		
1474	123	2123 Nov 18	03:07:26	154	1532	125	P	-t	-1.3389	0.3848	69.3S	25.9W	0	157		
1475	123	2124 May 14	01:59:10	155	1538	130	T	-p	0.5286	1.0464	50.3N	142.7E	58	167	182	03m34s
1476	123	2124 Nov 06	06:36:34	155	1544	135	A	-p	-0.5921	0.9724	51.6S	66.4E	53	18	123	02m26s
1477	124	2125 May 03	13:42:33	156	1550	140	A	nn	-0.2263	0.9915	3.0N	23.1W	77	349	31	00m59s
1478	124	2125 Oct 26	17:30:49	156	1556	145	T	n-	0.1461	1.0329	4.5S	84.0W	82	194	112	03m15s
1479	124	2126 Apr 22	18:04:22	157	1562	150	A-	t-	-1.0051	0.9514	71.1S	40.5W	0	311	-	-
1480	124	2126 Oct 16	09:12:51	158	1568	155	T	p-	0.8345	1.0534	45.3N	58.1E	33	203	319	04m00s
1481	124	2127 Mar 13	01:32:03	158	1573	122	P	-t	1.2208	0.5841	72.1N	80.0E	0	100		
1482	124	2127 Sep 06	15:24:16	159	1579	127	P	-t	-1.0822	0.8458	71.9S	120.6W	0	69		
1483	124	2128 Mar 01	07:48:32	159	1585	132	A	-n	0.4596	0.9940	18.9N	58.6E	63	163	24	00m37s
1484	124	2128 Aug 25	23:44:34	160	1591	137	A	-p	-0.3562	0.9694	9.8S	179.5E	69	15	117	03m41s
1485	124	2129 Feb 18	20:44:37	161	1597	142	T	n-	-0.2526	1.0411	25.6S	122.9W	75	344	142	03m38s
1486	124	2129 Aug 15	01:33:05	161	1603	147	A	p-	0.4055	0.9442	37.4N	165.3E	66	196	225	06m15s
1487	124	2130 Feb 08	12:35:23	162	1609	152	T	p-	-0.9212	1.0356	75.9S	51.3E	22	300	313	02m03s
1488	124	2130 Aug 04	02:38:44	162	1615	157	P	t-	1.1460	0.7158	69.9N	69.2W	0	330		
1489	125	2130 Dec 30	13:01:34	163	1620	124	P	-t	1.1730	0.6708	66.8N	9.3W	0	185		
1490	125	2131 Jun 25	00:43:16	164	1626	129	T	-p	-0.7813	1.0393	28.1S	174.3E	38	356	211	03m43s
1491	125	2131 Dec 19	17:06:50	164	1632	134	A	-p	0.5165	0.9267	7.6N	73.2W	59	186	321	10m14s
1492	125	2132 Jun 13	16:46:24	165	1638	139	Tm	nn	-0.0186	1.0788	22.3N	70.6W	89	350	255	06m55s
1493	125	2132 Dec 07	16:18:43	165	1644	144	A	nn	-0.1661	0.9215	32.2S	68.4W	80	13	301	09m33s
1494	125	2133 Jun 03	09:45:16	166	1650	149	T	p-	0.7247	1.0567	66.6N	10.2E	43	149	272	03m36s
1495	125	2133 Nov 26	18:05:55	167	1656	154	A	p-	-0.8473	0.9513	72.0S	144.0W	32	57	337	03m27s
1496	125	2134 Apr 24	10:59:59	167	1661	121	P	-t	-1.2052	0.6147	61.8S	80.0E	0	298		
1497	125	2134 May 23	23:01:18	167	1662	159	Pb	t-	1.5285	0.0309	63.7N	54.8E	0	37		
1498	125	2134 Oct 17	16:40:42	168	1667	126	P	-t	1.1931	0.6458	61.5N	0.9W	0	250		
1499	125	2134 Nov 16	03:12:08	168	1668	164	P	t-	-1.4857	0.1060	63.0S	2.6W	0	135		
1500	125	2135 Apr 13	13:27:05	168	1673	131	A	-p	-0.4973	0.9349	17.6S	7.0W	60	332	274	07m30s

Cat Num	Canon Plate	Calendar Date	TD of Greatest Eclipse	ΔT s	Luna Num	Saros Num	Ecl Type	QLE	Gamma	Ecl Mag	Lat °	Long °	Sun Alt °	Sun Azm °	Path Width km	Central Line Dur
1501	126	2135 Oct 07	09:00:03	169	1679	136	T	-p	0.4884	1.0603	20.3N	57.1E	61	210	224	04m50s
1502	126	2136 Apr 01	13:26:19	170	1685	141	A	nn	0.2295	0.9430	16.5N	26.5W	77	150	216	06m14s
1503	126	2136 Sep 26	00:12:14	170	1691	146	T	n-	-0.2309	1.0292	13.0S	168.9E	77	30	101	02m34s
1504	126	2137 Mar 21	18:16:38	171	1697	151	A	t-	0.9369	0.9769	55.6N	145.3W	20	121	233	01m40s
1505	126	2137 Sep 15	09:56:34	172	1703	156	P	t-	-1.0184	0.9436	61.0S	54.3W	0	84		
1506	126	2138 Feb 09	19:55:23	172	1708	123	P	-t	-1.0872	0.8453	62.1S	4.6E	0	238		
1507	126	2138 Aug 05	21:08:57	173	1714	128	P	-t	1.0781	0.8285	62.4N	9.8W	0	309		
1508	126	2139 Jan 30	11:42:25	174	1720	133	T	-n	-0.4255	1.0364	41.0S	20.1E	65	333	135	02m49s
1509	126	2139 Jul 25	23:26:33	174	1726	138	A	nn	0.2946	0.9778	35.8N	162.5W	73	202	83	02m13s
1510	126	2140 Jan 20	00:23:11	175	1732	143	A	n-	0.2676	0.9882	5.5S	172.9E	75	163	43	01m17s
1511	126	2140 Jul 14	08:36:11	175	1738	148	T	p-	-0.4861	1.0322	6.7S	45.9E	61	14	124	03m18s
1512	126	2141 Jan 08	06:12:38	176	1744	153	A+	p-	1.0024	0.9522	64.3N	57.2E	0	151	–	–
1513	127	2141 Jun 04	17:09:59	177	1749	120	P	-t	1.2981	0.4458	67.5N	106.1E	0	3		
1514	127	2141 Jul 03	23:53:38	177	1750	158	P	t-	-1.2029	0.6305	64.9S	157.5E	0	24		
1515	127	2141 Nov 28	10:59:33	177	1755	125	P	-t	-1.3552	0.3577	68.2S	155.5W	0	169		
1516	127	2142 May 25	09:32:37	178	1761	130	T	-p	0.5938	1.0449	57.4N	31.3E	53	171	187	03m17s
1517	127	2142 Nov 17	14:43:08	179	1767	135	A	-p	-0.6117	0.9727	56.4S	52.9W	52	14	124	02m19s
1518	127	2143 May 14	20:58:14	179	1773	140	Am	nn	-0.1638	0.9908	9.4N	133.2W	81	352	33	01m05s
1519	127	2143 Nov 07	01:51:16	180	1779	145	T	n-	0.1206	1.0326	9.4S	150.2E	83	191	111	03m14s
1520	127	2144 May 03	01:02:06	181	1785	150	A	t-	-0.9441	0.9363	53.6S	176.4W	19	341	727	06m09s
1521	127	2144 Oct 26	17:32:40	181	1791	155	T	p-	0.8037	1.0512	39.2N	71.7W	36	198	284	04m05s
1522	127	2145 Mar 23	09:09:38	182	1796	122	P	-t	1.2520	0.5311	72.1N	48.5W	0	86		
1523	127	2145 Sep 16	22:57:10	183	1802	127	P	-t	-1.1406	0.7368	72.1S	112.3E	0	83		
1524	127	2145 Oct 16	09:11:28	183	1803	165	Pb	t-	1.5190	0.0360	71.4N	101.1E	0	241		
1525	128	2146 Mar 12	15:58:15	183	1808	132	A	-p	0.4821	0.9995	24.4N	65.6W	61	161	2	00m03s
1526	128	2146 Sep 06	06:44:00	184	1814	137	A	-p	-0.4249	0.9640	17.8S	72.0E	65	18	143	04m13s
1527	128	2147 Mar 02	05:18:54	185	1820	142	T	n-	-0.2359	1.0452	20.5S	108.2E	76	343	155	04m02s
1528	128	2147 Aug 26	08:09:15	185	1826	147	A	pn	0.3271	0.9425	29.0N	64.7E	71	197	224	06m49s
1529	128	2148 Feb 19	21:18:00	186	1832	152	T	p-	-0.9111	1.0370	70.9S	88.9W	24	309	305	02m13s
1530	128	2148 Aug 14	09:22:21	187	1838	157	P	t-	1.0654	0.8563	70.7N	177.5E	0	318		
1531	128	2149 Jan 09	21:30:38	187	1843	124	P	-t	1.1802	0.6575	67.9N	147.3W	0	173		
1532	128	2149 Jul 05	07:59:34	188	1849	129	T	-p	-0.8544	1.0408	36.3S	61.8E	31	0	264	03m38s
1533	128	2149 Dec 30	01:13:04	189	1855	134	A	-p	0.5253	0.9245	8.6N	164.2E	58	182	334	10m42s
1534	128	2150 Jun 25	00:17:25	189	1861	139	T	nn	-0.0911	1.0802	18.3N	177.5E	85	356	260	07m14s
1535	128	2150 Dec 19	00:17:02	190	1867	144	A	nn	-0.1535	0.9211	32.3S	174.4E	81	8	302	09m46s
1536	128	2151 Jun 14	17:13:45	191	1873	149	T	p-	0.6561	1.0569	63.7N	90.0W	49	163	249	03m48s
1537	129	2151 Dec 08	02:18:31	191	1879	154	A	p-	-0.8320	0.9526	75.1S	102.6E	33	47	314	03m22s
1538	129	2152 May 04	18:14:02	192	1884	121	P	-t	-1.2680	0.5044	62.3S	37.4W	0	307		
1539	129	2152 Jun 03	06:11:19	192	1885	159	P	t-	1.4644	0.1479	64.5N	62.1W	0	28		
1540	129	2152 Oct 28	00:57:34	193	1890	126	P	-t	1.2213	0.5926	61.9N	133.8W	0	241		
1541	129	2152 Nov 26	11:41:08	193	1891	164	P	t-	-1.4665	0.1409	63.8S	139.0W	0	144		
1542	129	2153 Apr 23	20:29:24	193	1896	131	A	-p	-0.5557	0.9364	17.9S	112.4W	56	334	279	07m31s
1543	129	2153 Oct 17	17:12:17	194	1902	136	T	-p	0.5259	1.0560	18.8N	66.3W	58	208	214	04m36s
1544	129	2154 Apr 12	20:43:01	195	1908	141	A	nn	0.1794	0.9478	18.2N	134.8W	80	152	195	05m42s
1545	129	2154 Oct 07	08:03:50	196	1914	146	T	nn	-0.1867	1.0234	15.1S	51.5E	79	29	81	02m05s
1546	129	2155 Apr 02	02:06:34	196	1920	151	A	t-	0.8975	0.9844	55.6N	100.7E	26	123	123	01m07s
1547	129	2155 Sep 26	17:14:27	197	1926	156	A	t-	-0.9654	0.9593	58.6S	143.6W	15	68	569	02m55s
1548	129	2156 Feb 21	04:36:02	198	1931	123	P	-t	-1.0995	0.8230	61.6S	134.3W	0	247		
1549	130	2156 Aug 16	03:41:28	198	1937	128	P	-t	1.1584	0.6912	61.9N	116.7W	0	300		
1550	130	2157 Feb 09	20:25:36	199	1943	133	T	-p	-0.4358	1.0362	37.7S	109.0W	64	330	135	02m49s
1551	130	2157 Aug 05	06:14:19	200	1949	138	A	-p	0.3743	0.9792	37.1N	99.0E	68	207	80	01m59s
1552	130	2158 Jan 30	08:54:37	201	1955	143	A	n-	0.2619	0.9863	3.4S	44.9E	75	160	50	01m27s
1553	130	2158 Jul 25	15:49:17	201	1961	148	T	p-	-0.4086	1.0356	3.4S	62.4W	66	18	131	03m32s
1554	130	2159 Jan 19	14:23:26	202	1967	153	A+	p-	0.9974	0.9600	63.4N	74.8W	0	141	–	–
1555	130	2159 Jun 16	00:42:43	203	1972	120	P	-t	1.3668	0.3124	66.5N	17.6W	0	353		
1556	130	2159 Jul 15	07:20:50	203	1973	158	P	t-	-1.1288	0.7743	64.0S	36.1E	0	33		
1557	130	2159 Dec 09	18:58:33	203	1978	125	P	-t	-1.3664	0.3392	67.2S	73.8E	0	180		
1558	130	2160 Jun 04	16:58:36	204	1984	130	T	-p	0.6645	1.0428	64.5N	75.5W	48	178	192	02m58s
1559	130	2160 Nov 27	22:58:32	205	1990	135	A	-p	-0.6247	0.9734	60.1S	172.2W	51	8	123	02m11s
1560	130	2161 May 25	04:05:43	206	1996	140	A	nn	-0.0950	0.9898	15.7N	119.2E	85	355	36	01m12s

Cat Num	Canon Plate	Calendar Date	TD of Greatest Eclipse	ΔT s	Luna Num	Saros Num	Ecl Type	QLE	Gamma	Ecl Mag	Lat °	Long °	Sun Alt °	Sun Azm °	Path Width km	Central Line Dur
1561	131	2161 Nov 17	10:19:30	206	2002	145	T	n-	0.1012	1.0325	13.4S	23.0E	84	188	110	03m13s
1562	131	2162 May 14	07:52:46	207	2008	150	A	p-	-0.8775	0.9396	42.3S	72.2E	28	349	467	06m37s
1563	131	2162 Nov 07	01:59:40	208	2014	155	T	p-	0.7788	1.0489	34.1N	157.6E	39	193	258	04m05s
1564	131	2163 Apr 03	16:41:51	208	2019	122	P	-t	1.2876	0.4698	71.9N	175.6W	0	72		
1565	131	2163 Sep 28	06:34:34	209	2025	127	P	-t	-1.1943	0.6377	72.1S	16.2W	0	96		
1566	131	2163 Oct 27	17:20:52	209	2026	165	P	t-	1.4919	0.0889	70.8N	34.5W	0	227		
1567	131	2164 Mar 23	00:02:47	210	2031	132	H	-p	0.5096	1.0051	30.4N	171.4E	59	159	20	00m29s
1568	131	2164 Sep 16	13:48:20	211	2037	137	A	-p	-0.4885	0.9583	25.7S	36.9W	61	19	172	04m42s
1569	131	2165 Mar 12	13:45:50	211	2043	142	T	n-	-0.2130	1.0495	14.9S	19.4W	78	342	168	04m27s
1570	131	2165 Sep 05	14:52:45	212	2049	147	A	nn	0.2549	0.9406	20.7N	38.1W	75	198	227	07m22s
1571	131	2166 Mar 02	05:53:21	213	2055	152	T	p-	-0.8957	1.0388	65.4S	133.8E	26	317	294	02m26s
1572	131	2166 Aug 25	16:13:35	214	2061	157	An	t-	0.9900	0.9531	74.4N	40.9E	7	285	-	03m00s
1573	132	2167 Jan 21	05:56:25	214	2066	124	P	-t	1.1892	0.6414	68.9N	74.9E	0	162		
1574	132	2167 Jul 16	15:17:48	215	2072	129	T	-t	-0.9262	1.0410	46.8S	53.0W	22	6	368	03m19s
1575	132	2168 Jan 10	09:19:03	216	2078	134	A	-p	0.5337	0.9230	10.3N	41.5E	58	178	344	10m55s
1576	132	2168 Jul 05	07:45:23	217	2084	139	T	-n	-0.1660	1.0807	13.2N	65.8E	81	0	264	07m26s
1577	132	2168 Dec 29	08:19:32	217	2090	144	A	nn	-0.1444	0.9215	31.6S	56.1E	82	2	300	09m52s
1578	132	2169 Jun 25	00:37:09	218	2096	149	T	p-	0.5841	1.0562	59.2N	167.9E	54	173	229	03m58s
1579	132	2169 Dec 18	10:37:07	219	2102	154	A	p-	-0.8213	0.9544	77.3S	6.7W	34	31	295	03m15s
1580	132	2170 May 16	01:18:33	219	2107	121	P	-t	-1.3371	0.3831	63.0S	152.5W	0	316		
1581	132	2170 Jun 14	13:15:10	220	2108	159	P	t-	1.3963	0.2719	65.4N	177.8W	0	18		
1582	132	2170 Nov 08	09:23:07	220	2113	126	P	-t	1.2426	0.5524	62.5N	90.9E	0	232		
1583	132	2170 Dec 07	20:17:08	220	2114	164	P	t-	-1.4530	0.1654	64.7S	82.5E	0	154		
1584	132	2171 May 05	03:23:15	221	2119	131	A	-p	-0.6209	0.9378	19.4S	144.2E	51	337	289	07m32s
1585	133	2171 Oct 29	01:31:03	222	2125	136	T	-p	0.5577	1.0516	17.6N	168.4E	56	206	203	04m23s
1586	133	2172 Apr 23	03:53:15	223	2131	141	A	nn	0.1234	0.9528	19.2N	119.0E	83	154	174	05m11s
1587	133	2172 Oct 17	16:01:36	223	2137	146	H3	nn	-0.1484	1.0174	17.3S	67.2W	81	28	60	01m34s
1588	133	2173 Apr 12	09:49:40	224	2143	151	A	p-	0.8515	0.9919	56.2N	11.0W	31	126	53	00m34s
1589	133	2173 Oct 07	00:39:14	225	2149	156	A	p-	-0.9187	0.9558	57.8S	113.3E	23	62	402	03m17s
1590	133	2174 Mar 03	13:11:54	226	2154	123	P	-t	-1.1162	0.7924	61.3S	88.1E	0	256		
1591	133	2174 Apr 01	22:39:09	226	2155	161	Pb	t-	1.5106	0.0471	61.2N	103.2E	0	80		
1592	133	2174 Aug 27	10:19:55	226	2160	128	P	-t	1.2336	0.5630	61.4N	135.0E	0	291		
1593	133	2175 Feb 21	05:04:24	227	2166	133	T	-p	-0.4495	1.0362	34.2S	122.3E	63	328	135	02m50s
1594	133	2175 Aug 16	13:08:17	228	2172	138	A	-p	0.4497	0.9802	37.6N	1.2W	63	211	78	01m50s
1595	133	2176 Feb 10	17:21:21	229	2178	143	A	n-	0.2532	0.9849	0.9S	81.9W	75	156	55	01m34s
1596	133	2176 Aug 04	23:05:55	230	2184	148	T	p-	-0.3332	1.0383	1.3S	171.2W	71	21	136	03m40s
1597	134	2177 Jan 29	22:30:30	230	2190	153	An	p-	0.9897	0.9212	57.6N	164.5E	7	140	-	06m55s
1598	134	2177 Jun 26	08:13:27	231	2195	120	P	-t	1.4371	0.1758	65.5N	140.4W	0	343		
1599	134	2177 Jul 25	14:50:33	231	2196	158	P	t-	-1.0564	0.9150	63.2S	85.7W	0	43		
1600	134	2177 Dec 20	03:01:35	232	2201	125	P	-t	-1.3748	0.3251	66.1S	57.4W	0	191		
1601	134	2178 Jun 16	00:20:42	233	2207	130	T	-p	0.7379	1.0396	71.0N	175.9W	42	190	198	02m36s
1602	134	2178 Dec 09	07:20:02	233	2213	135	A	-p	-0.6338	0.9745	62.4S	69.3E	50	360	118	02m03s
1603	134	2179 Jun 05	11:05:36	234	2219	140	A	nn	-0.0209	0.9884	21.5N	14.3E	89	359	41	01m21s
1604	134	2179 Nov 28	18:54:18	235	2225	145	T	n-	0.0867	1.0325	16.5S	105.3W	85	184	110	03m12s
1605	134	2180 May 24	14:34:27	236	2231	150	A	p-	-0.8035	0.9422	32.6S	33.6W	36	354	359	06m59s
1606	134	2180 Nov 17	10:34:01	237	2237	155	T	p-	0.7605	1.0465	30.1N	25.8E	40	189	238	04m03s
1607	134	2181 Apr 14	00:04:05	237	2242	122	P	-t	1.3318	0.3931	71.5N	60.2E	0	59		
1608	134	2181 May 13	14:55:43	237	2243	160	Pb	t-	-1.5322	0.0511	69.4S	17.6W	0	335		
1609	135	2181 Oct 08	14:19:36	238	2248	127	P	-t	-1.2408	0.5529	71.9S	146.4W	0	110		
1610	135	2181 Nov 07	01:38:23	238	2249	165	P	t-	1.4718	0.1281	70.0N	171.6W	0	214		
1611	135	2182 Apr 03	07:59:43	239	2254	132	H	-p	0.5440	1.0108	36.9N	50.3E	57	159	44	00m58s
1612	135	2182 Sep 27	20:58:45	240	2260	137	A	-p	-0.5462	0.9527	33.5S	147.4W	57	21	205	05m05s
1613	135	2183 Mar 23	22:06:49	241	2266	142	T	n-	-0.1848	1.0540	8.9S	145.9W	79	342	181	04m54s
1614	135	2183 Sep 16	21:42:37	241	2272	147	A	nn	0.1877	0.9384	12.8N	142.6W	79	198	233	07m53s
1615	135	2184 Mar 12	14:22:32	242	2278	152	T	p-	-0.8755	1.0409	59.4S	0.9W	29	324	283	02m43s
1616	135	2184 Sep 04	23:11:00	243	2284	157	A	t-	0.9185	0.9576	67.1N	124.0W	23	227	393	03m12s
1617	135	2185 Jan 31	14:20:20	244	2289	124	P	-t	1.1992	0.6238	69.9N	63.1W	0	149		
1618	135	2185 Jul 26	22:38:16	245	2295	129	Ts	-t	-0.9967	1.0370	67.9S	179.2W	1	21	-	02m27s
1619	135	2186 Jan 20	17:23:44	245	2301	134	A	-p	0.5426	0.9221	12.8N	81.0W	57	174	350	10m53s
1620	135	2186 Jul 16	15:14:54	246	2307	139	T	-n	-0.2396	1.0805	7.4N	47.2W	76	4	267	07m29s

Cat Num	Canon Plate	Calendar Date	TD of Greatest Eclipse	ΔT s	Luna Num	Saros Num	Ecl Type	QLE	Gamma	Ecl Mag	Lat °	Long °	Sun Alt °	Sun Azm °	Path Width km	Central Line Dur
1621	136	2187 Jan 09	16:23:41	247	2313	144	A	nn	-0.1365	0.9224	30.0S	62.8W	82	358	296	09m51s
1622	136	2187 Jul 06	07:58:31	248	2319	149	T	p-	0.5109	1.0548	53.6N	63.2E	59	181	211	04m06s
1623	136	2187 Dec 29	18:59:03	249	2325	154	A	p-	-0.8126	0.9565	77.7S	111.9W	35	10	274	03m07s
1624	136	2188 May 26	08:15:53	249	2330	121	P	-t	-1.4109	0.2538	63.8S	94.0E	0	325		
1625	136	2188 Jun 24	20:14:38	250	2331	159	P	t-	1.3252	0.4008	66.4N	67.3E	0	8		
1626	136	2188 Nov 18	17:55:24	250	2336	126	P	-t	1.2591	0.5212	63.2N	46.2W	0	222		
1627	136	2188 Dec 18	04:56:59	250	2337	164	P	t-	-1.4420	0.1850	65.7S	57.3W	0	165		
1628	136	2189 May 15	10:08:34	251	2342	131	A	-p	-0.6928	0.9387	22.6S	42.6E	46	340	309	07m31s
1629	136	2189 Nov 08	09:57:28	252	2348	136	T	-p	0.5831	1.0474	16.5N	40.9E	54	202	192	04m10s
1630	136	2190 May 04	10:56:30	253	2354	141	A	nn	0.0608	0.9577	19.4N	14.7E	86	157	154	04m45s
1631	136	2190 Oct 29	00:05:50	254	2360	146	H	nn	-0.1160	1.0116	19.6S	172.5E	83	25	40	01m04s
1632	136	2191 Apr 23	17:26:06	255	2366	151	A	p-	0.7991	0.9993	57.0N	119.9W	37	130	4	00m03s
1633	137	2191 Oct 18	08:11:12	255	2372	156	A	p-	-0.8783	0.9516	58.7S	4.5E	28	59	365	03m39s
1634	137	2192 Mar 13	21:40:00	256	2377	123	P	-t	-1.1395	0.7490	61.1S	47.5W	0	265		
1635	137	2192 Apr 12	06:41:56	256	2378	161	P	t-	1.4678	0.1261	61.5N	26.1W	0	71		
1636	137	2192 Sep 06	17:05:08	257	2383	128	P	-t	1.3032	0.4444	61.2N	25.1E	0	282		
1637	137	2193 Mar 03	13:36:08	258	2389	133	T	-p	-0.4689	1.0365	30.9S	5.1W	62	327	137	02m53s
1638	137	2193 Aug 26	20:09:19	259	2395	138	A	-p	0.5200	0.9806	37.4N	103.6W	58	214	80	01m45s
1639	137	2194 Feb 21	01:41:31	260	2401	143	A	n-	-0.2396	0.9840	1.9N	152.8E	76	154	58	01m38s
1640	137	2194 Aug 16	06:28:08	260	2407	148	T	n-	-0.2616	1.0403	0.2S	78.9E	75	24	139	03m44s
1641	137	2195 Feb 10	06:34:27	261	2413	153	An	p-	0.9797	0.9218	55.2N	40.9E	11	136	-	06m52s
1642	137	2195 Jul 07	15:41:21	262	2418	120	Pe	-t	1.5095	0.0354	64.6N	97.8E	0	333		
1643	137	2195 Aug 05	22:21:03	262	2419	158	Ts	t-	-0.9843	1.0618	56.1S	165.7E	9	40	-	04m03s
1644	137	2195 Dec 31	11:09:22	263	2424	125	P	-t	-1.3797	0.3166	65.1S	170.7E	0	202		
1645	138	2196 Jun 26	07:37:40	264	2430	130	T	-p	0.8149	1.0356	76.3N	96.3E	35	213	208	02m12s
1646	138	2196 Dec 19	15:47:09	265	2436	135	A	-p	-0.6387	0.9762	63.1S	49.3W	50	350	111	01m53s
1647	138	2197 Jun 15	17:59:33	266	2442	140	A	nn	0.0574	0.9864	26.8N	88.3W	87	184	48	01m32s
1648	138	2197 Dec 09	03:35:07	266	2448	145	T	n-	0.0768	1.0329	18.5S	125.3E	86	180	111	03m13s
1649	138	2198 Jun 04	21:11:35	267	2454	150	A	p-	-0.7259	0.9443	24.2S	136.4W	43	359	299	07m13s
1650	138	2198 Nov 28	19:12:46	268	2460	155	T	p-	0.7459	1.0442	26.9N	106.7W	42	184	221	03m58s
1651	138	2199 Apr 25	07:21:51	269	2465	122	P	-t	1.3799	0.3085	70.8N	62.4W	0	46		
1652	138	2199 May 24	21:42:07	269	2466	160	P	t-	-1.4596	0.1743	68.5S	130.8W	0	347		
1653	138	2199 Oct 19	22:10:26	270	2471	127	P	-t	-1.2817	0.4790	71.4S	82.2E	0	124		
1654	138	2199 Nov 18	10:01:01	270	2472	165	P	t-	1.4563	0.1584	69.1N	50.6E	0	202		
1655	138	2200 Apr 14	15:49:57	271	2477	132	T	-p	0.5847	1.0165	43.8N	69.1W	54	158	69	01m23s
1656	138	2200 Oct 09	04:16:21	272	2483	137	A	-p	-0.5972	0.9470	41.1S	100.6E	53	22	241	05m25s
1657	139	2201 Apr 04	06:19:56	272	2489	142	T	n-	-0.1495	1.0584	2.7S	89.5E	81	343	194	05m20s
1658	139	2201 Sep 28	04:41:51	273	2495	147	A	nn	0.1281	0.9361	5.2N	110.6E	83	198	240	08m21s
1659	139	2202 Mar 24	22:42:58	274	2501	152	T	p-	-0.8441	1.0431	52.9S	132.6W	32	330	271	03m03s
1660	139	2202 Sep 17	06:18:53	275	2507	157	A	-t	0.8545	0.9597	57.1N	113.5E	31	214	281	03m24s
1661	139	2203 Feb 12	22:38:35	276	2512	124	P	-t	1.2128	0.5998	70.8N	159.7E	0	136		
1662	139	2203 Aug 08	06:01:56	277	2518	129	P	-t	-1.0650	0.8897	70.1S	56.3E	0	34		
1663	139	2203 Sep 06	14:50:22	277	2519	167	Pb	t-	1.5374	0.0068	71.8N	68.7E	0	291		
1664	139	2204 Feb 02	01:25:25	278	2524	134	A	-p	0.5535	0.9218	16.0N	157.1E	56	170	353	10m38s
1665	139	2204 Jul 27	22:44:32	279	2530	139	T	-n	-0.3129	1.0793	1.0N	160.8W	72	8	269	07m22s
1666	139	2205 Jan 21	00:27:32	280	2536	144	A	nn	-0.1281	0.9241	27.5S	177.9E	82	353	289	09m42s
1667	139	2205 Jul 17	15:18:00	280	2542	149	T	p-	0.4366	1.0525	47.2N	43.7W	64	186	193	04m10s
1668	139	2206 Jan 10	03:24:08	281	2548	154	A	p-	-0.8060	0.9593	75.9S	139.7E	36	351	252	02m57s
1669	140	2206 Jun 07	15:05:59	282	2553	121	Pe	-t	-1.4894	0.1166	64.7S	18.1W	0	335		
1670	140	2206 Jul 07	03:10:26	282	2554	159	P	t-	1.2516	0.5335	67.4N	47.1W	0	358		
1671	140	2206 Dec 01	02:33:55	283	2559	126	P	-t	1.2711	0.4985	64.1N	174.9E	0	212		
1672	140	2206 Dec 30	13:40:30	283	2560	164	P	t-	-1.4337	0.1997	66.8S	161.6E	0	175		
1673	140	2207 May 27	16:47:47	284	2565	131	A	-p	-0.7693	0.9393	27.5S	57.7W	40	343	347	07m25s
1674	140	2207 Nov 20	18:30:26	285	2571	136	T	-p	0.6028	1.0434	15.8N	88.5W	53	198	180	03m56s
1675	140	2208 May 15	17:53:06	286	2577	141	A	nn	-0.0080	0.9625	18.7N	87.8W	90	334	136	04m19s
1676	140	2208 Nov 09	08:17:12	287	2583	146	H	nn	-0.0905	1.0059	21.8S	50.7E	85	22	20	00m34s
1677	140	2209 May 05	00:56:53	288	2589	151	H	p-	0.7413	1.0066	57.7N	133.7E	42	136	34	00m28s
1678	140	2209 Oct 29	15:50:20	289	2595	156	A	p-	-0.8445	0.9472	60.7S	107.0W	32	56	358	04m02s
1679	140	2210 Mar 26	06:01:57	289	2600	123	P	-t	-1.1680	0.6954	61.1S	178.5E	0	274		
1680	140	2210 Apr 24	14:39:19	289	2601	161	P	t-	1.4202	0.2149	61.9N	154.2W	0	62		

Cat Num	Canon Plate	Calendar Date	TD of Greatest Eclipse	ΔT s	Luna Num	Saros Num	Ecl Type	QLE	Gamma	Ecl Mag	Lat °	Long °	Sun Alt °	Sun Azm °	Path Width km	Central Line Dur
1681	141	2210 Sep 18	23:59:09	290	2606	128	P	-t	1.3657	0.3384	61.0N	86.9W	0	274		
1682	141	2211 Mar 15	22:01:40	291	2612	133	T	-p	-0.4931	1.0368	27.8S	131.3W	60	327	140	02m57s
1683	141	2211 Sep 08	03:17:18	292	2618	138	A	-p	0.5855	0.9808	36.9N	151.8E	54	216	83	01m43s
1684	141	2212 Mar 04	09:55:00	293	2624	143	A	nn	0.2211	0.9834	4.9N	29.3E	77	152	60	01m40s
1685	141	2212 Aug 27	13:56:17	294	2630	148	T	n-	-0.1940	1.0416	0.1S	32.4W	79	27	142	03m45s
1686	141	2213 Feb 21	14:30:14	295	2636	153	A	p-	0.9635	0.9230	53.4N	79.4W	15	133	1080	06m44s
1687	141	2213 Aug 17	05:56:32	296	2642	158	T	t-	-0.9161	1.0653	46.0S	59.6E	23	36	525	04m35s
1688	141	2214 Jan 11	19:17:52	297	2647	125	P	-t	-1.3848	0.3078	64.1S	39.0E	0	212		
1689	141	2214 Jul 08	14:52:45	298	2653	130	T	-t	0.8925	1.0303	78.1N	27.5E	26	253	230	01m46s
1690	141	2215 Jan 01	00:16:36	298	2659	135	A	-p	-0.6427	0.9783	62.3S	168.7W	50	340	101	01m41s
1691	141	2215 Jun 28	00:48:45	299	2665	140	A	nn	0.1388	0.9839	31.4N	171.3E	82	189	58	01m44s
1692	141	2215 Dec 21	12:20:08	300	2671	145	T	n-	0.0701	1.0337	19.5S	4.9W	86	175	114	03m14s
1693	142	2216 Jun 16	03:41:04	301	2677	150	A	p-	-0.6420	0.9458	16.7S	123.8E	50	3	260	07m20s
1694	142	2216 Dec 10	03:57:51	302	2683	155	T	p-	0.7367	1.0421	24.8N	119.5E	42	180	208	03m51s
1695	142	2217 May 06	14:31:15	303	2688	122	P	-t	1.4355	0.2100	70.0N	177.7E	0	33		
1696	142	2217 Jun 05	04:22:20	303	2689	160	P	t-	-1.3806	0.3095	67.5S	118.1E	0	357		
1697	142	2217 Oct 31	06:08:54	304	2694	127	P	-t	-1.3157	0.4185	70.7S	50.6W	0	137		
1698	142	2217 Nov 29	18:29:51	304	2695	165	P	t-	1.4464	0.1783	68.1N	88.1W	0	190		
1699	142	2218 Apr 25	23:33:14	305	2700	132	T	-p	0.6321	1.0219	51.1N	173.6E	51	158	96	01m43s
1700	142	2218 Oct 20	11:41:55	306	2706	137	A	-p	-0.6411	0.9416	48.4S	12.8W	50	23	280	05m41s
1701	142	2219 Apr 15	14:26:33	307	2712	142	T	n-	-0.1086	1.0628	3.7N	33.6W	84	344	207	05m45s
1702	142	2219 Oct 09	11:48:35	308	2718	147	A	nn	0.0744	0.9338	2.0S	2.2E	86	197	248	08m46s
1703	142	2220 Apr 04	06:56:41	309	2724	152	T	p-	-0.8162	1.0454	46.2S	98.2E	35	335	260	03m26s
1704	142	2220 Sep 27	13:35:07	310	2730	157	A	p-	0.7966	0.9609	48.0N	3.6W	37	207	232	03m36s
1705	143	2221 Feb 23	06:50:48	311	2735	124	P	-t	1.2305	0.5688	71.5N	23.4E	0	123		
1706	143	2221 Aug 18	13:30:39	312	2741	129	P	-t	-1.1296	0.7673	70.9S	68.5W	0	47		
1707	143	2221 Sep 16	22:25:14	312	2742	167	P	t-	1.4775	0.1171	72.1N	58.8W	0	278		
1708	143	2222 Feb 12	09:23:17	313	2747	134	A	-p	0.5669	0.9220	20.0N	35.9E	55	166	355	10m14s
1709	143	2222 Aug 08	06:17:05	313	2753	139	T	-n	-0.3837	1.0774	6.0S	84.2E	67	11	270	07m06s
1710	143	2223 Feb 01	08:29:43	314	2759	144	A	nn	-0.1179	0.9263	24.1S	58.4E	83	349	279	09m26s
1711	143	2223 Jul 28	22:38:03	315	2765	149	T	n-	0.3636	1.0495	40.2N	152.5W	68	190	176	04m09s
1712	143	2224 Jan 21	11:48:53	316	2771	154	A	p-	-0.7984	0.9626	72.4S	24.4E	37	339	227	02m46s
1713	143	2224 Jul 17	10:03:58	317	2777	159	P	t-	1.1767	0.6678	68.4N	161.3W	0	348		
1714	143	2224 Dec 11	11:17:51	318	2782	126	P	-t	1.2791	0.4834	65.0N	34.4E	0	202		
1715	143	2225 Jan 09	22:25:24	318	2783	164	P	t-	-1.4263	0.2126	67.8S	19.6E	0	187		
1716	143	2225 Jun 06	23:21:31	319	2788	131	A	-p	-0.8497	0.9392	34.6S	157.3W	32	347	425	07m10s
1717	144	2225 Dec 01	03:08:36	320	2794	136	T	-p	0.6178	1.0398	15.4N	140.6E	52	194	169	03m43s
1718	144	2226 May 27	00:45:11	321	2800	141	A	nn	-0.0810	0.9670	16.8N	170.7E	85	344	119	03m55s
1719	144	2226 Nov 20	16:34:56	322	2806	146	Hm	nn	-0.0711	1.0005	23.7S	72.5W	86	19	2	00m03s
1720	144	2227 May 16	08:21:31	323	2812	151	T	p-	0.6774	1.0135	57.7N	30.0E	47	144	63	00m59s
1721	144	2227 Nov 09	23:36:42	324	2818	156	A	p-	-0.8171	0.9429	63.3S	139.9E	35	53	364	04m24s
1722	144	2228 Apr 05	14:15:36	325	2823	123	P	-t	-1.2036	0.6279	61.3S	46.5E	0	283		
1723	144	2228 May 04	22:28:44	325	2824	161	P	t-	1.3659	0.3174	62.4N	79.7E	0	53		
1724	144	2228 Sep 29	07:02:07	326	2829	128	P	-t	1.4212	0.2445	61.1N	158.9E	0	265		
1725	144	2228 Oct 29	00:15:43	326	2830	166	Pb	t-	-1.5410	0.0477	61.9S	57.0E	0	119		
1726	144	2229 Mar 26	06:17:34	327	2835	133	T	-p	-0.5251	1.0371	25.5S	104.7E	58	328	144	03m02s
1727	144	2229 Sep 18	10:34:51	328	2841	138	A	-p	0.6439	0.9805	36.2N	44.0E	50	217	89	01m44s
1728	144	2230 Mar 15	18:00:26	329	2847	143	A	nn	0.1964	0.9831	7.9N	92.1W	79	151	61	01m40s
1729	145	2230 Sep 07	21:30:39	330	2853	148	T	n-	-0.1308	1.0424	0.7S	145.3W	82	28	143	03m44s
1730	145	2231 Mar 04	22:20:23	331	2859	153	A	p-	0.9430	0.9246	52.4N	162.3E	19	130	838	06m32s
1731	145	2231 Aug 28	13:35:31	332	2865	158	T	p-	-0.8505	1.0661	41.4S	53.0W	31	36	402	04m43s
1732	145	2232 Jan 23	03:27:39	333	2870	125	P	-t	-1.3891	0.3001	63.3S	92.7W	0	222		
1733	145	2232 Jul 18	22:04:56	334	2876	130	T	-t	0.9717	1.0229	72.4N	34.2W	13	299	348	01m14s
1734	145	2233 Jan 11	08:49:17	335	2882	135	A	-p	-0.6447	0.9811	60.0S	69.6E	50	333	88	01m28s
1735	145	2233 Jul 08	07:35:24	336	2888	140	A	nn	0.2215	0.9809	35.1N	72.3E	77	194	70	01m59s
1736	145	2233 Dec 31	21:07:37	337	2894	145	T	n-	0.0649	1.0348	19.5S	135.5W	86	170	117	03m18s
1737	145	2234 Jun 27	10:09:34	338	2900	150	A	p-	-0.5572	0.9468	10.3S	25.3E	56	8	235	07m18s
1738	145	2234 Dec 21	12:46:02	339	2906	155	T	p-	0.7299	1.0403	23.5N	14.9W	43	175	197	03m42s
1739	145	2235 May 17	21:36:41	340	2911	122	Pe	-t	1.4946	0.1044	69.1N	59.5E	0	22		
1740	145	2235 Jun 16	11:00:35	340	2912	160	P	t-	-1.2990	0.4502	66.5S	8.0E	0	8		

Cat Num	Canon Plate	Calendar Date	TD of Greatest Eclipse	ΔT s	Luna Num	Saros Num	Ecl Type	QLE	Gamma	Ecl Mag	Lat °	Long °	Sun Alt °	Sun Azm °	Path Width km	Central Line Dur
1741	146	2235 Nov 11	14:13:08	341	2917	127	P	-t	-1.3444	0.3682	69.9S	175.8E	0	150		
1742	146	2235 Dec 11	03:02:34	341	2918	165	P	t-	1.4400	0.1914	67.1N	132.8E	0	179		
1743	146	2236 May 06	07:11:02	342	2923	132	T	-p	0.6848	1.0269	58.7N	58.1E	46	159	126	01m59s
1744	146	2236 Oct 30	19:15:14	343	2929	137	A	-p	-0.6779	0.9365	55.2S	127.2W	47	23	321	05m54s
1745	146	2237 Apr 25	22:25:03	344	2935	142	T	nn	-0.0606	1.0669	10.1N	154.5W	87	346	219	06m05s
1746	146	2237 Oct 19	19:06:03	345	2941	147	A	nn	0.0295	0.9316	8.6S	108.4W	88	196	256	09m07s
1747	146	2238 Apr 15	15:01:45	346	2947	152	T	p-	-0.7772	1.0475	39.3S	28.1W	39	340	250	03m49s
1748	146	2238 Oct 08	21:01:18	347	2953	157	A	p-	0.7459	0.9618	40.1N	120.5W	41	202	206	03m47s
1749	146	2239 Mar 06	14:54:58	348	2958	124	P	-t	1.2541	0.5278	72.0N	111.4W	0	109		
1750	146	2239 Aug 29	21:05:15	349	2964	129	P	-t	-1.1897	0.6529	71.5S	164.7E	0	60		
1751	146	2239 Sep 28	06:09:01	349	2965	167	P	t-	1.4239	0.2160	72.1N	171.2E	0	264		
1752	146	2240 Feb 23	17:14:11	350	2970	134	A	-p	0.5859	0.9228	24.7N	83.8W	54	163	356	09m41s
1753	147	2240 Aug 18	13:52:24	351	2976	139	T	-p	-0.4522	1.0746	13.3S	32.1W	63	14	270	06m40s
1754	147	2241 Feb 11	16:28:39	352	2982	144	A	nn	-0.1045	0.9292	19.9S	60.8W	84	347	267	09m04s
1755	147	2241 Aug 08	05:59:21	353	2988	149	T	n-	-0.2920	1.0457	32.9N	97.2E	73	193	159	04m02s
1756	147	2242 Jan 31	20:12:58	354	2994	154	A	p-	-0.7894	0.9665	67.9S	96.6W	38	333	197	02m31s
1757	147	2242 Jul 28	16:57:12	355	3000	159	P	t-	1.1020	0.8005	69.3N	83.9E	0	336		
1758	147	2242 Dec 22	20:06:40	356	3005	126	P	-t	1.2836	0.4750	66.0N	107.7W	0	192		
1759	147	2243 Jan 21	07:11:45	356	3006	164	P	t-	-1.4197	0.2239	68.9S	123.3W	0	198		
1760	147	2243 Jun 18	05:49:56	357	3011	131	A	-t	-0.9342	0.9380	45.6S	103.9E	20	351	652	06m41s
1761	147	2243 Dec 12	11:52:14	358	3017	136	T	-p	0.6284	1.0365	15.5N	8.2E	51	190	157	03m30s
1762	147	2244 Jun 06	07:33:12	359	3023	141	Am	nn	-0.1581	0.9712	13.8N	69.9E	81	349	105	03m31s
1763	147	2244 Dec 01	00:58:17	360	3029	146	A	nn	-0.0568	0.9955	25.1S	163.2E	87	14	16	00m27s
1764	147	2245 May 26	15:42:04	361	3035	151	T	p-	0.6089	1.0201	56.7N	72.2W	52	153	86	01m30s
1765	148	2245 Nov 20	07:29:36	362	3041	156	A	p-	-0.7954	0.9387	66.3S	26.3E	37	48	374	04m45s
1766	148	2246 Apr 16	22:23:23	363	3046	123	P	-t	-1.2445	0.5498	61.6S	84.0W	0	292		
1767	148	2246 May 16	06:14:10	363	3047	161	P	t-	1.3076	0.4285	63.1N	45.7W	0	44		
1768	148	2246 Oct 10	14:13:18	364	3052	128	P	-t	1.4705	0.1615	61.3N	42.6E	0	256		
1769	148	2246 Nov 09	07:47:02	364	3053	166	P	t-	-1.5082	0.1037	62.5S	64.6W	0	129		
1770	148	2247 Apr 06	14:26:51	365	3058	133	T	-p	-0.5624	1.0372	23.8S	17.7W	56	329	149	03m07s
1771	148	2247 Sep 29	18:01:05	366	3064	138	A	-p	0.6961	0.9801	35.6N	66.7W	46	216	96	01m47s
1772	148	2248 Mar 26	01:56:01	368	3070	143	A	nn	0.1643	0.9829	10.6N	149.3E	80	151	61	01m41s
1773	148	2248 Sep 18	05:13:07	369	3076	148	T	nn	-0.0738	1.0426	2.0S	99.8E	86	29	143	03m42s
1774	148	2249 Mar 15	06:00:45	370	3082	153	A	p-	0.9149	0.9266	52.0N	47.5E	23	128	666	06m18s
1775	148	2249 Sep 07	21:21:29	371	3088	158	T	p-	-0.7906	1.0656	39.4S	168.3W	38	37	343	04m42s
1776	148	2250 Feb 02	11:34:06	372	3093	125	P	-t	-1.3969	0.2864	62.5S	136.8E	0	231		
1777	149	2250 Jul 30	05:18:24	373	3099	130	P	-t	1.0490	0.9114	62.9N	125.6W	0	314		
1778	149	2250 Aug 28	13:51:18	373	3100	168	Pb	t-	-1.5277	0.0121	61.7S	97.5W	0	69		
1779	149	2251 Jan 22	17:21:41	374	3105	135	A	-p	-0.6481	0.9844	56.9S	54.0W	49	327	72	01m12s
1780	149	2251 Jul 19	14:18:46	375	3111	140	A	-p	0.3062	0.9773	38.0N	25.0W	72	200	85	02m16s
1781	149	2252 Jan 12	05:57:04	376	3117	145	T	n-	0.0607	1.0365	18.5S	93.2E	87	165	123	03m23s
1782	149	2252 Jul 07	16:34:11	377	3123	150	A	p-	-0.4686	0.9473	4.9S	71.4W	62	12	218	07m10s
1783	149	2252 Dec 31	21:37:06	378	3129	155	T	p-	0.7257	1.0389	23.1N	149.9W	43	170	189	03m33s
1784	149	2253 Jun 26	17:36:11	379	3135	160	P	t-	-1.2138	0.5982	65.5S	100.9W	0	18		
1785	149	2253 Nov 21	22:24:38	380	3140	127	P	-t	-1.3666	0.3297	68.9S	41.0E	0	162		
1786	149	2253 Dec 21	11:39:39	380	3141	165	P	t-	1.4374	0.1973	66.1N	6.8W	0	168		
1787	149	2254 May 17	14:43:39	381	3146	132	T	-p	0.7426	1.0315	66.7N	54.9W	42	161	160	02m09s
1788	149	2254 Nov 11	02:55:16	382	3152	137	A	-p	-0.7087	0.9317	61.4S	118.4E	45	21	363	06m05s
1789	150	2255 May 07	06:18:06	383	3158	142	T	nn	-0.0076	1.0706	16.4N	86.4E	90	346	230	06m22s
1790	150	2255 Oct 31	02:32:03	385	3164	147	A	nn	-0.0088	0.9295	14.5S	139.3E	89	11	264	09m24s
1791	150	2256 Apr 25	22:58:35	386	3170	152	T	p-	-0.7316	1.0495	32.3S	151.7W	43	344	240	04m14s
1792	150	2256 Oct 19	04:37:31	387	3176	157	A	p-	0.7025	0.9624	33.1N	121.4E	45	198	190	03m59s
1793	150	2257 Mar 16	22:51:29	388	3181	124	P	-t	1.2833	0.4770	72.2N	115.4E	0	95		
1794	150	2257 Apr 15	12:05:15	388	3182	162	Pb	t-	-1.5121	0.0634	71.3S	59.3E	0	302		
1795	150	2257 Sep 09	04:46:44	389	3187	129	P	-t	-1.2448	0.5480	71.9S	35.7E	0	73		
1796	150	2257 Oct 08	14:01:32	389	3188	167	P	t-	1.3765	0.3035	71.9N	39.2E	0	250		
1797	150	2258 Mar 06	00:58:23	390	3193	134	A	-p	0.6101	0.9239	30.2N	157.9E	52	160	358	09m04s
1798	150	2258 Aug 29	21:33:04	391	3199	139	T	-p	-0.5161	1.0712	20.9S	150.1W	59	17	269	06m09s
1799	150	2259 Feb 23	00:23:41	392	3205	144	A	nn	-0.0875	0.9326	15.0S	179.6W	85	345	253	08m36s
1800	150	2259 Aug 19	13:22:17	393	3211	149	T	nn	0.2226	1.0412	25.3N	14.5W	77	195	141	03m49s

Cat Num	Canon Plate	Calendar Date	TD of Greatest Eclipse	ΔT s	Luna Num	Saros Num	Ecl Type	QLE	Gamma	Ecl Mag	Lat °	Long °	Sun Alt °	Sun Azm °	Central Path Width km	Central Line Dur
1801	151	2260 Feb 12	04:34:24	394	3217	154	A	p-	-0.7776	0.9711	62.7S	139.3E	39	331	165	02m15s
1802	151	2260 Aug 07	23:51:13	395	3223	159	P	t-	1.0287	0.9294	70.2N	31.5W	0	325		
1803	151	2261 Jan 02	04:56:54	396	3228	126	P	-t	1.2873	0.4679	67.1N	109.4E	0	181		
1804	151	2261 Jan 31	15:55:00	397	3229	164	P	t-	-1.4107	0.2398	69.9S	93.9E	0	211		
1805	151	2261 Jun 28	12:16:27	398	3234	131	P	-t	-1.0198	0.9282	66.6S	5.1E	0	354		
1806	151	2261 Dec 22	20:38:49	399	3240	136	T	-p	0.6360	1.0337	16.1N	125.0W	50	185	147	03m17s
1807	151	2262 Jun 17	14:19:15	400	3246	141	A	nn	-0.2377	0.9750	9.8N	31.0W	76	353	92	03m08s
1808	151	2262 Dec 12	09:25:02	401	3252	146	A	nn	-0.0460	0.9910	25.8S	38.2E	87	10	32	00m56s
1809	151	2263 Jun 06	22:58:57	402	3258	151	T	p-	0.5366	1.0261	54.4N	174.0W	57	162	105	02m01s
1810	151	2263 Dec 01	15:28:45	403	3264	156	A	p-	-0.7794	0.9349	69.2S	86.6W	38	41	388	05m06s
1811	151	2264 Apr 27	06:21:41	404	3269	123	P	-t	-1.2931	0.4564	62.1S	147.7E	0	301		
1812	151	2264 May 26	13:52:06	404	3270	161	P	t-	1.2430	0.5526	63.9N	169.4W	0	35		
1813	152	2264 Oct 20	21:35:23	405	3275	128	P	-t	1.5111	0.0933	61.6N	76.5W	0	247		
1814	152	2264 Nov 19	15:28:12	405	3276	166	P	t-	-1.4830	0.1465	63.2S	171.2E	0	138		
1815	152	2265 Apr 16	22:26:19	406	3281	133	T	-p	-0.6073	1.0371	23.1S	137.7W	52	331	154	03m11s
1816	152	2265 Oct 10	01:37:34	408	3287	138	A	-p	0.7405	0.9796	35.1N	179.3E	42	215	105	01m51s
1817	152	2266 Apr 06	09:42:37	409	3293	143	Am	nn	0.1255	0.9829	12.9N	33.2E	83	151	61	01m42s
1818	152	2266 Sep 29	13:03:56	410	3299	148	T	nn	-0.0233	1.0425	3.7S	17.3W	89	28	142	03m40s
1819	152	2267 Mar 26	13:33:45	411	3305	153	A	p-	0.8810	0.9290	52.3N	64.5W	28	128	549	06m03s
1820	152	2267 Sep 19	05:12:14	412	3311	158	T	p-	-0.7348	1.0642	38.8S	75.1E	42	38	304	04m34s
1821	152	2268 Feb 13	19:39:31	413	3316	125	P	-t	-1.4059	0.2703	61.9S	6.7E	0	241		
1822	152	2268 Aug 09	12:32:04	414	3322	130	P	-t	1.1254	0.7683	62.2N	117.1E	0	305		
1823	152	2268 Sep 07	21:27:52	414	3323	168	P	t-	-1.4721	0.1194	61.4S	139.7E	0	78		
1824	152	2269 Feb 02	01:53:05	415	3328	135	A	-p	-0.6529	0.9883	53.2S	179.1W	49	323	54	00m54s
1825	153	2269 Jul 29	21:03:04	416	3334	140	A	-p	0.3893	0.9732	39.9N	122.1W	67	205	104	02m35s
1826	153	2270 Jan 22	14:46:28	418	3340	145	T	n-	0.0560	1.0386	16.7S	38.2W	87	161	130	03m29s
1827	153	2270 Jul 18	22:59:54	419	3346	150	A	p-	-0.3810	0.9474	0.7S	167.8W	68	16	208	06m57s
1828	153	2271 Jan 12	06:28:08	420	3352	155	T	p-	0.7217	1.0379	23.3N	75.1E	44	165	182	03m25s
1829	153	2271 Jul 08	00:13:01	421	3358	160	P	t-	-1.1284	0.7474	64.5S	150.2E	0	27		
1830	153	2271 Dec 03	06:40:47	422	3363	127	P	-t	-1.3843	0.2996	67.8S	94.3W	0	174		
1831	153	2272 Jan 01	20:17:51	422	3364	165	P	t-	1.4365	0.2000	65.1N	146.3W	0	158		
1832	153	2272 May 27	22:11:12	423	3369	132	T	-p	0.8053	1.0353	75.0N	164.1W	36	166	202	02m14s
1833	153	2272 Nov 21	10:42:52	424	3375	137	A	-p	-0.7327	0.9275	66.8S	5.1E	43	16	402	06m15s
1834	153	2273 May 17	14:04:30	426	3381	142	Tm	nn	0.0515	1.0738	22.5N	30.6W	87	173	240	06m31s
1835	153	2273 Nov 10	10:07:17	427	3387	147	A	nn	-0.0399	0.9278	19.6S	25.4E	88	10	272	09m34s
1836	153	2274 May 07	06:47:37	428	3393	152	T	p-	-0.6799	1.0510	25.5S	87.3E	47	348	230	04m37s
1837	154	2274 Oct 30	12:24:17	429	3399	157	A	p-	0.6666	0.9629	27.0N	1.5E	48	195	179	04m08s
1838	154	2275 Mar 28	06:37:50	430	3404	124	P	-t	1.3200	0.4133	72.2N	15.3W	0	81		
1839	154	2275 Apr 26	19:41:40	430	3405	162	P	t-	-1.4684	0.1424	70.7S	67.9W	0	315		
1840	154	2275 Sep 20	12:34:54	431	3410	129	P	-t	-1.2949	0.4526	72.0S	95.2W	0	87		
1841	154	2275 Oct 19	22:03:12	431	3411	167	P	t-	1.3358	0.3787	71.4N	94.8W	0	237		
1842	154	2276 Mar 16	08:34:02	432	3416	134	A	-p	0.6411	0.9253	36.4N	41.4E	50	158	362	08m23s
1843	154	2276 Sep 09	05:18:47	434	3422	139	T	-p	-0.5755	1.0671	28.5S	90.3E	55	20	266	05m33s
1844	154	2277 Mar 05	08:11:55	435	3428	144	A	nn	-0.0645	0.9366	9.5S	62.7E	86	343	236	08m04s
1845	154	2277 Aug 29	20:49:10	436	3434	149	T	nn	0.1572	1.0362	17.8N	127.6W	81	196	123	03m28s
1846	154	2278 Feb 22	12:52:47	437	3440	154	A	p-	-0.7628	0.9762	57.1S	13.9E	40	331	131	01m54s
1847	154	2278 Aug 19	06:46:22	438	3446	159	A	t-	0.9568	0.9712	75.8N	154.9E	16	257	367	01m53s
1848	154	2279 Jan 13	13:49:06	439	3451	126	P	-t	1.2899	0.4630	68.2N	34.6W	0	170		
1849	155	2279 Feb 12	00:37:05	440	3452	164	P	t-	-1.4003	0.2581	70.7S	49.2W	0	224		
1850	155	2279 Jul 09	18:41:12	441	3457	131	P	-t	-1.1065	0.7802	67.7S	101.6W	0	4		
1851	155	2280 Jan 03	05:28:11	442	3463	136	T	-p	0.6414	1.0314	17.2N	101.0E	50	180	138	03m04s
1852	155	2280 Jun 27	21:03:20	443	3469	141	A	nn	-0.3198	0.9784	4.6N	132.1W	71	357	81	02m45s
1853	155	2280 Dec 22	17:55:43	444	3475	146	A	nn	-0.0391	0.9870	25.8S	87.7W	88	5	46	01m23s
1854	155	2281 Jun 17	06:14:41	445	3481	151	T	p-	0.4621	1.0316	50.8N	83.3E	62	170	121	02m32s
1855	155	2281 Dec 11	23:31:24	447	3487	156	A	p-	-0.7667	0.9316	71.4S	162.8E	40	30	400	05m26s
1856	155	2282 May 08	14:15:15	448	3492	123	P	-t	-1.3458	0.3545	62.7S	20.4E	0	310		
1857	155	2282 Jun 06	21:28:19	448	3493	161	P	t-	1.1764	0.6815	64.8N	67.2E	0	25		
1858	155	2282 Nov 01	05:06:24	449	3498	128	Pe	-t	1.5448	0.0370	62.1N	162.1E	0	238		
1859	155	2282 Nov 30	23:15:22	449	3499	166	P	t-	-1.4624	0.1813	64.1S	45.2E	0	148		
1860	155	2283 Apr 28	06:18:21	450	3504	133	T	-p	-0.6581	1.0366	23.6S	104.1E	49	334	160	03m13s

Cat Num	Canon Plate	Calendar Date	TD of Greatest Eclipse	ΔT s	Luna Num	Saros Num	Ecl Type	QLE	Gamma	Ecl Mag	Lat °	Long °	Sun Alt °	Sun Azm °	Path Width km	Central Line Dur
1861	156	2283 Oct 21	09:23:10	451	3510	138	A	-p	0.7783	0.9790	34.9N	62.3E	39	212	116	01m56s
1862	156	2284 Apr 16	17:19:22	452	3516	143	A	nn	0.0792	0.9827	14.6N	80.1W	85	153	61	01m45s
1863	156	2284 Oct 09	21:03:48	454	3522	148	T	nn	0.0205	1.0420	5.7S	136.7W	89	209	140	03m39s
1864	156	2285 Apr 05	20:55:22	455	3528	153	A	p-	0.8378	0.9315	52.9N	172.3W	33	129	459	05m50s
1865	156	2285 Sep 29	13:11:37	456	3534	158	T	p-	-0.6859	1.0622	39.6S	43.8W	46	38	275	04m24s
1866	156	2286 Feb 24	03:39:23	457	3539	125	P	-t	-1.4204	0.2448	61.5S	121.9W	0	250		
1867	156	2286 Mar 25	20:37:47	457	3540	163	Pb	t-	1.5392	0.0473	61.0N	140.2E	0	86		
1868	156	2286 Aug 20	19:48:22	458	3545	130	P	-t	1.1987	0.6322	61.7N	0.7W	0	296		
1869	156	2286 Sep 19	05:10:03	458	3546	168	P	t-	-1.4214	0.2167	61.2S	15.6E	0	87		
1870	156	2287 Feb 13	10:21:24	459	3551	135	A	-p	-0.6613	0.9926	49.4S	55.4E	48	321	34	00m35s
1871	156	2287 Aug 10	03:47:41	461	3557	140	A	-p	0.4714	0.9686	41.0N	140.8E	62	210	127	02m56s
1872	156	2288 Feb 02	23:33:46	462	3563	145	T	n-	0.0492	1.0412	14.2S	169.3W	87	157	138	03m39s
1873	157	2288 Jul 29	05:25:23	463	3569	150	A	pn	-0.2929	0.9469	2.5N	96.5E	73	19	203	06m46s
1874	157	2289 Jan 22	15:19:24	464	3575	155	T	p-	0.7181	1.0374	24.3N	59.8W	44	161	178	03m18s
1875	157	2289 Jul 18	06:50:57	466	3581	160	P	t-	-1.0425	0.8980	63.6S	41.4E	0	37		
1876	157	2289 Dec 13	15:01:17	467	3586	127	P	-t	-1.3979	0.2767	66.8S	129.9E	0	185		
1877	157	2290 Jan 12	04:56:33	467	3587	165	P	t-	1.4365	0.2010	64.1N	74.5E	0	148		
1878	157	2290 Jun 08	05:35:48	468	3592	132	T	-p	0.8713	1.0382	83.8N	100.0E	29	182	265	02m14s
1879	157	2290 Dec 02	18:36:40	469	3598	137	A	-p	-0.7515	0.9237	70.9S	105.6W	41	7	439	06m23s
1880	157	2291 May 28	21:45:28	470	3604	142	T	nn	0.1153	1.0764	28.3N	145.4W	83	176	249	06m34s
1881	157	2291 Nov 21	17:50:53	472	3610	147	A	nn	-0.0644	0.9263	23.7S	89.9W	86	7	278	09m41s
1882	157	2292 May 17	14:29:32	473	3616	152	T	p-	-0.6224	1.0521	18.8S	31.3W	51	353	220	04m57s
1883	157	2292 Nov 09	20:20:06	474	3622	157	A	p-	0.6375	0.9635	22.0N	120.0W	50	191	171	04m14s
1884	157	2293 Apr 07	14:14:54	475	3627	124	P	-t	1.3632	0.3380	71.8N	143.5W	0	67		
1885	158	2293 May 07	03:09:46	475	3628	162	P	t-	-1.4186	0.2324	69.9S	167.6E	0	328		
1886	158	2293 Sep 30	20:31:27	476	3633	129	P	-t	-1.3386	0.3697	72.0S	131.8E	0	100		
1887	158	2293 Oct 30	06:13:45	477	3634	167	P	t-	1.3017	0.4416	70.7N	129.4E	0	223		
1888	158	2294 Mar 27	16:02:22	478	3639	134	A	-p	0.6777	0.9269	43.2N	73.5W	47	156	370	07m42s
1889	158	2294 Sep 20	13:09:57	479	3645	139	T	-p	-0.6300	1.0627	36.2S	30.9W	51	22	263	04m56s
1890	158	2295 Mar 16	15:54:34	480	3651	144	A	nn	-0.0362	0.9409	3.6S	53.9W	88	343	219	07m29s
1891	158	2295 Sep 10	04:20:19	481	3657	149	Tm	nn	0.0963	1.0307	10.3N	117.9E	84	197	104	03m01s
1892	158	2296 Mar 04	21:04:45	483	3663	154	A	p-	-0.7417	0.9819	51.1S	111.3W	42	333	95	01m31s
1893	158	2296 Aug 29	13:45:39	484	3669	159	A	p-	0.8888	0.9689	66.6N	14.0E	27	223	245	02m20s
1894	158	2297 Jan 23	22:39:47	485	3674	126	P	-t	1.2940	0.4550	69.2N	178.7W	0	158		
1895	158	2297 Feb 22	09:13:30	485	3675	164	P	t-	-1.3851	0.2854	71.4S	168.5E	0	237		
1896	158	2297 Jul 20	01:07:46	486	3680	131	P	-t	-1.1916	0.6346	68.7S	150.7E	0	15		
1897	159	2298 Jan 13	14:16:27	487	3686	136	T	-p	0.6474	1.0296	19.0N	32.9W	50	176	131	02m52s
1898	159	2298 Jul 09	03:49:01	489	3692	141	A	-p	-0.4013	0.9811	1.4S	125.6W	66	2	73	02m23s
1899	159	2299 Jan 03	02:27:42	490	3698	146	A	nn	-0.0341	0.9836	24.9S	146.0E	88	0	58	01m47s
1900	159	2299 Jun 28	13:27:43	491	3704	151	T	p-	0.3846	1.0365	46.0N	20.4W	67	176	133	03m03s
1901	159	2299 Dec 23	07:38:41	492	3710	156	A	p-	-0.7583	0.9288	72.5S	53.9E	40	16	412	05m45s
1902	159	2300 May 19	22:00:39	494	3715	123	P	-t	-1.4049	0.2399	63.4S	105.0W	0	319		
1903	159	2300 Jun 18	04:59:28	494	3716	161	P	t-	1.1056	0.8190	65.7N	55.4W	0	16		
1904	159	2300 Dec 12	07:09:43	495	3722	166	P	t-	-1.4473	0.2068	65.0S	82.8W	0	158		
1905	159	2301 May 09	14:00:58	496	3727	133	T	-p	-0.7161	1.0354	25.5S	12.0W	44	337	168	03m10s
1906	159	2301 Nov 01	17:19:33	497	3733	138	A	-p	0.8080	0.9786	34.8N	58.1W	36	209	126	02m01s
1907	159	2302 Apr 29	00:47:19	499	3739	143	A	nn	0.0262	0.9825	15.6N	169.0E	88	157	62	01m49s
1908	159	2302 Oct 22	05:11:15	500	3745	148	T	nn	0.0584	1.0413	7.8S	101.9E	87	207	139	03m38s
1909	160	2303 Apr 18	04:09:26	501	3751	153	A	p-	0.7888	0.9341	53.8N	82.8E	38	132	393	05m38s
1910	160	2303 Oct 11	21:17:24	502	3757	158	T	p-	-0.6424	1.0596	41.1S	164.1W	50	38	252	04m12s
1911	160	2304 Mar 07	11:34:23	504	3762	125	P	-t	-1.4389	0.2118	61.2S	110.9E	0	259		
1912	160	2304 Apr 06	04:00:21	504	3763	163	P	t-	1.4956	0.1190	61.2N	21.2E	0	77		
1913	160	2304 Sep 01	03:07:40	505	3768	130	P	-t	1.2684	0.5038	61.4N	119.1W	0	288		
1914	160	2304 Sep 30	12:58:17	505	3769	168	P	t-	-1.3760	0.3030	61.2S	110.0W	0	96		
1915	160	2305 Feb 24	18:46:09	506	3774	135	A	-p	-0.6732	0.9973	45.7S	70.2W	47	320	13	00m13s
1916	160	2305 Aug 21	10:35:44	507	3780	140	A	-p	0.5498	0.9637	41.5N	42.8E	56	214	155	03m21s
1917	160	2306 Feb 14	08:17:48	509	3786	145	T	nn	0.0394	1.0441	11.3S	60.1E	88	154	147	03m49s
1918	160	2306 Aug 10	11:55:09	510	3792	150	A	nn	-0.2083	0.9461	4.6N	0.1E	78	23	202	06m37s
1919	160	2307 Feb 04	00:08:00	511	3798	155	T	p-	0.7125	1.0373	25.7N	165.9E	44	156	176	03m12s
1920	160	2307 Jul 30	13:31:15	513	3804	160	A	t-	-0.9574	0.9602	50.0S	49.6W	16	30	500	03m37s

Cat Num	Canon Plate	Calendar Date	TD of Greatest Eclipse	ΔT s	Luna Num	Saros Num	Ecl Type	QLE	Gamma	Ecl Mag	Lat °	Long °	Sun Alt °	Sun Azm °	Path Width km	Central Line Dur
1921	161	2307 Dec 25	23:24:22	514	3809	127	P	-t	-1.4089	0.2584	65.7S	6.1W	0	195		
1922	161	2308 Jan 24	13:33:40	514	3810	165	P	t-	1.4358	0.2030	63.3N	63.9W	0	138		
1923	161	2308 Jun 19	12:57:53	515	3815	132	T	-t	0.9402	1.0396	84.1N	119.7E	19	313	401	02m08s
1924	161	2308 Dec 14	02:34:52	516	3821	137	A	-p	-0.7662	0.9207	73.4S	147.6E	40	353	470	06m31s
1925	161	2309 Jun 09	05:21:55	518	3827	142	T	-n	0.1833	1.0783	33.6N	101.7E	79	181	257	06m30s
1926	161	2309 Dec 03	01:42:04	519	3833	147	A	nn	-0.0833	0.9254	26.9S	153.6E	85	3	282	09m40s
1927	161	2310 May 29	22:04:49	520	3839	152	T	p-	-0.5599	1.0526	12.5S	147.5W	56	357	210	05m10s
1928	161	2310 Nov 22	04:24:19	522	3845	157	A	p-	0.6145	0.9642	17.9N	116.9E	52	187	164	04m16s
1929	161	2311 Apr 19	21:41:48	523	3850	124	P	-t	1.4139	0.2499	71.3N	91.4E	0	53		
1930	161	2311 May 19	10:28:45	523	3851	162	P	t-	-1.3620	0.3346	69.0S	45.9E	0	340		
1931	161	2311 Oct 13	04:36:08	524	3856	129	P	-t	-1.3762	0.2985	71.6S	3.1W	0	114		
1932	161	2311 Nov 11	14:33:19	524	3857	167	P	t-	1.2745	0.4920	69.9N	8.0W	0	211		
1933	162	2312 Apr 07	23:19:32	525	3862	134	A	-p	0.7231	0.9286	50.8N	173.7E	43	153	385	07m00s
1934	162	2312 Oct 01	21:08:25	527	3868	139	T	-p	-0.6783	1.0578	43.8S	153.9W	47	24	258	04m20s
1935	162	2313 Mar 27	23:29:30	528	3874	144	A	nn	-0.0010	0.9457	2.6N	168.9W	90	335	200	06m49s
1936	162	2313 Sep 21	11:57:00	529	3880	149	T	nn	0.0405	1.0249	3.0N	2.0E	88	198	85	02m30s
1937	162	2314 Mar 17	05:11:54	531	3886	154	A	p-	-0.7159	0.9880	44.9S	124.1E	44	335	60	01m03s
1938	162	2314 Sep 10	20:49:10	532	3892	159	A	p-	0.8247	0.9654	56.8N	104.3W	34	212	220	02m54s
1939	162	2315 Feb 05	07:29:49	533	3897	126	P	-t	1.2991	0.4453	70.1N	36.7E	0	145		
1940	162	2315 Mar 06	17:46:20	533	3898	164	P	t-	-1.3668	0.3188	71.9S	26.6E	0	251		
1941	162	2315 Aug 01	07:34:31	534	3903	131	P	-t	-1.2761	0.4898	69.6S	42.4E	0	27		
1942	162	2316 Jan 25	23:05:16	536	3909	136	T	-p	0.6527	1.0282	21.4N	166.9W	49	172	126	02m42s
1943	162	2316 Jul 20	10:36:17	537	3915	141	A	-p	-0.4819	0.9834	8.1S	22.2E	61	5	67	02m02s
1944	162	2317 Jan 14	10:59:37	538	3921	146	A	nn	-0.0298	0.9807	23.2S	19.5E	88	356	69	02m08s
1945	163	2317 Jul 09	20:42:40	540	3927	151	T	p-	0.3078	1.0406	40.4N	126.2W	72	182	143	03m32s
1946	163	2318 Jan 03	15:47:14	541	3933	156	A	p-	-0.7518	0.9265	71.9S	54.7W	41	1	422	06m02s
1947	163	2318 May 31	05:42:33	542	3938	123	Pe	-t	-1.4670	0.1192	64.2S	130.2E	0	329		
1948	163	2318 Jun 29	12:30:21	542	3939	161	P	t-	1.0340	0.9583	66.7N	178.2W	0	6		
1949	163	2318 Dec 23	15:07:25	544	3945	166	P	t-	-1.4346	0.2280	66.1S	147.9E	0	168		
1950	163	2319 May 20	21:37:22	545	3950	133	T	-p	-0.7786	1.0336	29.0S	126.7W	39	340	178	03m02s
1951	163	2319 Nov 13	01:24:38	546	3956	138	A	-p	0.8314	0.9784	35.0N	178.6E	33	205	136	02m04s
1952	163	2320 May 09	08:04:33	547	3962	143	A	nn	-0.0347	0.9820	15.6N	61.1E	88	337	64	01m56s
1953	163	2320 Nov 01	13:28:18	549	3968	148	Tm	nn	0.0888	1.0406	9.8S	21.8W	85	204	137	03m38s
1954	163	2321 Apr 28	11:12:58	550	3974	153	A	p-	0.7314	0.9367	54.5S	18.0W	43	136	341	05m30s
1955	163	2321 Oct 22	05:31:17	552	3980	158	T	p-	-0.6059	1.0567	43.3S	73.9E	52	37	233	04m00s
1956	163	2322 Mar 18	19:21:51	553	3985	125	P	-t	-1.4640	0.1671	61.1S	14.4W	0	268		
1957	164	2322 Apr 17	11:14:22	553	3986	163	P	t-	1.4445	0.2041	61.5N	95.8W	0	68		
1958	164	2322 Sep 12	10:32:06	554	3991	130	P	-t	1.3329	0.3865	61.1N	121.3E	0	279		
1959	164	2322 Oct 11	20:53:38	554	3992	168	P	t-	-1.3371	0.3764	61.4S	122.7E	0	105		
1960	164	2323 Mar 08	03:05:09	555	3997	135	H	-p	-0.6906	1.0023	42.4S	165.1E	46	320	11	00m11s
1961	164	2323 Sep 01	17:26:08	557	4003	140	A	-p	0.6253	0.9584	41.7N	56.2W	51	218	191	03m48s
1962	164	2324 Feb 25	16:57:31	558	4009	145	Tm	nn	0.0256	1.0475	8.1S	69.6W	89	152	158	04m02s
1963	164	2324 Aug 20	18:28:21	559	4015	150	A	nn	-0.1260	0.9449	5.7N	97.0W	83	25	205	06m33s
1964	164	2325 Feb 14	08:52:36	561	4021	155	T	p-	0.7038	1.0378	27.5N	32.9E	45	152	175	03m08s
1965	164	2325 Aug 09	20:16:23	562	4027	160	A	t-	-0.8749	0.9648	40.3S	147.1W	29	30	256	03m24s
1966	164	2326 Jan 05	07:49:42	563	4032	127	P	-t	-1.4177	0.2440	64.7S	142.1W	0	206		
1967	164	2326 Feb 03	22:08:48	564	4033	165	P	t-	1.4339	0.2069	62.6N	158.3E	0	128		
1968	164	2326 Jun 30	20:18:36	565	4038	132	P	-t	1.0107	0.9931	65.2N	36.3E	0	339		
1969	165	2326 Dec 25	10:36:52	566	4044	137	A	-p	-0.7774	0.9182	73.6S	42.3E	39	337	496	06m39s
1970	165	2327 Jun 20	12:55:00	567	4050	142	T	-n	0.2542	1.0795	38.3N	9.2W	75	186	265	06m21s
1971	165	2327 Dec 14	09:39:46	569	4056	147	A	nn	-0.0969	0.9250	28.8S	36.0E	84	358	284	09m34s
1972	165	2328 Jun 09	05:33:52	570	4062	152	T	p-	-0.4927	1.0524	6.7S	98.5E	60	1	199	05m16s
1973	165	2328 Dec 02	12:36:37	572	4068	157	A	p-	0.5974	0.9652	14.8N	7.9W	53	183	157	04m13s
1974	165	2329 Apr 30	04:59:57	573	4073	124	P	-t	1.4705	0.1514	70.6N	31.1W	0	40		
1975	165	2329 May 29	17:41:08	573	4074	162	P	t-	-1.3008	0.4449	68.1S	73.5W	0	351		
1976	165	2329 Oct 23	12:48:23	574	4079	129	P	-t	-1.4082	0.2383	71.1S	139.5W	0	127		
1977	165	2329 Nov 21	22:59:19	574	4080	167	P	t-	1.2521	0.5334	68.9N	146.4W	0	198		
1978	165	2330 Apr 19	06:29:24	576	4085	134	A	-p	0.7742	0.9302	59.0N	62.0E	39	151	412	06m19s
1979	165	2330 Oct 13	05:13:41	577	4091	139	T	-p	-0.7208	1.0528	51.2S	81.5E	44	27	251	03m46s
1980	165	2331 Apr 08	06:57:08	578	4097	144	A	nn	0.0408	0.9506	9.2N	78.0E	88	164	181	06m07s

Cat Num	Canon Plate	Calendar Date	TD of Greatest Eclipse	ΔT s	Luna Num	Saros Num	Ecl Type	QLE	Gamma	Ecl Mag	Lat °	Long °	Sun Alt °	Sun Azm °	Path Width km	Central Line Dur
1981	166	2331 Oct 02	19:39:15	580	4103	149	T	nn	-0.0097	1.0188	4.0S	115.2W	89	17	64	01m55s
1982	166	2332 Mar 27	13:11:33	581	4109	154	A	p-	-0.6831	0.9945	38.3S	1.1E	47	338	26	00m30s
1983	166	2332 Sep 21	03:59:09	582	4115	159	A	p-	0.7666	0.9613	47.9N	141.4E	40	207	216	03m34s
1984	166	2333 Feb 15	16:14:19	584	4120	126	P	-t	1.3087	0.4270	70.9N	107.2W	0	132		
1985	166	2333 Mar 17	02:10:52	584	4121	164	P	t-	-1.3417	0.3652	72.1S	113.4W	0	265		
1986	166	2333 Aug 11	14:06:47	585	4126	131	P	-t	-1.3558	0.3534	70.5S	67.9W	0	38		
1987	166	2333 Sep 10	05:41:59	585	4127	169	Pb	t-	1.5299	0.0592	72.0N	158.1W	0	286		
1988	166	2334 Feb 05	07:50:29	586	4132	136	T	-p	0.6603	1.0272	24.6N	59.8E	49	168	123	02m33s
1989	166	2334 Jul 31	17:26:33	588	4138	141	A	-p	-0.5608	0.9851	15.6S	82.8W	56	9	64	01m45s
1990	166	2335 Jan 25	19:29:43	589	4144	146	A	nn	-0.0247	0.9784	20.6S	106.9W	88	352	77	02m25s
1991	166	2335 Jul 21	03:57:48	591	4150	151	T	n-	0.2306	1.0440	34.0N	126.4E	76	186	151	03m58s
1992	166	2336 Jan 14	23:56:41	592	4156	156	A	p-	-0.7462	0.9250	69.6S	165.9W	41	349	427	06m18s
1993	167	2336 Jul 09	19:58:21	593	4162	161	T	t-	0.9598	1.0657	83.2N	48.4E	16	345	799	03m18s
1994	167	2337 Jan 02	23:09:43	595	4168	166	P	t-	-1.4251	0.2435	67.2S	17.0E	0	179		
1995	167	2337 May 31	05:05:56	596	4173	133	T	-t	-0.8470	1.0309	34.6S	120.2E	32	344	195	02m46s
1996	167	2337 Nov 23	09:37:55	597	4179	138	A	-p	0.8488	0.9786	35.5N	52.8E	32	200	142	02m05s
1997	167	2338 May 20	15:14:19	599	4185	143	A	nn	-0.1011	0.9812	14.5N	45.0W	84	342	67	02m07s
1998	167	2338 Nov 12	21:52:53	600	4191	148	T	nn	0.1132	1.0399	11.7S	147.4W	84	201	134	03m38s
1999	167	2339 May 09	18:08:03	602	4197	153	A	p-	0.6672	0.9392	54.7N	115.5W	48	143	300	05m24s
2000	167	2339 Nov 02	13:51:49	603	4203	158	T	p-	-0.5751	1.0536	45.8S	49.3W	55	34	215	03m47s
2001	167	2340 Mar 29	03:03:37	604	4208	125	P	-t	-1.4941	0.1131	61.2S	138.3W	0	277		
2002	167	2340 Apr 27	18:21:32	605	4209	163	P	t-	1.3873	0.3006	62.0N	148.8E	0	59		
2003	167	2340 Sep 22	18:01:33	606	4214	130	P	-t	1.3925	0.2793	61.1N	0.4E	0	270		
2004	167	2340 Oct 22	04:55:28	606	4215	168	P	t-	-1.3037	0.4387	61.7S	6.3W	0	114		
2005	168	2341 Mar 18	11:18:19	607	4220	135	H	-p	-0.7137	1.0075	39.8S	41.6E	44	321	36	00m36s
2006	168	2341 Sep 12	00:22:46	609	4226	140	A	-p	0.6950	0.9529	41.7N	157.4W	46	220	234	04m19s
2007	168	2342 Mar 08	01:32:13	610	4232	145	T	nn	0.0072	1.0511	4.9S	161.9E	90	149	169	04m16s
2008	168	2342 Sep 01	01:06:54	612	4238	150	A	nn	-0.0480	0.9434	6.1N	164.7E	87	28	209	06m34s
2009	168	2343 Feb 25	17:32:17	613	4244	155	T	p-	0.6913	1.0385	29.6N	98.7W	46	149	175	03m06s
2010	168	2343 Aug 21	03:07:04	614	4250	160	A	p-	-0.7956	0.9679	35.1S	111.8E	37	31	186	03m09s
2011	168	2344 Jan 16	16:13:40	616	4255	127	P	-t	-1.4270	0.2288	63.8S	82.5E	0	216		
2012	168	2344 Feb 15	06:37:57	616	4256	165	P	t-	1.4280	0.2179	62.0N	22.3E	0	119		
2013	168	2344 Jul 11	03:39:14	617	4261	132	P	-t	1.0818	0.8591	64.3N	83.4W	0	330		
2014	168	2344 Aug 09	11:59:04	617	4262	170	Pb	t-	-1.4974	0.0789	62.3S	53.2W	0	54		
2015	168	2345 Jan 04	18:40:23	618	4267	137	A	-p	-0.7872	0.9165	71.9S	65.6W	38	323	517	06m45s
2016	168	2345 Jun 30	20:26:17	620	4273	142	T	-n	0.3267	1.0797	42.1N	118.7W	71	192	272	06m07s
2017	169	2345 Dec 24	17:41:04	621	4279	147	Am	nn	-0.1082	0.9252	29.7S	82.1W	84	353	284	09m21s
2018	169	2346 Jun 20	12:58:43	623	4285	152	T	p-	-0.4224	1.0515	1.5S	13.7W	65	5	188	05m12s
2019	169	2346 Dec 13	20:55:35	624	4291	157	A	p-	0.5848	0.9665	12.8N	134.1W	54	178	149	04m04s
2020	169	2347 May 11	12:07:07	625	4296	124	Pe	-t	1.5351	0.0391	69.7N	150.1W	0	28		
2021	169	2347 Jun 10	00:44:41	626	4297	162	P	t-	-1.2329	0.5671	67.1S	169.8E	0	1		
2022	169	2347 Nov 03	21:09:18	627	4302	129	P	-t	-1.4337	0.1903	70.4S	82.4E	0	140		
2023	169	2347 Dec 03	07:33:33	627	4303	167	P	t-	1.2358	0.5635	67.9N	73.8E	0	187		
2024	169	2348 Apr 29	13:29:00	628	4308	134	A	-p	0.8338	0.9315	68.1N	49.8W	33	145	466	05m40s
2025	169	2348 Oct 23	13:26:55	630	4314	139	T	-p	-0.7564	1.0476	58.2S	44.6W	41	28	242	03m14s
2026	169	2349 Apr 18	14:16:51	631	4320	144	A	nn	0.0900	0.9557	16.0N	33.1W	85	165	162	05m23s
2027	169	2349 Oct 13	03:28:53	633	4326	149	H	nn	-0.0532	1.0126	10.6S	126.1E	87	16	43	01m18s
2028	169	2350 Apr 07	21:06:02	634	4332	154	H	p-	-0.6452	1.0011	31.7S	120.7W	50	340	5	00m06s
2029	170	2350 Oct 02	11:14:07	636	4338	159	A	p-	0.7131	0.9560	30.0N	27.7E	44	203	222	04m21s
2030	170	2351 Feb 27	00:56:11	637	4343	126	P	-t	1.3209	0.4037	71.5N	109.1E	0	119		
2031	170	2351 Mar 28	10:30:56	637	4344	164	P	t-	-1.3126	0.4196	72.1S	107.5E	0	279		
2032	170	2351 Aug 22	20:42:46	638	4349	131	P	-t	-1.4322	0.2228	71.2S	179.6W	0	51		
2033	170	2351 Sep 21	12:33:26	639	4350	169	P	t-	1.4664	0.1681	72.2N	85.2E	0	273		
2034	170	2352 Feb 16	16:32:05	640	4355	136	T	-p	0.6709	1.0266	28.5N	72.8W	48	164	121	02m25s
2035	170	2352 Aug 11	00:21:34	641	4361	141	A	-p	-0.6366	0.9862	23.6S	170.2E	50	13	63	01m32s
2036	170	2353 Feb 05	03:56:54	643	4367	146	A	nn	-0.0179	0.9766	17.1S	127.0E	89	349	84	02m38s
2037	170	2353 Jul 31	11:17:05	644	4373	151	T	n-	0.1559	1.0467	27.2N	16.8E	81	190	158	04m20s
2038	170	2354 Jan 25	08:03:20	646	4379	156	A	p-	-0.7388	0.9240	66.0S	79.5E	42	341	427	06m35s
2039	170	2354 Jul 21	03:28:21	647	4385	161	T	t-	0.8870	1.0697	81.4N	170.7E	27	221	499	03m51s
2040	170	2355 Jan 14	07:12:19	649	4391	166	P	t-	-1.4157	0.2589	68.2S	114.4W	0	190		

Cat Num	Canon Plate	Calendar Date	TD of Greatest Eclipse	ΔT s	Luna Num	Saros Num	Ecl Type	QLE	Gamma	Ecl Mag	Lat °	Long °	Sun Alt °	Sun Azm °	Path Width km	Central Line Dur
2041	171	2355 Jun 11	12:28:17	650	4396	133	T	-t	-0.9196	1.0269	43.3S	8.2E	23	348	233	02m18s
2042	171	2355 Dec 04	17:58:36	651	4402	138	A	-p	0.8609	0.9792	36.0N	75.4W	30	195	145	02m02s
2043	171	2356 May 30	22:15:18	653	4408	143	A	nn	-0.1735	0.9800	12.2N	149.0W	80	346	72	02m21s
2044	171	2356 Nov 23	06:24:55	654	4414	148	T	-n	0.1317	1.0394	13.2S	85.3E	83	197	133	03m40s
2045	171	2357 May 20	00:54:22	656	4420	153	A	p-	0.5960	0.9415	53.9N	149.9E	53	150	269	05m24s
2046	171	2357 Nov 12	22:20:22	657	4426	158	T	p-	-0.5514	1.0505	48.4S	173.7W	56	31	200	03m35s
2047	171	2358 Apr 09	10:37:39	659	4431	125	Pe	-t	-1.5309	0.0467	61.4S	99.7E	0	286		
2048	171	2358 May 09	01:21:14	659	4432	163	P	t-	1.3230	0.4098	62.6N	35.1E	0	50		
2049	171	2358 Oct 04	01:36:38	660	4437	130	P	-t	1.4465	0.1835	61.1N	121.8W	0	261		
2050	171	2358 Nov 02	13:03:59	660	4438	168	P	t-	-1.2765	0.4890	62.2S	137.1W	0	123		
2051	171	2359 Mar 29	19:24:46	662	4443	135	T	-p	-0.7430	1.0129	37.9S	80.3W	42	323	65	01m02s
2052	171	2359 Sep 23	07:24:41	663	4449	140	A	-p	0.7595	0.9471	41.9N	99.6E	40	221	291	04m53s
2053	172	2360 Mar 18	09:59:21	665	4455	145	T	nn	-0.0177	1.0549	1.8S	35.4E	89	331	181	04m33s
2054	172	2360 Sep 11	07:52:24	666	4461	150	Am	nn	0.0244	0.9415	5.7N	64.6E	89	208	217	06m41s
2055	172	2361 Mar 08	02:05:55	668	4467	155	T	p-	0.6743	1.0396	31.9N	131.7E	47	146	176	03m06s
2056	172	2361 Aug 31	10:04:30	669	4473	160	A	p-	-0.7211	0.9701	32.2S	8.7E	44	33	151	02m54s
2057	172	2362 Jan 27	00:35:59	670	4478	127	P	-t	-1.4368	0.2125	62.9S	52.1W	0	225		
2058	172	2362 Feb 25	15:02:02	671	4479	165	P	t-	1.4189	0.2345	61.6N	112.3W	0	109		
2059	172	2362 Jul 22	11:01:14	672	4484	132	P	-t	1.1522	0.7255	63.5N	156.9E	0	321		
2060	172	2362 Aug 20	19:18:10	672	4485	170	P	t-	-1.4239	0.2149	61.8S	171.7W	0	63		
2061	172	2363 Jan 16	02:45:06	673	4490	137	A	-p	-0.7955	0.9154	68.8S	178.6W	37	314	532	06m52s
2062	172	2363 Jul 12	03:55:03	675	4496	142	T	-p	0.4012	1.0792	45.0N	133.4E	66	198	279	05m51s
2063	172	2364 Jan 05	01:46:48	676	4502	147	A	nn	-0.1161	0.9259	29.4S	158.7E	83	348	281	09m03s
2064	172	2364 Jun 30	20:19:47	678	4508	152	T	n-	-0.3493	1.0499	2.9N	124.3W	70	9	176	05m00s
2065	173	2364 Dec 24	05:18:58	679	4514	157	A	p-	0.5752	0.9683	11.6N	98.8E	55	174	139	03m48s
2066	173	2365 Jun 20	07:44:13	681	4520	162	P	t-	-1.1623	0.6935	66.1S	54.7E	0	12		
2067	173	2365 Nov 14	05:37:33	682	4525	129	P	-t	-1.4540	0.1526	69.5S	56.9W	0	153		
2068	173	2365 Dec 13	16:12:41	683	4526	167	P	t-	1.2230	0.5873	66.8N	66.7W	0	176		
2069	173	2366 May 10	20:22:07	684	4531	134	A	-t	0.8981	0.9323	77.9N	170.5W	26	129	583	05m03s
2070	173	2366 Nov 03	21:46:04	685	4537	139	T	-p	-0.7868	1.0426	64.8S	171.2W	38	29	231	02m46s
2071	173	2367 Apr 29	21:30:02	687	4543	144	Am	nn	0.1451	0.9607	22.8N	142.2W	82	167	144	04m38s
2072	173	2367 Oct 24	11:25:03	688	4549	149	H	nn	-0.0902	1.0065	16.7S	6.3E	85	15	22	00m40s
2073	173	2368 Apr 18	04:51:37	690	4555	154	H	p-	-0.5992	1.0079	24.8S	119.8E	53	344	34	00m47s
2074	173	2368 Oct 12	18:37:19	691	4561	159	A	p-	0.6672	0.9522	32.5N	86.9W	48	199	233	05m13s
2075	173	2369 Mar 09	09:30:23	693	4566	126	P	-t	1.3392	0.3686	71.9N	33.2W	0	105		
2076	173	2369 Apr 07	18:42:10	693	4567	164	P	t-	-1.2763	0.4881	71.8S	29.1W	0	293		
2077	174	2369 Sep 02	03:25:55	694	4572	131	Pe	-t	-1.5027	0.1025	71.7S	66.3E	0	64		
2078	174	2369 Oct 01	19:33:30	695	4573	169	P	t-	1.4094	0.2652	72.1N	33.7W	0	259		
2079	174	2370 Feb 27	01:07:02	696	4578	136	T	-p	0.6865	1.0262	33.2N	156.0E	46	161	122	02m17s
2080	174	2370 Aug 22	07:22:20	697	4584	141	A	-p	-0.7082	0.9867	32.0S	61.0E	45	17	66	01m22s
2081	174	2371 Feb 16	12:18:48	699	4590	146	A	nn	-0.0075	0.9753	12.9S	1.7E	89	348	88	02m48s
2082	174	2371 Aug 11	18:38:03	700	4596	151	T	nn	0.0820	1.0487	19.9N	94.0W	85	192	162	04m36s
2083	174	2372 Feb 05	16:07:47	702	4602	156	A	p-	-0.7301	0.9237	61.5S	38.0W	43	336	422	06m50s
2084	174	2372 Jul 31	10:58:29	704	4608	161	T	p-	0.8144	1.0717	71.0N	44.5E	35	209	404	04m18s
2085	174	2373 Jan 24	15:14:58	705	4614	166	P	t-	-1.4062	0.2742	69.3S	113.5E	0	202		
2086	174	2373 Jun 21	19:45:28	706	4619	133	Ts	-t	-0.9954	1.0191	62.7S	101.1W	3	349	-	01m24s
2087	174	2373 Dec 15	02:25:54	708	4625	138	A	-p	0.8678	0.9803	36.7N	154.4E	29	190	141	01m56s
2088	174	2374 Jun 11	05:09:55	709	4631	143	A	-p	-0.2505	0.9784	8.8N	108.1E	76	351	79	02m39s
2089	175	2374 Dec 04	15:02:55	711	4637	148	T	-n	0.1455	1.0390	14.1S	43.4W	82	193	132	03m42s
2090	175	2375 May 31	07:34:33	713	4643	153	A	p-	0.5200	0.9436	52.0N	56.9E	58	158	243	05m26s
2091	175	2375 Nov 24	06:54:53	714	4649	158	T	p-	-0.5327	1.0474	50.7S	61.2E	58	26	186	03m23s
2092	175	2376 May 19	08:14:43	716	4655	163	P	t-	1.2528	0.5304	63.3N	77.1W	0	41		
2093	175	2376 Oct 14	09:18:27	717	4660	130	P	-t	1.4941	0.1003	61.4N	114.3E	0	252		
2094	175	2376 Nov 12	21:19:05	717	4661	168	P	t-	-1.2551	0.5280	62.8S	90.3E	0	132		
2095	175	2377 Apr 09	03:25:10	719	4666	135	T	-p	-0.7780	1.0180	37.1S	159.1E	39	325	96	01m28s
2096	175	2377 Oct 03	14:33:16	720	4672	140	A	-p	0.8178	0.9413	42.6N	5.8W	35	220	366	05m29s
2097	175	2378 Mar 29	18:20:22	722	4678	145	T	nn	-0.0480	1.0587	1.1N	89.6W	87	331	193	04m51s
2098	175	2378 Sep 22	14:45:47	723	4684	150	A	nn	0.0904	0.9396	4.8N	37.6W	85	209	225	06m54s
2099	175	2379 Mar 19	10:31:46	725	4690	155	T	p-	0.6511	1.0409	34.3N	4.6E	49	144	177	03m07s
2100	175	2379 Sep 11	17:09:31	726	4696	160	A	p-	-0.6517	0.9717	30.9S	96.4W	49	34	130	02m42s

Cat Num	Canon Plate	Calendar Date	TD of Greatest Eclipse	ΔT s	Luna Num	Saros Num	Ecl Type	QLE	Gamma	Ecl Mag	Lat °	Long °	Sun Alt °	Sun Azm °	Path Width km	Central Line Dur
2101	176	2380 Feb 07	08:54:00	728	4701	127	P	-t	-1.4496	0.1909	62.2S	174.6E	0	235		
2102	176	2380 Mar 07	23:17:51	728	4702	165	P	t-	1.4038	0.2616	61.3N	115.3E	0	100		
2103	176	2380 Aug 01	18:26:16	729	4707	132	P	-t	1.2208	0.5949	62.8N	36.6E	0	312		
2104	176	2380 Aug 31	02:44:38	730	4708	170	P	t-	-1.3552	0.3423	61.4S	68.1E	0	72		
2105	176	2381 Jan 26	10:46:37	731	4713	137	A	-p	-0.8064	0.9149	65.3S	65.8E	36	309	546	06m57s
2106	176	2381 Jul 22	11:25:01	733	4719	142	T	-p	0.4749	1.0777	46.9N	25.9E	61	205	285	05m32s
2107	176	2382 Jan 15	09:53:21	734	4725	147	A	nn	-0.1242	0.9274	28.1S	39.1E	83	343	275	08m40s
2108	176	2382 Jul 12	03:37:51	736	4731	152	T	n-	-0.2743	1.0475	6.5N	126.4E	74	13	164	04m41s
2109	176	2383 Jan 04	13:46:25	737	4737	157	A	p-	0.5682	0.9706	11.4N	29.2W	55	169	127	03m26s
2110	176	2383 Jul 01	14:37:41	739	4743	162	P	t-	-1.0870	0.8276	65.1S	58.6W	0	21		
2111	176	2383 Nov 25	14:13:31	740	4748	129	P	-t	-1.4683	0.1260	68.6S	162.4E	0	165		
2112	176	2383 Dec 25	00:57:03	740	4749	167	P	t-	1.2144	0.6034	65.8N	152.1E	0	165		
2113	177	2384 May 21	03:05:25	742	4754	134	A	-t	0.9702	0.9317	80.8N	1.9W	13	40	1116	04m28s
2114	177	2384 Nov 14	06:13:19	743	4760	139	T	-p	-0.8102	1.0377	70.9S	62.4E	36	28	217	02m22s
2115	177	2385 May 10	04:36:48	745	4766	144	A	nn	0.2063	0.9657	29.5N	110.8E	78	169	126	03m53s
2116	177	2385 Nov 03	19:27:29	747	4772	149	H	-n	-0.1212	1.0004	22.1S	114.5W	83	13	2	00m03s
2117	177	2386 Apr 29	12:32:24	748	4778	154	H2	p-	-0.5483	1.0147	18.1S	1.8E	57	347	60	01m30s
2118	177	2386 Oct 24	02:06:43	750	4784	159	A	p-	0.6267	0.9475	26.1N	157.7E	51	196	246	06m09s
2119	177	2387 Mar 20	17:59:08	751	4790	126	P	t-	1.3624	0.3241	72.1N	174.3W	0	90		
2120	177	2387 Apr 19	02:47:05	751	4790	164	P	t-	-1.2345	0.5678	71.3S	163.8W	0	306		
2121	177	2387 Oct 13	02:41:03	753	4796	169	P	t-	1.3579	0.3524	71.8N	154.4W	0	245		
2122	177	2388 Mar 09	09:36:20	754	4801	136	T	-p	0.7065	1.0260	38.5N	26.0E	45	158	124	02m10s
2123	177	2388 Sep 01	14:30:25	756	4807	141	A	-p	-0.7744	0.9867	40.7S	51.2W	39	22	73	01m15s
2124	177	2389 Feb 26	20:33:51	758	4813	146	A	nn	0.0078	0.9744	8.1S	122.4W	90	162	92	02m55s
2125	178	2389 Aug 22	02:05:53	759	4819	151	T	nn	0.0133	1.0500	12.5N	152.8E	89	193	166	04m45s
2126	178	2390 Feb 16	00:06:58	761	4825	156	A	p-	-0.7177	0.9239	56.4S	156.7W	44	335	411	07m06s
2127	178	2390 Aug 11	18:31:26	762	4831	161	T	p-	0.7440	1.0724	61.3N	73.6W	42	206	353	04m41s
2128	178	2391 Feb 04	23:15:05	764	4837	166	P	t-	-1.3944	0.2934	70.3S	18.6W	0	215		
2129	178	2391 Jul 03	02:58:52	765	4842	133	P	-t	-1.0732	0.8664	67.1S	141.9E	0	358		
2130	178	2391 Aug 01	11:14:31	766	4843	171	Pb	t-	1.4924	0.0767	69.6N	166.8E	0	332		
2131	178	2391 Dec 26	10:57:14	767	4848	138	A	-p	0.8724	0.9820	37.6N	23.0E	29	184	131	01m46s
2132	178	2392 Jun 21	11:57:57	769	4854	143	A	-p	-0.3319	0.9762	4.1N	6.2E	71	355	90	03m02s
2133	178	2392 Dec 14	23:46:26	770	4860	148	T	-n	0.1550	1.0391	14.5S	173.5W	81	188	133	03m46s
2134	178	2393 Jun 10	14:08:40	772	4866	153	A	p-	0.4389	0.9453	48.7N	35.5W	64	166	224	05m34s
2135	178	2393 Dec 04	15:34:35	774	4872	158	T	p-	-0.5188	1.0445	52.6S	64.1W	59	20	174	03m13s
2136	178	2394 May 30	15:03:02	775	4878	163	P	t-	1.1775	0.6610	64.1N	171.6E	0	32		
2137	179	2394 Oct 25	17:07:12	777	4883	130	Pe	-t	1.5351	0.0298	61.8N	11.4W	0	243		
2138	179	2394 Nov 24	05:40:35	777	4884	168	P	t-	-1.2398	0.5556	63.6S	44.1W	0	142		
2139	179	2395 Apr 20	11:17:14	778	4889	135	T	-p	-0.8204	1.0230	37.7S	40.8E	35	327	134	01m52s
2140	179	2395 Oct 14	21:49:15	780	4895	140	A	-p	0.8691	0.9354	44.0N	113.5W	29	219	471	06m07s
2141	179	2396 Apr 09	02:33:16	781	4901	145	T	nn	-0.0851	1.0625	3.4N	147.6E	85	332	206	05m12s
2142	179	2396 Oct 02	21:48:06	783	4907	150	A	nn	0.1494	0.9375	3.5N	142.3W	81	209	234	07m12s
2143	179	2397 Mar 29	18:49:51	785	4913	155	T	p-	0.6221	1.0423	36.7N	119.9W	51	144	178	03m11s
2144	179	2397 Sep 22	00:23:54	786	4919	160	A	p-	-0.5891	0.9728	30.9S	156.1E	54	34	118	02m34s
2145	179	2398 Feb 17	17:08:13	788	4924	127	P	-t	-1.4648	0.1650	61.7S	42.5E	0	244		
2146	179	2398 Mar 19	07:27:07	788	4925	165	P	t-	1.3843	0.2966	61.2N	15.5W	0	91		
2147	179	2398 Aug 13	01:53:36	789	4930	132	P	-t	1.2878	0.4668	62.2N	84.0W	0	303		
2148	179	2398 Sep 11	10:16:33	790	4931	170	P	t-	-1.2902	0.4633	61.2S	53.4W	0	81		
2149	180	2399 Feb 06	18:46:43	791	4936	137	A	-p	-0.8180	0.9150	61.6S	52.0W	35	307	557	07m01s
2150	180	2399 Aug 02	18:55:13	793	4942	142	T	-p	0.5482	1.0754	48.0N	81.5W	57	211	291	05m14s
2151	180	2400 Jan 26	18:00:09	794	4948	147	A	nn	-0.1322	0.9295	26.0S	80.9W	82	339	267	08m13s
2152	180	2400 Jul 22	10:54:47	796	4954	152	T	nn	-0.1992	1.0444	9.1N	17.9E	79	17	151	04m17s
2153	180	2401 Jan 14	22:15:19	798	4960	157	A	p-	0.5617	0.9735	11.9N	157.5W	56	165	114	03m00s
2154	180	2401 Jul 11	21:29:19	799	4966	162	P	t-	-1.0110	0.9620	64.2S	171.0W	0	31		
2155	180	2401 Dec 05	22:53:36	801	4971	129	P	-t	-1.4797	0.1049	67.5S	21.3E	0	176		
2156	180	2402 Jan 04	09:42:27	801	4972	167	P	t-	1.2063	0.6185	64.7N	11.1E	0	155		
2157	180	2402 Jun 01	09:44:37	802	4977	134	P	-t	1.0452	0.8834	67.8N	136.9W	0	6		
2158	180	2402 Nov 25	14:45:40	804	4983	139	T	-p	-0.8292	1.0332	76.2S	60.7W	34	22	202	02m02s
2159	180	2403 May 21	11:36:54	806	4989	144	A	nn	0.2737	0.9705	36.1N	6.3E	74	173	110	03m10s
2160	180	2403 Nov 15	03:36:24	807	4995	149	A	-n	-0.1461	0.9947	26.8S	123.8E	81	9	19	00m33s

Cat Num	Canon Plate	Calendar Date	TD of Greatest Eclipse	ΔT s	Luna Num	Saros Num	Ecl Type	QLE	Gamma	Ecl Mag	Lat °	Long °	Sun Alt °	Sun Azm °	Path Width km	Central Line Dur
2161	181	2404 May 09	20:05:44	809	5001	154	T	p-	-0.4901	1.0212	11.4S	113.9W	61	350	83	02m14s
2162	181	2404 Nov 03	09:44:07	811	5007	159	A	p-	0.5934	0.9430	20.5N	40.9E	53	193	260	07m05s
2163	181	2405 Mar 31	02:18:51	812	5012	126	P	-t	1.3929	0.2654	71.9N	46.8E	0	76		
2164	181	2405 Apr 29	10:43:54	812	5013	164	P	t-	-1.1858	0.6613	70.6S	64.2E	0	319		
2165	181	2405 Oct 23	09:58:54	814	5019	169	P	t-	1.3141	0.4262	71.3N	82.7E	0	232		
2166	181	2406 Mar 20	17:57:22	815	5024	136	T	-p	0.7327	1.0258	44.6N	102.4W	43	155	128	02m03s
2167	181	2406 Sep 12	21:45:22	817	5030	141	A	-p	-0.8356	0.9862	49.6S	166.6W	33	27	88	01m11s
2168	181	2407 Mar 10	04:41:40	819	5036	146	A	nn	0.0283	0.9739	2.7S	115.0E	88	163	93	02m59s
2169	181	2407 Sep 02	09:38:24	820	5042	151	T	nn	-0.0518	1.0506	5.1N	38.1E	87	17	168	04m48s
2170	181	2408 Feb 27	07:59:39	822	5048	156	A	p-	-0.7004	0.9249	50.8S	84.4E	45	334	394	07m22s
2171	181	2408 Aug 22	02:07:38	824	5054	161	T	p-	0.6766	1.0720	52.3N	168.9E	47	204	317	05m00s
2172	181	2409 Feb 15	07:12:29	826	5060	166	P	t-	-1.3802	0.3164	71.1S	150.7W	0	228		
2173	182	2409 Jul 13	10:09:33	827	5065	133	P	-t	-1.1523	0.7186	68.1S	23.5E	0	9		
2174	182	2409 Aug 11	18:38:30	827	5066	171	P	t-	1.4271	0.2022	70.4N	43.7E	0	320		
2175	182	2410 Jan 05	19:31:38	829	5071	138	A	-p	0.8749	0.9842	38.8N	109.3W	29	179	116	01m31s
2176	182	2410 Jul 02	18:42:29	830	5077	143	A	-p	-0.4152	0.9735	1.6S	95.5W	65	359	104	03m25s
2177	182	2410 Dec 26	08:33:57	832	5083	148	T	-n	0.1614	1.0395	14.1S	55.5E	81	184	134	03m50s
2178	182	2411 Jun 21	20:37:43	834	5089	153	A	pn	0.3537	0.9467	44.2N	128.0W	69	173	210	05m46s
2179	182	2411 Dec 16	00:19:06	835	5095	158	T	p-	-0.5093	1.0419	53.6S	170.1E	59	13	163	03m04s
2180	182	2412 Jun 09	21:48:03	837	5101	163	P	t-	1.0987	0.7984	65.0N	61.0E	0	22		
2181	182	2412 Dec 04	14:06:30	839	5107	168	P	t-	-1.2288	0.5751	64.5S	179.8W	0	152		
2182	182	2413 Apr 30	19:03:56	840	5112	135	T	-p	-0.8677	1.0274	40.0S	76.1W	30	330	183	02m13s
2183	182	2413 Oct 25	05:13:19	842	5118	140	A	-p	0.9130	0.9298	46.2N	136.2E	24	218	628	06m43s
2184	182	2414 Apr 20	10:39:38	844	5124	145	T	-n	-0.1279	1.0661	5.0N	26.6E	83	334	218	05m33s
2185	183	2414 Oct 14	04:58:49	845	5130	150	A	nn	0.2016	0.9355	2.2N	110.7E	78	207	245	07m34s
2186	183	2415 Apr 10	02:59:34	847	5136	155	T	p-	0.5866	1.0437	38.9N	118.5E	54	144	178	03m16s
2187	183	2415 Oct 03	07:47:47	849	5142	160	A	p-	-0.5334	0.9736	31.8S	46.3E	58	34	110	02m27s
2188	183	2416 Feb 29	01:13:31	850	5147	127	P	-t	-1.4865	0.1279	61.3S	87.3W	0	253		
2189	183	2416 Mar 29	15:24:53	851	5148	165	P	t-	1.3563	0.3467	61.2N	143.3W	0	82		
2190	183	2416 Aug 23	09:26:37	852	5153	132	P	-t	1.3505	0.3467	61.8N	154.1E	0	294		
2191	183	2416 Sep 21	17:57:50	852	5154	170	P	t-	-1.2320	0.5716	61.1S	177.1W	0	89		
2192	183	2417 Feb 17	02:40:41	854	5159	137	A	-p	-0.8345	0.9155	58.3S	169.4W	33	306	574	07m04s
2193	183	2417 Aug 13	02:28:05	855	5165	142	T	-p	0.6190	1.0723	48.3N	170.3E	52	216	297	04m55s
2194	183	2418 Feb 06	02:04:03	857	5171	147	A	nn	-0.1431	0.9322	23.3S	159.4E	82	336	256	07m43s
2195	183	2418 Aug 02	18:11:10	859	5177	152	T	nn	-0.1242	1.0406	10.9N	90.1W	83	21	137	03m50s
2196	183	2419 Jan 26	06:44:36	861	5183	157	A	p-	0.5549	0.9770	13.2N	74.1E	56	161	97	02m30s
2197	184	2419 Jul 23	04:16:44	862	5189	162	A	t-	-0.9321	0.9754	45.6S	97.1E	21	24	242	02m17s
2198	184	2419 Dec 17	07:40:06	864	5194	129	P	-t	-1.4865	0.0925	66.5S	120.8W	0	187		
2199	184	2420 Jan 15	18:30:38	864	5195	167	P	t-	1.2004	0.6299	63.8N	130.3W	0	145		
2200	184	2420 Jun 11	16:17:01	865	5200	134	P	-t	1.1257	0.7469	66.8N	114.5E	0	355		
2201	184	2420 Dec 05	23:23:51	867	5206	139	T	-p	-0.8431	1.0291	80.2S	175.1W	32	6	185	01m44s
2202	184	2421 May 31	18:32:58	869	5212	144	A	-p	0.3452	0.9750	42.4N	96.1W	70	177	95	02m32s
2203	184	2421 Nov 25	11:51:40	871	5218	149	A	-n	-0.1652	0.9893	30.4S	1.3E	80	6	38	01m06s
2204	184	2422 May 21	03:34:50	872	5224	154	T	p-	-0.4278	1.0275	5.0S	132.0E	65	354	103	02m56s
2205	184	2422 Nov 14	17:27:39	874	5230	159	A	p-	0.5657	0.9386	15.8N	76.9W	55	189	275	08m01s
2206	184	2423 Apr 11	10:32:40	876	5235	126	P	-t	1.4283	0.1970	71.6N	90.2W	0	63		
2207	184	2423 May 10	18:35:16	876	5236	164	P	t-	-1.1323	0.7648	69.7S	65.9W	0	332		
2208	184	2423 Nov 03	17:24:50	878	5242	169	P	t-	1.2769	0.4888	70.5N	41.6W	0	219		
2209	185	2424 Mar 31	02:10:09	879	5247	136	T	-p	0.7652	1.0254	51.3N	130.8E	40	152	133	01m55s
2210	185	2424 Sep 23	05:09:45	881	5253	141	A	-p	-0.8896	0.9853	58.6S	73.0E	27	36	114	01m08s
2211	185	2425 Mar 20	12:41:11	883	5259	146	A	nn	0.0546	0.9735	3.1N	5.8W	87	162	95	03m02s
2212	185	2425 Sep 12	17:18:07	884	5265	151	Tm	nn	-0.1114	1.0507	2.3S	78.6W	84	17	169	04m47s
2213	185	2426 Mar 09	15:44:44	886	5271	156	A	p-	-0.6773	0.9262	44.7S	33.6W	47	336	374	07m38s
2214	185	2426 Sep 02	09:48:46	888	5277	161	T	p-	0.6133	1.0709	43.8N	50.5E	52	203	291	05m14s
2215	185	2427 Feb 26	15:03:44	890	5283	166	P	t-	-1.3606	0.3485	71.7S	78.2E	0	241		
2216	185	2427 Jul 24	17:18:10	891	5288	133	P	-t	-1.2318	0.5708	69.1S	94.8W	0	20		
2217	185	2427 Aug 23	02:04:50	891	5289	171	P	t-	1.3642	0.3223	71.1N	80.5W	0	308		
2218	185	2428 Jan 17	04:07:20	893	5294	138	A	-p	0.8770	0.9870	40.5N	118.0E	28	173	96	01m13s
2219	185	2428 Jul 13	01:23:54	895	5300	143	A	-p	-0.4999	0.9703	8.3S	162.8E	60	3	123	03m50s
2220	185	2429 Jan 05	17:22:55	896	5306	148	T	-n	0.1666	1.0404	13.0S	76.0W	80	179	137	03m56s

Cat Num	Canon Plate	Calendar Date	TD of Greatest Eclipse	ΔT s	Luna Num	Saros Num	Ecl Type	QLE	Gamma	Ecl Mag	Lat °	Long °	Sun Alt °	Sun Azm °	Path Width km	Central Line Dur
2221	186	2429 Jul 02	03:04:29	898	5312	153	A	pn	0.2668	0.9476	38.6N	138.5E	74	179	200	06m01s
2222	186	2429 Dec 26	09:07:19	900	5318	158	T	n-	-0.5035	1.0397	53.7S	43.8E	60	6	155	02m57s
2223	186	2430 Jun 21	04:29:26	902	5324	163	P	t-	1.0160	0.9439	66.0N	49.1W	0	13		
2224	186	2430 Dec 15	22:37:28	903	5330	168	P	t-	-1.2227	0.5858	65.5S	42.9E	0	162		
2225	186	2431 May 12	02:43:29	905	5335	135	T	-p	-0.9214	1.0310	44.8S	169.3E	22	332	268	02m27s
2226	186	2431 Nov 05	12:45:39	907	5341	140	A	-t	0.9497	0.9242	49.5N	23.4E	18	216	902	07m15s
2227	186	2432 Apr 30	18:37:30	909	5347	145	T	-n	-0.1780	1.0694	5.8N	92.1W	80	337	229	05m56s
2228	186	2432 Oct 24	12:19:57	910	5353	150	A	nn	0.2455	0.9335	0.8N	1.0E	76	205	255	08m01s
2229	186	2433 Apr 20	11:01:31	912	5359	155	T	p-	0.5450	1.0449	40.8N	0.2W	57	146	177	03m21s
2230	186	2433 Oct 13	15:20:15	914	5365	160	A	p-	-0.4840	0.9742	33.4S	65.3W	61	33	104	02m23s
2231	186	2434 Mar 11	09:12:46	915	5370	127	P	-t	-1.5122	0.0837	61.1S	144.5E	0	263		
2232	186	2434 Apr 09	23:15:23	916	5371	165	P	t-	1.3232	0.4059	61.4N	90.6E	0	73		
2233	187	2434 Sep 03	17:04:07	917	5376	132	P	-t	1.4099	0.2331	61.5N	31.1E	0	285		
2234	187	2434 Oct 03	01:46:02	917	5377	170	P	t-	-1.1789	0.6706	61.1S	57.4E	0	98		
2235	187	2435 Feb 28	10:29:44	919	5382	137	A	-p	-0.8546	0.9165	55.4S	73.9E	31	306	599	07m05s
2236	187	2435 Aug 24	10:03:11	921	5388	142	T	-p	0.6876	1.0684	48.2N	61.1E	46	221	304	04m35s
2237	187	2436 Feb 17	10:05:23	923	5394	147	A	nn	-0.1567	0.9355	20.2S	40.0E	81	333	243	07m12s
2238	187	2436 Aug 13	01:29:32	924	5400	152	Tm	nn	-0.0517	1.0361	11.8N	161.6E	87	25	122	03m21s
2239	187	2437 Feb 05	15:11:24	926	5406	157	A	p-	0.5453	0.9810	14.9N	53.6W	57	157	79	01m58s
2240	187	2437 Aug 02	11:06:00	928	5412	162	A	p-	-0.8552	0.9741	37.4S	4.0W	31	26	175	02m33s
2241	187	2437 Dec 27	16:29:06	929	5417	129	P	-t	-1.4920	0.0824	65.5S	96.9E	0	198		
2242	187	2438 Jan 26	03:17:36	930	5418	167	P	t-	1.1929	0.6441	63.0N	89.0E	0	135		
2243	187	2438 Jun 22	22:46:46	931	5423	134	P	-t	1.2079	0.6068	65.8N	7.0E	0	345		
2244	187	2438 Dec 17	08:05:39	933	5429	139	T	-p	-0.8539	1.0254	81.7S	83.1E	31	336	168	01m30s
2245	188	2439 Jun 12	01:25:21	935	5435	144	A	-p	0.4207	0.9791	48.2N	164.0E	65	183	82	01m59s
2246	188	2439 Dec 06	20:11:46	937	5441	149	A	-n	-0.1794	0.9844	33.0S	121.6W	79	1	56	01m36s
2247	188	2440 May 31	10:58:14	938	5447	154	T	p-	-0.3597	1.0334	1.0N	19.9E	69	358	121	03m33s
2248	188	2440 Nov 25	01:18:38	940	5453	159	A	p-	0.5445	0.9347	12.2N	163.8E	57	185	290	08m51s
2249	188	2441 Apr 21	18:37:49	942	5458	126	P	-t	1.4707	0.1149	71.0N	135.3E	0	50		
2250	188	2441 May 21	02:20:10	942	5459	164	P	t-	-1.0733	0.8795	68.8S	166.2E	0	343		
2251	188	2441 Nov 14	00:59:16	944	5465	169	P	t-	1.2459	0.5405	69.6N	167.4W	0	206		
2252	188	2442 Apr 11	10:14:03	945	5470	136	T	-p	0.8046	1.0248	58.7N	5.1E	36	148	142	01m45s
2253	188	2442 Oct 04	12:42:59	947	5476	141	A	-p	-0.9371	0.9838	67.3S	55.8W	20	50	166	01m08s
2254	188	2443 Mar 31	20:30:25	949	5482	146	A	nn	0.0890	0.9734	9.3N	124.2W	85	163	95	03m02s
2255	188	2443 Sep 24	01:04:46	951	5488	151	T	nn	-0.1657	1.0502	9.6S	163.0E	80	18	169	04m39s
2256	188	2444 Mar 19	23:21:37	953	5494	156	A	p-	-0.6476	0.9280	38.3S	150.2W	49	337	351	07m53s
2257	189	2444 Sep 12	17:35:34	954	5500	161	T	p-	0.5548	1.0688	35.7N	69.0W	56	202	268	05m24s
2258	189	2445 Mar 08	22:49:33	956	5506	166	P	t-	-1.3361	0.3892	72.1S	52.1W	0	255		
2259	189	2445 Aug 04	00:27:21	958	5511	133	P	-t	-1.3097	0.4272	70.0S	146.1E	0	31		
2260	189	2445 Sep 02	09:35:13	958	5512	171	P	t-	1.3049	0.4345	71.7N	153.8E	0	295		
2261	189	2446 Jan 27	12:43:50	960	5517	138	A	-p	0.8790	0.9903	42.7N	15.0W	28	168	72	00m53s
2262	189	2446 Jul 24	08:03:10	962	5523	143	A	-p	-0.5854	0.9665	16.0S	60.7E	54	7	149	04m13s
2263	189	2447 Jan 17	02:14:02	963	5529	148	T	-n	0.1703	1.0417	11.1S	151.8E	80	175	141	04m03s
2264	189	2447 Jul 13	09:29:34	965	5535	153	A	nn	0.1786	0.9481	32.2N	44.0E	80	183	194	06m18s
2265	189	2448 Jan 06	17:57:06	967	5541	158	T	n-	-0.4991	1.0380	52.6S	83.1W	60	358	147	02m51s
2266	189	2448 Jul 01	11:10:15	969	5547	163	A	t-	-0.9316	0.9620	87.6N	136.4W	21	25	388	02m26s
2267	189	2448 Dec 26	07:10:40	971	5553	168	P	t-	-1.2190	0.5919	66.5S	95.4W	0	172		
2268	189	2449 May 22	10:19:14	972	5558	135	T	-t	-0.9790	1.0328	54.4S	57.9E	11	332	567	02m24s
2269	190	2449 Nov 15	20:23:55	974	5564	140	An	-t	0.9810	0.9186	54.9N	90.2W	10	214	–	07m35s
2270	190	2450 May 12	02:29:43	976	5570	145	T	-n	-0.2331	1.0722	5.6N	150.6E	77	340	241	06m19s
2271	190	2450 Nov 04	19:49:30	978	5576	150	A	nn	0.2828	0.9318	0.5S	111.0W	74	203	264	08m30s
2272	190	2451 May 01	18:53:36	980	5582	155	T	p-	0.4957	1.0459	42.1N	115.4W	60	149	175	03m28s
2273	190	2451 Oct 24	23:03:08	981	5588	160	A	p-	-0.4423	0.9746	35.3S	179.4W	64	31	101	02m21s
2274	190	2452 Mar 21	17:01:30	983	5593	127	Pe	-t	-1.5455	0.0261	61.1S	19.0E	0	272		
2275	190	2452 Apr 20	06:54:26	983	5594	165	P	t-	1.2818	0.4798	61.8N	32.7W	0	64		
2276	190	2452 Sep 14	00:49:16	985	5599	132	P	-t	1.4635	0.1307	61.3N	93.6W	0	276		
2277	190	2452 Oct 13	09:44:04	985	5600	170	P	t-	-1.1333	0.7554	61.3S	70.5W	0	107		
2278	190	2453 Mar 10	18:09:41	987	5605	137	A	-p	-0.8820	0.9177	53.6S	40.3W	28	306	647	07m04s
2279	190	2453 Sep 03	17:43:47	989	5611	142	T	-p	0.7513	1.0638	48.0N	50.2W	41	224	312	04m15s
2280	190	2454 Feb 27	18:01:46	990	5617	147	A	nn	-0.1750	0.9393	17.0S	78.4W	80	331	228	06m40s

Cat Num	Canon Plate	Calendar Date	TD of Greatest Eclipse	ΔT s	Luna Num	Saros Num	Ecl Type	QLE	Gamma	Ecl Mag	Lat °	Long °	Sun Alt °	Sun Azm °	Path Width km	Central Line Dur
2281	191	2454 Aug 24	08:48:46	992	5623	152	T	nn	0.0195	1.0310	11.9N	53.2E	89	205	105	02m50s
2282	191	2455 Feb 16	23:36:26	994	5629	157	A	p-	0.5334	0.9857	17.1N	179.2E	58	154	59	01m25s
2283	191	2455 Aug 13	17:54:36	996	5635	162	A	p-	-0.7781	0.9716	32.3S	105.3W	39	28	158	02m52s
2284	191	2456 Jan 08	01:21:03	998	5640	129	P	-t	-1.4955	0.0759	64.5S	45.7W	0	208		
2285	191	2456 Feb 06	12:03:14	998	5641	167	P	t-	1.1842	0.6608	62.3N	51.2W	0	125		
2286	191	2456 Jul 03	05:13:15	1000	5646	134	P	-t	1.2925	0.4621	64.9N	99.2W	0	336		
2287	191	2456 Dec 27	16:51:24	1001	5652	139	T	-p	-0.8614	1.0222	79.8S	23.2W	30	311	151	01m19s
2288	191	2457 Jun 22	08:16:12	1003	5658	144	A	-p	0.4980	0.9827	53.2N	66.3E	60	190	71	01m32s
2289	191	2457 Dec 17	04:35:26	1005	5664	149	A	-n	-0.1900	0.9799	34.4S	115.0E	79	356	73	02m04s
2290	191	2458 Jun 11	18:19:39	1007	5670	154	T	n-	-0.2891	1.0388	6.3N	91.1W	73	2	136	04m04s
2291	191	2458 Dec 06	09:14:45	1009	5676	159	A	p-	0.5280	0.9312	9.5N	43.6E	58	181	303	09m34s
2292	191	2459 May 03	02:35:53	1010	5681	126	Pe	-t	1.5188	0.0214	70.3N	3.2E	0	37		
2293	192	2459 Jun 01	09:59:49	1011	5682	164	T-	t-	-1.0096	1.0038	67.8S	40.2E	0	354	-	-
2294	192	2459 Nov 25	08:41:40	1013	5688	169	P	t-	1.2211	0.5819	68.6N	65.4E	0	194		
2295	192	2460 Apr 21	18:09:48	1014	5693	136	T	-p	0.8503	1.0237	66.8N	120.9W	31	142	154	01m34s
2296	192	2460 Oct 14	20:25:56	1016	5699	141	A	-p	-0.9775	0.9817	73.9S	154.9E	11	82	328	01m09s
2297	192	2461 Apr 11	04:10:34	1018	5705	146	A	nn	0.1300	0.9732	15.8N	119.7E	82	164	97	03m02s
2298	192	2461 Oct 04	09:00:21	1020	5711	151	T	-n	-0.2131	1.0495	16.5S	42.6E	78	18	168	04m30s
2299	192	2462 Mar 31	06:49:43	1022	5717	156	A	p-	-0.6111	0.9302	31.7S	95.1E	52	340	327	08m07s
2300	192	2462 Sep 24	01:28:07	1024	5723	161	T	p-	0.5013	1.0662	28.1N	170.3E	60	200	249	05m28s
2301	192	2463 Mar 20	06:27:53	1026	5729	166	P	t-	-1.3050	0.4411	72.3S	179.4E	0	270		
2302	192	2463 Aug 15	07:37:34	1027	5734	133	P	-t	-1.3853	0.2891	70.8S	26.2E	0	43		
2303	192	2463 Sep 13	17:10:27	1027	5735	171	P	t-	1.2504	0.5368	72.0N	26.4E	0	281		
2304	192	2464 Feb 07	21:17:15	1029	5740	138	A	-p	0.8840	0.9941	45.7N	147.5W	28	163	44	00m31s
2305	193	2464 Aug 03	14:42:59	1031	5746	143	A	-p	-0.6693	0.9621	24.5S	42.4W	48	11	184	04m32s
2306	193	2465 Jan 27	11:03:48	1033	5752	148	T	-n	0.1752	1.0435	8.3S	19.7E	80	171	147	04m11s
2307	193	2465 Jul 23	15:54:47	1035	5758	153	A	nn	0.0904	0.9482	25.0N	51.8W	85	187	191	06m35s
2308	193	2466 Jan 17	02:47:00	1037	5764	158	T	n-	-0.4953	1.0366	50.4S	149.1E	60	352	142	02m48s
2309	193	2466 Jul 12	17:50:50	1039	5770	163	A	t-	0.8460	0.9676	79.5N	66.9W	32	196	221	02m18s
2310	193	2467 Jan 06	15:46:08	1040	5776	168	P	t-	-1.2179	0.5934	67.6S	125.3E	0	183		
2311	193	2467 Jun 02	17:48:23	1042	5781	135	P	-t	-1.0425	0.9314	64.5S	51.9W	0	331		
2312	193	2467 Nov 27	04:10:20	1044	5787	140	A+	-t	1.0051	0.9433	63.7N	157.2E	0	216	-	-
2313	193	2468 May 22	10:15:10	1046	5793	145	T	-n	-0.2937	1.0744	22.4N	34.9E	73	344	252	06m41s
2314	193	2468 Nov 15	03:28:22	1048	5799	150	A	-n	0.3126	0.9304	1.5S	134.5E	72	199	273	08m59s
2315	193	2469 May 12	02:39:06	1050	5805	155	T	p-	0.4416	1.0466	42.6N	131.7E	64	153	172	03m36s
2316	193	2469 Nov 04	06:55:36	1052	5811	160	A	p-	-0.4081	0.9750	37.5S	64.5E	66	29	97	02m19s
2317	194	2470 May 01	14:25:39	1054	5817	165	P	t-	1.2347	0.5638	62.3N	154.1W	0	55		
2318	194	2470 Sep 25	08:39:56	1055	5822	132	Pe	-t	1.5130	0.0365	61.3N	140.2E	0	268		
2319	194	2470 Oct 24	17:49:28	1056	5823	170	P	t-	-1.0932	0.8298	61.7S	159.7E	0	116		
2320	194	2471 Mar 22	01:43:36	1057	5828	137	A	-p	-0.9141	0.9190	52.9S	152.5W	24	307	738	07m00s
2321	194	2471 Sep 15	01:29:10	1059	5834	142	T	-p	0.8109	1.0585	48.0N	163.3W	36	226	323	03m54s
2322	194	2472 Mar 10	01:52:10	1061	5840	147	A	nn	-0.1989	0.9436	13.9S	164.5E	78	331	212	06m08s
2323	194	2472 Sep 03	16:12:53	1063	5846	152	T	nn	0.0857	1.0255	11.3N	56.5W	85	208	87	02m19s
2324	194	2473 Feb 27	07:56:50	1065	5852	157	A	p-	0.5168	0.9908	19.6N	53.4E	59	151	37	00m53s
2325	194	2473 Aug 24	00:46:31	1067	5858	162	A	p-	-0.7042	0.9684	29.3S	152.5E	45	30	156	03m12s
2326	194	2474 Jan 18	10:12:10	1068	5863	129	P	-t	-1.5000	0.0673	63.6S	172.3E	0	218		
2327	194	2474 Feb 16	20:44:51	1069	5864	167	P	t-	1.1720	0.6842	61.7N	169.8E	0	116		
2328	194	2474 Jul 14	11:40:29	1070	5869	134	P	-t	1.3764	0.3182	64.0N	154.7E	0	327		
2329	195	2474 Aug 13	02:43:55	1071	5870	172	Pb	t-	-1.4827	0.1380	62.1S	84.1E	0	58		
2330	195	2475 Jan 08	01:37:51	1072	5875	139	T	-p	-0.8680	1.0196	76.2S	142.9W	29	299	136	01m10s
2331	195	2475 Jul 03	15:05:21	1074	5881	144	A	-p	0.5775	0.9858	57.3N	28.9W	54	199	62	01m11s
2332	195	2475 Dec 28	13:01:53	1076	5887	149	A	-n	-0.1977	0.9760	34.7S	8.8W	78	350	87	02m27s
2333	195	2476 Jun 22	01:38:28	1078	5893	154	T	n-	-0.2152	1.0435	11.1N	159.3E	78	6	149	04m25s
2334	195	2476 Dec 16	17:15:17	1080	5899	159	A	p-	0.5154	0.9282	7.7N	77.5W	59	176	314	10m04s
2335	195	2477 Jun 11	17:35:28	1082	5905	164	T	t-	-0.9422	1.0647	47.7S	82.0W	19	3	642	04m53s
2336	195	2477 Dec 05	16:32:04	1084	5911	169	P	t-	1.2019	0.6137	67.5N	63.2W	0	183		
2337	195	2478 May 03	01:55:58	1086	5916	136	T	-t	0.9034	1.0218	75.7N	106.5E	25	128	176	01m20s
2338	195	2478 Oct 26	04:18:20	1088	5922	141	P	-t	-1.0109	0.9644	71.0S	14.5W	0	132		
2339	195	2479 Apr 22	11:40:29	1090	5928	146	A	nn	0.1790	0.9731	22.5N	6.4E	80	165	98	03m01s
2340	195	2479 Oct 15	17:04:10	1091	5934	151	T	-n	-0.2538	1.0484	23.0S	79.4W	75	17	166	04m18s

Cat Num	Canon Plate	Calendar Date	TD of Greatest Eclipse	ΔT s	Luna Num	Saros Num	Ecl Type	QLE	Gamma	Ecl Mag	Lat °	Long °	Sun Alt °	Sun Azm °	Path Width km	Central Line Dur
2341	196	2480 Apr 10	14:07:45	1093	5940	156	A	p-	-0.5664	0.9326	24.8S	17.1W	55	342	303	08m18s
2342	196	2480 Oct 04	09:27:57	1095	5946	161	T	p-	0.4542	1.0631	21.1N	48.0E	63	198	231	05m26s
2343	196	2481 Mar 30	14:00:06	1097	5952	166	P	t-	-1.2684	0.5028	72.1S	52.3E	0	284		
2344	196	2481 Aug 25	14:49:24	1099	5957	133	P	-t	-1.4585	0.1568	71.4S	94.6W	0	56		
2345	196	2481 Sep 24	00:49:50	1099	5958	171	P	t-	1.1997	0.6308	72.1N	102.2W	0	268		
2346	196	2482 Feb 18	05:48:51	1101	5963	138	A	-p	0.8912	0.9982	49.3N	80.0E	27	157	14	00m09s
2347	196	2482 Aug 14	21:23:34	1103	5969	143	A	-p	-0.7516	0.9573	33.8S	147.0W	41	16	234	04m45s
2348	196	2483 Feb 07	19:51:55	1105	5975	148	T	-n	0.1818	1.0457	4.8S	112.3W	80	168	155	04m20s
2349	196	2483 Aug 03	22:21:16	1107	5981	153	A	nn	0.0029	0.9479	17.4N	148.9W	90	186	192	06m50s
2350	196	2484 Jan 28	11:35:52	1109	5987	158	T	n-	-0.4909	1.0358	47.2S	20.4E	60	347	138	02m48s
2351	196	2484 Jul 23	00:34:33	1111	5993	163	A	p-	0.7618	0.9720	68.9N	167.2W	40	198	156	02m10s
2352	196	2485 Jan 17	00:19:52	1113	5999	168	P	t-	-1.2161	0.5963	68.6S	14.1W	0	195		
2353	197	2485 Jun 13	01:16:17	1115	6004	135	P	-t	-1.1076	0.8094	65.4S	173.5W	0	341		
2354	197	2485 Jul 12	09:35:01	1115	6005	173	Pb	t-	1.4713	0.1260	68.0N	146.4W	0	352		
2355	197	2485 Dec 07	12:01:58	1116	6010	140	A+	-t	1.0243	0.9099	64.7N	30.1E	0	206	-	-
2356	197	2486 Jun 02	17:55:27	1118	6016	145	T	-n	-0.3588	1.0760	1.8N	79.9W	69	348	263	06m59s
2357	197	2486 Nov 26	11:15:06	1120	6022	150	A	-n	0.3364	0.9294	2.1S	18.0E	70	195	280	09m26s
2358	197	2487 May 23	10:16:14	1122	6028	155	T	n-	0.3811	1.0467	42.1N	21.5E	67	159	168	03m43s
2359	197	2487 Nov 15	14:57:34	1124	6034	160	A	-p	-0.3807	0.9756	39.5S	53.4W	67	25	94	02m16s
2360	197	2488 May 11	21:45:54	1126	6040	165	P	t-	1.1793	0.6627	62.9N	87.1E	0	46		
2361	197	2488 Nov 04	02:04:55	1128	6046	170	P	t-	-1.0609	0.8899	62.3S	27.3E	0	125		
2362	197	2489 Apr 01	09:07:53	1130	6051	137	A	-t	-0.9541	0.9200	54.4S	100.1E	17	305	997	06m50s
2363	197	2489 Sep 25	09:20:21	1132	6057	142	T	-p	0.8655	1.0527	48.6N	81.7E	30	227	341	03m32s
2364	197	2490 Mar 21	09:36:10	1134	6063	147	A	nn	-0.2288	0.9483	11.1S	48.9E	77	330	195	05m36s
2365	198	2490 Sep 14	23:40:37	1136	6069	152	T	-n	0.1484	1.0195	10.3N	167.3W	81	209	67	01m47s
2366	198	2491 Mar 10	16:11:56	1138	6075	157	A	p-	0.4951	0.9964	22.2N	70.8W	60	149	14	00m20s
2367	198	2491 Sep 04	07:41:14	1140	6081	162	A	p-	-0.6332	0.9646	27.7S	49.7E	51	32	161	03m34s
2368	198	2492 Jan 29	19:03:42	1142	6086	129	P	-t	-1.5046	0.0582	62.9S	30.5E	0	228		
2369	198	2492 Feb 28	05:22:52	1142	6087	167	P	t-	1.1567	0.7136	61.4N	31.9E	0	107		
2370	198	2492 Jul 24	18:08:31	1144	6092	134	P	-t	1.4595	0.1755	63.2N	48.7E	0	317		
2371	198	2492 Aug 23	09:17:48	1144	6093	172	P	t-	-1.4042	0.2724	61.6S	23.0W	0	67		
2372	198	2493 Jan 18	10:24:29	1146	6098	139	T	-p	-0.8743	1.0174	72.2S	89.7E	29	294	123	01m02s
2373	198	2493 Jul 13	21:56:35	1148	6104	144	A	-p	0.6562	0.9882	60.3N	122.5W	49	209	55	00m56s
2374	198	2494 Jan 07	21:30:20	1150	6110	149	A	-n	-0.2034	0.9727	33.7S	133.2W	78	345	100	02m46s
2375	198	2494 Jul 03	08:56:15	1152	6116	154	T	nn	-0.1397	1.0477	15.0N	50.5E	82	11	160	04m40s
2376	198	2494 Dec 28	01:19:27	1154	6122	159	A	p-	0.5061	0.9257	6.9N	160.7E	60	172	323	10m22s
2377	199	2495 Jun 23	01:08:05	1156	6128	164	T	t-	-0.8718	1.0696	37.2S	161.5E	29	8	464	05m39s
2378	199	2495 Dec 17	00:27:37	1158	6134	169	P	t-	1.1867	0.6390	66.4N	167.6E	0	172		
2379	199	2496 May 13	09:34:24	1160	6139	136	T	-t	0.9622	1.0185	81.0N	71.6W	15	65	243	01m02s
2380	199	2496 Nov 05	12:20:22	1162	6145	141	P	-t	-1.0373	0.9173	70.2S	147.6W	0	145		
2381	199	2497 May 02	19:01:51	1164	6151	146	A	-n	0.2341	0.9728	29.2N	104.4W	76	167	100	02m59s
2382	199	2497 Oct 26	01:15:22	1166	6157	151	T	-n	-0.2889	1.0472	29.1S	157.3E	73	16	164	04m06s
2383	199	2498 Apr 21	21:17:11	1168	6163	156	A	p-	-0.5148	0.9351	17.9S	127.1W	59	345	280	08m26s
2384	199	2498 Oct 15	17:34:43	1170	6169	161	T	n-	0.4130	1.0597	14.6N	75.6W	66	196	215	05m21s
2385	199	2499 Apr 10	21:22:38	1172	6175	166	P	t-	-1.2233	0.5798	71.8S	72.0W	0	298		
2386	199	2499 Sep 05	22:05:17	1173	6180	133	Pe	-t	-1.5274	0.0340	71.9S	143.1E	0	69		
2387	199	2499 Oct 05	08:36:22	1174	6181	171	P	t-	1.1554	0.7120	71.9N	127.4E	0	254		
2388	199	2500 Mar 01	14:14:46	1176	6186	138	H	-p	0.9038	1.0026	53.9N	51.9W	25	151	21	00m12s
2389	200	2500 Aug 26	04:08:15	1178	6192	143	A	-p	-0.8297	0.9518	43.8S	105.7E	34	21	313	04m53s

Appendix B

Solar Eclipse Maps: 1501 to 2500

Key to Solar Eclipse Maps

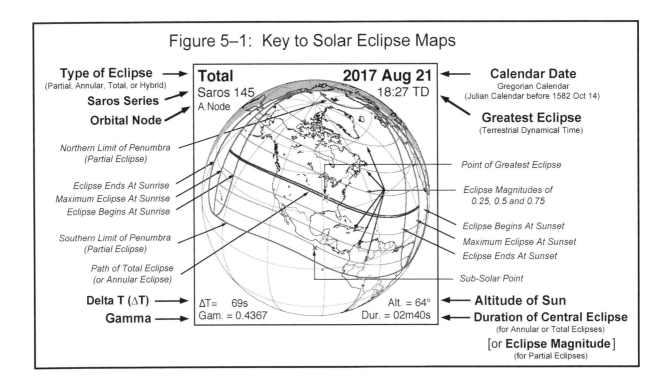

Figure 5–1: Key to Solar Eclipse Maps

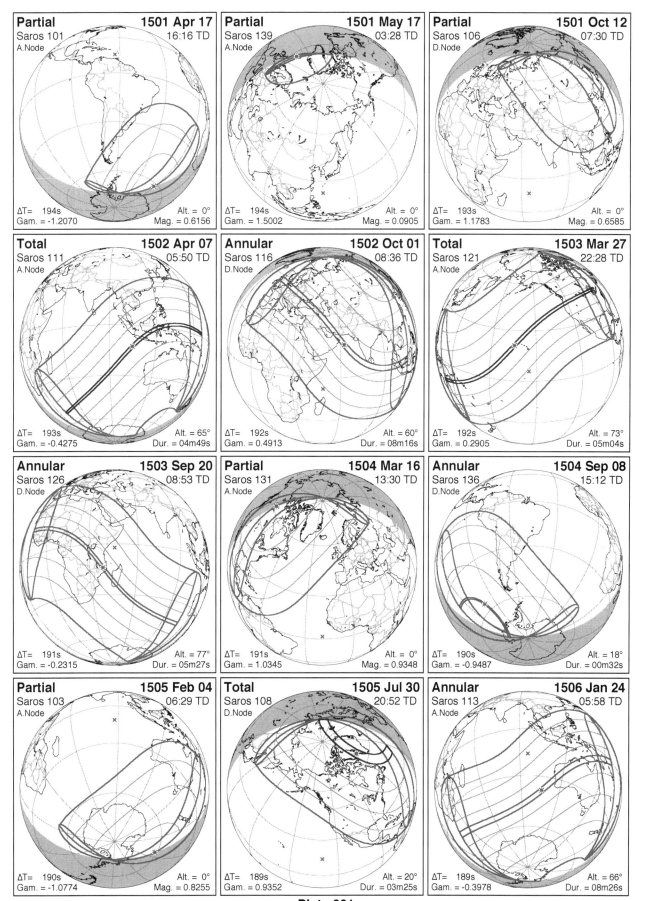

Partial 1501 Apr 17 Saros 101 16:16 TD A.Node ΔT= 194s Alt. = 0° Gam. = -1.2070 Mag. = 0.6156	**Partial** 1501 May 17 Saros 139 03:28 TD A.Node ΔT= 194s Alt. = 0° Gam. = 1.5002 Mag. = 0.0905	**Partial** 1501 Oct 12 Saros 106 07:30 TD D.Node ΔT= 193s Alt. = 0° Gam. = 1.1783 Mag. = 0.6585
Total 1502 Apr 07 Saros 111 05:50 TD A.Node ΔT= 193s Alt. = 65° Gam. = -0.4275 Dur. = 04m49s	**Annular** 1502 Oct 01 Saros 116 08:36 TD D.Node ΔT= 192s Alt. = 60° Gam. = 0.4913 Dur. = 08m16s	**Total** 1503 Mar 27 Saros 121 22:28 TD A.Node ΔT= 192s Alt. = 73° Gam. = 0.2905 Dur. = 05m04s
Annular 1503 Sep 20 Saros 126 08:53 TD D.Node ΔT= 191s Alt. = 77° Gam. = -0.2315 Dur. = 05m27s	**Partial** 1504 Mar 16 Saros 131 13:30 TD A.Node ΔT= 191s Alt. = 0° Gam. = 1.0345 Mag. = 0.9348	**Annular** 1504 Sep 08 Saros 136 15:12 TD D.Node ΔT= 190s Alt. = 18° Gam. = -0.9487 Dur. = 00m32s
Partial 1505 Feb 04 Saros 103 06:29 TD A.Node ΔT= 190s Alt. = 0° Gam. = -1.0774 Mag. = 0.8255	**Total** 1505 Jul 30 Saros 108 20:52 TD D.Node ΔT= 189s Alt. = 20° Gam. = 0.9352 Dur. = 03m25s	**Annular** 1506 Jan 24 Saros 113 05:58 TD A.Node ΔT= 189s Alt. = 66° Gam. = -0.3978 Dur. = 08m26s

Plate 001

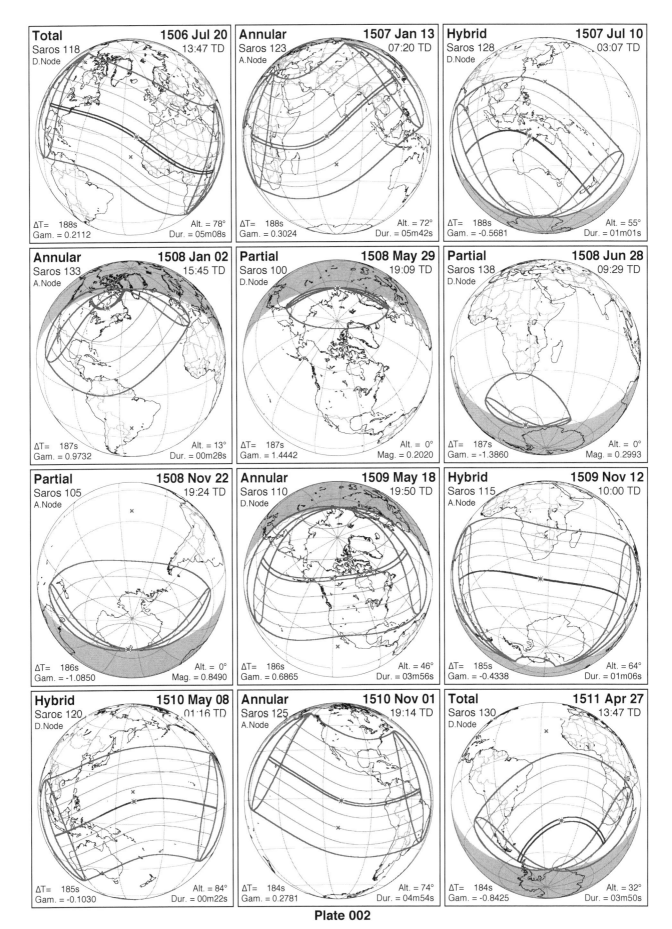

Total	1506 Jul 20
Saros 118	13:47 TD
D.Node	
ΔT = 188s	Alt. = 78°
Gam. = 0.2112	Dur. = 05m08s

Annular	1507 Jan 13
Saros 123	07:20 TD
A.Node	
ΔT = 188s	Alt. = 72°
Gam. = 0.3024	Dur. = 05m42s

Hybrid	1507 Jul 10
Saros 128	03:07 TD
D.Node	
ΔT = 188s	Alt. = 55°
Gam. = -0.5681	Dur. = 01m01s

Annular	1508 Jan 02
Saros 133	15:45 TD
A.Node	
ΔT = 187s	Alt. = 13°
Gam. = 0.9732	Dur. = 00m28s

Partial	1508 May 29
Saros 100	19:09 TD
D.Node	
ΔT = 187s	Alt. = 0°
Gam. = 1.4442	Mag. = 0.2020

Partial	1508 Jun 28
Saros 138	09:29 TD
D.Node	
ΔT = 187s	Alt. = 0°
Gam. = -1.3860	Mag. = 0.2993

Partial	1508 Nov 22
Saros 105	19:24 TD
A.Node	
ΔT = 186s	Alt. = 0°
Gam. = -1.0850	Mag. = 0.8490

Annular	1509 May 18
Saros 110	19:50 TD
D.Node	
ΔT = 186s	Alt. = 46°
Gam. = 0.6865	Dur. = 03m56s

Hybrid	1509 Nov 12
Saros 115	10:00 TD
A.Node	
ΔT = 185s	Alt. = 64°
Gam. = -0.4338	Dur. = 01m06s

Hybrid	1510 May 08
Saros 120	01:16 TD
D.Node	
ΔT = 185s	Alt. = 84°
Gam. = -0.1030	Dur. = 00m22s

Annular	1510 Nov 01
Saros 125	19:14 TD
A.Node	
ΔT = 184s	Alt. = 74°
Gam. = 0.2781	Dur. = 04m54s

Total	1511 Apr 27
Saros 130	13:47 TD
D.Node	
ΔT = 184s	Alt. = 32°
Gam. = -0.8425	Dur. = 03m50s

Plate 002

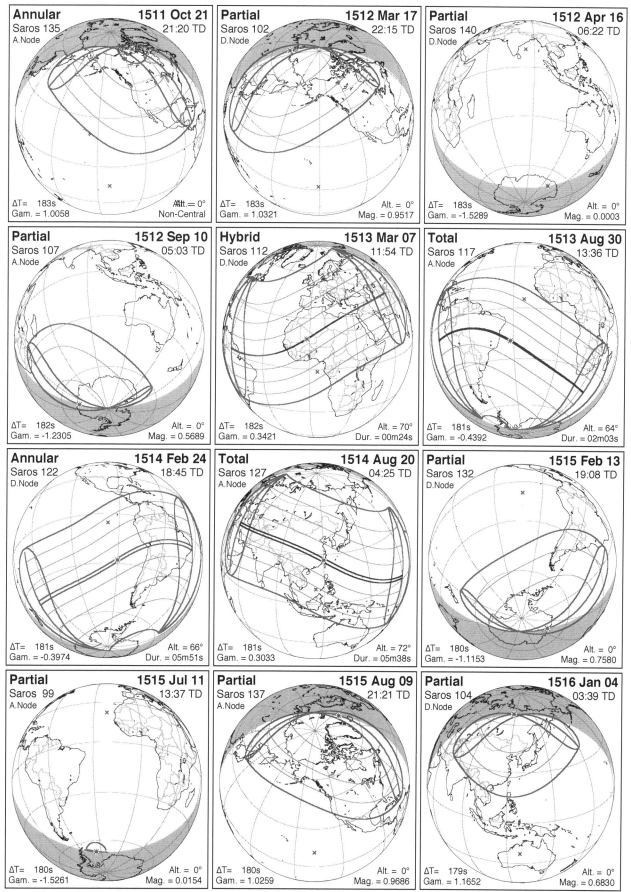

Annular **1511 Oct 21** Saros 135 21:20 TD A.Node ΔT= 183s AAlt.= 0° Gam. = 1.0058 Non-Central	**Partial** **1512 Mar 17** Saros 102 22:15 TD D.Node ΔT= 183s Alt. = 0° Gam. = 1.0321 Mag. = 0.9517	**Partial** **1512 Apr 16** Saros 140 06:22 TD D.Node ΔT= 183s Alt. = 0° Gam. = -1.5289 Mag. = 0.0003
Partial **1512 Sep 10** Saros 107 05:03 TD A.Node ΔT= 182s Alt. = 0° Gam. = -1.2305 Mag. = 0.5689	**Hybrid** **1513 Mar 07** Saros 112 11:54 TD D.Node ΔT= 182s Alt. = 70° Gam. = 0.3421 Dur. = 00m24s	**Total** **1513 Aug 30** Saros 117 13:36 TD A.Node ΔT= 181s Alt. = 64° Gam. = -0.4392 Dur. = 02m03s
Annular **1514 Feb 24** Saros 122 18:45 TD D.Node ΔT= 181s Alt. = 66° Gam. = -0.3974 Dur. = 05m51s	**Total** **1514 Aug 20** Saros 127 04:25 TD A.Node ΔT= 181s Alt. = 72° Gam. = 0.3033 Dur. = 05m38s	**Partial** **1515 Feb 13** Saros 132 19:08 TD D.Node ΔT= 180s Alt. = 0° Gam. = -1.1153 Mag. = 0.7580
Partial **1515 Jul 11** Saros 99 13:37 TD A.Node ΔT= 180s Alt. = 0° Gam. = -1.5261 Mag. = 0.0154	**Partial** **1515 Aug 09** Saros 137 21:21 TD A.Node ΔT= 180s Alt. = 0° Gam. = 1.0259 Mag. = 0.9686	**Partial** **1516 Jan 04** Saros 104 03:39 TD D.Node ΔT= 179s Alt. = 0° Gam. = 1.1652 Mag. = 0.6830

Plate 003

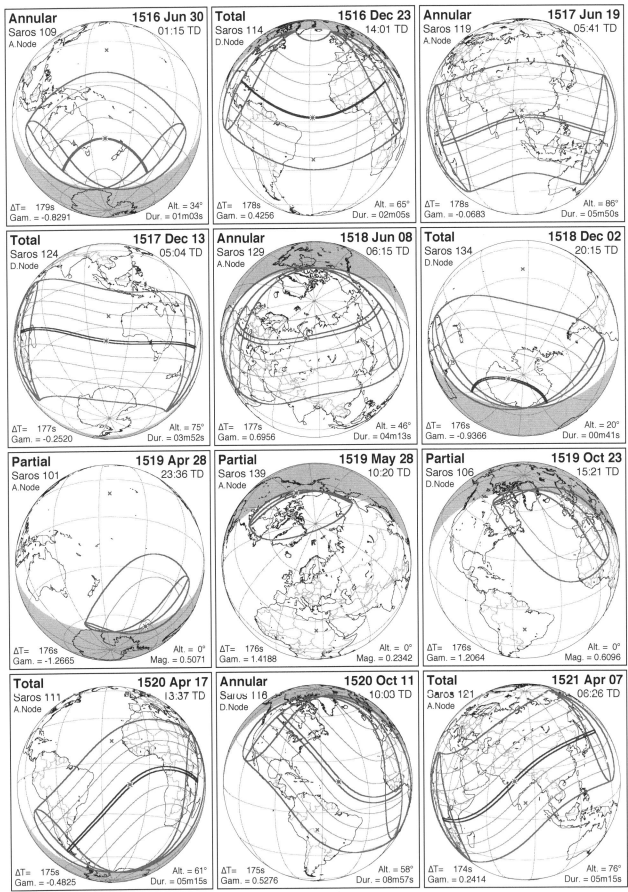

Annular	1516 Jun 30
Saros 109	01:15 TD
A.Node	
ΔT= 179s	Alt. = 34°
Gam. = -0.8291	Dur. = 01m03s

Total	1516 Dec 23
Saros 114	14:01 TD
D.Node	
ΔT= 178s	Alt. = 65°
Gam. = 0.4256	Dur. = 02m05s

Annular	1517 Jun 19
Saros 119	05:41 TD
A.Node	
ΔT= 178s	Alt. = 86°
Gam. = -0.0683	Dur. = 05m50s

Total	1517 Dec 13
Saros 124	05:04 TD
D.Node	
ΔT= 177s	Alt. = 75°
Gam. = -0.2520	Dur. = 03m52s

Annular	1518 Jun 08
Saros 129	06:15 TD
A.Node	
ΔT= 177s	Alt. = 46°
Gam. = 0.6956	Dur. = 04m13s

Total	1518 Dec 02
Saros 134	20:15 TD
D.Node	
ΔT= 176s	Alt. = 20°
Gam. = -0.9366	Dur. = 00m41s

Partial	1519 Apr 28
Saros 101	23:36 TD
A.Node	
ΔT= 176s	Alt. = 0°
Gam. = -1.2665	Mag. = 0.5071

Partial	1519 May 28
Saros 139	10:20 TD
A.Node	
ΔT= 176s	Alt. = 0°
Gam. = 1.4188	Mag. = 0.2342

Partial	1519 Oct 23
Saros 106	15:21 TD
D.Node	
ΔT= 176s	Alt. = 0°
Gam. = 1.2064	Mag. = 0.6096

Total	1520 Apr 17
Saros 111	13:37 TD
A.Node	
ΔT= 175s	Alt. = 61°
Gam. = -0.4825	Dur. = 05m15s

Annular	1520 Oct 11
Saros 116	10:03 TD
D.Node	
ΔT= 175s	Alt. = 58°
Gam. = 0.5276	Dur. = 08m57s

Total	1521 Apr 07
Saros 121	06:26 TD
A.Node	
ΔT= 174s	Alt. = 76°
Gam. = 0.2414	Dur. = 05m15s

Plate 004

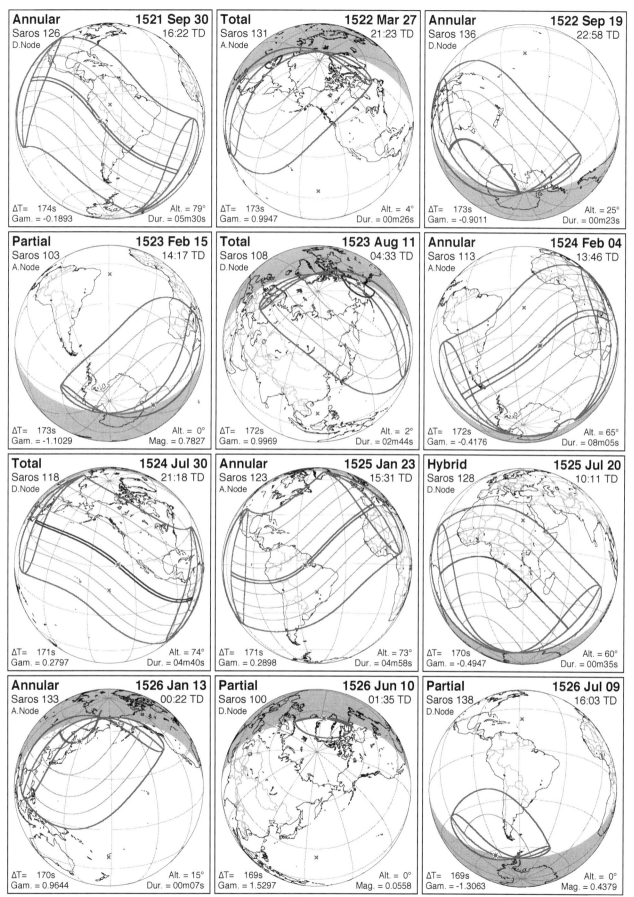

Annular 1521 Sep 30	
Saros 126 16:22 TD	
D.Node	
ΔT= 174s	Alt. = 79°
Gam. = -0.1893	Dur. = 05m30s

Total 1522 Mar 27	
Saros 131 21:23 TD	
A.Node	
ΔT= 173s	Alt. = 4°
Gam. = 0.9947	Dur. = 00m26s

Annular 1522 Sep 19	
Saros 136 22:58 TD	
D.Node	
ΔT= 173s	Alt. = 25°
Gam. = -0.9011	Dur. = 00m23s

Partial 1523 Feb 15	
Saros 103 14:17 TD	
A.Node	
ΔT= 173s	Alt. = 0°
Gam. = -1.1029	Mag. = 0.7827

Total 1523 Aug 11	
Saros 108 04:33 TD	
D.Node	
ΔT= 172s	Alt. = 2°
Gam. = 0.9969	Dur. = 02m44s

Annular 1524 Feb 04	
Saros 113 13:46 TD	
A.Node	
ΔT= 172s	Alt. = 65°
Gam. = -0.4176	Dur. = 08m05s

Total 1524 Jul 30	
Saros 118 21:18 TD	
D.Node	
ΔT= 171s	Alt. = 74°
Gam. = 0.2797	Dur. = 04m40s

Annular 1525 Jan 23	
Saros 123 15:31 TD	
A.Node	
ΔT= 171s	Alt. = 73°
Gam. = 0.2898	Dur. = 04m58s

Hybrid 1525 Jul 20	
Saros 128 10:11 TD	
D.Node	
ΔT= 170s	Alt. = 60°
Gam. = -0.4947	Dur. = 00m35s

Annular 1526 Jan 13	
Saros 133 00:22 TD	
A.Node	
ΔT= 170s	Alt. = 15°
Gam. = 0.9644	Dur. = 00m07s

Partial 1526 Jun 10	
Saros 100 01:35 TD	
D.Node	
ΔT= 169s	Alt. = 0°
Gam. = 1.5297	Mag. = 0.0558

Partial 1526 Jul 09	
Saros 138 16:03 TD	
D.Node	
ΔT= 169s	Alt. = 0°
Gam. = -1.3063	Mag. = 0.4379

Plate 005

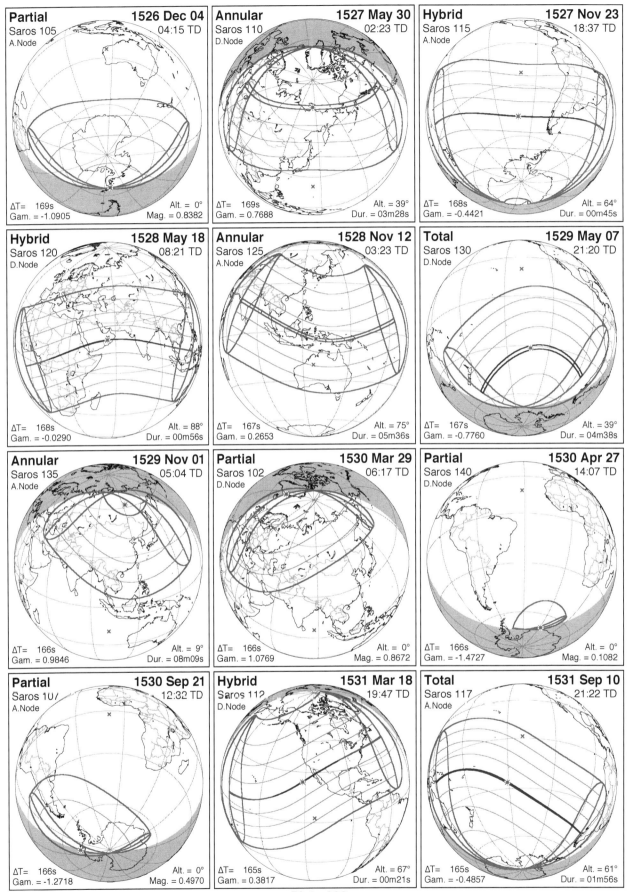

Partial — **1526 Dec 04**
Saros 105 — 04:15 TD
A.Node
ΔT= 169s — Alt. = 0°
Gam. = -1.0905 — Mag. = 0.8382

Annular — **1527 May 30**
Saros 110 — 02:23 TD
D.Node
ΔT= 169s — Alt. = 39°
Gam. = 0.7688 — Dur. = 03m28s

Hybrid — **1527 Nov 23**
Saros 115 — 18:37 TD
A.Node
ΔT= 168s — Alt. = 64°
Gam. = -0.4421 — Dur. = 00m45s

Hybrid — **1528 May 18**
Saros 120 — 08:21 TD
D.Node
ΔT= 168s — Alt. = 88°
Gam. = -0.0290 — Dur. = 00m56s

Annular — **1528 Nov 12**
Saros 125 — 03:23 TD
A.Node
ΔT= 167s — Alt. = 75°
Gam. = 0.2653 — Dur. = 05m36s

Total — **1529 May 07**
Saros 130 — 21:20 TD
D.Node
ΔT= 167s — Alt. = 39°
Gam. = -0.7760 — Dur. = 04m38s

Annular — **1529 Nov 01**
Saros 135 — 05:04 TD
A.Node
ΔT= 166s — Alt. = 9°
Gam. = 0.9846 — Dur. = 08m09s

Partial — **1530 Mar 29**
Saros 102 — 06:17 TD
D.Node
ΔT= 166s — Alt. = 0°
Gam. = 1.0769 — Mag. = 0.8672

Partial — **1530 Apr 27**
Saros 140 — 14:07 TD
D.Node
ΔT= 166s — Alt. = 0°
Gam. = -1.4727 — Mag. = 0.1082

Partial — **1530 Sep 21**
Saros 107 — 12:32 TD
A.Node
ΔT= 166s — Alt. = 0°
Gam. = -1.2718 — Mag. = 0.4970

Hybrid — **1531 Mar 18**
Saros 112 — 19:47 TD
D.Node
ΔT= 165s — Alt. = 67°
Gam. = 0.3817 — Dur. = 00m21s

Total — **1531 Sep 10**
Saros 117 — 21:22 TD
A.Node
ΔT= 165s — Alt. = 61°
Gam. = -0.4857 — Dur. = 01m56s

Plate 006

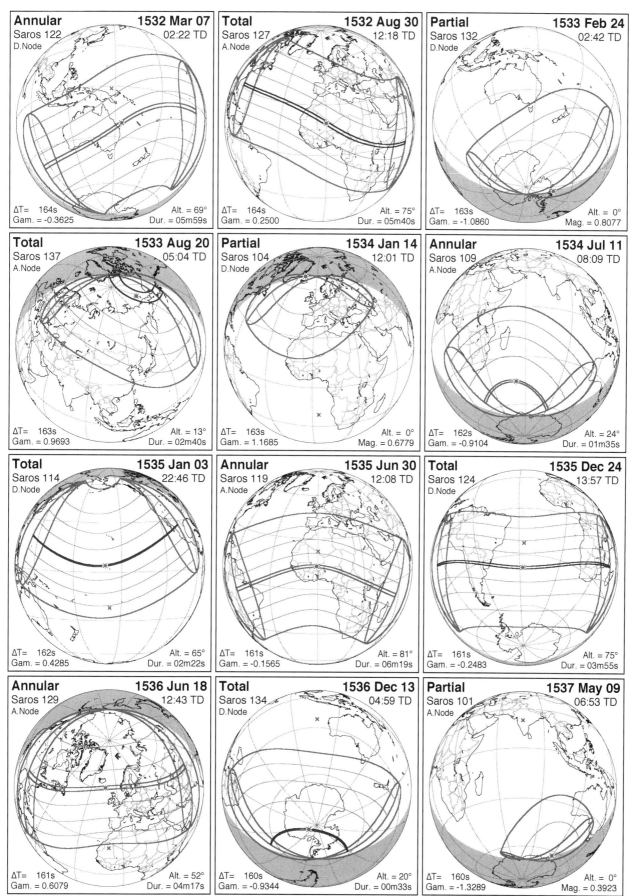

Annular   **1532 Mar 07**
Saros 122   02:22 TD
D.Node
ΔT= 164s   Alt. = 69°
Gam. = -0.3625   Dur. = 05m59s

Total   **1532 Aug 30**
Saros 127   12:18 TD
A.Node
ΔT= 164s   Alt. = 75°
Gam. = 0.2500   Dur. = 05m40s

Partial   **1533 Feb 24**
Saros 132   02:42 TD
D.Node
ΔT= 163s   Alt. = 0°
Gam. = -1.0860   Mag. = 0.8077

Total   **1533 Aug 20**
Saros 137   05:04 TD
A.Node
ΔT= 163s   Alt. = 13°
Gam. = 0.9693   Dur. = 02m40s

Partial   **1534 Jan 14**
Saros 104   12:01 TD
D.Node
ΔT= 163s   Alt. = 0°
Gam. = 1.1685   Mag. = 0.6779

Annular   **1534 Jul 11**
Saros 109   08:09 TD
A.Node
ΔT= 162s   Alt. = 24°
Gam. = -0.9104   Dur. = 01m35s

Total   **1535 Jan 03**
Saros 114   22:46 TD
D.Node
ΔT= 162s   Alt. = 65°
Gam. = 0.4285   Dur. = 02m22s

Annular   **1535 Jun 30**
Saros 119   12:08 TD
A.Node
ΔT= 161s   Alt. = 81°
Gam. = -0.1565   Dur. = 06m19s

Total   **1535 Dec 24**
Saros 124   13:57 TD
D.Node
ΔT= 161s   Alt. = 75°
Gam. = -0.2483   Dur. = 03m55s

Annular   **1536 Jun 18**
Saros 129   12:43 TD
A.Node
ΔT= 161s   Alt. = 52°
Gam. = 0.6079   Dur. = 04m17s

Total   **1536 Dec 13**
Saros 134   04:59 TD
D.Node
ΔT= 160s   Alt. = 20°
Gam. = -0.9344   Dur. = 00m33s

Partial   **1537 May 09**
Saros 101   06:53 TD
A.Node
ΔT= 160s   Alt. = 0°
Gam. = -1.3289   Mag. = 0.3923

Plate 007

101

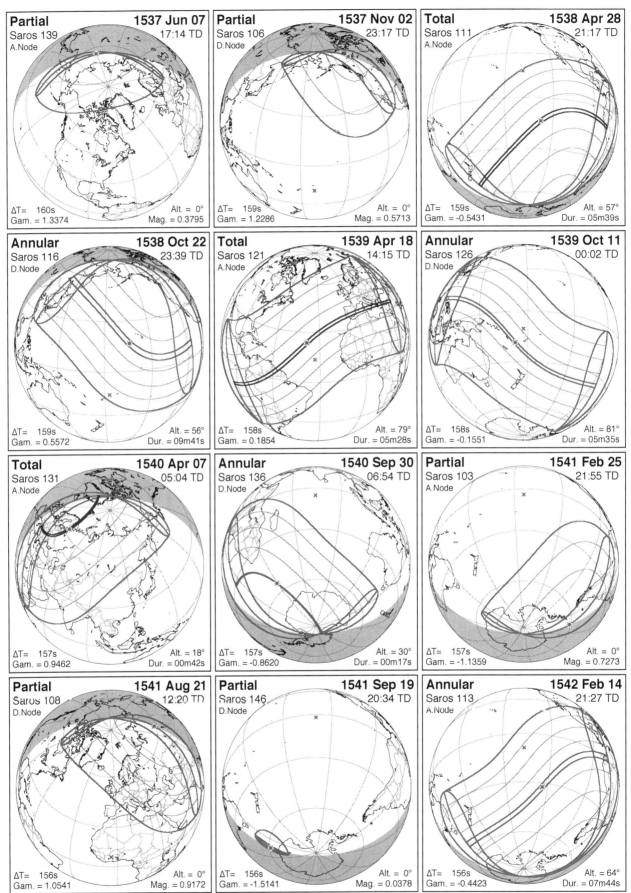

Partial	1537 Jun 07
Saros 139	17:14 TD
A.Node	
ΔT= 160s	Alt. = 0°
Gam. = 1.3374	Mag. = 0.3795

Partial	1537 Nov 02
Saros 106	23:17 TD
D.Node	
ΔT= 159s	Alt. = 0°
Gam. = 1.2286	Mag. = 0.5713

Total	1538 Apr 28
Saros 111	21:17 TD
A.Node	
ΔT= 159s	Alt. = 57°
Gam. = -0.5431	Dur. = 05m39s

Annular	1538 Oct 22
Saros 116	23:39 TD
D.Node	
ΔT= 159s	Alt. = 56°
Gam. = 0.5572	Dur. = 09m41s

Total	1539 Apr 18
Saros 121	14:15 TD
A.Node	
ΔT= 158s	Alt. = 79°
Gam. = 0.1854	Dur. = 05m28s

Annular	1539 Oct 11
Saros 126	00:02 TD
D.Node	
ΔT= 158s	Alt. = 81°
Gam. = -0.1551	Dur. = 05m35s

Total	1540 Apr 07
Saros 131	05:04 TD
A.Node	
ΔT= 157s	Alt. = 18°
Gam. = 0.9462	Dur. = 00m42s

Annular	1540 Sep 30
Saros 136	06:54 TD
D.Node	
ΔT= 157s	Alt. = 30°
Gam. = -0.8620	Dur. = 00m17s

Partial	1541 Feb 25
Saros 103	21:55 TD
A.Node	
ΔT= 157s	Alt. = 0°
Gam. = -1.1359	Mag. = 0.7273

Partial	1541 Aug 21
Saros 108	12:20 TD
D.Node	
ΔT= 156s	Alt. = 0°
Gam. = 1.0541	Mag. = 0.9172

Partial	1541 Sep 19
Saros 146	20:34 TD
D.Node	
ΔT= 156s	Alt. = 0°
Gam. = -1.5141	Mag. = 0.0378

Annular	1542 Feb 14
Saros 113	21:27 TD
A.Node	
ΔT= 156s	Alt. = 64°
Gam. = -0.4423	Dur. = 07m44s

Plate 008

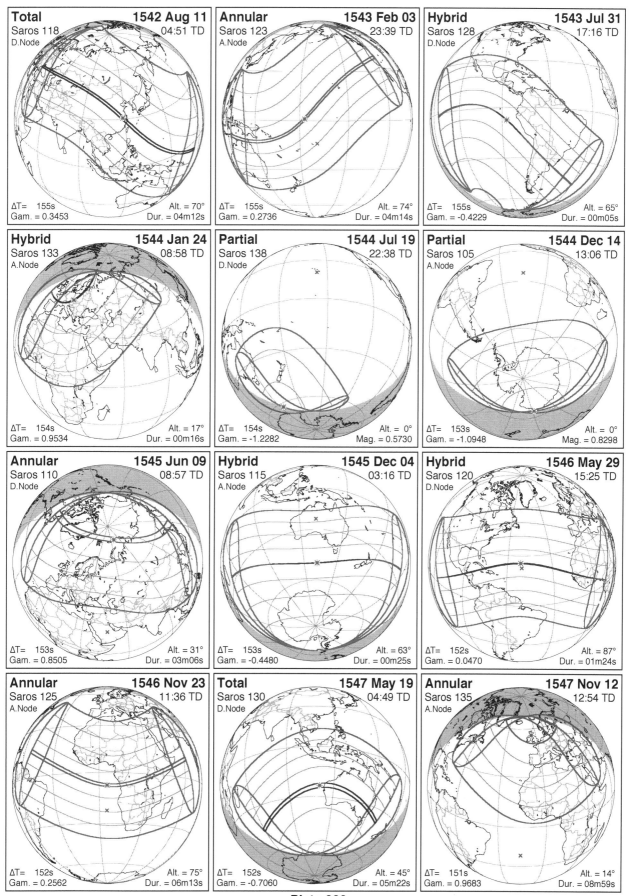

Total — **1542 Aug 11**
Saros 118 — 04:51 TD
D.Node
ΔT= 155s — Alt. = 70°
Gam. = 0.3453 — Dur. = 04m12s

Annular — **1543 Feb 03**
Saros 123 — 23:39 TD
A.Node
ΔT= 155s — Alt. = 74°
Gam. = 0.2736 — Dur. = 04m14s

Hybrid — **1543 Jul 31**
Saros 128 — 17:16 TD
D.Node
ΔT= 155s — Alt. = 65°
Gam. = -0.4229 — Dur. = 00m05s

Hybrid — **1544 Jan 24**
Saros 133 — 08:58 TD
A.Node
ΔT= 154s — Alt. = 17°
Gam. = 0.9534 — Dur. = 00m16s

Partial — **1544 Jul 19**
Saros 138 — 22:38 TD
D.Node
ΔT= 154s — Alt. = 0°
Gam. = -1.2282 — Mag. = 0.5730

Partial — **1544 Dec 14**
Saros 105 — 13:06 TD
A.Node
ΔT= 153s — Alt. = 0°
Gam. = -1.0948 — Mag. = 0.8298

Annular — **1545 Jun 09**
Saros 110 — 08:57 TD
D.Node
ΔT= 153s — Alt. = 31°
Gam. = 0.8505 — Dur. = 03m06s

Hybrid — **1545 Dec 04**
Saros 115 — 03:16 TD
A.Node
ΔT= 153s — Alt. = 63°
Gam. = -0.4480 — Dur. = 00m25s

Hybrid — **1546 May 29**
Saros 120 — 15:25 TD
D.Node
ΔT= 152s — Alt. = 87°
Gam. = 0.0470 — Dur. = 01m24s

Annular — **1546 Nov 23**
Saros 125 — 11:36 TD
A.Node
ΔT= 152s — Alt. = 75°
Gam. = 0.2562 — Dur. = 06m13s

Total — **1547 May 19**
Saros 130 — 04:49 TD
D.Node
ΔT= 152s — Alt. = 45°
Gam. = -0.7060 — Dur. = 05m22s

Annular — **1547 Nov 12**
Saros 135 — 12:54 TD
A.Node
ΔT= 151s — Alt. = 14°
Gam. = 0.9683 — Dur. = 08m59s

Plate 009

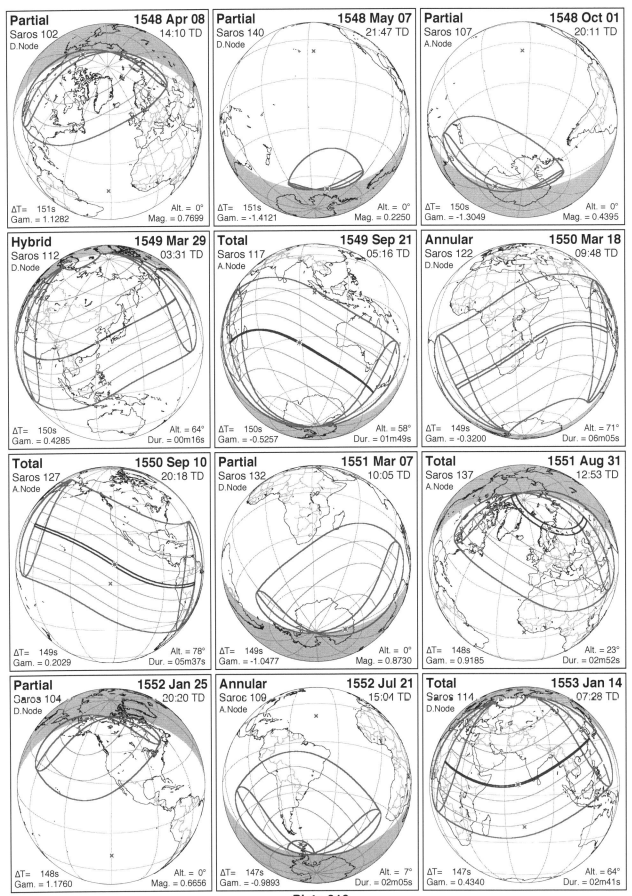

Partial — 1548 Apr 08
Saros 102 · 14:10 TD · D.Node
ΔT= 151s · Gam. = 1.1282 · Alt. = 0° · Mag. = 0.7699

Partial — 1548 May 07
Saros 140 · 21:47 TD · D.Node
ΔT= 151s · Gam. = -1.4121 · Alt. = 0° · Mag. = 0.2250

Partial — 1548 Oct 01
Saros 107 · 20:11 TD · A.Node
ΔT= 150s · Gam. = -1.3049 · Alt. = 0° · Mag. = 0.4395

Hybrid — 1549 Mar 29
Saros 112 · 03:31 TD · D.Node
ΔT= 150s · Gam. = 0.4285 · Alt. = 64° · Dur. = 00m16s

Total — 1549 Sep 21
Saros 117 · 05:16 TD · A.Node
ΔT= 150s · Gam. = -0.5257 · Alt. = 58° · Dur. = 01m49s

Annular — 1550 Mar 18
Saros 122 · 09:48 TD · D.Node
ΔT= 149s · Gam. = -0.3200 · Alt. = 71° · Dur. = 06m05s

Total — 1550 Sep 10
Saros 127 · 20:18 TD · A.Node
ΔT= 149s · Gam. = 0.2029 · Alt. = 78° · Dur. = 05m37s

Partial — 1551 Mar 07
Saros 132 · 10:05 TD · D.Node
ΔT= 149s · Gam. = -1.0477 · Alt. = 0° · Mag. = 0.8730

Total — 1551 Aug 31
Saros 137 · 12:53 TD · A.Node
ΔT= 148s · Gam. = 0.9185 · Alt. = 23° · Dur. = 02m52s

Partial — 1552 Jan 25
Saros 104 · 20:20 TD · D.Node
ΔT= 148s · Gam. = 1.1760 · Alt. = 0° · Mag. = 0.6656

Annular — 1552 Jul 21
Saros 109 · 15:04 TD · A.Node
ΔT= 147s · Gam. = -0.9893 · Alt. = 7° · Dur. = 02m05s

Total — 1553 Jan 14
Saros 114 · 07:28 TD · D.Node
ΔT= 147s · Gam. = 0.4340 · Alt. = 64° · Dur. = 02m41s

Plate 010

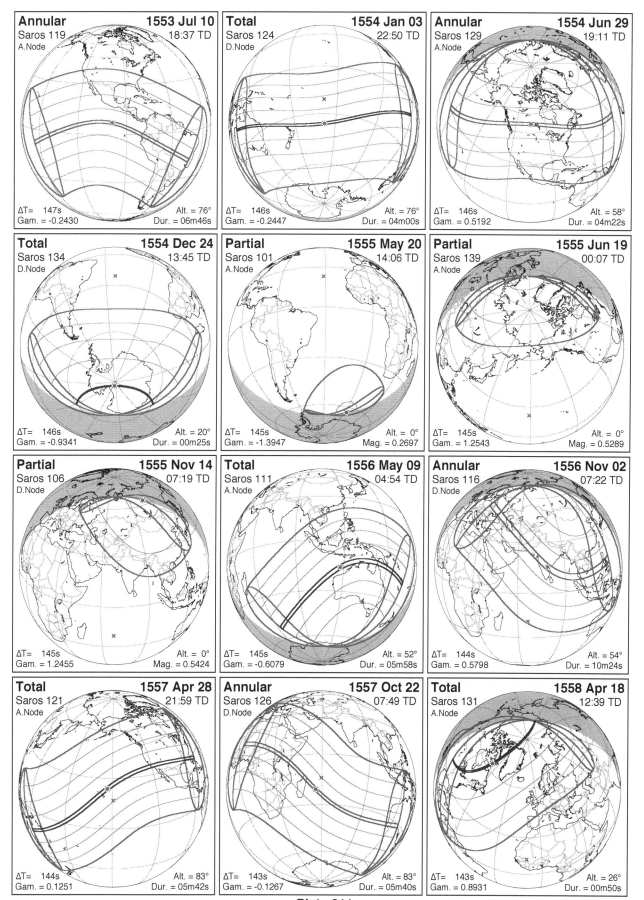

Annular   **1553 Jul 10**
Saros 119   18:37 TD
A.Node
ΔT= 147s   Alt. = 76°
Gam. = -0.2430   Dur. = 06m46s

Total   **1554 Jan 03**
Saros 124   22:50 TD
D.Node
ΔT= 146s   Alt. = 76°
Gam. = -0.2447   Dur. = 04m00s

Annular   **1554 Jun 29**
Saros 129   19:11 TD
A.Node
ΔT= 146s   Alt. = 58°
Gam. = 0.5192   Dur. = 04m22s

Total   **1554 Dec 24**
Saros 134   13:45 TD
D.Node
ΔT= 146s   Alt. = 20°
Gam. = -0.9341   Dur. = 00m25s

Partial   **1555 May 20**
Saros 101   14:06 TD
A.Node
ΔT= 145s   Alt. = 0°
Gam. = -1.3947   Mag. = 0.2697

Partial   **1555 Jun 19**
Saros 139   00:07 TD
A.Node
ΔT= 145s   Alt. = 0°
Gam. = 1.2543   Mag. = 0.5289

Partial   **1555 Nov 14**
Saros 106   07:19 TD
D.Node
ΔT= 145s   Alt. = 0°
Gam. = 1.2455   Mag. = 0.5424

Total   **1556 May 09**
Saros 111   04:54 TD
A.Node
ΔT= 145s   Alt. = 52°
Gam. = -0.6079   Dur. = 05m58s

Annular   **1556 Nov 02**
Saros 116   07:22 TD
D.Node
ΔT= 144s   Alt. = 54°
Gam. = 0.5798   Dur. = 10m24s

Total   **1557 Apr 28**
Saros 121   21:59 TD
A.Node
ΔT= 144s   Alt. = 83°
Gam. = 0.1251   Dur. = 05m42s

Annular   **1557 Oct 22**
Saros 126   07:49 TD
D.Node
ΔT= 143s   Alt. = 83°
Gam. = -0.1267   Dur. = 05m40s

Total   **1558 Apr 18**
Saros 131   12:39 TD
A.Node
ΔT= 143s   Alt. = 26°
Gam. = 0.8931   Dur. = 00m50s

Plate 011

105

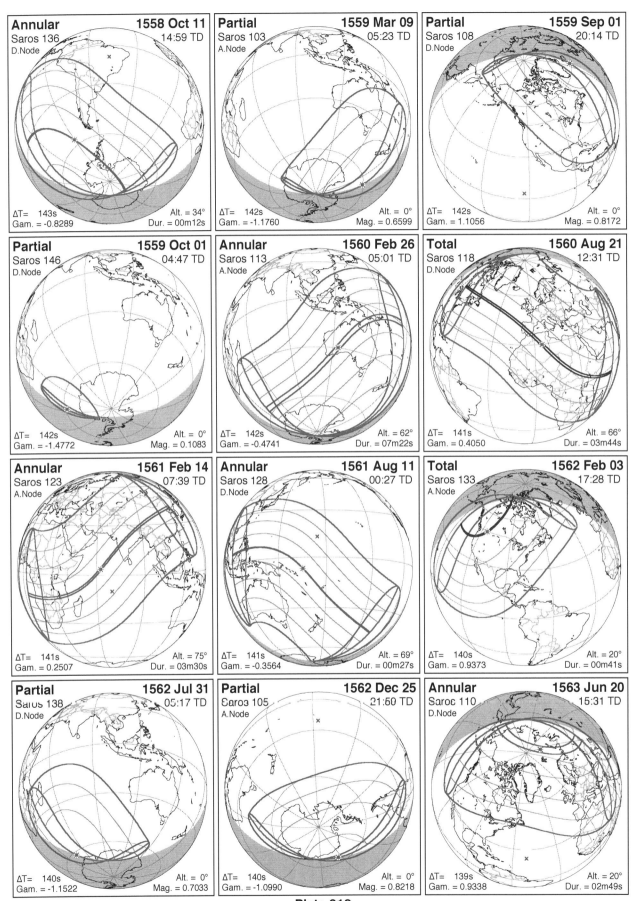

Annular   **1558 Oct 11**
Saros 136   14:59 TD
D.Node
ΔT= 143s   Alt. = 34°
Gam. = -0.8289   Dur. = 00m12s

Partial   **1559 Mar 09**
Saros 103   05:23 TD
A.Node
ΔT= 142s   Alt. = 0°
Gam. = -1.1760   Mag. = 0.6599

Partial   **1559 Sep 01**
Saros 108   20:14 TD
D.Node
ΔT= 142s   Alt. = 0°
Gam. = 1.1056   Mag. = 0.8172

Partial   **1559 Oct 01**
Saros 146   04:47 TD
D.Node
ΔT= 142s   Alt. = 0°
Gam. = -1.4772   Mag. = 0.1083

Annular   **1560 Feb 26**
Saros 113   05:01 TD
A.Node
ΔT= 142s   Alt. = 62°
Gam. = -0.4741   Dur. = 07m22s

Total   **1560 Aug 21**
Saros 118   12:31 TD
D.Node
ΔT= 141s   Alt. = 66°
Gam. = 0.4050   Dur. = 03m44s

Annular   **1561 Feb 14**
Saros 123   07:39 TD
A.Node
ΔT= 141s   Alt. = 75°
Gam. = 0.2507   Dur. = 03m30s

Annular   **1561 Aug 11**
Saros 128   00:27 TD
D.Node
ΔT= 141s   Alt. = 69°
Gam. = -0.3564   Dur. = 00m27s

Total   **1562 Feb 03**
Saros 133   17:28 TD
A.Node
ΔT= 140s   Alt. = 20°
Gam. = 0.9373   Dur. = 00m41s

Partial   **1562 Jul 31**
Saros 138   05:17 TD
D.Node
ΔT= 140s   Alt. = 0°
Gam. = -1.1522   Mag. = 0.7033

Partial   **1562 Dec 25**
Saros 105   21:50 TD
A.Node
ΔT= 140s   Alt. = 0°
Gam. = -1.0990   Mag. = 0.8218

Annular   **1563 Jun 20**
Saros 110   15:31 TD
D.Node
ΔT= 139s   Alt. = 20°
Gam. = 0.9338   Dur. = 02m49s

Plate 012

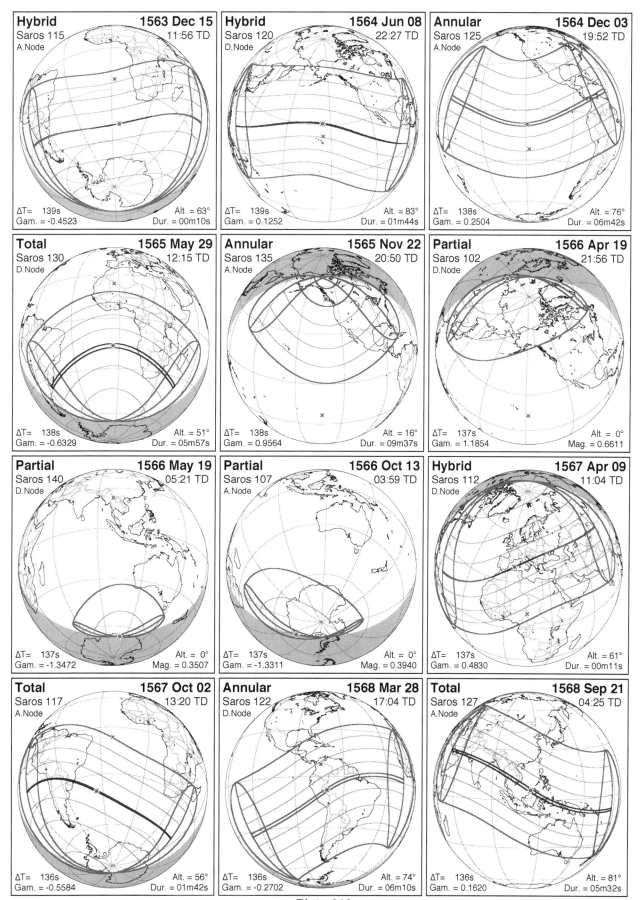

Hybrid 1563 Dec 15	**Hybrid** 1564 Jun 08	**Annular** 1564 Dec 03
Saros 115 11:56 TD	Saros 120 22:27 TD	Saros 125 19:52 TD
A.Node	D.Node	A.Node
ΔT= 139s Alt. = 63°	ΔT= 139s Alt. = 83°	ΔT= 138s Alt. = 76°
Gam. = -0.4523 Dur. = 00m10s	Gam. = 0.1252 Dur. = 01m44s	Gam. = 0.2504 Dur. = 06m42s
Total 1565 May 29	**Annular** 1565 Nov 22	**Partial** 1566 Apr 19
Saros 130 12:15 TD	Saros 135 20:50 TD	Saros 102 21:56 TD
D.Node	A.Node	D.Node
ΔT= 138s Alt. = 51°	ΔT= 138s Alt. = 16°	ΔT= 137s Alt. = 0°
Gam. = -0.6329 Dur. = 05m57s	Gam. = 0.9564 Dur. = 09m37s	Gam. = 1.1854 Mag. = 0.6611
Partial 1566 May 19	**Partial** 1566 Oct 13	**Hybrid** 1567 Apr 09
Saros 140 05:21 TD	Saros 107 03:59 TD	Saros 112 11:04 TD
D.Node	A.Node	D.Node
ΔT= 137s Alt. = 0°	ΔT= 137s Alt. = 0°	ΔT= 137s Alt. = 61°
Gam. = -1.3472 Mag. = 0.3507	Gam. = -1.3311 Mag. = 0.3940	Gam. = 0.4830 Dur. = 00m11s
Total 1567 Oct 02	**Annular** 1568 Mar 28	**Total** 1568 Sep 21
Saros 117 13:20 TD	Saros 122 17:04 TD	Saros 127 04:25 TD
A.Node	D.Node	A.Node
ΔT= 136s Alt. = 56°	ΔT= 136s Alt. = 74°	ΔT= 136s Alt. = 81°
Gam. = -0.5584 Dur. = 01m42s	Gam. = -0.2702 Dur. = 06m10s	Gam. = 0.1620 Dur. = 05m32s

Plate 013

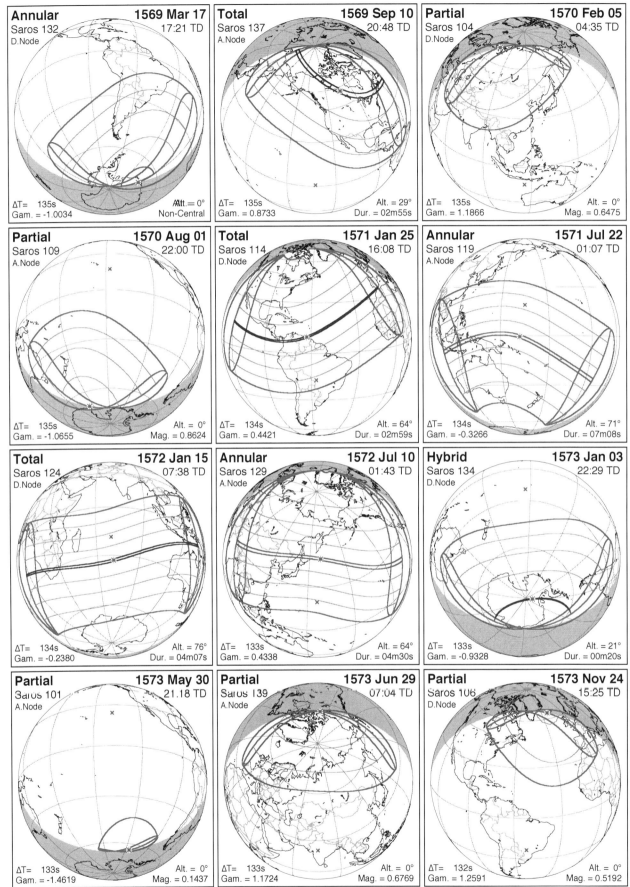

Annular **1569 Mar 17**	
Saros 132 17:21 TD	
D.Node	
ΔT= 135s Alt. = 0°	
Gam. = -1.0034 Non-Central	

Total **1569 Sep 10**	
Saros 137 20:48 TD	
A.Node	
ΔT= 135s Alt. = 29°	
Gam. = 0.8733 Dur. = 02m55s	

Partial **1570 Feb 05**	
Saros 104 04:35 TD	
D.Node	
ΔT= 135s Alt. = 0°	
Gam. = 1.1866 Mag. = 0.6475	

Partial **1570 Aug 01**	
Saros 109 22:00 TD	
A.Node	
ΔT= 135s Alt. = 0°	
Gam. = -1.0655 Mag. = 0.8624	

Total **1571 Jan 25**	
Saros 114 16:08 TD	
D.Node	
ΔT= 134s Alt. = 64°	
Gam. = 0.4421 Dur. = 02m59s	

Annular **1571 Jul 22**	
Saros 119 01:07 TD	
A.Node	
ΔT= 134s Alt. = 71°	
Gam. = -0.3266 Dur. = 07m08s	

Total **1572 Jan 15**	
Saros 124 07:38 TD	
D.Node	
ΔT= 134s Alt. = 76°	
Gam. = -0.2380 Dur. = 04m07s	

Annular **1572 Jul 10**	
Saros 129 01:43 TD	
A.Node	
ΔT= 133s Alt. = 64°	
Gam. = 0.4338 Dur. = 04m30s	

Hybrid **1573 Jan 03**	
Saros 134 22:29 TD	
D.Node	
ΔT= 133s Alt. = 21°	
Gam. = -0.9328 Dur. = 00m20s	

Partial **1573 May 30**	
Saros 101 21.18 TD	
A.Node	
ΔT= 133s Alt. = 0°	
Gam. = -1.4619 Mag. = 0.1437	

Partial **1573 Jun 29**	
Saros 139 07:04 TD	
A.Node	
ΔT= 133s Alt. = 0°	
Gam. = 1.1724 Mag. = 0.6769	

Partial **1573 Nov 24**	
Saros 106 15:25 TD	
D.Node	
ΔT= 132s Alt. = 0°	
Gam. = 1.2591 Mag. = 0.5192	

Plate 014

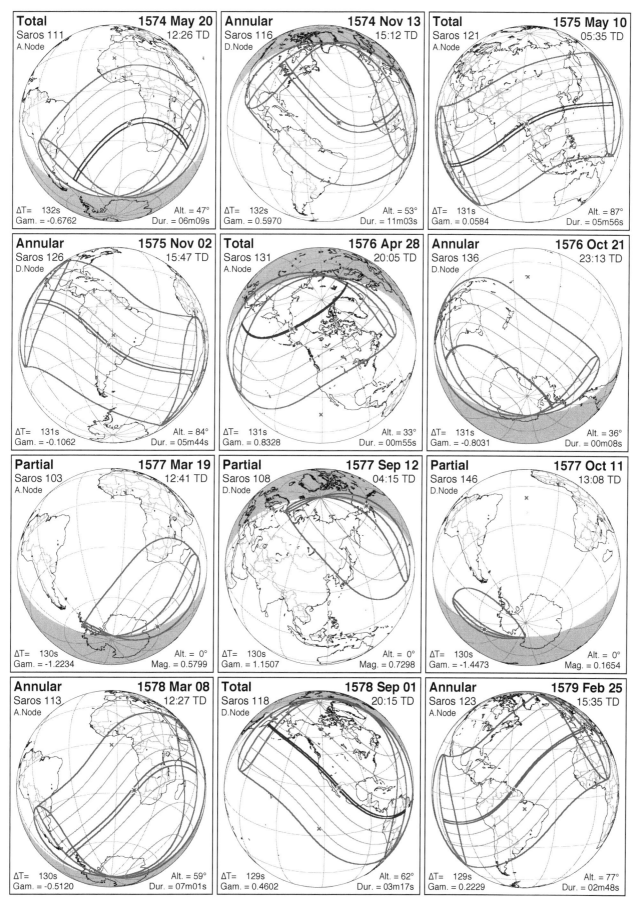

Total 1574 May 20	
Saros 111 12:26 TD	
A.Node	
ΔT= 132s	Alt. = 47°
Gam. = -0.6762	Dur. = 06m09s

Annular 1574 Nov 13	
Saros 116 15:12 TD	
D.Node	
ΔT= 132s	Alt. = 53°
Gam. = 0.5970	Dur. = 11m03s

Total 1575 May 10	
Saros 121 05:35 TD	
A.Node	
ΔT= 131s	Alt. = 87°
Gam. = 0.0584	Dur. = 05m56s

Annular 1575 Nov 02	
Saros 126 15:47 TD	
D.Node	
ΔT= 131s	Alt. = 84°
Gam. = -0.1062	Dur. = 05m44s

Total 1576 Apr 28	
Saros 131 20:05 TD	
A.Node	
ΔT= 131s	Alt. = 33°
Gam. = 0.8328	Dur. = 00m55s

Annular 1576 Oct 21	
Saros 136 23:13 TD	
D.Node	
ΔT= 131s	Alt. = 36°
Gam. = -0.8031	Dur. = 00m08s

Partial 1577 Mar 19	
Saros 103 12:41 TD	
A.Node	
ΔT= 130s	Alt. = 0°
Gam. = -1.2234	Mag. = 0.5799

Partial 1577 Sep 12	
Saros 108 04:15 TD	
D.Node	
ΔT= 130s	Alt. = 0°
Gam. = 1.1507	Mag. = 0.7298

Partial 1577 Oct 11	
Saros 146 13:08 TD	
D.Node	
ΔT= 130s	Alt. = 0°
Gam. = -1.4473	Mag. = 0.1654

Annular 1578 Mar 08	
Saros 113 12:27 TD	
A.Node	
ΔT= 130s	Alt. = 59°
Gam. = -0.5120	Dur. = 07m01s

Total 1578 Sep 01	
Saros 118 20:15 TD	
D.Node	
ΔT= 129s	Alt. = 62°
Gam. = 0.4602	Dur. = 03m17s

Annular 1579 Feb 25	
Saros 123 15:35 TD	
A.Node	
ΔT= 129s	Alt. = 77°
Gam. = 0.2229	Dur. = 02m48s

Plate 015

109

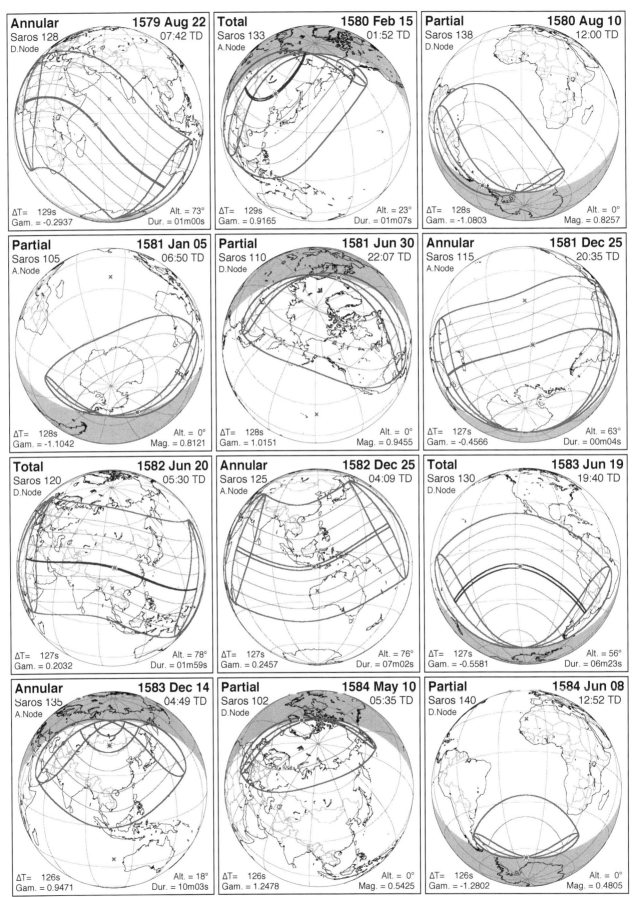

Annular **1579 Aug 22** Saros 128 07:42 TD D.Node ΔT= 129s Alt. = 73° Gam. = -0.2937 Dur. = 01m00s	**Total** **1580 Feb 15** Saros 133 01:52 TD A.Node ΔT= 129s Alt. = 23° Gam. = 0.9165 Dur. = 01m07s	**Partial** **1580 Aug 10** Saros 138 12:00 TD D.Node ΔT= 128s Alt. = 0° Gam. = -1.0803 Mag. = 0.8257
Partial **1581 Jan 05** Saros 105 06:50 TD A.Node ΔT= 128s Alt. = 0° Gam. = -1.1042 Mag. = 0.8121	**Partial** **1581 Jun 30** Saros 110 22:07 TD D.Node ΔT= 128s Alt. = 0° Gam. = 1.0151 Mag. = 0.9455	**Annular** **1581 Dec 25** Saros 115 20:35 TD A.Node ΔT= 127s Alt. = 63° Gam. = -0.4566 Dur. = 00m04s
Total **1582 Jun 20** Saros 120 05:30 TD D.Node ΔT= 127s Alt. = 78° Gam. = 0.2032 Dur. = 01m59s	**Annular** **1582 Dec 25** Saros 125 04:09 TD A.Node ΔT= 127s Alt. = 76° Gam. = 0.2457 Dur. = 07m02s	**Total** **1583 Jun 19** Saros 130 19:40 TD D.Node ΔT= 127s Alt. = 56° Gam. = -0.5581 Dur. = 06m23s
Annular **1583 Dec 14** Saros 135 04:49 TD A.Node ΔT= 126s Alt. = 18° Gam. = 0.9471 Dur. = 10m03s	**Partial** **1584 May 10** Saros 102 05:35 TD D.Node ΔT= 126s Alt. = 0° Gam. = 1.2478 Mag. = 0.5425	**Partial** **1584 Jun 08** Saros 140 12:52 TD D.Node ΔT= 126s Alt. = 0° Gam. = -1.2802 Mag. = 0.4805

Plate 016

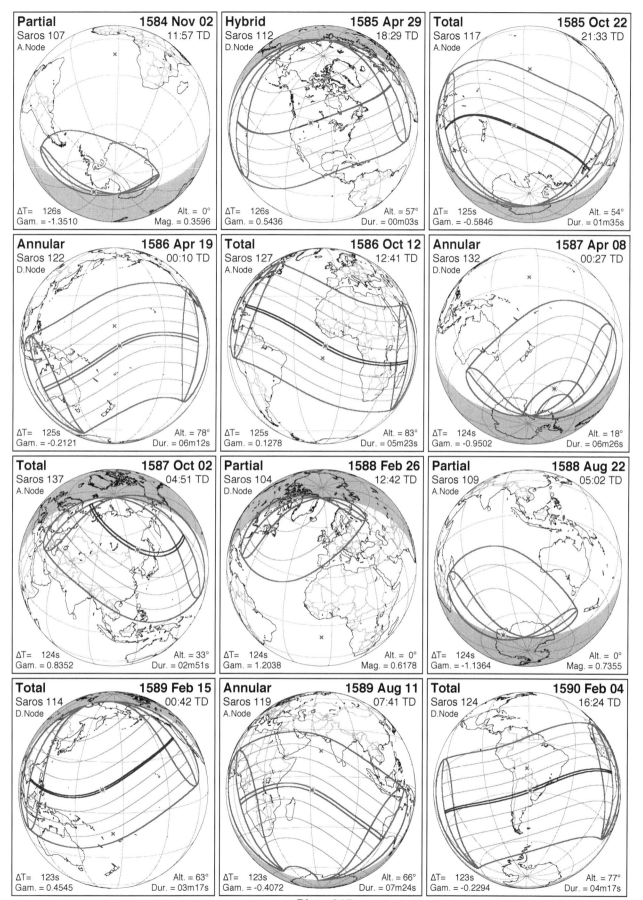

Partial	1584 Nov 02
Saros 107	11:57 TD
A.Node	
ΔT= 126s	Alt. = 0°
Gam. = -1.3510	Mag. = 0.3596

Hybrid	1585 Apr 29
Saros 112	18:29 TD
D.Node	
ΔT= 126s	Alt. = 57°
Gam. = 0.5436	Dur. = 00m03s

Total	1585 Oct 22
Saros 117	21:33 TD
A.Node	
ΔT= 125s	Alt. = 54°
Gam. = -0.5846	Dur. = 01m35s

Annular	1586 Apr 19
Saros 122	00:10 TD
D.Node	
ΔT= 125s	Alt. = 78°
Gam. = -0.2121	Dur. = 06m12s

Total	1586 Oct 12
Saros 127	12:41 TD
A.Node	
ΔT= 125s	Alt. = 83°
Gam. = 0.1278	Dur. = 05m23s

Annular	1587 Apr 08
Saros 132	00:27 TD
D.Node	
ΔT= 124s	Alt. = 18°
Gam. = -0.9502	Dur. = 06m26s

Total	1587 Oct 02
Saros 137	04:51 TD
A.Node	
ΔT= 124s	Alt. = 33°
Gam. = 0.8352	Dur. = 02m51s

Partial	1588 Feb 26
Saros 104	12:42 TD
D.Node	
ΔT= 124s	Alt. = 0°
Gam. = 1.2038	Mag. = 0.6178

Partial	1588 Aug 22
Saros 109	05:02 TD
A.Node	
ΔT= 124s	Alt. = 0°
Gam. = -1.1364	Mag. = 0.7355

Total	1589 Feb 15
Saros 114	00:42 TD
D.Node	
ΔT= 123s	Alt. = 63°
Gam. = 0.4545	Dur. = 03m17s

Annular	1589 Aug 11
Saros 119	07:41 TD
A.Node	
ΔT= 123s	Alt. = 66°
Gam. = -0.4072	Dur. = 07m24s

Total	1590 Feb 04
Saros 124	16:24 TD
D.Node	
ΔT= 123s	Alt. = 77°
Gam. = -0.2294	Dur. = 04m17s

Plate 017

111

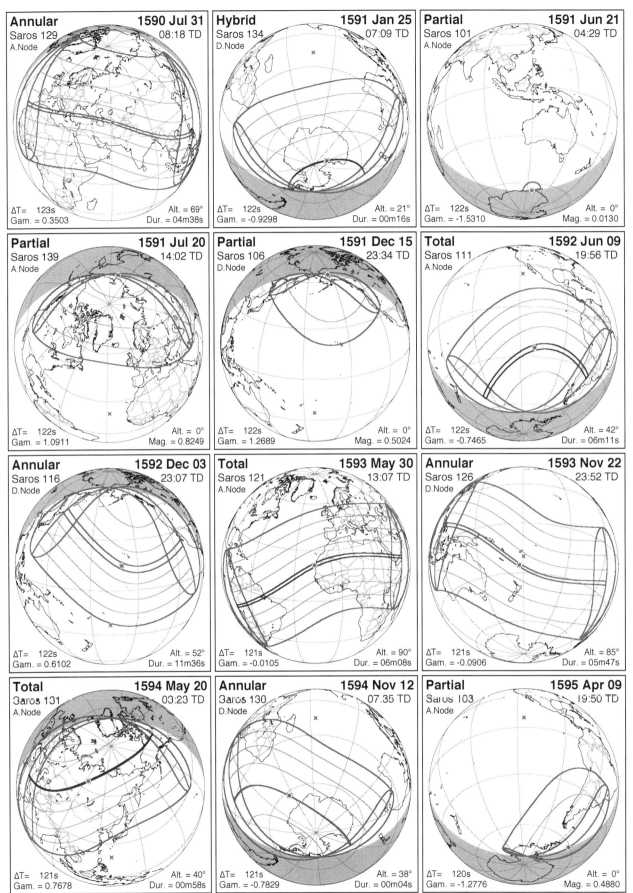

Annular 1590 Jul 31	**Hybrid** 1591 Jan 25	**Partial** 1591 Jun 21
Saros 129 08:18 TD	Saros 134 07:09 TD	Saros 101 04:29 TD
A.Node	D.Node	A.Node
ΔT= 123s Alt. = 69°	ΔT= 122s Alt. = 21°	ΔT= 122s Alt. = 0°
Gam. = 0.3503 Dur. = 04m38s	Gam. = -0.9298 Dur. = 00m16s	Gam. = -1.5310 Mag. = 0.0130
Partial 1591 Jul 20	**Partial** 1591 Dec 15	**Total** 1592 Jun 09
Saros 139 14:02 TD	Saros 106 23:34 TD	Saros 111 19:56 TD
A.Node	D.Node	A.Node
ΔT= 122s Alt. = 0°	ΔT= 122s Alt. = 0°	ΔT= 122s Alt. = 42°
Gam. = 1.0911 Mag. = 0.8249	Gam. = 1.2689 Mag. = 0.5024	Gam. = -0.7465 Dur. = 06m11s
Annular 1592 Dec 03	**Total** 1593 May 30	**Annular** 1593 Nov 22
Saros 116 23:07 TD	Saros 121 13:07 TD	Saros 126 23:52 TD
D.Node	A.Node	D.Node
ΔT= 122s Alt. = 52°	ΔT= 121s Alt. = 90°	ΔT= 121s Alt. = 85°
Gam. = 0.6102 Dur. = 11m36s	Gam. = -0.0105 Dur. = 06m08s	Gam. = -0.0906 Dur. = 05m47s
Total 1594 May 20	**Annular** 1594 Nov 12	**Partial** 1595 Apr 09
Saros 131 03:23 TD	Saros 130 07:35 TD	Saros 103 19:50 TD
A.Node	D.Node	A.Node
ΔT= 121s Alt. = 40°	ΔT= 121s Alt. = 38°	ΔT= 120s Alt. = 0°
Gam. = 0.7678 Dur. = 00m58s	Gam. = -0.7829 Dur. = 00m04s	Gam. = -1.2776 Mag. = 0.4880

Plate 018

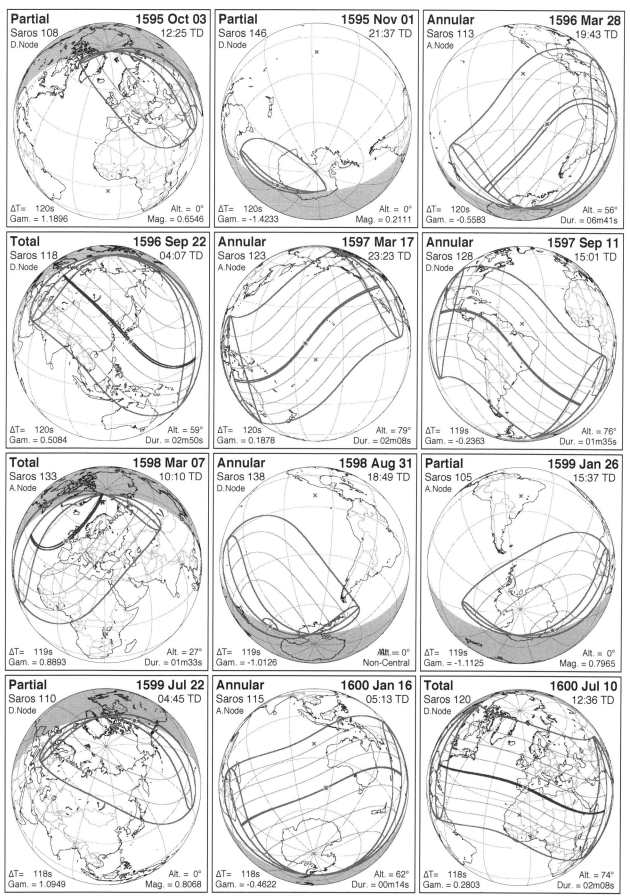

Partial — **1595 Oct 03**
Saros 108 — 12:25 TD
D.Node
ΔT= 120s — Alt. = 0°
Gam. = 1.1896 — Mag. = 0.6546

Partial — **1595 Nov 01**
Saros 146 — 21:37 TD
D.Node
ΔT= 120s — Alt. = 0°
Gam. = -1.4233 — Mag. = 0.2111

Annular — **1596 Mar 28**
Saros 113 — 19:43 TD
A.Node
ΔT= 120s — Alt. = 56°
Gam. = -0.5583 — Dur. = 06m41s

Total — **1596 Sep 22**
Saros 118 — 04:07 TD
D.Node
ΔT= 120s — Alt. = 59°
Gam. = 0.5084 — Dur. = 02m50s

Annular — **1597 Mar 17**
Saros 123 — 23:23 TD
A.Node
ΔT= 120s — Alt. = 79°
Gam. = 0.1878 — Dur. = 02m08s

Annular — **1597 Sep 11**
Saros 128 — 15:01 TD
D.Node
ΔT= 119s — Alt. = 76°
Gam. = -0.2363 — Dur. = 01m35s

Total — **1598 Mar 07**
Saros 133 — 10:10 TD
A.Node
ΔT= 119s — Alt. = 27°
Gam. = 0.8893 — Dur. = 01m33s

Annular — **1598 Aug 31**
Saros 138 — 18:49 TD
D.Node
ΔT= 119s — Alt. = 0°
Gam. = -1.0126 — Non-Central

Partial — **1599 Jan 26**
Saros 105 — 15:37 TD
A.Node
ΔT= 119s — Alt. = 0°
Gam. = -1.1125 — Mag. = 0.7965

Partial — **1599 Jul 22**
Saros 110 — 04:45 TD
D.Node
ΔT= 118s — Alt. = 0°
Gam. = 1.0949 — Mag. = 0.8068

Annular — **1600 Jan 16**
Saros 115 — 05:13 TD
A.Node
ΔT= 118s — Alt. = 62°
Gam. = -0.4622 — Dur. = 00m14s

Total — **1600 Jul 10**
Saros 120 — 12:36 TD
D.Node
ΔT= 118s — Alt. = 74°
Gam. = 0.2803 — Dur. = 02m08s

Plate 019

113

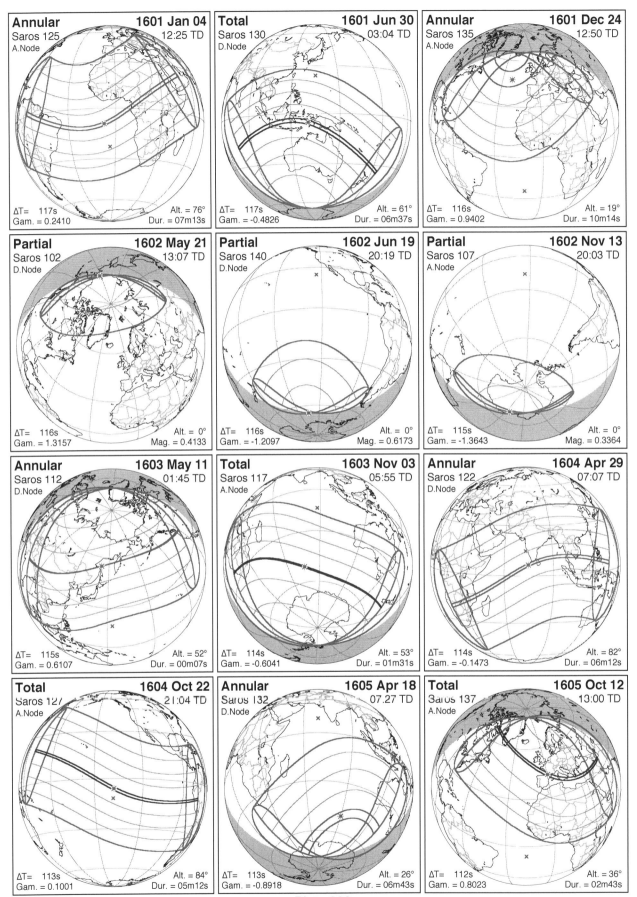

Annular 1601 Jan 04 Saros 125 A.Node 12:25 TD ΔT= 117s Alt. = 76° Gam. = 0.2410 Dur. = 07m13s	**Total** 1601 Jun 30 Saros 130 D.Node 03:04 TD ΔT= 117s Alt. = 61° Gam. = -0.4826 Dur. = 06m37s	**Annular** 1601 Dec 24 Saros 135 A.Node 12:50 TD ΔT= 116s Alt. = 19° Gam. = 0.9402 Dur. = 10m14s
Partial 1602 May 21 Saros 102 D.Node 13:07 TD ΔT= 116s Alt. = 0° Gam. = 1.3157 Mag. = 0.4133	**Partial** 1602 Jun 19 Saros 140 D.Node 20:19 TD ΔT= 116s Alt. = 0° Gam. = -1.2097 Mag. = 0.6173	**Partial** 1602 Nov 13 Saros 107 A.Node 20:03 TD ΔT= 115s Alt. = 0° Gam. = -1.3643 Mag. = 0.3364
Annular 1603 May 11 Saros 112 D.Node 01:45 TD ΔT= 115s Alt. = 52° Gam. = 0.6107 Dur. = 00m07s	**Total** 1603 Nov 03 Saros 117 A.Node 05:55 TD ΔT= 114s Alt. = 53° Gam. = -0.6041 Dur. = 01m31s	**Annular** 1604 Apr 29 Saros 122 D.Node 07:07 TD ΔT= 114s Alt. = 82° Gam. = -0.1473 Dur. = 06m12s
Total 1604 Oct 22 Saros 127 A.Node 21:04 TD ΔT= 113s Alt. = 84° Gam. = 0.1001 Dur. = 05m12s	**Annular** 1605 Apr 18 Saros 132 D.Node 07.27 TD ΔT= 113s Alt. = 26° Gam. = -0.8918 Dur. = 06m43s	**Total** 1605 Oct 12 Saros 137 A.Node 13:00 TD ΔT= 112s Alt. = 36° Gam. = 0.8023 Dur. = 02m43s

Plate 020

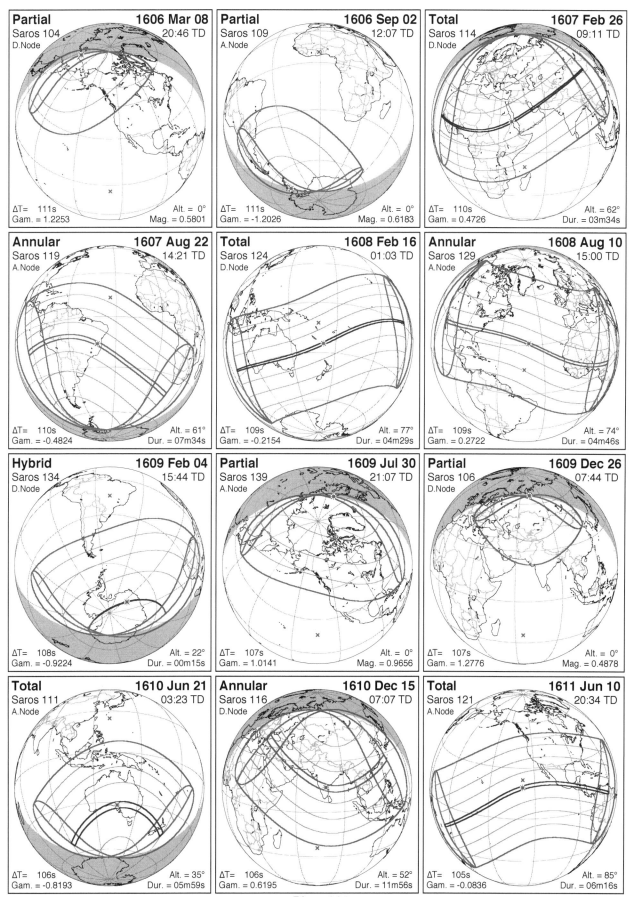

Partial	**1606 Mar 08**
Saros 104	20:46 TD
D.Node	
ΔT= 111s	Alt. = 0°
Gam. = 1.2253	Mag. = 0.5801

Partial	**1606 Sep 02**
Saros 109	12:07 TD
A.Node	
ΔT= 111s	Alt. = 0°
Gam. = -1.2026	Mag. = 0.6183

Total	**1607 Feb 26**
Saros 114	09:11 TD
D.Node	
ΔT= 110s	Alt. = 62°
Gam. = 0.4726	Dur. = 03m34s

Annular	**1607 Aug 22**
Saros 119	14:21 TD
A.Node	
ΔT= 110s	Alt. = 61°
Gam. = -0.4824	Dur. = 07m34s

Total	**1608 Feb 16**
Saros 124	01:03 TD
D.Node	
ΔT= 109s	Alt. = 77°
Gam. = -0.2154	Dur. = 04m29s

Annular	**1608 Aug 10**
Saros 129	15:00 TD
A.Node	
ΔT= 109s	Alt. = 74°
Gam. = 0.2722	Dur. = 04m46s

Hybrid	**1609 Feb 04**
Saros 134	15:44 TD
D.Node	
ΔT= 108s	Alt. = 22°
Gam. = -0.9224	Dur. = 00m15s

Partial	**1609 Jul 30**
Saros 139	21:07 TD
A.Node	
ΔT= 107s	Alt. = 0°
Gam. = 1.0141	Mag. = 0.9656

Partial	**1609 Dec 26**
Saros 106	07:44 TD
D.Node	
ΔT= 107s	Alt. = 0°
Gam. = 1.2776	Mag. = 0.4878

Total	**1610 Jun 21**
Saros 111	03:23 TD
A.Node	
ΔT= 106s	Alt. = 35°
Gam. = -0.8193	Dur. = 05m59s

Annular	**1610 Dec 15**
Saros 116	07:07 TD
D.Node	
ΔT= 106s	Alt. = 52°
Gam. = 0.6195	Dur. = 11m56s

Total	**1611 Jun 10**
Saros 121	20:34 TD
A.Node	
ΔT= 105s	Alt. = 85°
Gam. = -0.0836	Dur. = 06m16s

Plate 021

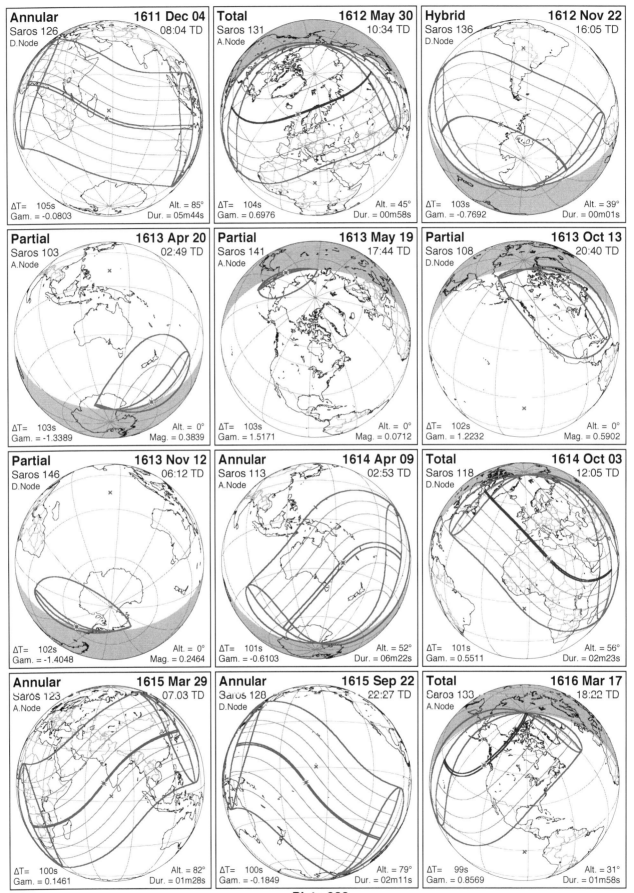

Annular   **1611 Dec 04**
Saros 126   08:04 TD
D.Node
ΔT= 105s   Alt. = 85°
Gam. = -0.0803   Dur. = 05m44s

Total   **1612 May 30**
Saros 131   10:34 TD
A.Node
ΔT= 104s   Alt. = 45°
Gam. = 0.6976   Dur. = 00m58s

Hybrid   **1612 Nov 22**
Saros 136   16:05 TD
D.Node
ΔT= 103s   Alt. = 39°
Gam. = -0.7692   Dur. = 00m01s

Partial   **1613 Apr 20**
Saros 103   02:49 TD
A.Node
ΔT= 103s   Alt. = 0°
Gam. = -1.3389   Mag. = 0.3839

Partial   **1613 May 19**
Saros 141   17:44 TD
A.Node
ΔT= 103s   Alt. = 0°
Gam. = 1.5171   Mag. = 0.0712

Partial   **1613 Oct 13**
Saros 108   20:40 TD
D.Node
ΔT= 102s   Alt. = 0°
Gam. = 1.2232   Mag. = 0.5902

Partial   **1613 Nov 12**
Saros 146   06:12 TD
D.Node
ΔT= 102s   Alt. = 0°
Gam. = -1.4048   Mag. = 0.2464

Annular   **1614 Apr 09**
Saros 113   02:53 TD
A.Node
ΔT= 101s   Alt. = 52°
Gam. = -0.6103   Dur. = 06m22s

Total   **1614 Oct 03**
Saros 118   12:05 TD
D.Node
ΔT= 101s   Alt. = 56°
Gam. = 0.5511   Dur. = 02m23s

Annular   **1615 Mar 29**
Saros 123   07.03 TD
A.Node
ΔT= 100s   Alt. = 82°
Gam. = 0.1461   Dur. = 01m28s

Annular   **1615 Sep 22**
Saros 128   22:27 TD
D.Node
ΔT= 100s   Alt. = 79°
Gam. = -0.1849   Dur. = 02m11s

Total   **1616 Mar 17**
Saros 133   18:22 TD
A.Node
ΔT= 99s   Alt. = 31°
Gam. = 0.8569   Dur. = 01m58s

Plate 022

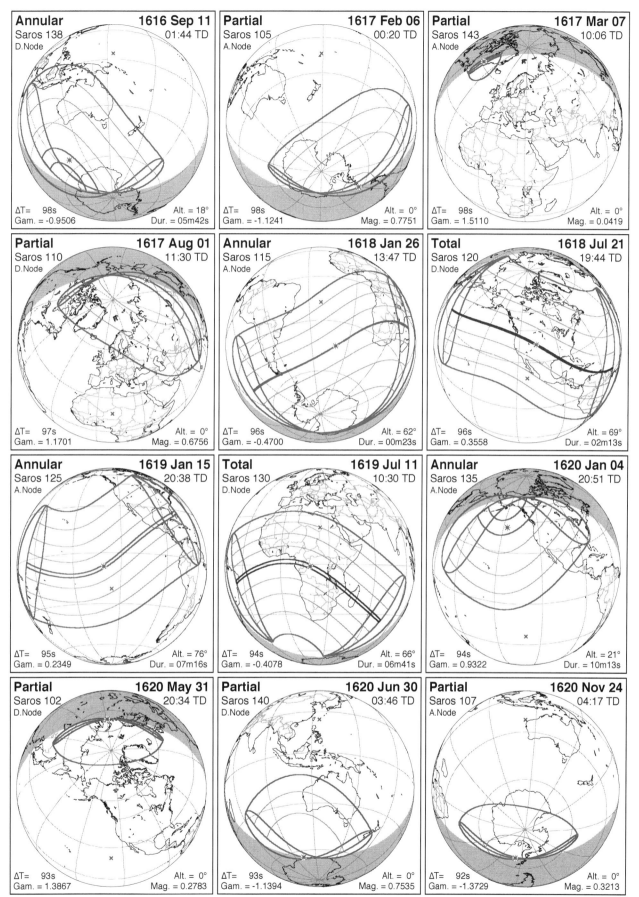

Annular	1616 Sep 11
Saros 138	01:44 TD
D.Node	
ΔT= 98s	Alt. = 18°
Gam. = -0.9506	Dur. = 05m42s

Partial	1617 Feb 06
Saros 105	00:20 TD
A.Node	
ΔT= 98s	Alt. = 0°
Gam. = -1.1241	Mag. = 0.7751

Partial	1617 Mar 07
Saros 143	10:06 TD
A.Node	
ΔT= 98s	Alt. = 0°
Gam. = 1.5110	Mag. = 0.0419

Partial	1617 Aug 01
Saros 110	11:30 TD
D.Node	
ΔT= 97s	Alt. = 0°
Gam. = 1.1701	Mag. = 0.6756

Annular	1618 Jan 26
Saros 115	13:47 TD
A.Node	
ΔT= 96s	Alt. = 62°
Gam. = -0.4700	Dur. = 00m23s

Total	1618 Jul 21
Saros 120	19:44 TD
D.Node	
ΔT= 96s	Alt. = 69°
Gam. = 0.3558	Dur. = 02m13s

Annular	1619 Jan 15
Saros 125	20:38 TD
A.Node	
ΔT= 95s	Alt. = 76°
Gam. = 0.2349	Dur. = 07m16s

Total	1619 Jul 11
Saros 130	10:30 TD
D.Node	
ΔT= 94s	Alt. = 66°
Gam. = -0.4078	Dur. = 06m41s

Annular	1620 Jan 04
Saros 135	20:51 TD
A.Node	
ΔT= 94s	Alt. = 21°
Gam. = 0.9322	Dur. = 10m13s

Partial	1620 May 31
Saros 102	20:34 TD
D.Node	
ΔT= 93s	Alt. = 0°
Gam. = 1.3867	Mag. = 0.2783

Partial	1620 Jun 30
Saros 140	03:46 TD
D.Node	
ΔT= 93s	Alt. = 0°
Gam. = -1.1394	Mag. = 0.7535

Partial	1620 Nov 24
Saros 107	04:17 TD
A.Node	
ΔT= 92s	Alt. = 0°
Gam. = -1.3729	Mag. = 0.3213

Plate 023

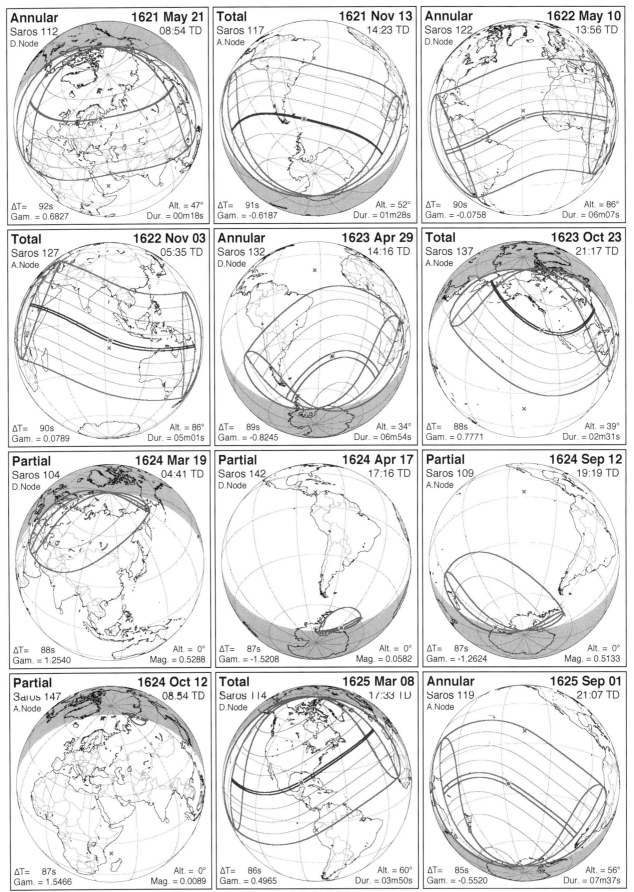

Annular	1621 May 21
Saros 112	08:54 TD
D.Node	
ΔT= 92s	Alt. = 47°
Gam. = 0.6827	Dur. = 00m18s

Total	1621 Nov 13
Saros 117	14:23 TD
A.Node	
ΔT= 91s	Alt. = 52°
Gam. = -0.6187	Dur. = 01m28s

Annular	1622 May 10
Saros 122	13:56 TD
D.Node	
ΔT= 90s	Alt. = 86°
Gam. = -0.0758	Dur. = 06m07s

Total	1622 Nov 03
Saros 127	05:35 TD
A.Node	
ΔT= 90s	Alt. = 86°
Gam. = 0.0789	Dur. = 05m01s

Annular	1623 Apr 29
Saros 132	14:16 TD
D.Node	
ΔT= 89s	Alt. = 34°
Gam. = -0.8245	Dur. = 06m54s

Total	1623 Oct 23
Saros 137	21:17 TD
A.Node	
ΔT= 88s	Alt. = 39°
Gam. = 0.7771	Dur. = 02m31s

Partial	1624 Mar 19
Saros 104	04:41 TD
D.Node	
ΔT= 88s	Alt. = 0°
Gam. = 1.2540	Mag. = 0.5288

Partial	1624 Apr 17
Saros 142	17:16 TD
D.Node	
ΔT= 87s	Alt. = 0°
Gam. = -1.5208	Mag. = 0.0582

Partial	1624 Sep 12
Saros 109	19:19 TD
A.Node	
ΔT= 87s	Alt. = 0°
Gam. = -1.2624	Mag. = 0.5133

Partial	1624 Oct 12
Saros 147	08.54 TD
A.Node	
ΔT= 87s	Alt. = 0°
Gam. = 1.5466	Mag. = 0.0089

Total	1625 Mar 08
Saros 114	17:33 TD
D.Node	
ΔT= 86s	Alt. = 60°
Gam. = 0.4965	Dur. = 03m50s

Annular	1625 Sep 01
Saros 119	21:07 TD
A.Node	
ΔT= 85s	Alt. = 56°
Gam. = -0.5520	Dur. = 07m37s

Plate 024

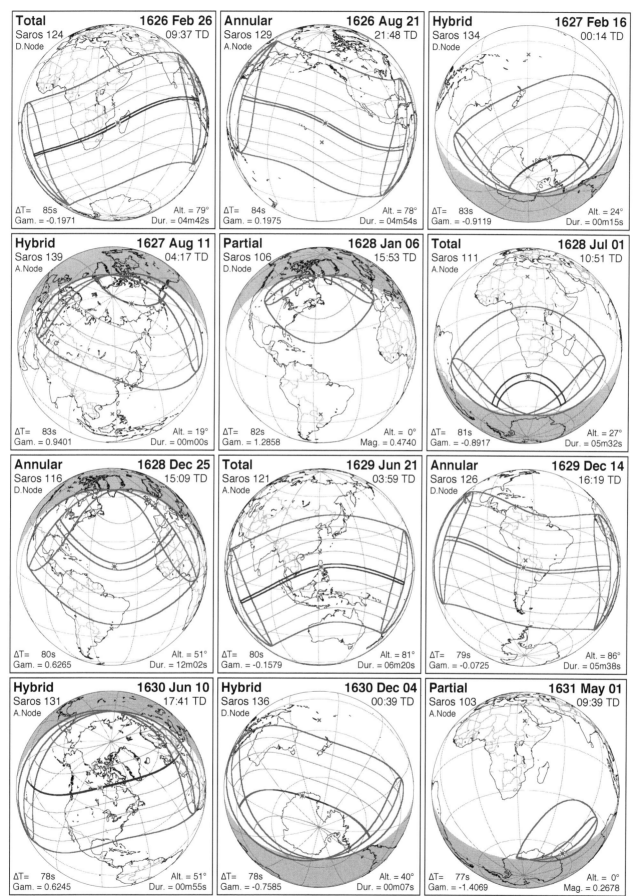

Total 1626 Feb 26 Saros 124 09:37 TD D.Node ΔT= 85s Alt. = 79° Gam. = -0.1971 Dur. = 04m42s	**Annular** 1626 Aug 21 Saros 129 21:48 TD A.Node ΔT= 84s Alt. = 78° Gam. = 0.1975 Dur. = 04m54s	**Hybrid** 1627 Feb 16 Saros 134 00:14 TD D.Node ΔT= 83s Alt. = 24° Gam. = -0.9119 Dur. = 00m15s
Hybrid 1627 Aug 11 Saros 139 04:17 TD A.Node ΔT= 83s Alt. = 19° Gam. = 0.9401 Dur. = 00m00s	**Partial** 1628 Jan 06 Saros 106 15:53 TD D.Node ΔT= 82s Alt. = 0° Gam. = 1.2858 Mag. = 0.4740	**Total** 1628 Jul 01 Saros 111 10:51 TD A.Node ΔT= 81s Alt. = 27° Gam. = -0.8917 Dur. = 05m32s
Annular 1628 Dec 25 Saros 116 15:09 TD D.Node ΔT= 80s Alt. = 51° Gam. = 0.6265 Dur. = 12m02s	**Total** 1629 Jun 21 Saros 121 03:59 TD A.Node ΔT= 80s Alt. = 81° Gam. = -0.1579 Dur. = 06m20s	**Annular** 1629 Dec 14 Saros 126 16:19 TD D.Node ΔT= 79s Alt. = 86° Gam. = -0.0725 Dur. = 05m38s
Hybrid 1630 Jun 10 Saros 131 17:41 TD A.Node ΔT= 78s Alt. = 51° Gam. = 0.6245 Dur. = 00m55s	**Hybrid** 1630 Dec 04 Saros 136 00:39 TD D.Node ΔT= 78s Alt. = 40° Gam. = -0.7585 Dur. = 00m07s	**Partial** 1631 May 01 Saros 103 09:39 TD A.Node ΔT= 77s Alt. = 0° Gam. = -1.4069 Mag. = 0.2678

Plate 025

119

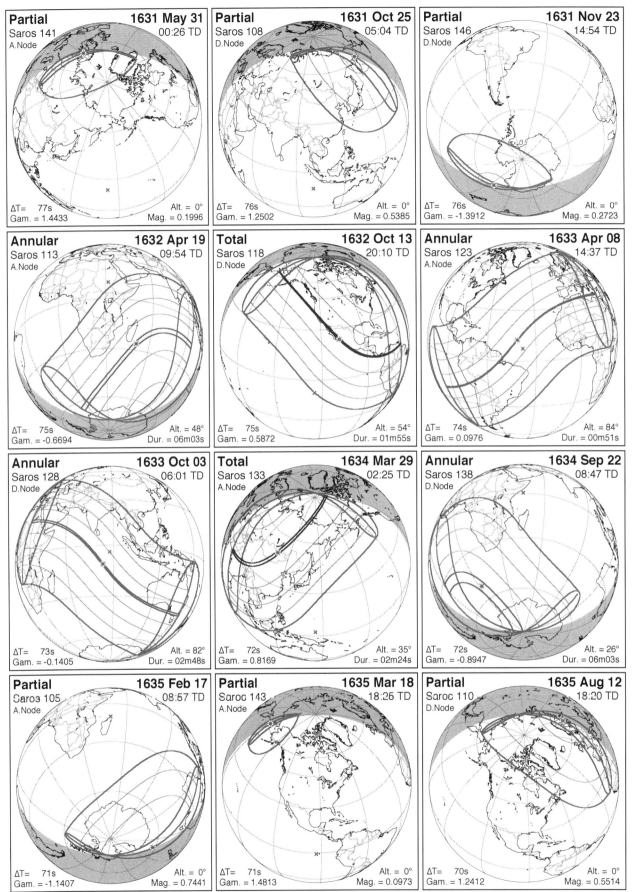

Partial **1631 May 31**	**Partial** **1631 Oct 25**	**Partial** **1631 Nov 23**
Saros 141 00:26 TD A.Node	Saros 108 05:04 TD D.Node	Saros 146 14:54 TD D.Node
ΔT= 77s Alt. = 0° Gam. = 1.4433 Mag. = 0.1996	ΔT= 76s Alt. = 0° Gam. = 1.2502 Mag. = 0.5385	ΔT= 76s Alt. = 0° Gam. = -1.3912 Mag. = 0.2723
Annular **1632 Apr 19**	**Total** **1632 Oct 13**	**Annular** **1633 Apr 08**
Saros 113 09:54 TD A.Node	Saros 118 20:10 TD D.Node	Saros 123 14:37 TD A.Node
ΔT= 75s Alt. = 48° Gam. = -0.6694 Dur. = 06m03s	ΔT= 75s Alt. = 54° Gam. = 0.5872 Dur. = 01m55s	ΔT= 74s Alt. = 84° Gam. = 0.0976 Dur. = 00m51s
Annular **1633 Oct 03**	**Total** **1634 Mar 29**	**Annular** **1634 Sep 22**
Saros 128 06:01 TD D.Node	Saros 133 02:25 TD A.Node	Saros 138 08:47 TD D.Node
ΔT= 73s Alt. = 82° Gam. = -0.1405 Dur. = 02m48s	ΔT= 72s Alt. = 35° Gam. = 0.8169 Dur. = 02m24s	ΔT= 72s Alt. = 26° Gam. = -0.8947 Dur. = 06m03s
Partial **1635 Feb 17**	**Partial** **1635 Mar 18**	**Partial** **1635 Aug 12**
Saros 105 08:57 TD A.Node	Saros 143 18:26 TD A.Node	Saros 110 18:20 TD D.Node
ΔT= 71s Alt. = 0° Gam. = -1.1407 Mag. = 0.7441	ΔT= 71s Alt. = 0° Gam. = 1.4813 Mag. = 0.0973	ΔT= 70s Alt. = 0° Gam. = 1.2412 Mag. = 0.5514

Plate 026

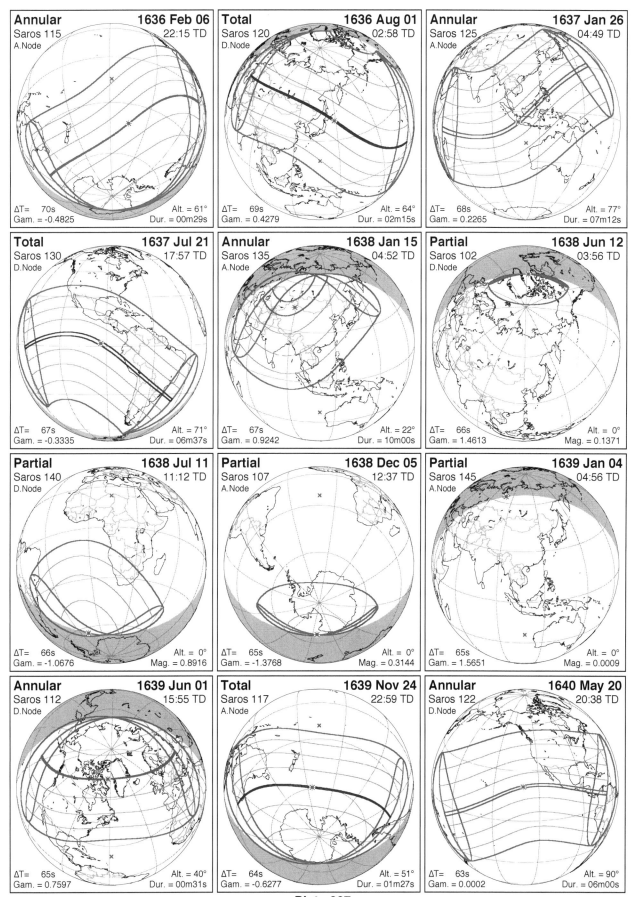

Annular   **1636 Feb 06**
Saros 115   22:15 TD
A.Node
ΔT= 70s   Alt. = 61°
Gam. = -0.4825   Dur. = 00m29s

Total   **1636 Aug 01**
Saros 120   02:58 TD
D.Node
ΔT= 69s   Alt. = 64°
Gam. = 0.4279   Dur. = 02m15s

Annular   **1637 Jan 26**
Saros 125   04:49 TD
A.Node
ΔT= 68s   Alt. = 77°
Gam. = 0.2265   Dur. = 07m12s

Total   **1637 Jul 21**
Saros 130   17:57 TD
D.Node
ΔT= 67s   Alt. = 71°
Gam. = -0.3335   Dur. = 06m37s

Annular   **1638 Jan 15**
Saros 135   04:52 TD
A.Node
ΔT= 67s   Alt. = 22°
Gam. = 0.9242   Dur. = 10m00s

Partial   **1638 Jun 12**
Saros 102   03:56 TD
D.Node
ΔT= 66s   Alt. = 0°
Gam. = 1.4613   Mag. = 0.1371

Partial   **1638 Jul 11**
Saros 140   11:12 TD
D.Node
ΔT= 66s   Alt. = 0°
Gam. = -1.0676   Mag. = 0.8916

Partial   **1638 Dec 05**
Saros 107   12:37 TD
A.Node
ΔT= 65s   Alt. = 0°
Gam. = -1.3768   Mag. = 0.3144

Partial   **1639 Jan 04**
Saros 145   04:56 TD
A.Node
ΔT= 65s   Alt. = 0°
Gam. = 1.5651   Mag. = 0.0009

Annular   **1639 Jun 01**
Saros 112   15:55 TD
D.Node
ΔT= 65s   Alt. = 40°
Gam. = 0.7597   Dur. = 00m31s

Total   **1639 Nov 24**
Saros 117   22:59 TD
A.Node
ΔT= 64s   Alt. = 51°
Gam. = -0.6277   Dur. = 01m27s

Annular   **1640 May 20**
Saros 122   20:38 TD
D.Node
ΔT= 63s   Alt. = 90°
Gam. = 0.0002   Dur. = 06m00s

Plate 027

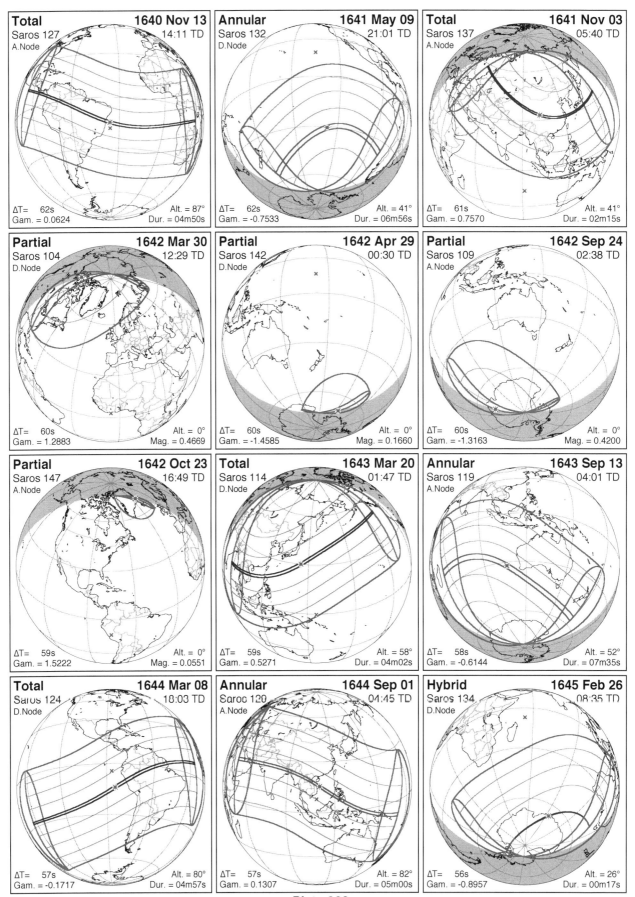

Total **1640 Nov 13** Saros 127 14:11 TD A.Node ΔT= 62s Alt. = 87° Gam. = 0.0624 Dur. = 04m50s	**Annular** **1641 May 09** Saros 132 21:01 TD D.Node ΔT= 62s Alt. = 41° Gam. = -0.7533 Dur. = 06m56s	**Total** **1641 Nov 03** Saros 137 05:40 TD A.Node ΔT= 61s Alt. = 41° Gam. = 0.7570 Dur. = 02m15s
Partial **1642 Mar 30** Saros 104 12:29 TD D.Node ΔT= 60s Alt. = 0° Gam. = 1.2883 Mag. = 0.4669	**Partial** **1642 Apr 29** Saros 142 00:30 TD D.Node ΔT= 60s Alt. = 0° Gam. = -1.4585 Mag. = 0.1660	**Partial** **1642 Sep 24** Saros 109 02:38 TD A.Node ΔT= 60s Alt. = 0° Gam. = -1.3163 Mag. = 0.4200
Partial **1642 Oct 23** Saros 147 16:49 TD A.Node ΔT= 59s Alt. = 0° Gam. = 1.5222 Mag. = 0.0551	**Total** **1643 Mar 20** Saros 114 01:47 TD D.Node ΔT= 59s Alt. = 58° Gam. = 0.5271 Dur. = 04m02s	**Annular** **1643 Sep 13** Saros 119 04:01 TD A.Node ΔT= 58s Alt. = 52° Gam. = -0.6144 Dur. = 07m35s
Total **1644 Mar 08** Saros 124 18:03 TD D.Node ΔT= 57s Alt. = 80° Gam. = -0.1717 Dur. = 04m57s	**Annular** **1644 Sep 01** Saros 120 04:45 TD A.Node ΔT= 57s Alt. = 82° Gam. = 0.1307 Dur. = 05m00s	**Hybrid** **1645 Feb 26** Saros 134 08:35 TD D.Node ΔT= 56s Alt. = 26° Gam. = -0.8957 Dur. = 00m17s

Plate 028

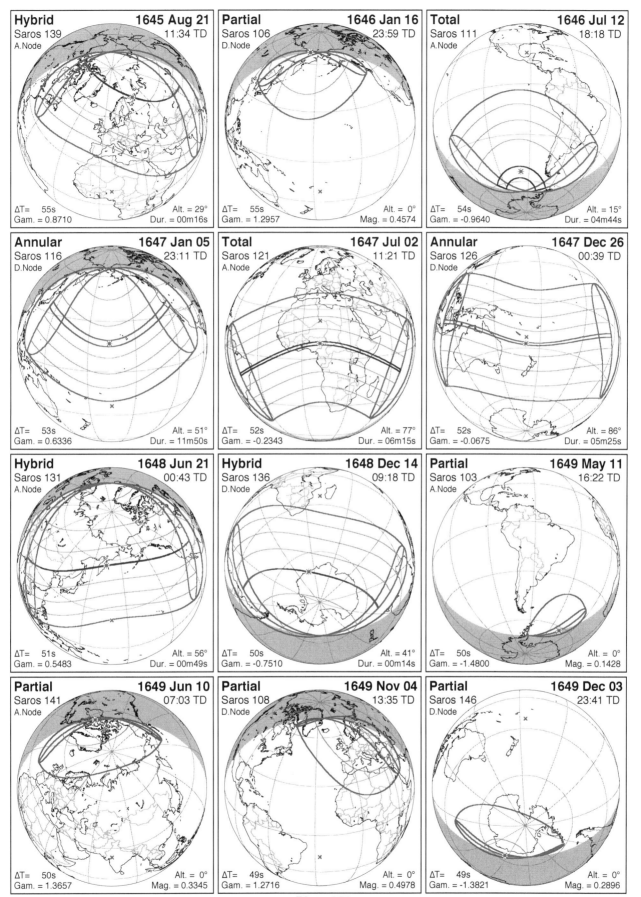

Hybrid	1645 Aug 21
Saros 139	11:34 TD
A.Node	
ΔT= 55s	Alt. = 29°
Gam. = 0.8710	Dur. = 00m16s

Partial	1646 Jan 16
Saros 106	23:59 TD
D.Node	
ΔT= 55s	Alt. = 0°
Gam. = 1.2957	Mag. = 0.4574

Total	1646 Jul 12
Saros 111	18:18 TD
A.Node	
ΔT= 54s	Alt. = 15°
Gam. = -0.9640	Dur. = 04m44s

Annular	1647 Jan 05
Saros 116	23:11 TD
D.Node	
ΔT= 53s	Alt. = 51°
Gam. = 0.6336	Dur. = 11m50s

Total	1647 Jul 02
Saros 121	11:21 TD
A.Node	
ΔT= 52s	Alt. = 77°
Gam. = -0.2343	Dur. = 06m15s

Annular	1647 Dec 26
Saros 126	00:39 TD
D.Node	
ΔT= 52s	Alt. = 86°
Gam. = -0.0675	Dur. = 05m25s

Hybrid	1648 Jun 21
Saros 131	00:43 TD
A.Node	
ΔT= 51s	Alt. = 56°
Gam. = 0.5483	Dur. = 00m49s

Hybrid	1648 Dec 14
Saros 136	09:18 TD
D.Node	
ΔT= 50s	Alt. = 41°
Gam. = -0.7510	Dur. = 00m14s

Partial	1649 May 11
Saros 103	16:22 TD
A.Node	
ΔT= 50s	Alt. = 0°
Gam. = -1.4800	Mag. = 0.1428

Partial	1649 Jun 10
Saros 141	07:03 TD
A.Node	
ΔT= 50s	Alt. = 0°
Gam. = 1.3657	Mag. = 0.3345

Partial	1649 Nov 04
Saros 108	13:35 TD
D.Node	
ΔT= 49s	Alt. = 0°
Gam. = 1.2716	Mag. = 0.4978

Partial	1649 Dec 03
Saros 146	23:41 TD
D.Node	
ΔT= 49s	Alt. = 0°
Gam. = -1.3821	Mag. = 0.2896

Plate 029

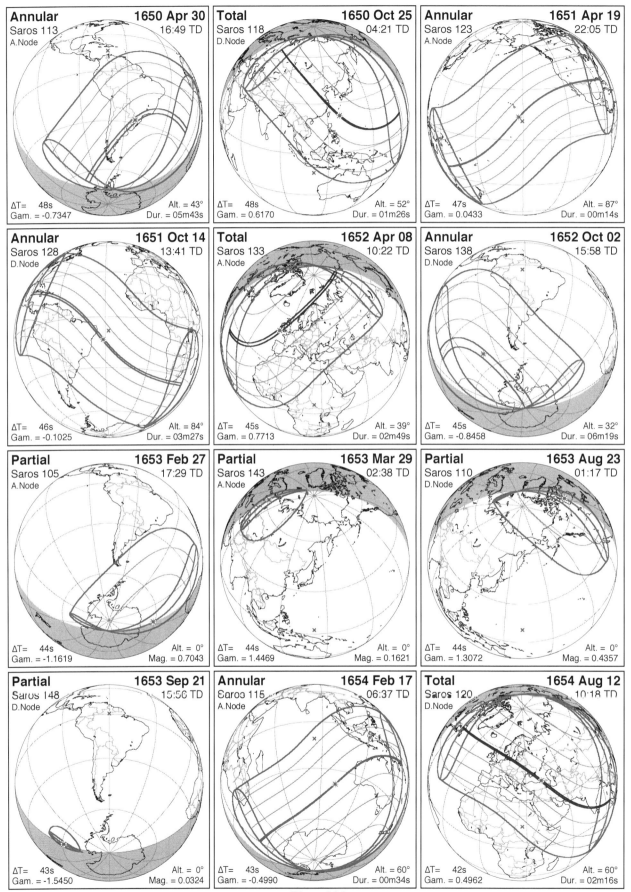

Annular 1650 Apr 30 Saros 113 16:49 TD A.Node ΔT= 48s Alt. = 43° Gam. = -0.7347 Dur. = 05m43s	**Total** 1650 Oct 25 Saros 118 04:21 TD D.Node ΔT= 48s Alt. = 52° Gam. = 0.6170 Dur. = 01m26s	**Annular** 1651 Apr 19 Saros 123 22:05 TD A.Node ΔT= 47s Alt. = 87° Gam. = 0.0433 Dur. = 00m14s
Annular 1651 Oct 14 Saros 128 13:41 TD D.Node ΔT= 46s Alt. = 84° Gam. = -0.1025 Dur. = 03m27s	**Total** 1652 Apr 08 Saros 133 10:22 TD A.Node ΔT= 45s Alt. = 39° Gam. = 0.7713 Dur. = 02m49s	**Annular** 1652 Oct 02 Saros 138 15:58 TD D.Node ΔT= 45s Alt. = 32° Gam. = -0.8458 Dur. = 06m19s
Partial 1653 Feb 27 Saros 105 17:29 TD A.Node ΔT= 44s Alt. = 0° Gam. = -1.1619 Mag. = 0.7043	**Partial** 1653 Mar 29 Saros 143 02:38 TD A.Node ΔT= 44s Alt. = 0° Gam. = 1.4469 Mag. = 0.1621	**Partial** 1653 Aug 23 Saros 110 01:17 TD D.Node ΔT= 44s Alt. = 0° Gam. = 1.3072 Mag. = 0.4357
Partial 1653 Sep 21 Saros 148 15:56 TD D.Node ΔT= 43s Alt. = 0° Gam. = -1.5450 Mag. = 0.0324	**Annular** 1654 Feb 17 Saros 115 06:37 TD A.Node ΔT= 43s Alt. = 60° Gam. = -0.4990 Dur. = 00m34s	**Total** 1654 Aug 12 Saros 120 10:18 TD D.Node ΔT= 42s Alt. = 60° Gam. = 0.4962 Dur. = 02m16s

Plate 030

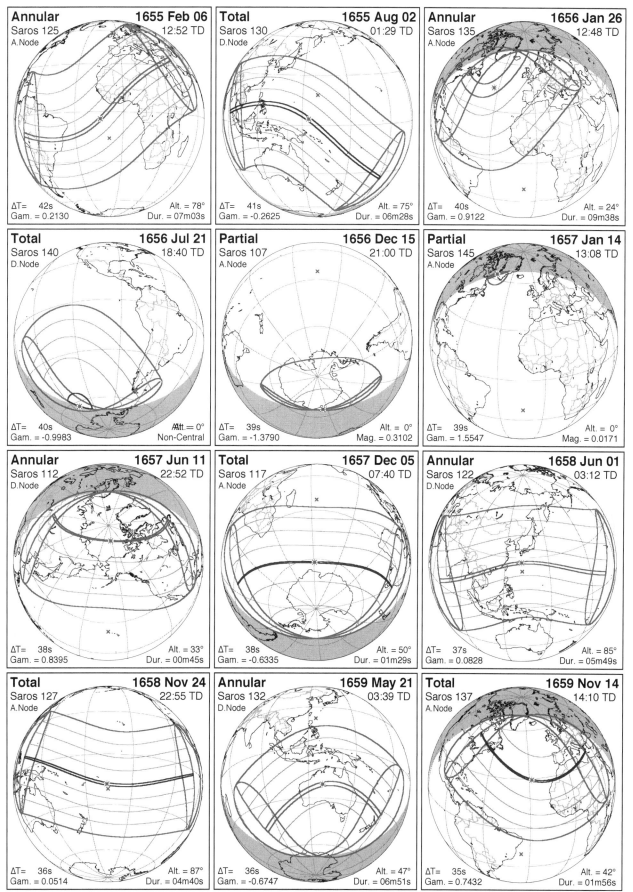

Annular	1655 Feb 06
Saros 125	12:52 TD
A.Node	
ΔT= 42s	Alt. = 78°
Gam. = 0.2130	Dur. = 07m03s

Total	1655 Aug 02
Saros 130	01:29 TD
D.Node	
ΔT= 41s	Alt. = 75°
Gam. = -0.2625	Dur. = 06m28s

Annular	1656 Jan 26
Saros 135	12:48 TD
A.Node	
ΔT= 40s	Alt. = 24°
Gam. = 0.9122	Dur. = 09m38s

Total	1656 Jul 21
Saros 140	18:40 TD
D.Node	
ΔT= 40s	Alt.= 0°
Gam. = -0.9983	Non-Central

Partial	1656 Dec 15
Saros 107	21:00 TD
A.Node	
ΔT= 39s	Alt. = 0°
Gam. = -1.3790	Mag. = 0.3102

Partial	1657 Jan 14
Saros 145	13:08 TD
A.Node	
ΔT= 39s	Alt. = 0°
Gam. = 1.5547	Mag. = 0.0171

Annular	1657 Jun 11
Saros 112	22:52 TD
D.Node	
ΔT= 38s	Alt. = 33°
Gam. = 0.8395	Dur. = 00m45s

Total	1657 Dec 05
Saros 117	07:40 TD
A.Node	
ΔT= 38s	Alt. = 50°
Gam. = -0.6335	Dur. = 01m29s

Annular	1658 Jun 01
Saros 122	03:12 TD
D.Node	
ΔT= 37s	Alt. = 85°
Gam. = 0.0828	Dur. = 05m49s

Total	1658 Nov 24
Saros 127	22:55 TD
A.Node	
ΔT= 36s	Alt. = 87°
Gam. = 0.0514	Dur. = 04m40s

Annular	1659 May 21
Saros 132	03:39 TD
D.Node	
ΔT= 36s	Alt. = 47°
Gam. = -0.6747	Dur. = 06m51s

Total	1659 Nov 14
Saros 137	14:10 TD
A.Node	
ΔT= 35s	Alt. = 42°
Gam. = 0.7432	Dur. = 01m56s

Plate 031

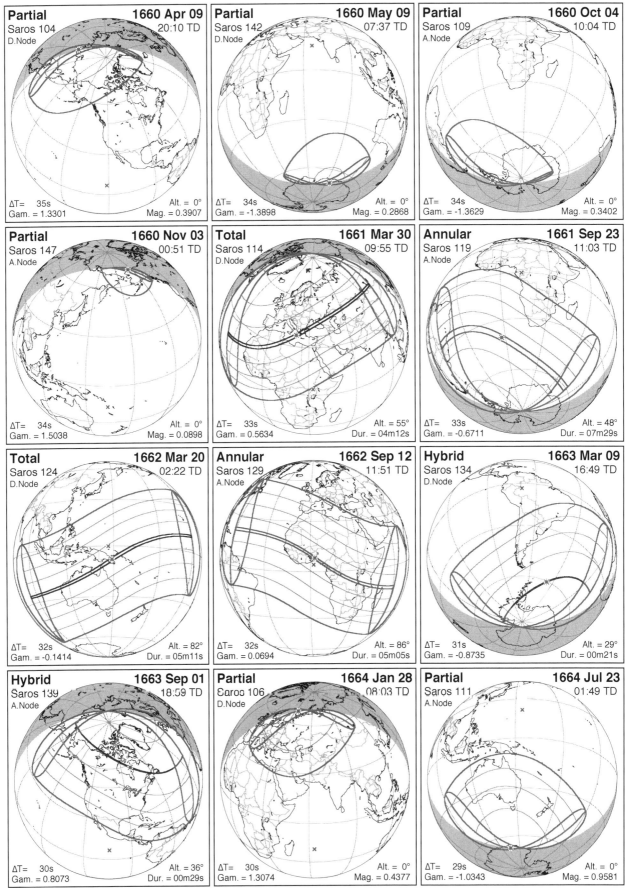

Partial 1660 Apr 09 Saros 104 20:10 TD D.Node ΔT= 35s Alt. = 0° Gam. = 1.3301 Mag. = 0.3907	**Partial** 1660 May 09 Saros 142 07:37 TD D.Node ΔT= 34s Alt. = 0° Gam. = -1.3898 Mag. = 0.2868	**Partial** 1660 Oct 04 Saros 109 10:04 TD A.Node ΔT= 34s Alt. = 0° Gam. = -1.3629 Mag. = 0.3402
Partial 1660 Nov 03 Saros 147 00:51 TD A.Node ΔT= 34s Alt. = 0° Gam. = 1.5038 Mag. = 0.0898	**Total** 1661 Mar 30 Saros 114 09:55 TD D.Node ΔT= 33s Alt. = 55° Gam. = 0.5634 Dur. = 04m12s	**Annular** 1661 Sep 23 Saros 119 11:03 TD A.Node ΔT= 33s Alt. = 48° Gam. = -0.6711 Dur. = 07m29s
Total 1662 Mar 20 Saros 124 02:22 TD D.Node ΔT= 32s Alt. = 82° Gam. = -0.1414 Dur. = 05m11s	**Annular** 1662 Sep 12 Saros 129 11:51 TD A.Node ΔT= 32s Alt. = 86° Gam. = 0.0694 Dur. = 05m05s	**Hybrid** 1663 Mar 09 Saros 134 16:49 TD D.Node ΔT= 31s Alt. = 29° Gam. = -0.8735 Dur. = 00m21s
Hybrid 1663 Sep 01 Saros 139 18:59 TD A.Node ΔT= 30s Alt. = 36° Gam. = 0.8073 Dur. = 00m29s	**Partial** 1664 Jan 28 Saros 106 08:03 TD D.Node ΔT= 30s Alt. = 0° Gam. = 1.3074 Mag. = 0.4377	**Partial** 1664 Jul 23 Saros 111 01:49 TD A.Node ΔT= 29s Alt. = 0° Gam. = -1.0343 Mag. = 0.9581

Plate 032

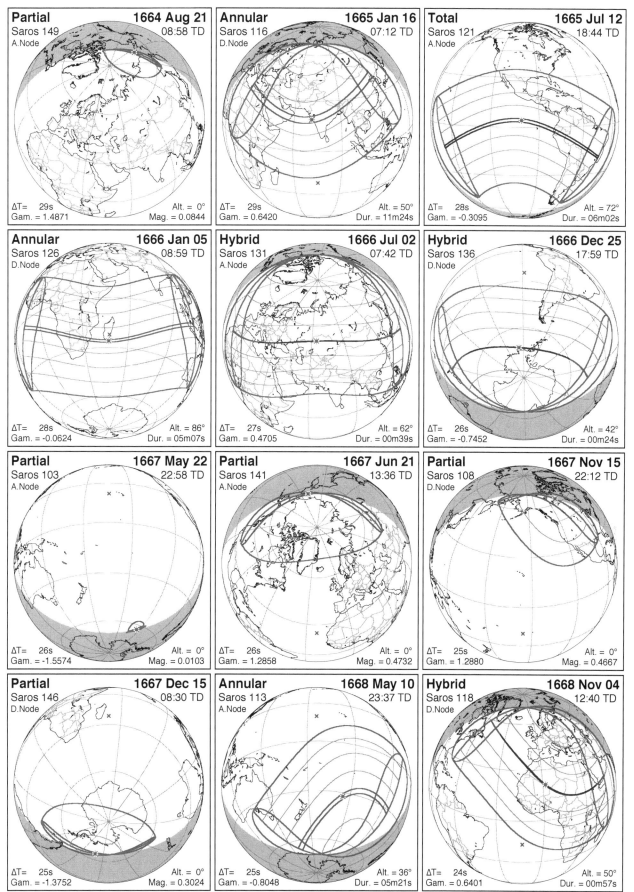

Partial   1664 Aug 21
Saros 149   08:58 TD
A.Node
ΔT= 29s   Alt. = 0°
Gam. = 1.4871   Mag. = 0.0844

Annular   1665 Jan 16
Saros 116   07:12 TD
D.Node
ΔT= 29s   Alt. = 50°
Gam. = 0.6420   Dur. = 11m24s

Total   1665 Jul 12
Saros 121   18:44 TD
A.Node
ΔT= 28s   Alt. = 72°
Gam. = -0.3095   Dur. = 06m02s

Annular   1666 Jan 05
Saros 126   08:59 TD
D.Node
ΔT= 28s   Alt. = 86°
Gam. = -0.0624   Dur. = 05m07s

Hybrid   1666 Jul 02
Saros 131   07:42 TD
A.Node
ΔT= 27s   Alt. = 62°
Gam. = 0.4705   Dur. = 00m39s

Hybrid   1666 Dec 25
Saros 136   17:59 TD
D.Node
ΔT= 26s   Alt. = 42°
Gam. = -0.7452   Dur. = 00m24s

Partial   1667 May 22
Saros 103   22:58 TD
A.Node
ΔT= 26s   Alt. = 0°
Gam. = -1.5574   Mag. = 0.0103

Partial   1667 Jun 21
Saros 141   13:36 TD
A.Node
ΔT= 26s   Alt. = 0°
Gam. = 1.2858   Mag. = 0.4732

Partial   1667 Nov 15
Saros 108   22:12 TD
D.Node
ΔT= 25s   Alt. = 0°
Gam. = 1.2880   Mag. = 0.4667

Partial   1667 Dec 15
Saros 146   08:30 TD
D.Node
ΔT= 25s   Alt. = 0°
Gam. = -1.3752   Mag. = 0.3024

Annular   1668 May 10
Saros 113   23:37 TD
A.Node
ΔT= 25s   Alt. = 36°
Gam. = -0.8048   Dur. = 05m21s

Hybrid   1668 Nov 04
Saros 118   12:40 TD
D.Node
ΔT= 24s   Alt. = 50°
Gam. = 0.6401   Dur. = 00m57s

Plate 033

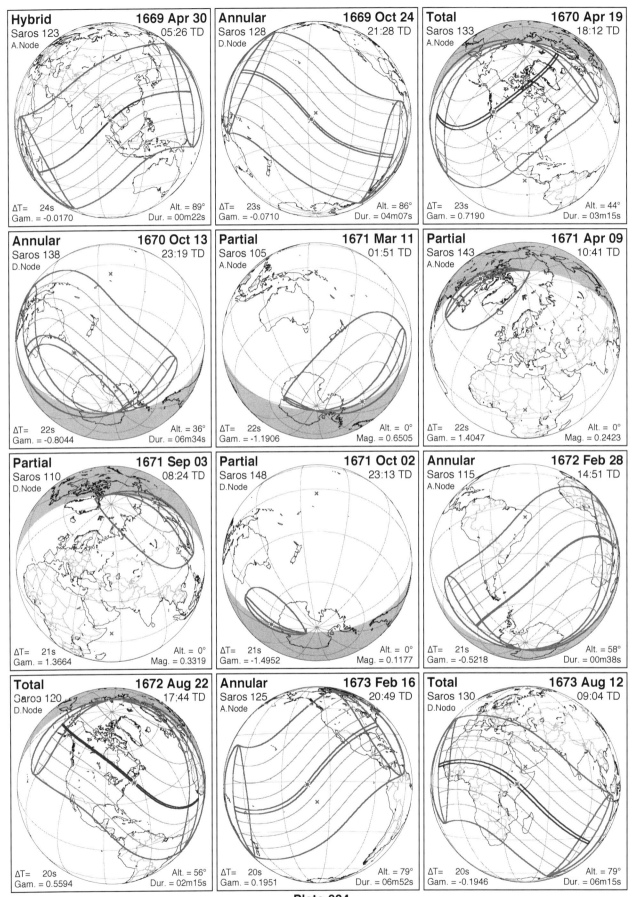

Hybrid 1669 Apr 30	**Annular** 1669 Oct 24	**Total** 1670 Apr 19
Saros 123 · 05:26 TD · A.Node	Saros 128 · 21:28 TD · D.Node	Saros 133 · 18:12 TD · A.Node
ΔT= 24s · Gam. = -0.0170 · Alt. = 89° · Dur. = 00m22s	ΔT= 23s · Gam. = -0.0710 · Alt. = 86° · Dur. = 04m07s	ΔT= 23s · Gam. = 0.7190 · Alt. = 44° · Dur. = 03m15s
Annular 1670 Oct 13	**Partial** 1671 Mar 11	**Partial** 1671 Apr 09
Saros 138 · 23:19 TD · D.Node	Saros 105 · 01:51 TD · A.Node	Saros 143 · 10:41 TD · A.Node
ΔT= 22s · Gam. = -0.8044 · Alt. = 36° · Dur. = 06m34s	ΔT= 22s · Gam. = -1.1906 · Alt. = 0° · Mag. = 0.6505	ΔT= 22s · Gam. = 1.4047 · Alt. = 0° · Mag. = 0.2423
Partial 1671 Sep 03	**Partial** 1671 Oct 02	**Annular** 1672 Feb 28
Saros 110 · 08:24 TD · D.Node	Saros 148 · 23:13 TD · D.Node	Saros 115 · 14:51 TD · A.Node
ΔT= 21s · Gam. = 1.3664 · Alt. = 0° · Mag. = 0.3319	ΔT= 21s · Gam. = -1.4952 · Alt. = 0° · Mag. = 0.1177	ΔT= 21s · Gam. = -0.5218 · Alt. = 58° · Dur. = 00m38s
Total 1672 Aug 22	**Annular** 1673 Feb 16	**Total** 1673 Aug 12
Saros 120 · 17:44 TD · D.Node	Saros 125 · 20:49 TD · A.Node	Saros 130 · 09:04 TD · D.Node
ΔT= 20s · Gam. = 0.5594 · Alt. = 56° · Dur. = 02m15s	ΔT= 20s · Gam. = 0.1951 · Alt. = 79° · Dur. = 06m52s	ΔT= 20s · Gam. = -0.1946 · Alt. = 79° · Dur. = 06m15s

Plate 034

128

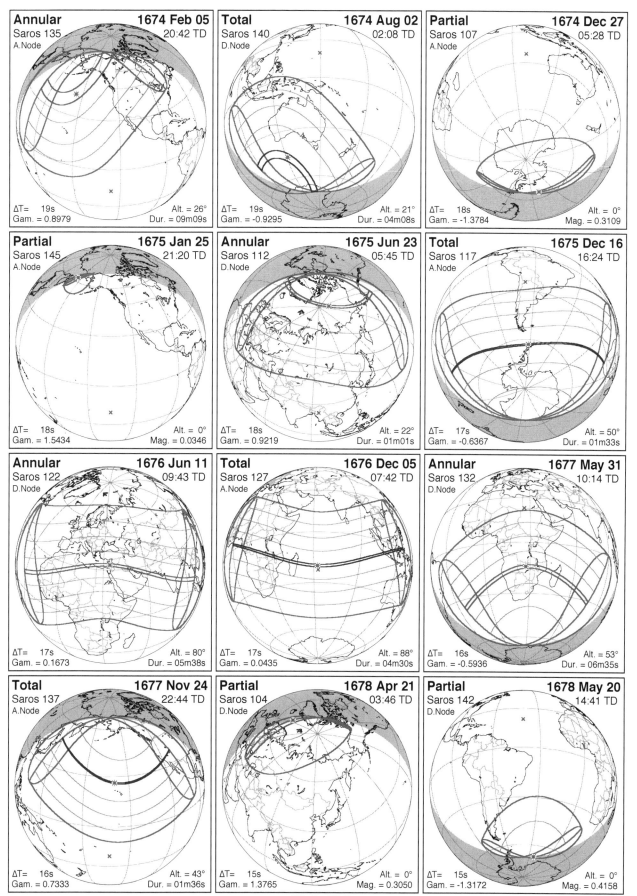

Annular **1674 Feb 05** Saros 135 20:42 TD A.Node ΔT= 19s Alt. = 26° Gam. = 0.8979 Dur. = 09m09s	**Total** **1674 Aug 02** Saros 140 02:08 TD D.Node ΔT= 19s Alt. = 21° Gam. = -0.9295 Dur. = 04m08s	**Partial** **1674 Dec 27** Saros 107 05:28 TD A.Node ΔT= 18s Alt. = 0° Gam. = -1.3784 Mag. = 0.3109
Partial **1675 Jan 25** Saros 145 21:20 TD A.Node ΔT= 18s Alt. = 0° Gam. = 1.5434 Mag. = 0.0346	**Annular** **1675 Jun 23** Saros 112 05:45 TD D.Node ΔT= 18s Alt. = 22° Gam. = 0.9219 Dur. = 01m01s	**Total** **1675 Dec 16** Saros 117 16:24 TD A.Node ΔT= 17s Alt. = 50° Gam. = -0.6367 Dur. = 01m33s
Annular **1676 Jun 11** Saros 122 09:43 TD D.Node ΔT= 17s Alt. = 80° Gam. = 0.1673 Dur. = 05m38s	**Total** **1676 Dec 05** Saros 127 07:42 TD A.Node ΔT= 17s Alt. = 88° Gam. = 0.0435 Dur. = 04m30s	**Annular** **1677 May 31** Saros 132 10:14 TD D.Node ΔT= 16s Alt. = 53° Gam. = -0.5936 Dur. = 06m35s
Total **1677 Nov 24** Saros 137 22:44 TD A.Node ΔT= 16s Alt. = 43° Gam. = 0.7333 Dur. = 01m36s	**Partial** **1678 Apr 21** Saros 104 03:46 TD D.Node ΔT= 15s Alt. = 0° Gam. = 1.3765 Mag. = 0.3050	**Partial** **1678 May 20** Saros 142 14:41 TD D.Node ΔT= 15s Alt. = 0° Gam. = -1.3172 Mag. = 0.4158

Plate 035

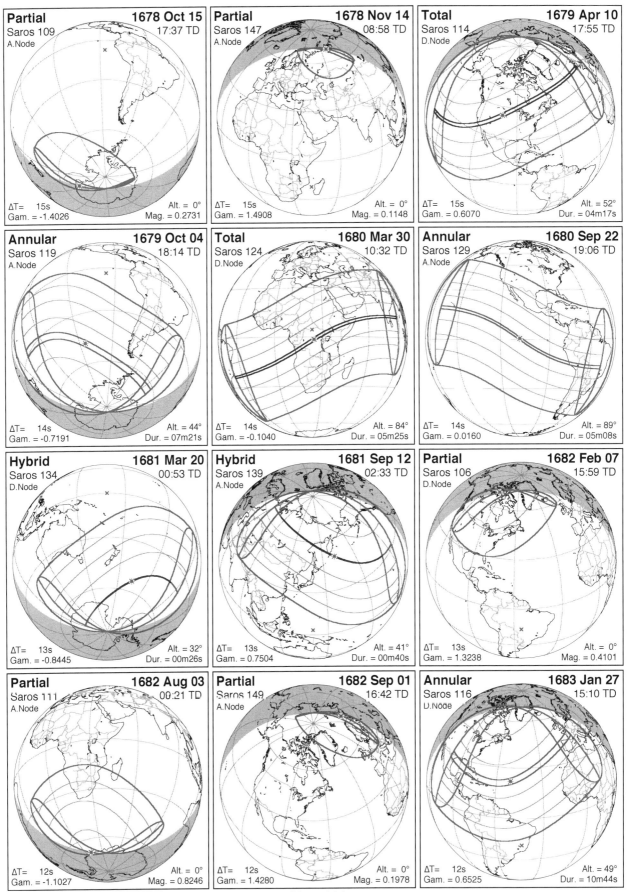

Partial **1678 Oct 15** Saros 109 17:37 TD A.Node ΔT= 15s Alt. = 0° Gam. = -1.4026 Mag. = 0.2731	**Partial** **1678 Nov 14** Saros 147 08:58 TD A.Node ΔT= 15s Alt. = 0° Gam. = 1.4908 Mag. = 0.1148
Total **1679 Apr 10** Saros 114 17:55 TD D.Node ΔT= 15s Alt. = 52° Gam. = 0.6070 Dur. = 04m17s	
Annular **1679 Oct 04** Saros 119 18:14 TD A.Node ΔT= 14s Alt. = 44° Gam. = -0.7191 Dur. = 07m21s	**Total** **1680 Mar 30** Saros 124 10:32 TD D.Node ΔT= 14s Alt. = 84° Gam. = -0.1040 Dur. = 05m25s
Annular **1680 Sep 22** Saros 129 19:06 TD A.Node ΔT= 14s Alt. = 89° Gam. = 0.0160 Dur. = 05m08s	
Hybrid **1681 Mar 20** Saros 134 00:53 TD D.Node ΔT= 13s Alt. = 32° Gam. = -0.8445 Dur. = 00m26s	**Hybrid** **1681 Sep 12** Saros 139 02:33 TD A.Node ΔT= 13s Alt. = 41° Gam. = 0.7504 Dur. = 00m40s
Partial **1682 Feb 07** Saros 106 15:59 TD D.Node ΔT= 13s Alt. = 0° Gam. = 1.3238 Mag. = 0.4101	
Partial **1682 Aug 03** Saros 111 00:21 TD A.Node ΔT= 12s Alt. = 0° Gam. = -1.1027 Mag. = 0.8246	**Partial** **1682 Sep 01** Saros 149 16:42 TD A.Node ΔT= 12s Alt. = 0° Gam. = 1.4280 Mag. = 0.1978
Annular **1683 Jan 27** Saros 116 15:10 TD D.Node ΔT= 12s Alt. = 49° Gam. = 0.6525 Dur. = 10m44s	

Plate 036

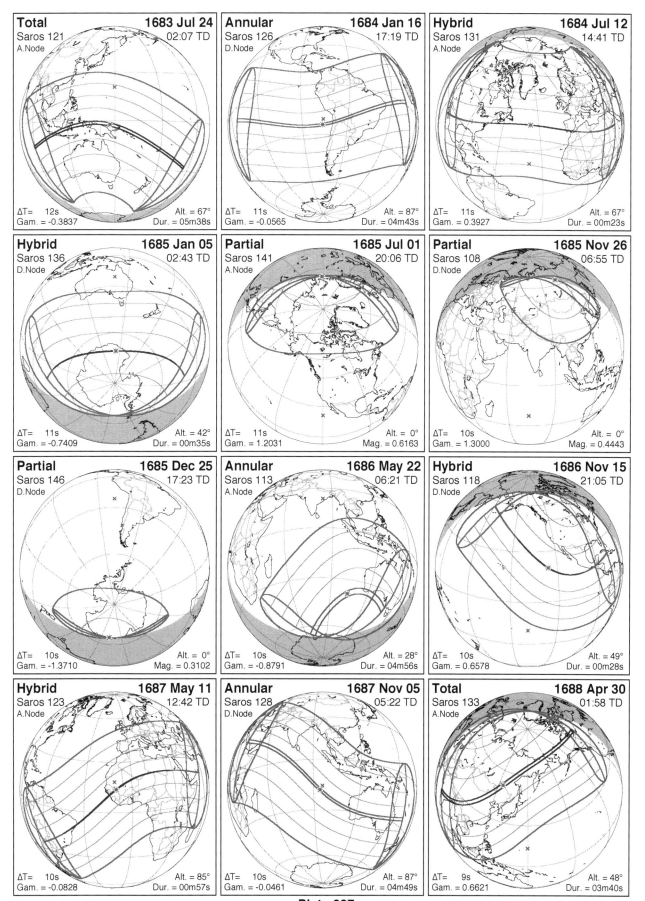

Total	1683 Jul 24
Saros 121	02:07 TD
A.Node	
ΔT= 12s	Alt. = 67°
Gam. = -0.3837	Dur. = 05m38s

Annular	1684 Jan 16
Saros 126	17:19 TD
D.Node	
ΔT= 11s	Alt. = 87°
Gam. = -0.0565	Dur. = 04m43s

Hybrid	1684 Jul 12
Saros 131	14:41 TD
A.Node	
ΔT= 11s	Alt. = 67°
Gam. = 0.3927	Dur. = 00m23s

Hybrid	1685 Jan 05
Saros 136	02:43 TD
D.Node	
ΔT= 11s	Alt. = 42°
Gam. = -0.7409	Dur. = 00m35s

Partial	1685 Jul 01
Saros 141	20:06 TD
A.Node	
ΔT= 11s	Alt. = 0°
Gam. = 1.2031	Mag. = 0.6163

Partial	1685 Nov 26
Saros 108	06:55 TD
D.Node	
ΔT= 10s	Alt. = 0°
Gam. = 1.3000	Mag. = 0.4443

Partial	1685 Dec 25
Saros 146	17:23 TD
D.Node	
ΔT= 10s	Alt. = 0°
Gam. = -1.3710	Mag. = 0.3102

Annular	1686 May 22
Saros 113	06:21 TD
A.Node	
ΔT= 10s	Alt. = 28°
Gam. = -0.8791	Dur. = 04m56s

Hybrid	1686 Nov 15
Saros 118	21:05 TD
D.Node	
ΔT= 10s	Alt. = 49°
Gam. = 0.6578	Dur. = 00m28s

Hybrid	1687 May 11
Saros 123	12:42 TD
A.Node	
ΔT= 10s	Alt. = 85°
Gam. = -0.0828	Dur. = 00m57s

Annular	1687 Nov 05
Saros 128	05:22 TD
D.Node	
ΔT= 10s	Alt. = 87°
Gam. = -0.0461	Dur. = 04m49s

Total	1688 Apr 30
Saros 133	01:58 TD
A.Node	
ΔT= 9s	Alt. = 48°
Gam. = 0.6621	Dur. = 03m40s

Plate 037

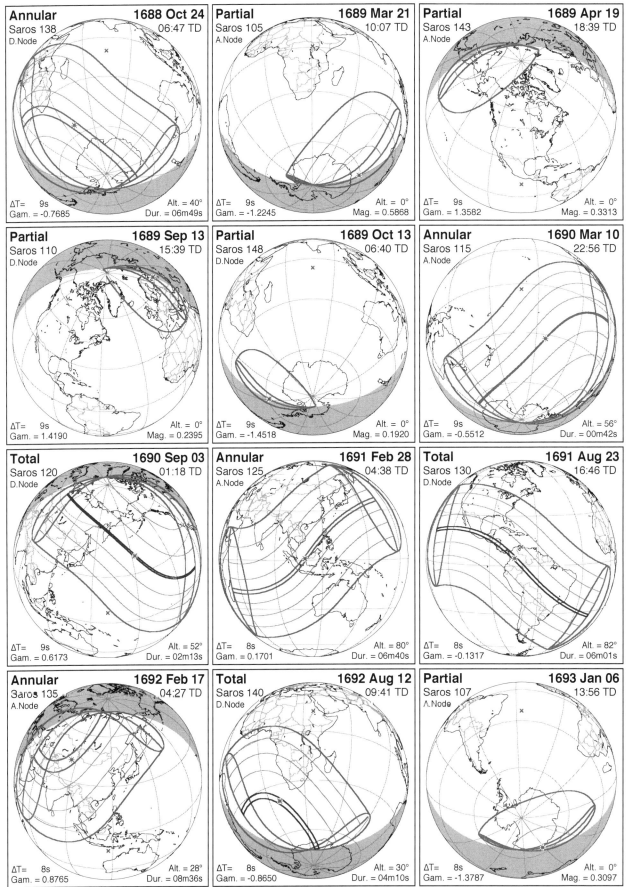

Annular 1688 Oct 24	**Partial** 1689 Mar 21	**Partial** 1689 Apr 19
Saros 138 06:47 TD	Saros 105 10:07 TD	Saros 143 18:39 TD
D.Node	A.Node	A.Node
ΔT= 9s Alt. = 40°	ΔT= 9s Alt. = 0°	ΔT= 9s Alt. = 0°
Gam. = -0.7685 Dur. = 06m49s	Gam. = -1.2245 Mag. = 0.5868	Gam. = 1.3582 Mag. = 0.3313
Partial 1689 Sep 13	**Partial** 1689 Oct 13	**Annular** 1690 Mar 10
Saros 110 15:39 TD	Saros 148 06:40 TD	Saros 115 22:56 TD
D.Node	D.Node	A.Node
ΔT= 9s Alt. = 0°	ΔT= 9s Alt. = 0°	ΔT= 9s Alt. = 56°
Gam. = 1.4190 Mag. = 0.2395	Gam. = -1.4518 Mag. = 0.1920	Gam. = -0.5512 Dur. = 00m42s
Total 1690 Sep 03	**Annular** 1691 Feb 28	**Total** 1691 Aug 23
Saros 120 01:18 TD	Saros 125 04:38 TD	Saros 130 16:46 TD
D.Node	A.Node	D.Node
ΔT= 9s Alt. = 52°	ΔT= 8s Alt. = 80°	ΔT= 8s Alt. = 82°
Gam. = 0.6173 Dur. = 02m13s	Gam. = 0.1701 Dur. = 06m40s	Gam. = -0.1317 Dur. = 06m01s
Annular 1692 Feb 17	**Total** 1692 Aug 12	**Partial** 1693 Jan 06
Saros 135 04:27 TD	Saros 140 09:41 TD	Saros 107 13:56 TD
A.Node	D.Node	A.Node
ΔT= 8s Alt. = 28°	ΔT= 8s Alt. = 30°	ΔT= 8s Alt. = 0°
Gam. = 0.8765 Dur. = 08m36s	Gam. = -0.8650 Dur. = 04m10s	Gam. = -1.3787 Mag. = 0.3097

Plate 038

132

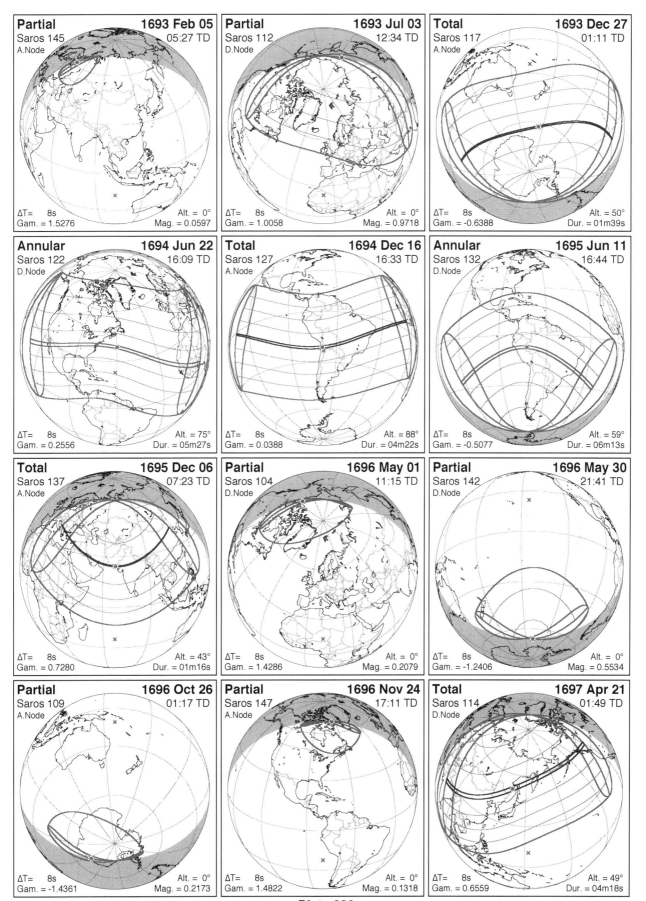

Partial **1693 Feb 05**	
Saros 145 05:27 TD	
A.Node	
ΔT= 8s Alt. = 0°	
Gam. = 1.5276 Mag. = 0.0597	

Partial   **1693 Feb 05**
Saros 145   05:27 TD
A.Node
ΔT= 8s   Alt. = 0°
Gam. = 1.5276   Mag. = 0.0597

Partial   **1693 Jul 03**
Saros 112   12:34 TD
D.Node
ΔT= 8s   Alt. = 0°
Gam. = 1.0058   Mag. = 0.9718

Total   **1693 Dec 27**
Saros 117   01:11 TD
A.Node
ΔT= 8s   Alt. = 50°
Gam. = -0.6388   Dur. = 01m39s

Annular   **1694 Jun 22**
Saros 122   16:09 TD
D.Node
ΔT= 8s   Alt. = 75°
Gam. = 0.2556   Dur. = 05m27s

Total   **1694 Dec 16**
Saros 127   16:33 TD
A.Node
ΔT= 8s   Alt. = 88°
Gam. = 0.0388   Dur. = 04m22s

Annular   **1695 Jun 11**
Saros 132   16:44 TD
D.Node
ΔT= 8s   Alt. = 59°
Gam. = -0.5077   Dur. = 06m13s

Total   **1695 Dec 06**
Saros 137   07:23 TD
A.Node
ΔT= 8s   Alt. = 43°
Gam. = 0.7280   Dur. = 01m16s

Partial   **1696 May 01**
Saros 104   11:15 TD
D.Node
ΔT= 8s   Alt. = 0°
Gam. = 1.4286   Mag. = 0.2079

Partial   **1696 May 30**
Saros 142   21:41 TD
D.Node
ΔT= 8s   Alt. = 0°
Gam. = -1.2406   Mag. = 0.5534

Partial   **1696 Oct 26**
Saros 109   01:17 TD
A.Node
ΔT= 8s   Alt. = 0°
Gam. = -1.4361   Mag. = 0.2173

Partial   **1696 Nov 24**
Saros 147   17:11 TD
A.Node
ΔT= 8s   Alt. = 0°
Gam. = 1.4822   Mag. = 0.1318

Total   **1697 Apr 21**
Saros 114   01:49 TD
D.Node
ΔT= 8s   Alt. = 49°
Gam. = 0.6559   Dur. = 04m18s

Plate 039

133

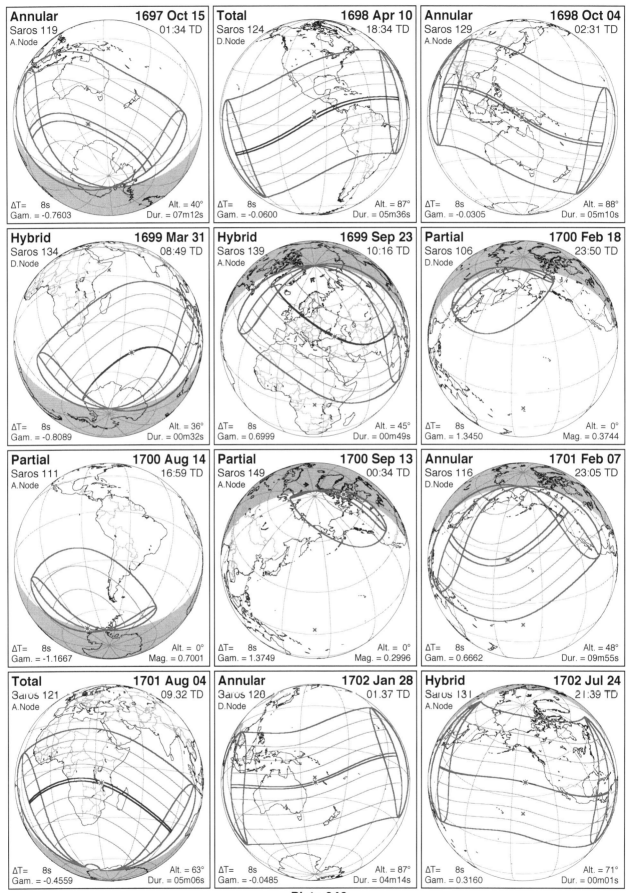

Annular	1697 Oct 15
Saros 119	01:34 TD
A.Node	
ΔT= 8s	Alt. = 40°
Gam. = -0.7603	Dur. = 07m12s

Total	1698 Apr 10
Saros 124	18:34 TD
D.Node	
ΔT= 8s	Alt. = 87°
Gam. = -0.0600	Dur. = 05m36s

Annular	1698 Oct 04
Saros 129	02:31 TD
A.Node	
ΔT= 8s	Alt. = 88°
Gam. = -0.0305	Dur. = 05m10s

Hybrid	1699 Mar 31
Saros 134	08:49 TD
D.Node	
ΔT= 8s	Alt. = 36°
Gam. = -0.8089	Dur. = 00m32s

Hybrid	1699 Sep 23
Saros 139	10:16 TD
A.Node	
ΔT= 8s	Alt. = 45°
Gam. = 0.6999	Dur. = 00m49s

Partial	1700 Feb 18
Saros 106	23:50 TD
D.Node	
ΔT= 8s	Alt. = 0°
Gam. = 1.3450	Mag. = 0.3744

Partial	1700 Aug 14
Saros 111	16:59 TD
A.Node	
ΔT= 8s	Alt. = 0°
Gam. = -1.1667	Mag. = 0.7001

Partial	1700 Sep 13
Saros 149	00:34 TD
A.Node	
ΔT= 8s	Alt. = 0°
Gam. = 1.3749	Mag. = 0.2996

Annular	1701 Feb 07
Saros 116	23:05 TD
D.Node	
ΔT= 8s	Alt. = 48°
Gam. = 0.6662	Dur. = 09m55s

Total	1701 Aug 04
Saros 121	09.32 TD
A.Node	
ΔT= 8s	Alt. = 63°
Gam. = -0.4559	Dur. = 05m06s

Annular	1702 Jan 28
Saros 126	01.37 TD
D.Node	
ΔT= 8s	Alt. = 87°
Gam. = -0.0485	Dur. = 04m14s

Hybrid	1702 Jul 24
Saros 131	21:39 TD
A.Node	
ΔT= 8s	Alt. = 71°
Gam. = 0.3160	Dur. = 00m01s

Plate 040

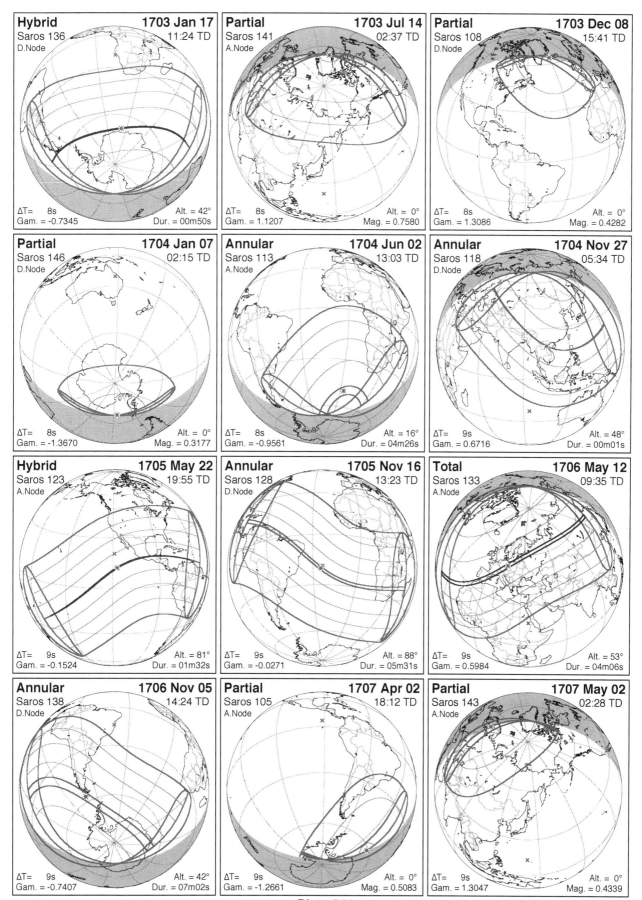

Hybrid	1703 Jan 17
Saros 136	11:24 TD
D.Node	
ΔT= 8s	Alt. = 42°
Gam. = -0.7345	Dur. = 00m50s

Partial	1703 Jul 14
Saros 141	02:37 TD
A.Node	
ΔT= 8s	Alt. = 0°
Gam. = 1.1207	Mag. = 0.7580

Partial	1703 Dec 08
Saros 108	15:41 TD
D.Node	
ΔT= 8s	Alt. = 0°
Gam. = 1.3086	Mag. = 0.4282

Partial	1704 Jan 07
Saros 146	02:15 TD
D.Node	
ΔT= 8s	Alt. = 0°
Gam. = -1.3670	Mag. = 0.3177

Annular	1704 Jun 02
Saros 113	13:03 TD
A.Node	
ΔT= 8s	Alt. = 16°
Gam. = -0.9561	Dur. = 04m26s

Annular	1704 Nov 27
Saros 118	05:34 TD
D.Node	
ΔT= 9s	Alt. = 48°
Gam. = 0.6716	Dur. = 00m01s

Hybrid	1705 May 22
Saros 123	19:55 TD
A.Node	
ΔT= 9s	Alt. = 81°
Gam. = -0.1524	Dur. = 01m32s

Annular	1705 Nov 16
Saros 128	13:23 TD
D.Node	
ΔT= 9s	Alt. = 88°
Gam. = -0.0271	Dur. = 05m31s

Total	1706 May 12
Saros 133	09:35 TD
A.Node	
ΔT= 9s	Alt. = 53°
Gam. = 0.5984	Dur. = 04m06s

Annular	1706 Nov 05
Saros 138	14:24 TD
D.Node	
ΔT= 9s	Alt. = 42°
Gam. = -0.7407	Dur. = 07m02s

Partial	1707 Apr 02
Saros 105	18:12 TD
A.Node	
ΔT= 9s	Alt. = 0°
Gam. = -1.2661	Mag. = 0.5083

Partial	1707 May 02
Saros 143	02:28 TD
A.Node	
ΔT= 9s	Alt. = 0°
Gam. = 1.3047	Mag. = 0.4339

Plate 041

135

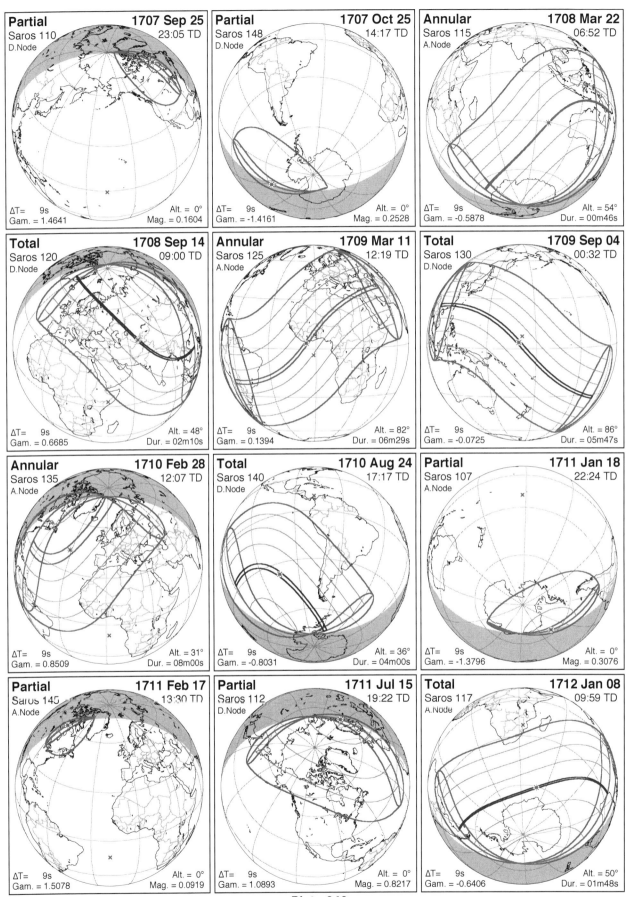

Partial 1707 Sep 25	**Partial** 1707 Oct 25	**Annular** 1708 Mar 22
Saros 110 — 23:05 TD	Saros 148 — 14:17 TD	Saros 115 — 06:52 TD
D.Node	D.Node	A.Node
ΔT= 9s — Alt. = 0°	ΔT= 9s — Alt. = 0°	ΔT= 9s — Alt. = 54°
Gam. = 1.4641 — Mag. = 0.1604	Gam. = -1.4161 — Mag. = 0.2528	Gam. = -0.5878 — Dur. = 00m46s
Total 1708 Sep 14	**Annular** 1709 Mar 11	**Total** 1709 Sep 04
Saros 120 — 09:00 TD	Saros 125 — 12:19 TD	Saros 130 — 00:32 TD
D.Node	A.Node	D.Node
ΔT= 9s — Alt. = 48°	ΔT= 9s — Alt. = 82°	ΔT= 9s — Alt. = 86°
Gam. = 0.6685 — Dur. = 02m10s	Gam. = 0.1394 — Dur. = 06m29s	Gam. = -0.0725 — Dur. = 05m47s
Annular 1710 Feb 28	**Total** 1710 Aug 24	**Partial** 1711 Jan 18
Saros 135 — 12:07 TD	Saros 140 — 17:17 TD	Saros 107 — 22:24 TD
A.Node	D.Node	A.Node
ΔT= 9s — Alt. = 31°	ΔT= 9s — Alt. = 36°	ΔT= 9s — Alt. = 0°
Gam. = 0.8509 — Dur. = 08m00s	Gam. = -0.8031 — Dur. = 04m00s	Gam. = -1.3796 — Mag. = 0.3076
Partial 1711 Feb 17	**Partial** 1711 Jul 15	**Total** 1712 Jan 08
Saros 145 — 13:30 TD	Saros 112 — 19:22 TD	Saros 117 — 09:59 TD
A.Node	D.Node	A.Node
ΔT= 9s — Alt. = 0°	ΔT= 9s — Alt. = 0°	ΔT= 9s — Alt. = 50°
Gam. = 1.5078 — Mag. = 0.0919	Gam. = 1.0893 — Mag. = 0.8217	Gam. = -0.6406 — Dur. = 01m48s

Plate 042

136

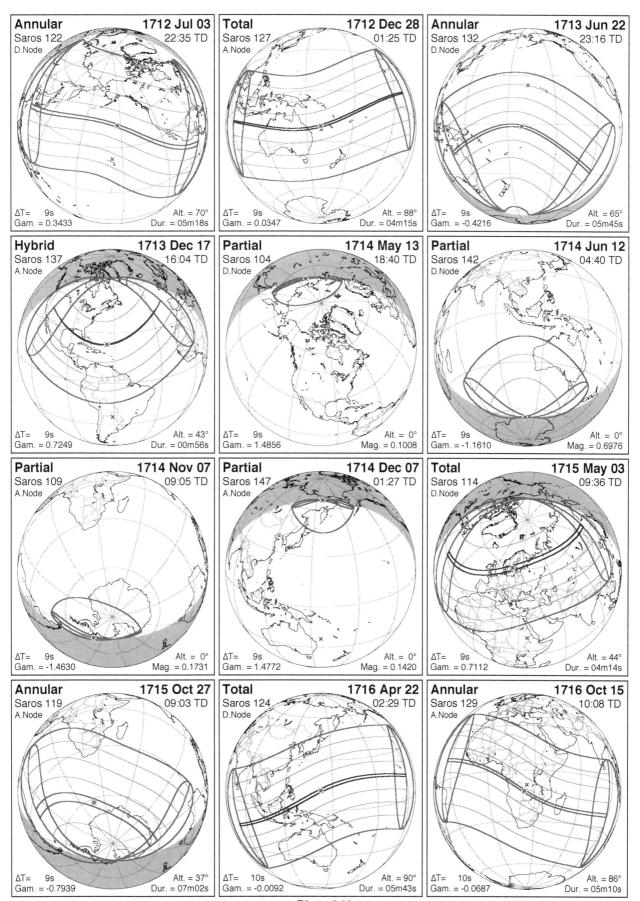

Annular 1712 Jul 03 Saros 122 22:35 TD D.Node ΔT= 9s Alt. = 70° Gam. = 0.3433 Dur. = 05m18s	**Total** 1712 Dec 28 Saros 127 01:25 TD A.Node ΔT= 9s Alt. = 88° Gam. = 0.0347 Dur. = 04m15s	**Annular** 1713 Jun 22 Saros 132 23:16 TD D.Node ΔT= 9s Alt. = 65° Gam. = -0.4216 Dur. = 05m45s
Hybrid 1713 Dec 17 Saros 137 16:04 TD A.Node ΔT= 9s Alt. = 43° Gam. = 0.7249 Dur. = 00m56s	**Partial** 1714 May 13 Saros 104 18:40 TD D.Node ΔT= 9s Alt. = 0° Gam. = 1.4856 Mag. = 0.1008	**Partial** 1714 Jun 12 Saros 142 04:40 TD D.Node ΔT= 9s Alt. = 0° Gam. = -1.1610 Mag. = 0.6976
Partial 1714 Nov 07 Saros 109 09:05 TD A.Node ΔT= 9s Alt. = 0° Gam. = -1.4630 Mag. = 0.1731	**Partial** 1714 Dec 07 Saros 147 01:27 TD A.Node ΔT= 9s Alt. = 0° Gam. = 1.4772 Mag. = 0.1420	**Total** 1715 May 03 Saros 114 09:36 TD D.Node ΔT= 9s Alt. = 44° Gam. = 0.7112 Dur. = 04m14s
Annular 1715 Oct 27 Saros 119 09:03 TD A.Node ΔT= 9s Alt. = 37° Gam. = -0.7939 Dur. = 07m02s	**Total** 1716 Apr 22 Saros 124 02:29 TD D.Node ΔT= 10s Alt. = 90° Gam. = -0.0092 Dur. = 05m43s	**Annular** 1716 Oct 15 Saros 129 10:08 TD A.Node ΔT= 10s Alt. = 86° Gam. = -0.0687 Dur. = 05m10s

Plate 043

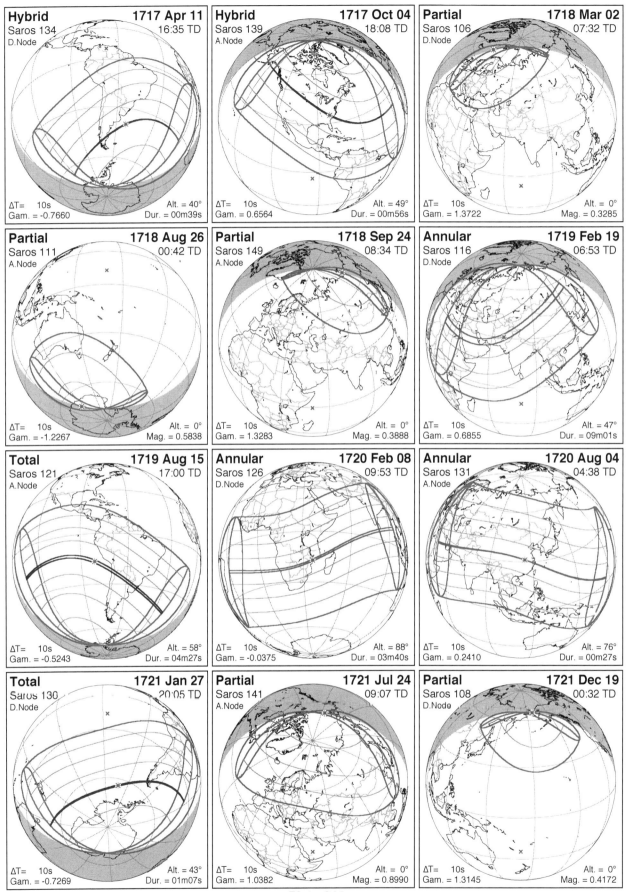

Hybrid	1717 Apr 11
Saros 134	16:35 TD
D.Node	
ΔT= 10s	Alt. = 40°
Gam. = -0.7660	Dur. = 00m39s

Hybrid	1717 Oct 04
Saros 139	18:08 TD
A.Node	
ΔT= 10s	Alt. = 49°
Gam. = 0.6564	Dur. = 00m56s

Partial	1718 Mar 02
Saros 106	07:32 TD
D.Node	
ΔT= 10s	Alt. = 0°
Gam. = 1.3722	Mag. = 0.3285

Partial	1718 Aug 26
Saros 111	00:42 TD
A.Node	
ΔT= 10s	Alt. = 0°
Gam. = -1.2267	Mag. = 0.5838

Partial	1718 Sep 24
Saros 149	08:34 TD
A.Node	
ΔT= 10s	Alt. = 0°
Gam. = 1.3283	Mag. = 0.3888

Annular	1719 Feb 19
Saros 116	06:53 TD
D.Node	
ΔT= 10s	Alt. = 47°
Gam. = 0.6855	Dur. = 09m01s

Total	1719 Aug 15
Saros 121	17:00 TD
A.Node	
ΔT= 10s	Alt. = 58°
Gam. = -0.5243	Dur. = 04m27s

Annular	1720 Feb 08
Saros 126	09:53 TD
D.Node	
ΔT= 10s	Alt. = 88°
Gam. = -0.0375	Dur. = 03m40s

Annular	1720 Aug 04
Saros 131	04:38 TD
A.Node	
ΔT= 10s	Alt. = 76°
Gam. = 0.2410	Dur. = 00m27s

Total	1721 Jan 27
Saros 130	20:05 TD
D.Node	
ΔT= 10s	Alt. = 43°
Gam. = -0.7269	Dur. = 01m07s

Partial	1721 Jul 24
Saros 141	09:07 TD
A.Node	
ΔT= 10s	Alt. = 0°
Gam. = 1.0382	Mag. = 0.8990

Partial	1721 Dec 19
Saros 108	00:32 TD
D.Node	
ΔT= 10s	Alt. = 0°
Gam. = 1.3145	Mag. = 0.4172

Plate 044

138

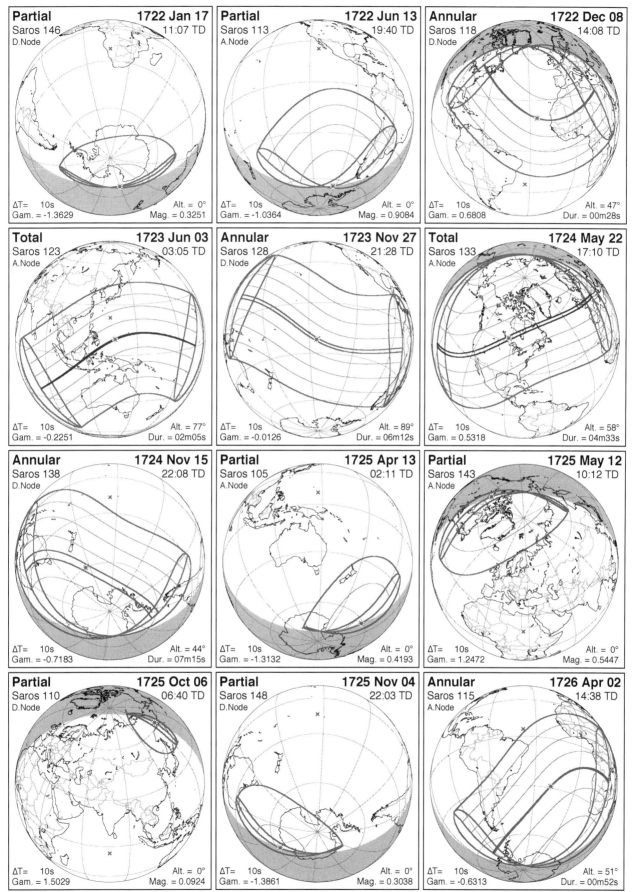

Partial	1722 Jan 17
Saros 146	11:07 TD
D.Node	
ΔT= 10s	Alt. = 0°
Gam. = -1.3629	Mag. = 0.3251

Partial	1722 Jun 13
Saros 113	19:40 TD
A.Node	
ΔT= 10s	Alt. = 0°
Gam. = -1.0364	Mag. = 0.9084

Annular	1722 Dec 08
Saros 118	14:08 TD
D.Node	
ΔT= 10s	Alt. = 47°
Gam. = 0.6808	Dur. = 00m28s

Total	1723 Jun 03
Saros 123	03:05 TD
A.Node	
ΔT= 10s	Alt. = 77°
Gam. = -0.2251	Dur. = 02m05s

Annular	1723 Nov 27
Saros 128	21:28 TD
D.Node	
ΔT= 10s	Alt. = 89°
Gam. = -0.0126	Dur. = 06m12s

Total	1724 May 22
Saros 133	17:10 TD
A.Node	
ΔT= 10s	Alt. = 58°
Gam. = 0.5318	Dur. = 04m33s

Annular	1724 Nov 15
Saros 138	22:08 TD
D.Node	
ΔT= 10s	Alt. = 44°
Gam. = -0.7183	Dur. = 07m15s

Partial	1725 Apr 13
Saros 105	02:11 TD
A.Node	
ΔT= 10s	Alt. = 0°
Gam. = -1.3132	Mag. = 0.4193

Partial	1725 May 12
Saros 143	10:12 TD
A.Node	
ΔT= 10s	Alt. = 0°
Gam. = 1.2472	Mag. = 0.5447

Partial	1725 Oct 06
Saros 110	06:40 TD
D.Node	
ΔT= 10s	Alt. = 0°
Gam. = 1.5029	Mag. = 0.0924

Partial	1725 Nov 04
Saros 148	22:03 TD
D.Node	
ΔT= 10s	Alt. = 0°
Gam. = -1.3861	Mag. = 0.3038

Annular	1726 Apr 02
Saros 115	14:38 TD
A.Node	
ΔT= 10s	Alt. = 51°
Gam. = -0.6313	Dur. = 00m52s

Plate 045

139

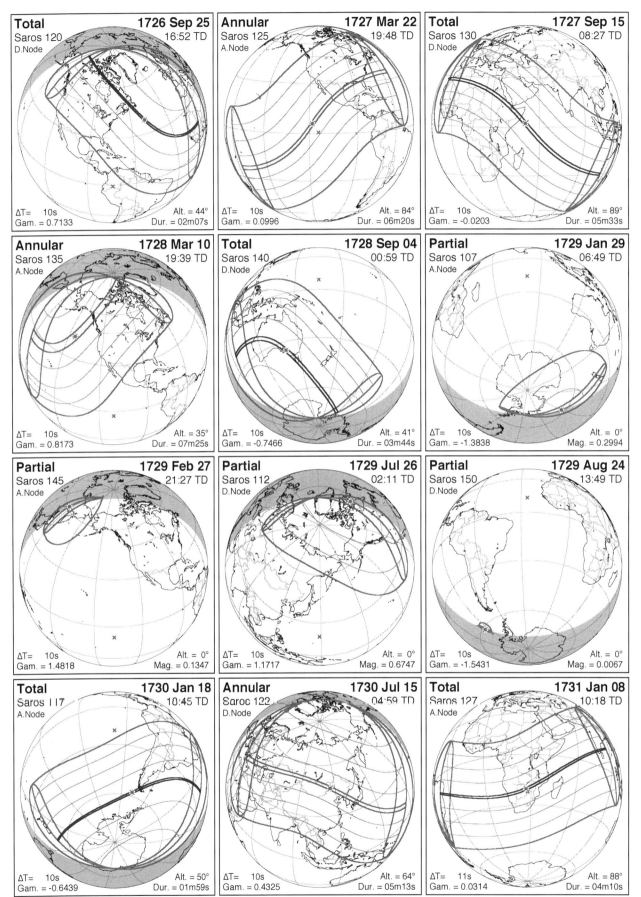

Total 1726 Sep 25	
Saros 120 16:52 TD	
D.Node	
ΔT= 10s Alt. = 44°	
Gam. = 0.7133 Dur. = 02m07s	

| **Annular** 1727 Mar 22 |
| Saros 125 19:48 TD |
| A.Node |
| ΔT= 10s Alt. = 84° |
| Gam. = 0.0996 Dur. = 06m20s |

| **Total** 1727 Sep 15 |
| Saros 130 08:27 TD |
| D.Node |
| ΔT= 10s Alt. = 89° |
| Gam. = -0.0203 Dur. = 05m33s |

| **Annular** 1728 Mar 10 |
| Saros 135 19:39 TD |
| A.Node |
| ΔT= 10s Alt. = 35° |
| Gam. = 0.8173 Dur. = 07m25s |

| **Total** 1728 Sep 04 |
| Saros 140 00:59 TD |
| D.Node |
| ΔT= 10s Alt. = 41° |
| Gam. = -0.7466 Dur. = 03m44s |

| **Partial** 1729 Jan 29 |
| Saros 107 06:49 TD |
| A.Node |
| ΔT= 10s Alt. = 0° |
| Gam. = -1.3838 Mag. = 0.2994 |

| **Partial** 1729 Feb 27 |
| Saros 145 21:27 TD |
| A.Node |
| ΔT= 10s Alt. = 0° |
| Gam. = 1.4818 Mag. = 0.1347 |

| **Partial** 1729 Jul 26 |
| Saros 112 02:11 TD |
| D.Node |
| ΔT= 10s Alt. = 0° |
| Gam. = 1.1717 Mag. = 0.6747 |

| **Partial** 1729 Aug 24 |
| Saros 150 13:49 TD |
| D.Node |
| ΔT= 10s Alt. = 0° |
| Gam. = -1.5431 Mag. = 0.0067 |

| **Total** 1730 Jan 18 |
| Saros 117 10:45 TD |
| A.Node |
| ΔT= 10s Alt. = 50° |
| Gam. = -0.6439 Dur. = 01m59s |

| **Annular** 1730 Jul 15 |
| Saros 122 04:59 TD |
| D.Node |
| ΔT= 10s Alt. = 64° |
| Gam. = 0.4325 Dur. = 05m13s |

| **Total** 1731 Jan 08 |
| Saros 127 10:18 TD |
| A.Node |
| ΔT= 11s Alt. = 88° |
| Gam. = 0.0314 Dur. = 04m10s |

Plate 046

140

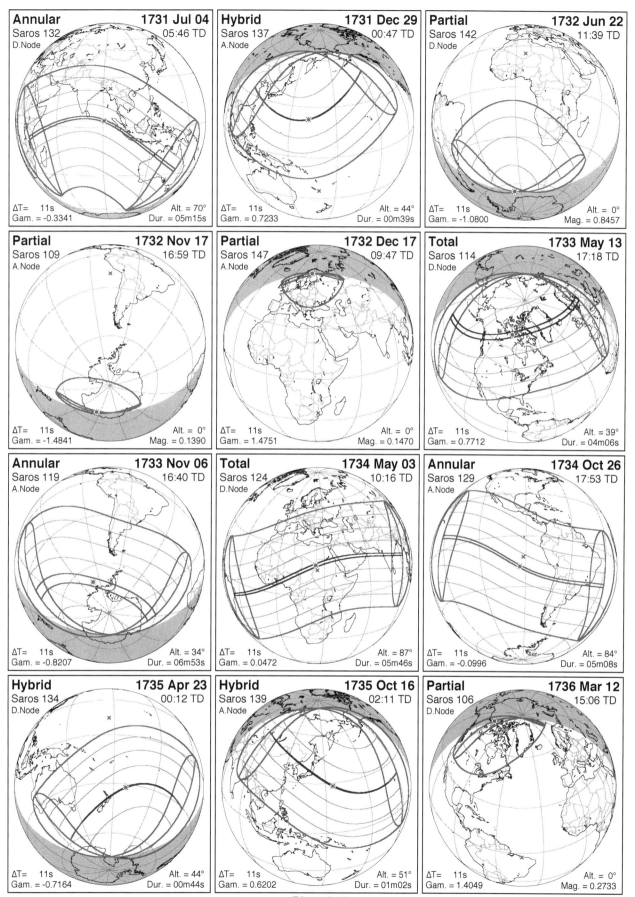

Annular	**1731 Jul 04**
Saros 132	05:46 TD
D.Node	
ΔT= 11s	Alt. = 70°
Gam. = -0.3341	Dur. = 05m15s

Hybrid	**1731 Dec 29**
Saros 137	00:47 TD
A.Node	
ΔT= 11s	Alt. = 44°
Gam. = 0.7233	Dur. = 00m39s

Partial	**1732 Jun 22**
Saros 142	11:39 TD
D.Node	
ΔT= 11s	Alt. = 0°
Gam. = -1.0800	Mag. = 0.8457

Partial	**1732 Nov 17**
Saros 109	16:59 TD
A.Node	
ΔT= 11s	Alt. = 0°
Gam. = -1.4841	Mag. = 0.1390

Partial	**1732 Dec 17**
Saros 147	09:47 TD
A.Node	
ΔT= 11s	Alt. = 0°
Gam. = 1.4751	Mag. = 0.1470

Total	**1733 May 13**
Saros 114	17:18 TD
D.Node	
ΔT= 11s	Alt. = 39°
Gam. = 0.7712	Dur. = 04m06s

Annular	**1733 Nov 06**
Saros 119	16:40 TD
A.Node	
ΔT= 11s	Alt. = 34°
Gam. = -0.8207	Dur. = 06m53s

Total	**1734 May 03**
Saros 124	10:16 TD
D.Node	
ΔT= 11s	Alt. = 87°
Gam. = 0.0472	Dur. = 05m46s

Annular	**1734 Oct 26**
Saros 129	17:53 TD
A.Node	
ΔT= 11s	Alt. = 84°
Gam. = -0.0996	Dur. = 05m08s

Hybrid	**1735 Apr 23**
Saros 134	00:12 TD
D.Node	
ΔT= 11s	Alt. = 44°
Gam. = -0.7164	Dur. = 00m44s

Hybrid	**1735 Oct 16**
Saros 139	02:11 TD
A.Node	
ΔT= 11s	Alt. = 51°
Gam. = 0.6202	Dur. = 01m02s

Partial	**1736 Mar 12**
Saros 106	15:06 TD
D.Node	
ΔT= 11s	Alt. = 0°
Gam. = 1.4049	Mag. = 0.2733

Plate 047

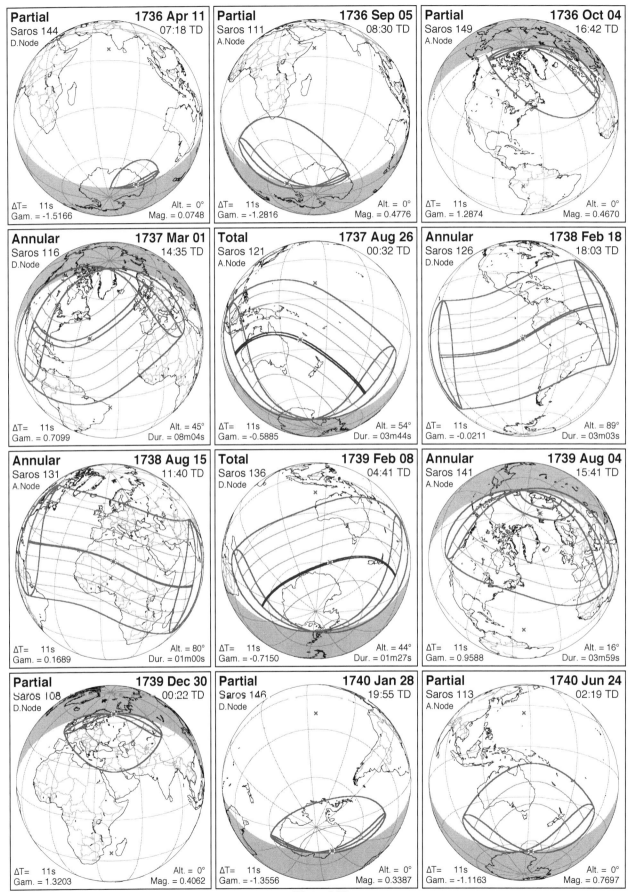

Partial 1736 Apr 11	**Partial** 1736 Sep 05	**Partial** 1736 Oct 04
Saros 144 07:18 TD D.Node	Saros 111 08:30 TD A.Node	Saros 149 16:42 TD A.Node
ΔT= 11s Alt. = 0° Gam. = -1.5166 Mag. = 0.0748	ΔT= 11s Alt. = 0° Gam. = -1.2816 Mag. = 0.4776	ΔT= 11s Alt. = 0° Gam. = 1.2874 Mag. = 0.4670
Annular 1737 Mar 01	**Total** 1737 Aug 26	**Annular** 1738 Feb 18
Saros 116 14:35 TD D.Node	Saros 121 00:32 TD A.Node	Saros 126 18:03 TD D.Node
ΔT= 11s Alt. = 45° Gam. = 0.7099 Dur. = 08m04s	ΔT= 11s Alt. = 54° Gam. = -0.5885 Dur. = 03m44s	ΔT= 11s Alt. = 89° Gam. = -0.0211 Dur. = 03m03s
Annular 1738 Aug 15	**Total** 1739 Feb 08	**Annular** 1739 Aug 04
Saros 131 11:40 TD A.Node	Saros 136 04:41 TD D.Node	Saros 141 15:41 TD A.Node
ΔT= 11s Alt. = 80° Gam. = 0.1689 Dur. = 01m00s	ΔT= 11s Alt. = 44° Gam. = -0.7150 Dur. = 01m27s	ΔT= 11s Alt. = 16° Gam. = 0.9588 Dur. = 03m59s
Partial 1739 Dec 30	**Partial** 1740 Jan 28	**Partial** 1740 Jun 24
Saros 108 00:22 TD D.Node	Saros 146 19:55 TD D.Node	Saros 113 02:19 TD A.Node
ΔT= 11s Alt. = 0° Gam. = 1.3203 Mag. = 0.4062	ΔT= 11s Alt. = 0° Gam. = -1.3556 Mag. = 0.3387	ΔT= 11s Alt. = 0° Gam. = -1.1163 Mag. = 0.7697

Plate 048

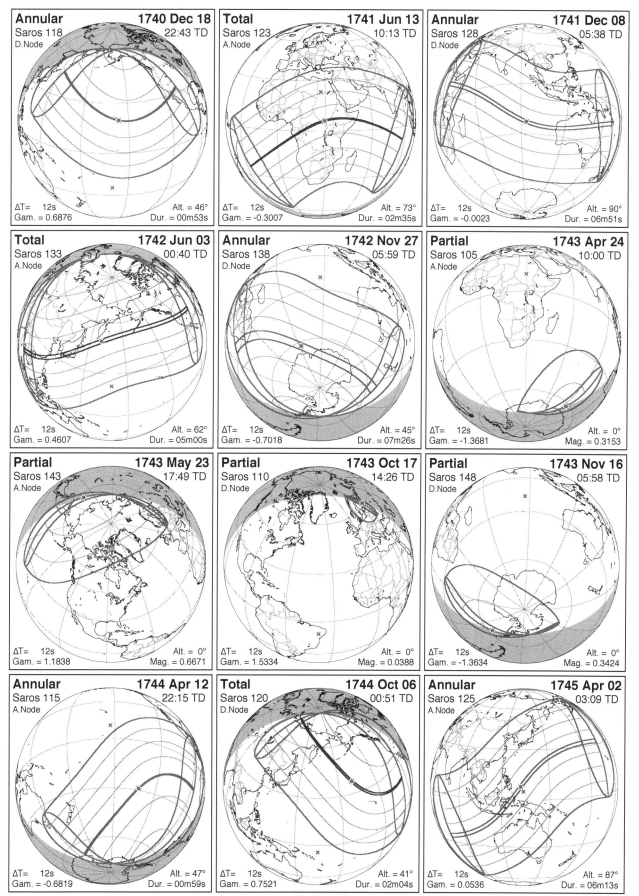

Annular	1740 Dec 18
Saros 118	22:43 TD
D.Node	
ΔT= 12s	Alt. = 46°
Gam. = 0.6876	Dur. = 00m53s

Total	1741 Jun 13
Saros 123	10:13 TD
A.Node	
ΔT= 12s	Alt. = 73°
Gam. = -0.3007	Dur. = 02m35s

Annular	1741 Dec 08
Saros 128	05:38 TD
D.Node	
ΔT= 12s	Alt. = 90°
Gam. = -0.0023	Dur. = 06m51s

Total	1742 Jun 03
Saros 133	00:40 TD
A.Node	
ΔT= 12s	Alt. = 62°
Gam. = 0.4607	Dur. = 05m00s

Annular	1742 Nov 27
Saros 138	05:59 TD
D.Node	
ΔT= 12s	Alt. = 45°
Gam. = -0.7018	Dur. = 07m26s

Partial	1743 Apr 24
Saros 105	10:00 TD
A.Node	
ΔT= 12s	Alt. = 0°
Gam. = -1.3681	Mag. = 0.3153

Partial	1743 May 23
Saros 143	17:49 TD
A.Node	
ΔT= 12s	Alt. = 0°
Gam. = 1.1838	Mag. = 0.6671

Partial	1743 Oct 17
Saros 110	14:26 TD
D.Node	
ΔT= 12s	Alt. = 0°
Gam. = 1.5334	Mag. = 0.0388

Partial	1743 Nov 16
Saros 148	05:58 TD
D.Node	
ΔT= 12s	Alt. = 0°
Gam. = -1.3634	Mag. = 0.3424

Annular	1744 Apr 12
Saros 115	22:15 TD
A.Node	
ΔT= 12s	Alt. = 47°
Gam. = -0.6819	Dur. = 00m59s

Total	1744 Oct 06
Saros 120	00:51 TD
D.Node	
ΔT= 12s	Alt. = 41°
Gam. = 0.7521	Dur. = 02m04s

Annular	1745 Apr 02
Saros 125	03:09 TD
A.Node	
ΔT= 12s	Alt. = 87°
Gam. = 0.0536	Dur. = 06m13s

Plate 049

143

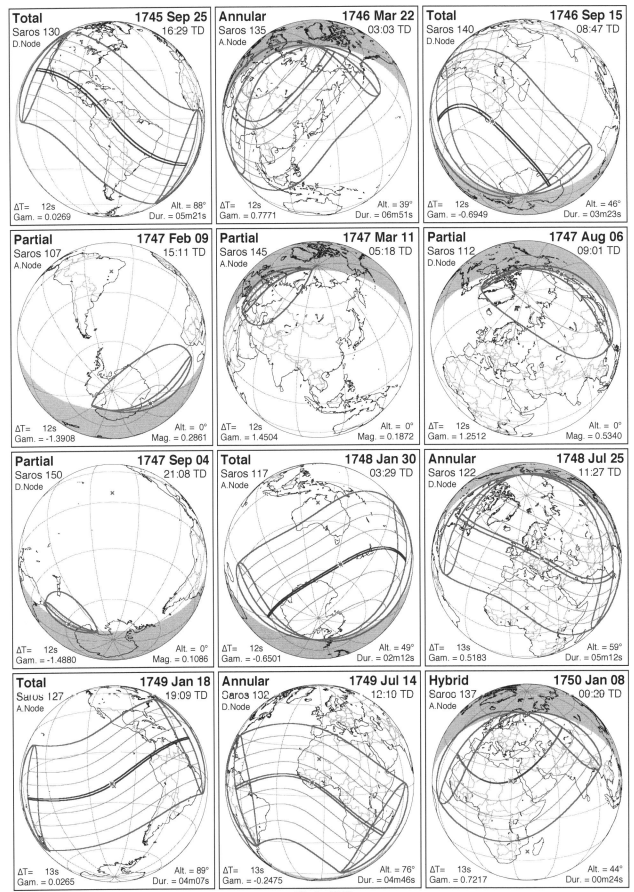

Total — 1745 Sep 25
Saros 130
D.Node
16:29 TD
ΔT= 12s
Gam. = 0.0269
Alt. = 88°
Dur. = 05m21s

Annular — 1746 Mar 22
Saros 135
A.Node
03:03 TD
ΔT= 12s
Gam. = 0.7771
Alt. = 39°
Dur. = 06m51s

Total — 1746 Sep 15
Saros 140
D.Node
08:47 TD
ΔT= 12s
Gam. = -0.6949
Alt. = 46°
Dur. = 03m23s

Partial — 1747 Feb 09
Saros 107
A.Node
15:11 TD
ΔT= 12s
Gam. = -1.3908
Alt. = 0°
Mag. = 0.2861

Partial — 1747 Mar 11
Saros 145
A.Node
05:18 TD
ΔT= 12s
Gam. = 1.4504
Alt. = 0°
Mag. = 0.1872

Partial — 1747 Aug 06
Saros 112
D.Node
09:01 TD
ΔT= 12s
Gam. = 1.2512
Alt. = 0°
Mag. = 0.5340

Partial — 1747 Sep 04
Saros 150
D.Node
21:08 TD
ΔT= 12s
Gam. = -1.4880
Alt. = 0°
Mag. = 0.1086

Total — 1748 Jan 30
Saros 117
A.Node
03:29 TD
ΔT= 12s
Gam. = -0.6501
Alt. = 49°
Dur. = 02m12s

Annular — 1748 Jul 25
Saros 122
D.Node
11:27 TD
ΔT= 13s
Gam. = 0.5183
Alt. = 59°
Dur. = 05m12s

Total — 1749 Jan 18
Saros 127
A.Node
19:09 TD
ΔT= 13s
Gam. = 0.0265
Alt. = 89°
Dur. = 04m07s

Annular — 1749 Jul 14
Saros 132
D.Node
12:10 TD
ΔT= 13s
Gam. = -0.2475
Alt. = 76°
Dur. = 04m46s

Hybrid — 1750 Jan 08
Saros 137
A.Node
00:20 TD
ΔT= 13s
Gam. = 0.7217
Alt. = 44°
Dur. = 00m24s

Plate 050

144

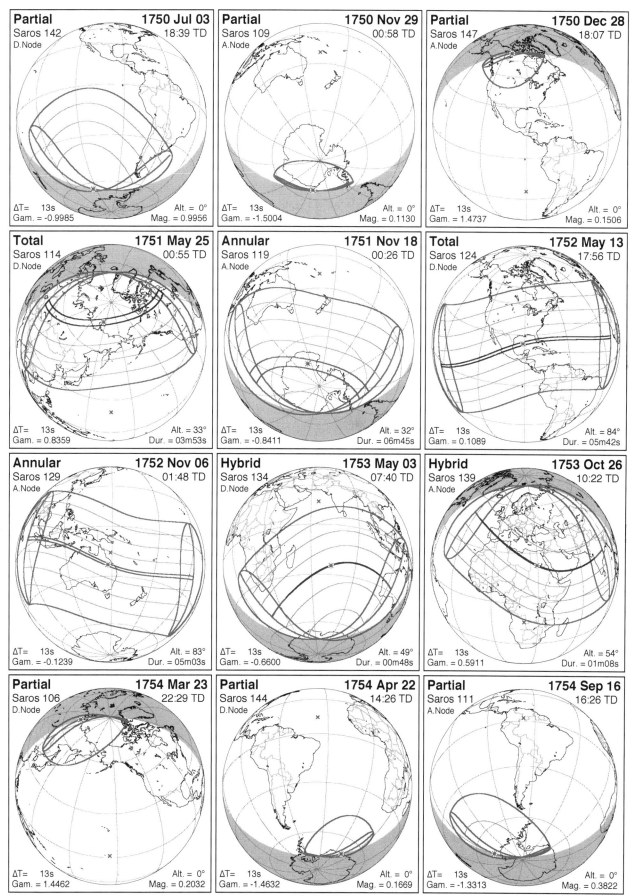

Partial	1750 Jul 03
Saros 142	18:39 TD
D.Node	
ΔT= 13s	Alt. = 0°
Gam. = -0.9985	Mag. = 0.9956

Partial	1750 Nov 29
Saros 109	00:58 TD
A.Node	
ΔT= 13s	Alt. = 0°
Gam. = -1.5004	Mag. = 0.1130

Partial	1750 Dec 28
Saros 147	18:07 TD
A.Node	
ΔT= 13s	Alt. = 0°
Gam. = 1.4737	Mag. = 0.1506

Total	1751 May 25
Saros 114	00:55 TD
D.Node	
ΔT= 13s	Alt. = 33°
Gam. = 0.8359	Dur. = 03m53s

Annular	1751 Nov 18
Saros 119	00:26 TD
A.Node	
ΔT= 13s	Alt. = 32°
Gam. = -0.8411	Dur. = 06m45s

Total	1752 May 13
Saros 124	17:56 TD
D.Node	
ΔT= 13s	Alt. = 84°
Gam. = 0.1089	Dur. = 05m42s

Annular	1752 Nov 06
Saros 129	01:48 TD
A.Node	
ΔT= 13s	Alt. = 83°
Gam. = -0.1239	Dur. = 05m03s

Hybrid	1753 May 03
Saros 134	07:40 TD
D.Node	
ΔT= 13s	Alt. = 49°
Gam. = -0.6600	Dur. = 00m48s

Hybrid	1753 Oct 26
Saros 139	10:22 TD
A.Node	
ΔT= 13s	Alt. = 54°
Gam. = 0.5911	Dur. = 01m08s

Partial	1754 Mar 23
Saros 106	22:29 TD
D.Node	
ΔT= 13s	Alt. = 0°
Gam. = 1.4462	Mag. = 0.2032

Partial	1754 Apr 22
Saros 144	14:26 TD
D.Node	
ΔT= 13s	Alt. = 0°
Gam. = -1.4632	Mag. = 0.1669

Partial	1754 Sep 16
Saros 111	16:26 TD
A.Node	
ΔT= 13s	Alt. = 0°
Gam. = -1.3313	Mag. = 0.3822

Plate 051

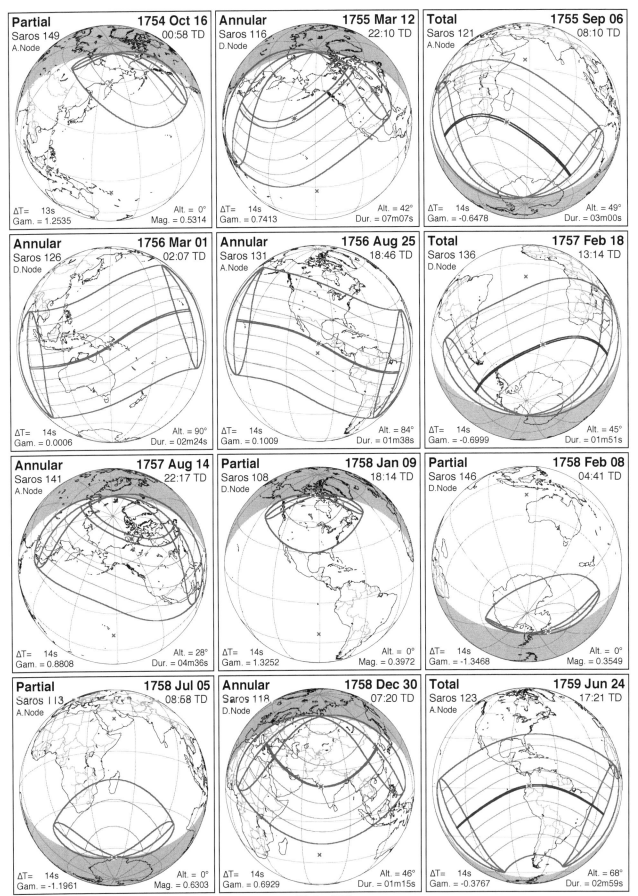

Partial   **1754 Oct 16**
Saros 149   00:58 TD
A.Node
ΔT= 13s   Alt. = 0°
Gam. = 1.2535   Mag. = 0.5314

Annular   **1755 Mar 12**
Saros 116   22:10 TD
D.Node
ΔT= 14s   Alt. = 42°
Gam. = 0.7413   Dur. = 07m07s

Total   **1755 Sep 06**
Saros 121   08:10 TD
A.Node
ΔT= 14s   Alt. = 49°
Gam. = -0.6478   Dur. = 03m00s

Annular   **1756 Mar 01**
Saros 126   02:07 TD
D.Node
ΔT= 14s   Alt. = 90°
Gam. = 0.0006   Dur. = 02m24s

Annular   **1756 Aug 25**
Saros 131   18:46 TD
A.Node
ΔT= 14s   Alt. = 84°
Gam. = 0.1009   Dur. = 01m38s

Total   **1757 Feb 18**
Saros 136   13:14 TD
D.Node
ΔT= 14s   Alt. = 45°
Gam. = -0.6999   Dur. = 01m51s

Annular   **1757 Aug 14**
Saros 141   22:17 TD
A.Node
ΔT= 14s   Alt. = 28°
Gam. = 0.8808   Dur. = 04m36s

Partial   **1758 Jan 09**
Saros 108   18:14 TD
D.Node
ΔT= 14s   Alt. = 0°
Gam. = 1.3252   Mag. = 0.3972

Partial   **1758 Feb 08**
Saros 146   04:41 TD
D.Node
ΔT= 14s   Alt. = 0°
Gam. = -1.3468   Mag. = 0.3549

Partial   **1758 Jul 05**
Saros 113   08:58 TD
A.Node
ΔT= 14s   Alt. = 0°
Gam. = -1.1961   Mag. = 0.6303

Annular   **1758 Dec 30**
Saros 118   07:20 TD
D.Node
ΔT= 14s   Alt. = 46°
Gam. = 0.6929   Dur. = 01m15s

Total   **1759 Jun 24**
Saros 123   17:21 TD
A.Node
ΔT= 14s   Alt. = 68°
Gam. = -0.3767   Dur. = 02m59s

Plate 052

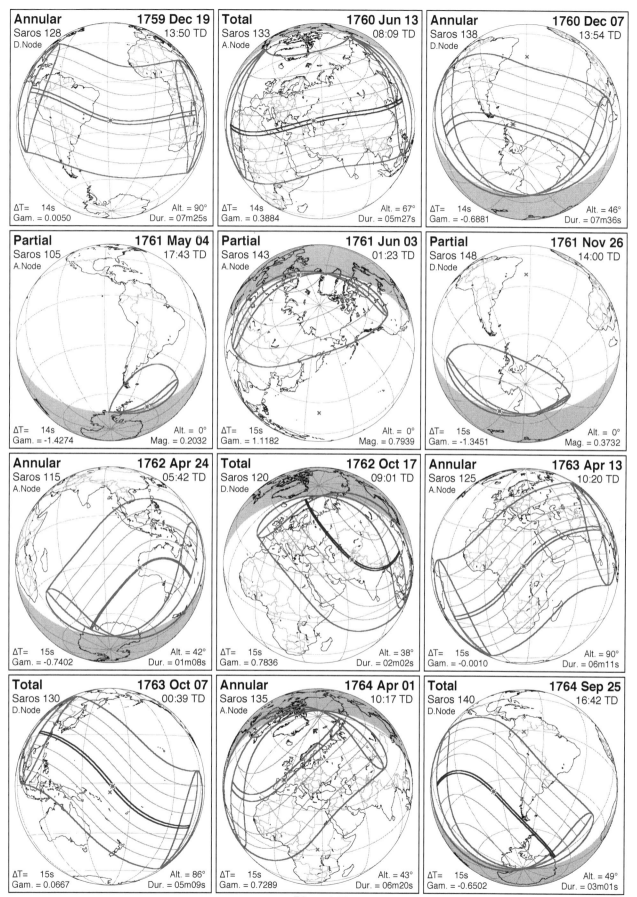

Annular 1759 Dec 19	**Total** 1760 Jun 13	**Annular** 1760 Dec 07
Saros 128 13:50 TD	Saros 133 08:09 TD	Saros 138 13:54 TD
D.Node	A.Node	D.Node
ΔT= 14s Alt. = 90°	ΔT= 14s Alt. = 67°	ΔT= 14s Alt. = 46°
Gam. = 0.0050 Dur. = 07m25s	Gam. = 0.3884 Dur. = 05m27s	Gam. = -0.6881 Dur. = 07m36s
Partial 1761 May 04	**Partial** 1761 Jun 03	**Partial** 1761 Nov 26
Saros 105 17:43 TD	Saros 143 01:23 TD	Saros 148 14:00 TD
A.Node	A.Node	D.Node
ΔT= 14s Alt. = 0°	ΔT= 15s Alt. = 0°	ΔT= 15s Alt. = 0°
Gam. = -1.4274 Mag. = 0.2032	Gam. = 1.1182 Mag. = 0.7939	Gam. = -1.3451 Mag. = 0.3732
Annular 1762 Apr 24	**Total** 1762 Oct 17	**Annular** 1763 Apr 13
Saros 115 05:42 TD	Saros 120 09:01 TD	Saros 125 10:20 TD
A.Node	D.Node	A.Node
ΔT= 15s Alt. = 42°	ΔT= 15s Alt. = 38°	ΔT= 15s Alt. = 90°
Gam. = -0.7402 Dur. = 01m08s	Gam. = 0.7836 Dur. = 02m02s	Gam. = -0.0010 Dur. = 06m11s
Total 1763 Oct 07	**Annular** 1764 Apr 01	**Total** 1764 Sep 25
Saros 130 00:39 TD	Saros 135 10:17 TD	Saros 140 16:42 TD
D.Node	A.Node	D.Node
ΔT= 15s Alt. = 86°	ΔT= 15s Alt. = 43°	ΔT= 15s Alt. = 49°
Gam. = 0.0667 Dur. = 05m09s	Gam. = 0.7289 Dur. = 06m20s	Gam. = -0.6502 Dur. = 03m01s

Plate 053

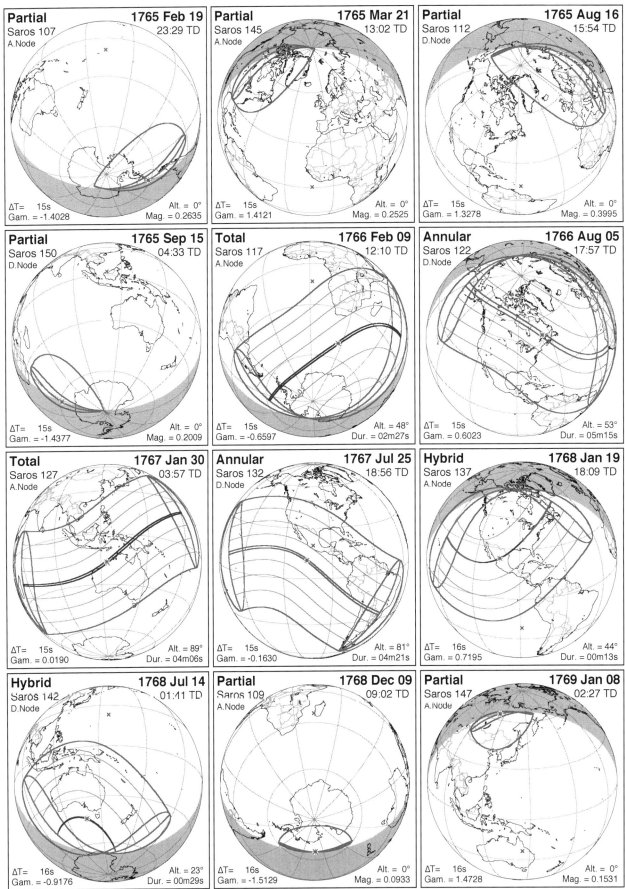

Partial	1765 Feb 19
Saros 107	23:29 TD
A.Node	
ΔT= 15s	Alt. = 0°
Gam. = -1.4028	Mag. = 0.2635

Partial	1765 Mar 21
Saros 145	13:02 TD
A.Node	
ΔT= 15s	Alt. = 0°
Gam. = 1.4121	Mag. = 0.2525

Partial	1765 Aug 16
Saros 112	15:54 TD
D.Node	
ΔT= 15s	Alt. = 0°
Gam. = 1.3278	Mag. = 0.3995

Partial	1765 Sep 15
Saros 150	04:33 TD
D.Node	
ΔT= 15s	Alt. = 0°
Gam. = -1.4377	Mag. = 0.2009

Total	1766 Feb 09
Saros 117	12:10 TD
A.Node	
ΔT= 15s	Alt. = 48°
Gam. = -0.6597	Dur. = 02m27s

Annular	1766 Aug 05
Saros 122	17:57 TD
D.Node	
ΔT= 15s	Alt. = 53°
Gam. = 0.6023	Dur. = 05m15s

Total	1767 Jan 30
Saros 127	03:57 TD
A.Node	
ΔT= 15s	Alt. = 89°
Gam. = 0.0190	Dur. = 04m06s

Annular	1767 Jul 25
Saros 132	18:56 TD
D.Node	
ΔT= 15s	Alt. = 81°
Gam. = -0.1630	Dur. = 04m21s

Hybrid	1768 Jan 19
Saros 137	18:09 TD
A.Node	
ΔT= 16s	Alt. = 44°
Gam. = 0.7195	Dur. = 00m13s

Hybrid	1768 Jul 14
Saros 142	01:41 TD
D.Node	
ΔT= 16s	Alt. = 23°
Gam. = -0.9176	Dur. = 00m29s

Partial	1768 Dec 09
Saros 109	09:02 TD
A.Node	
ΔT= 16s	Alt. = 0°
Gam. = -1.5129	Mag. = 0.0933

Partial	1769 Jan 08
Saros 147	02:27 TD
A.Node	
ΔT= 16s	Alt. = 0°
Gam. = 1.4728	Mag. = 0.1531

Plate 054

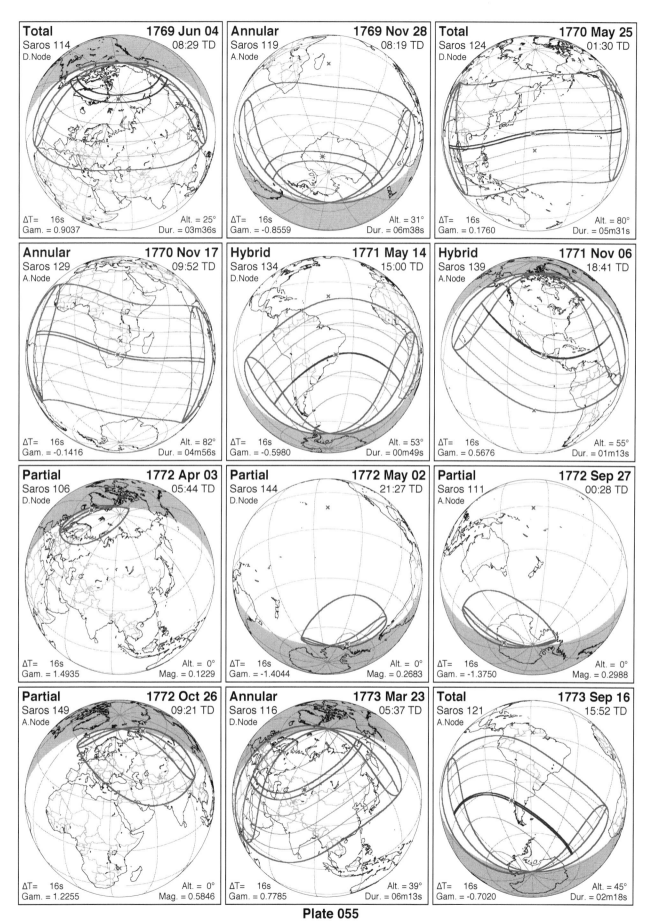

Total	**1769 Jun 04**
Saros 114	08:29 TD
D.Node	
ΔT= 16s	Alt. = 25°
Gam. = 0.9037	Dur. = 03m36s

Annular	**1769 Nov 28**
Saros 119	08:19 TD
A.Node	
ΔT= 16s	Alt. = 31°
Gam. = -0.8559	Dur. = 06m38s

Total	**1770 May 25**
Saros 124	01:30 TD
D.Node	
ΔT= 16s	Alt. = 80°
Gam. = 0.1760	Dur. = 05m31s

Annular	**1770 Nov 17**
Saros 129	09:52 TD
A.Node	
ΔT= 16s	Alt. = 82°
Gam. = -0.1416	Dur. = 04m56s

Hybrid	**1771 May 14**
Saros 134	15:00 TD
D.Node	
ΔT= 16s	Alt. = 53°
Gam. = -0.5980	Dur. = 00m49s

Hybrid	**1771 Nov 06**
Saros 139	18:41 TD
A.Node	
ΔT= 16s	Alt. = 55°
Gam. = 0.5676	Dur. = 01m13s

Partial	**1772 Apr 03**
Saros 106	05:44 TD
D.Node	
ΔT= 16s	Alt. = 0°
Gam. = 1.4935	Mag. = 0.1229

Partial	**1772 May 02**
Saros 144	21:27 TD
D.Node	
ΔT= 16s	Alt. = 0°
Gam. = -1.4044	Mag. = 0.2683

Partial	**1772 Sep 27**
Saros 111	00:28 TD
A.Node	
ΔT= 16s	Alt. = 0°
Gam. = -1.3750	Mag. = 0.2988

Partial	**1772 Oct 26**
Saros 149	09:21 TD
A.Node	
ΔT= 16s	Alt. = 0°
Gam. = 1.2255	Mag. = 0.5846

Annular	**1773 Mar 23**
Saros 116	05:37 TD
D.Node	
ΔT= 16s	Alt. = 39°
Gam. = 0.7785	Dur. = 06m13s

Total	**1773 Sep 16**
Saros 121	15:52 TD
A.Node	
ΔT= 16s	Alt. = 45°
Gam. = -0.7020	Dur. = 02m18s

Plate 055

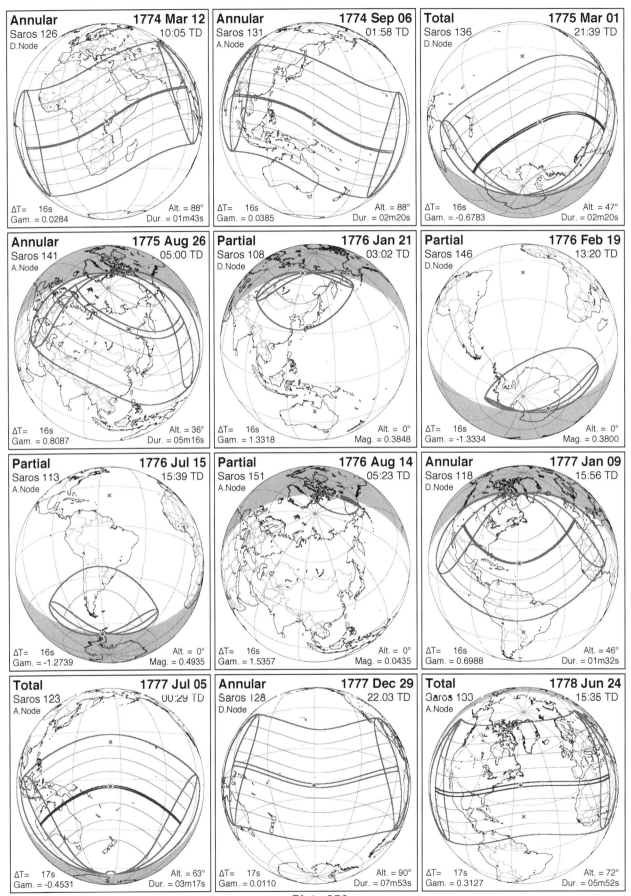

Annular   1774 Mar 12
Saros 126   10:05 TD
D.Node
ΔT=   16s   Alt. = 88°
Gam. = 0.0284   Dur. = 01m43s

Annular   1774 Sep 06
Saros 131   01:58 TD
A.Node
ΔT=   16s   Alt. = 88°
Gam. = 0.0385   Dur. = 02m20s

Total   1775 Mar 01
Saros 136   21:39 TD
D.Node
ΔT=   16s   Alt. = 47°
Gam. = -0.6783   Dur. = 02m20s

Annular   1775 Aug 26
Saros 141   05:00 TD
A.Node
ΔT=   16s   Alt. = 36°
Gam. = 0.8087   Dur. = 05m16s

Partial   1776 Jan 21
Saros 108   03:02 TD
D.Node
ΔT=   16s   Alt. = 0°
Gam. = 1.3318   Mag. = 0.3848

Partial   1776 Feb 19
Saros 146   13:20 TD
D.Node
ΔT=   16s   Alt. = 0°
Gam. = -1.3334   Mag. = 0.3800

Partial   1776 Jul 15
Saros 113   15:39 TD
A.Node
ΔT=   16s   Alt. = 0°
Gam. = -1.2739   Mag. = 0.4935

Partial   1776 Aug 14
Saros 151   05:23 TD
A.Node
ΔT=   16s   Alt. = 0°
Gam. = 1.5357   Mag. = 0.0435

Annular   1777 Jan 09
Saros 118   15:56 TD
D.Node
ΔT=   16s   Alt. = 46°
Gam. = 0.6988   Dur. = 01m32s

Total   1777 Jul 05
Saros 123   00:29 TD
A.Node
ΔT=   17s   Alt. = 63°
Gam. = -0.4531   Dur. = 03m17s

Annular   1777 Dec 29
Saros 128   22.03 TD
D.Node
ΔT=   17s   Alt. = 90°
Gam. = 0.0110   Dur. = 07m53s

Total   1778 Jun 24
Saros 130   15:35 TD
A.Node
ΔT=   17s   Alt. = 72°
Gam. = 0.3127   Dur. = 05m52s

Plate 056

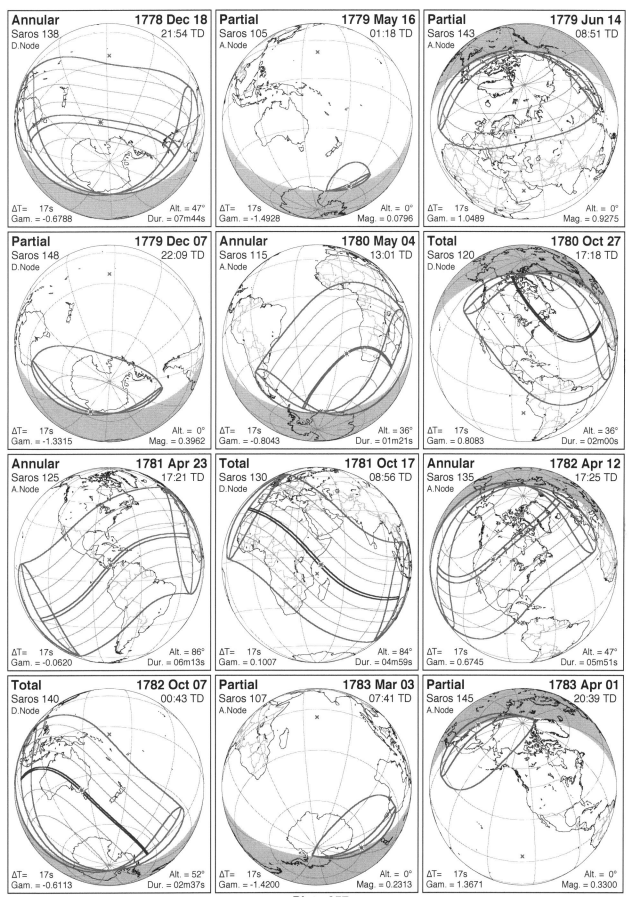

Annular **1778 Dec 18**	**Partial** **1779 May 16**	**Partial** **1779 Jun 14**
Saros 138 21:54 TD	Saros 105 01:18 TD	Saros 143 08:51 TD
D.Node	A.Node	A.Node
ΔT= 17s Alt. = 47°	ΔT= 17s Alt. = 0°	ΔT= 17s Alt. = 0°
Gam. = -0.6788 Dur. = 07m44s	Gam. = -1.4928 Mag. = 0.0796	Gam. = 1.0489 Mag. = 0.9275
Partial **1779 Dec 07**	**Annular** **1780 May 04**	**Total** **1780 Oct 27**
Saros 148 22:09 TD	Saros 115 13:01 TD	Saros 120 17:18 TD
D.Node	A.Node	D.Node
ΔT= 17s Alt. = 0°	ΔT= 17s Alt. = 36°	ΔT= 17s Alt. = 36°
Gam. = -1.3315 Mag. = 0.3962	Gam. = -0.8043 Dur. = 01m21s	Gam. = 0.8083 Dur. = 02m00s
Annular **1781 Apr 23**	**Total** **1781 Oct 17**	**Annular** **1782 Apr 12**
Saros 125 17:21 TD	Saros 130 08:56 TD	Saros 135 17:25 TD
A.Node	D.Node	A.Node
ΔT= 17s Alt. = 86°	ΔT= 17s Alt. = 84°	ΔT= 17s Alt. = 47°
Gam. = -0.0620 Dur. = 06m13s	Gam. = 0.1007 Dur. = 04m59s	Gam. = 0.6745 Dur. = 05m51s
Total **1782 Oct 07**	**Partial** **1783 Mar 03**	**Partial** **1783 Apr 01**
Saros 140 00:43 TD	Saros 107 07:41 TD	Saros 145 20:39 TD
D.Node	A.Node	A.Node
ΔT= 17s Alt. = 52°	ΔT= 17s Alt. = 0°	ΔT= 17s Alt. = 0°
Gam. = -0.6113 Dur. = 02m37s	Gam. = -1.4200 Mag. = 0.2313	Gam. = 1.3671 Mag. = 0.3300

Plate 057

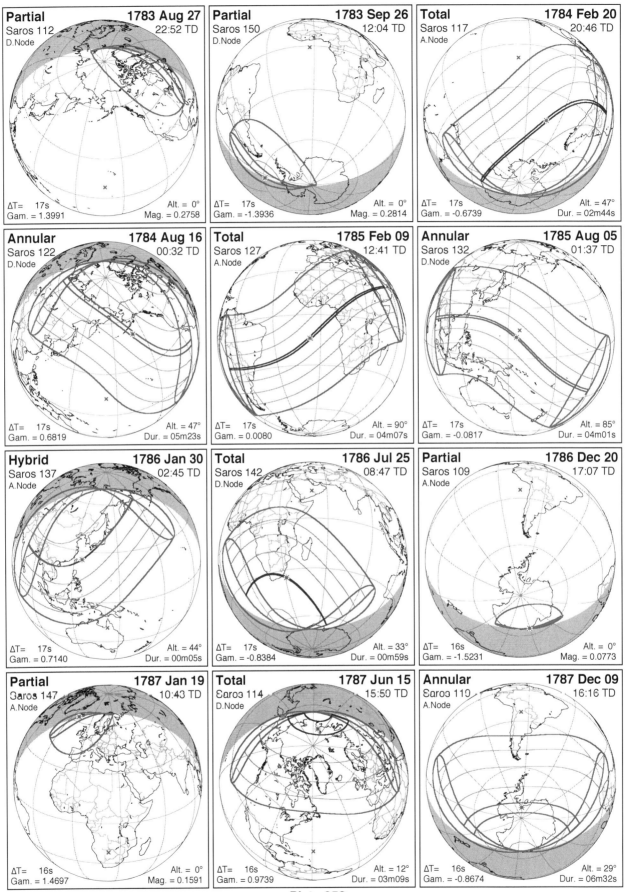

Partial   **1783 Aug 27**
Saros 112   22:52 TD
D.Node
ΔT= 17s   Alt. = 0°
Gam. = 1.3991   Mag. = 0.2758

Partial   **1783 Sep 26**
Saros 150   12:04 TD
D.Node
ΔT= 17s   Alt. = 0°
Gam. = -1.3936   Mag. = 0.2814

Total   **1784 Feb 20**
Saros 117   20:46 TD
A.Node
ΔT= 17s   Alt. = 47°
Gam. = -0.6739   Dur. = 02m44s

Annular   **1784 Aug 16**
Saros 122   00:32 TD
D.Node
ΔT= 17s   Alt. = 47°
Gam. = 0.6819   Dur. = 05m23s

Total   **1785 Feb 09**
Saros 127   12:41 TD
A.Node
ΔT= 17s   Alt. = 90°
Gam. = 0.0080   Dur. = 04m07s

Annular   **1785 Aug 05**
Saros 132   01:37 TD
D.Node
ΔT= 17s   Alt. = 85°
Gam. = -0.0817   Dur. = 04m01s

Hybrid   **1786 Jan 30**
Saros 137   02:45 TD
A.Node
ΔT= 17s   Alt. = 44°
Gam. = 0.7140   Dur. = 00m05s

Total   **1786 Jul 25**
Saros 142   08:47 TD
D.Node
ΔT= 17s   Alt. = 33°
Gam. = -0.8384   Dur. = 00m59s

Partial   **1786 Dec 20**
Saros 109   17:07 TD
A.Node
ΔT= 16s   Alt. = 0°
Gam. = -1.5231   Mag. = 0.0773

Partial   **1787 Jan 19**
Saros 147   10:43 TD
A.Node
ΔT= 16s   Alt. = 0°
Gam. = 1.4697   Mag. = 0.1591

Total   **1787 Jun 15**
Saros 114   15:50 TD
D.Node
ΔT= 16s   Alt. = 12°
Gam. = 0.9739   Dur. = 03m09s

Annular   **1787 Dec 09**
Saros 119   16:16 TD
A.Node
ΔT= 16s   Alt. = 29°
Gam. = -0.8674   Dur. = 06m32s

Plate 058

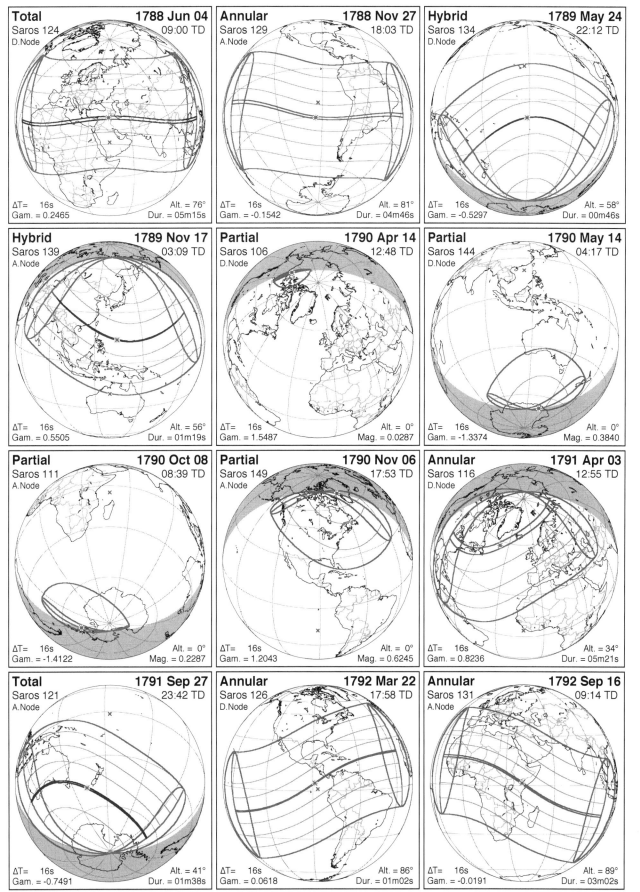

Total	1788 Jun 04
Saros 124	09:00 TD
D.Node	
ΔT= 16s	Alt. = 76°
Gam. = 0.2465	Dur. = 05m15s

Annular	1788 Nov 27
Saros 129	18:03 TD
A.Node	
ΔT= 16s	Alt. = 81°
Gam. = -0.1542	Dur. = 04m46s

Hybrid	1789 May 24
Saros 134	22:12 TD
D.Node	
ΔT= 16s	Alt. = 58°
Gam. = -0.5297	Dur. = 00m46s

Hybrid	1789 Nov 17
Saros 139	03:09 TD
A.Node	
ΔT= 16s	Alt. = 56°
Gam. = 0.5505	Dur. = 01m19s

Partial	1790 Apr 14
Saros 106	12:48 TD
D.Node	
ΔT= 16s	Alt. = 0°
Gam. = 1.5487	Mag. = 0.0287

Partial	1790 May 14
Saros 144	04:17 TD
D.Node	
ΔT= 16s	Alt. = 0°
Gam. = -1.3374	Mag. = 0.3840

Partial	1790 Oct 08
Saros 111	08:39 TD
A.Node	
ΔT= 16s	Alt. = 0°
Gam. = -1.4122	Mag. = 0.2287

Partial	1790 Nov 06
Saros 149	17:53 TD
A.Node	
ΔT= 16s	Alt. = 0°
Gam. = 1.2043	Mag. = 0.6245

Annular	1791 Apr 03
Saros 116	12:55 TD
D.Node	
ΔT= 16s	Alt. = 34°
Gam. = 0.8236	Dur. = 05m21s

Total	1791 Sep 27
Saros 121	23:42 TD
A.Node	
ΔT= 16s	Alt. = 41°
Gam. = -0.7491	Dur. = 01m38s

Annular	1792 Mar 22
Saros 126	17:58 TD
D.Node	
ΔT= 16s	Alt. = 86°
Gam. = 0.0618	Dur. = 01m02s

Annular	1792 Sep 16
Saros 131	09:14 TD
A.Node	
ΔT= 16s	Alt. = 89°
Gam. = -0.0191	Dur. = 03m02s

Plate 059

153

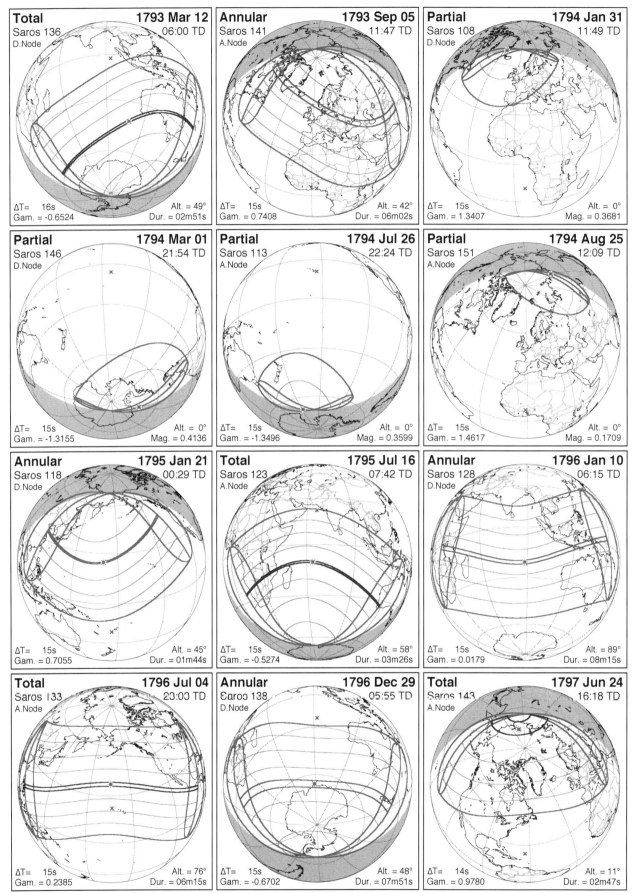

Total	1793 Mar 12
Saros 136	06:00 TD
D.Node	
ΔT= 16s	Alt. = 49°
Gam. = -0.6524	Dur. = 02m51s

Annular	1793 Sep 05
Saros 141	11:47 TD
A.Node	
ΔT= 15s	Alt. = 42°
Gam. = 0.7408	Dur. = 06m02s

Partial	1794 Jan 31
Saros 108	11:49 TD
D.Node	
ΔT= 15s	Alt. = 0°
Gam. = 1.3407	Mag. = 0.3681

Partial	1794 Mar 01
Saros 146	21:54 TD
D.Node	
ΔT= 15s	Alt. = 0°
Gam. = -1.3155	Mag. = 0.4136

Partial	1794 Jul 26
Saros 113	22:24 TD
A.Node	
ΔT= 15s	Alt. = 0°
Gam. = -1.3496	Mag. = 0.3599

Partial	1794 Aug 25
Saros 151	12:09 TD
A.Node	
ΔT= 15s	Alt. = 0°
Gam. = 1.4617	Mag. = 0.1709

Annular	1795 Jan 21
Saros 118	00:29 TD
D.Node	
ΔT= 15s	Alt. = 45°
Gam. = 0.7055	Dur. = 01m44s

Total	1795 Jul 16
Saros 123	07:42 TD
A.Node	
ΔT= 15s	Alt. = 58°
Gam. = -0.5274	Dur. = 03m26s

Annular	1796 Jan 10
Saros 128	06:15 TD
D.Node	
ΔT= 15s	Alt. = 89°
Gam. = 0.0179	Dur. = 08m15s

Total	1796 Jul 04
Saros 133	20:03 TD
A.Node	
ΔT= 15s	Alt. = 76°
Gam. = 0.2385	Dur. = 06m15s

Annular	1796 Dec 29
Saros 138	05:55 TD
D.Node	
ΔT= 15s	Alt. = 48°
Gam. = -0.6702	Dur. = 07m51s

Total	1797 Jun 24
Saros 143	16:18 TD
A.Node	
ΔT= 14s	Alt. = 11°
Gam. = 0.9780	Dur. = 02m47s

Plate 060

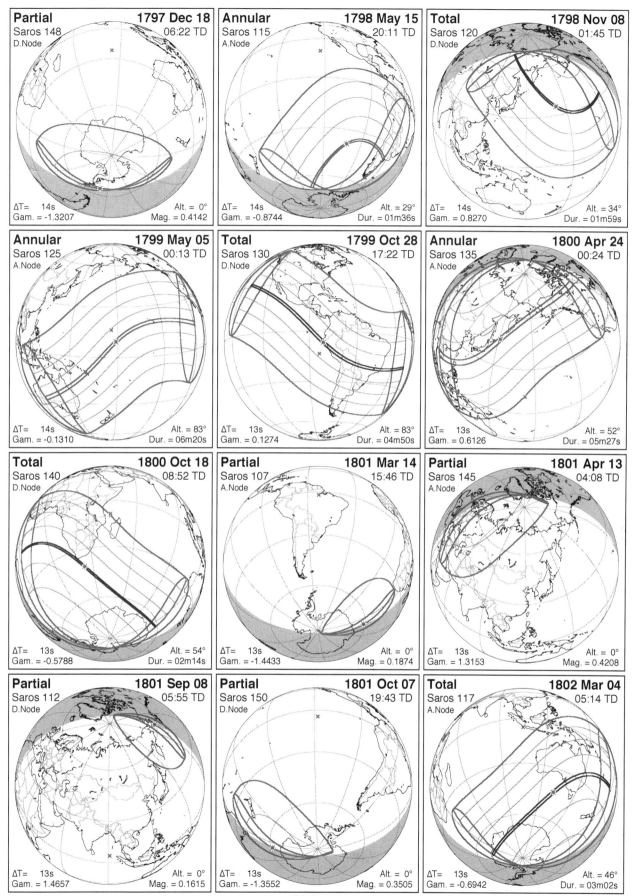

Partial	1797 Dec 18
Saros 148	06:22 TD
D.Node	
ΔT= 14s	Alt. = 0°
Gam. = -1.3207	Mag. = 0.4142

Annular	1798 May 15
Saros 115	20:11 TD
A.Node	
ΔT= 14s	Alt. = 29°
Gam. = -0.8744	Dur. = 01m36s

Total	1798 Nov 08
Saros 120	01:45 TD
D.Node	
ΔT= 14s	Alt. = 34°
Gam. = 0.8270	Dur. = 01m59s

Annular	1799 May 05
Saros 125	00:13 TD
A.Node	
ΔT= 14s	Alt. = 83°
Gam. = -0.1310	Dur. = 06m20s

Total	1799 Oct 28
Saros 130	17:22 TD
D.Node	
ΔT= 13s	Alt. = 83°
Gam. = 0.1274	Dur. = 04m50s

Annular	1800 Apr 24
Saros 135	00:24 TD
A.Node	
ΔT= 13s	Alt. = 52°
Gam. = 0.6126	Dur. = 05m27s

Total	1800 Oct 18
Saros 140	08:52 TD
D.Node	
ΔT= 13s	Alt. = 54°
Gam. = -0.5788	Dur. = 02m14s

Partial	1801 Mar 14
Saros 107	15:46 TD
A.Node	
ΔT= 13s	Alt. = 0°
Gam. = -1.4433	Mag. = 0.1874

Partial	1801 Apr 13
Saros 145	04:08 TD
A.Node	
ΔT= 13s	Alt. = 0°
Gam. = 1.3153	Mag. = 0.4208

Partial	1801 Sep 08
Saros 112	05:55 TD
D.Node	
ΔT= 13s	Alt. = 0°
Gam. = 1.4657	Mag. = 0.1615

Partial	1801 Oct 07
Saros 150	19:43 TD
D.Node	
ΔT= 13s	Alt. = 0°
Gam. = -1.3552	Mag. = 0.3505

Total	1802 Mar 04
Saros 117	05:14 TD
A.Node	
ΔT= 13s	Alt. = 46°
Gam. = -0.6942	Dur. = 03m02s

Plate 061

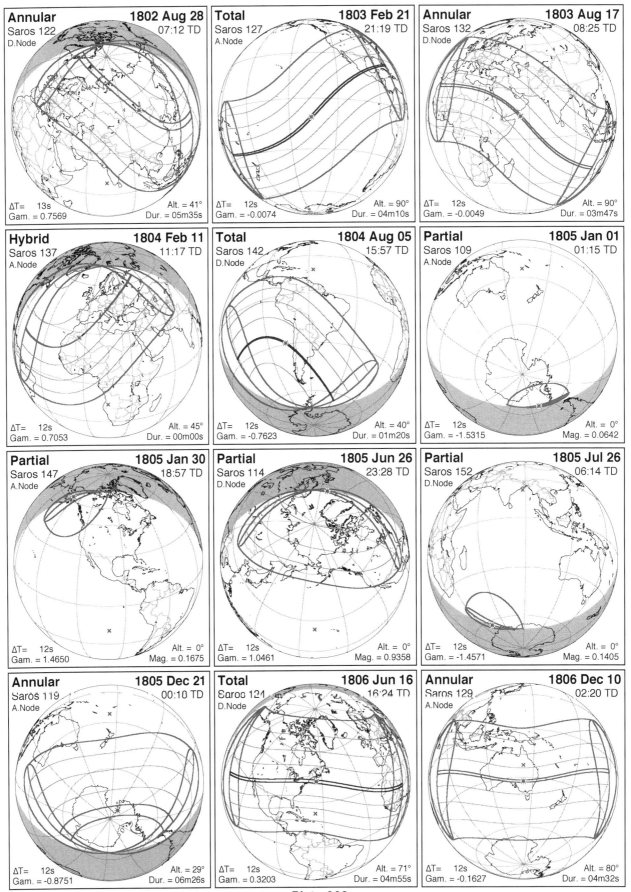

Annular	1802 Aug 28
Saros 122	07:12 TD
D.Node	
ΔT= 13s	Alt. = 41°
Gam. = 0.7569	Dur = 05m35s

Total	1803 Feb 21
Saros 127	21:19 TD
A.Node	
ΔT= 12s	Alt. = 90°
Gam. = -0.0074	Dur = 04m10s

Annular	1803 Aug 17
Saros 132	08:25 TD
D.Node	
ΔT= 12s	Alt. = 90°
Gam. = -0.0049	Dur = 03m47s

Hybrid	1804 Feb 11
Saros 137	11:17 TD
A.Node	
ΔT= 12s	Alt. = 45°
Gam. = 0.7053	Dur = 00m00s

Total	1804 Aug 05
Saros 142	15:57 TD
D.Node	
ΔT= 12s	Alt. = 40°
Gam. = -0.7623	Dur = 01m20s

Partial	1805 Jan 01
Saros 109	01:15 TD
A.Node	
ΔT= 12s	Alt. = 0°
Gam. = -1.5315	Mag. = 0.0642

Partial	1805 Jan 30
Saros 147	18:57 TD
A.Node	
ΔT= 12s	Alt. = 0°
Gam. = 1.4650	Mag. = 0.1675

Partial	1805 Jun 26
Saros 114	23:28 TD
D.Node	
ΔT= 12s	Alt. = 0°
Gam. = 1.0461	Mag. = 0.9358

Partial	1805 Jul 26
Saros 152	06:14 TD
D.Node	
ΔT= 12s	Alt. = 0°
Gam. = -1.4571	Mag. = 0.1405

Annular	1805 Dec 21
Saros 119	00:10 TD
A.Node	
ΔT= 12s	Alt. = 29°
Gam. = -0.8751	Dur = 06m26s

Total	1806 Jun 16
Saros 124	16:24 TD
D.Node	
ΔT= 12s	Alt. = 71°
Gam. = 0.3203	Dur = 04m55s

Annular	1806 Dec 10
Saros 129	02:20 TD
A.Node	
ΔT= 12s	Alt. = 80°
Gam. = -0.1627	Dur = 04m32s

Plate 062

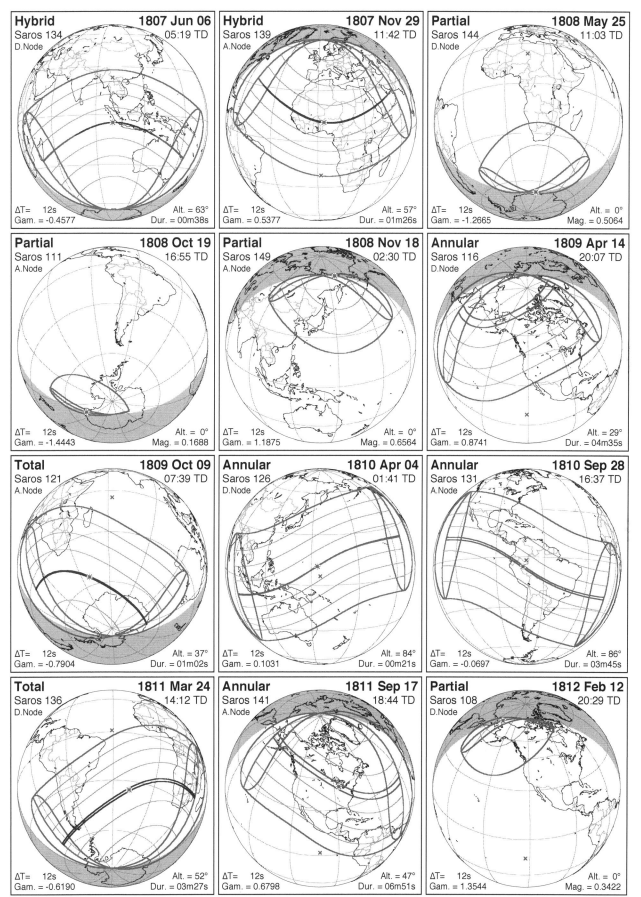

Hybrid **1807 Jun 06**	
Saros 134 05:19 TD	
D.Node	
ΔT= 12s Alt. = 63°	
Gam. = -0.4577 Dur. = 00m38s	

| **Hybrid** **1807 Nov 29** |
| Saros 139 11:42 TD |
| A.Node |
| ΔT= 12s Alt. = 57° |
| Gam. = 0.5377 Dur. = 01m26s |

| **Partial** **1808 May 25** |
| Saros 144 11:03 TD |
| D.Node |
| ΔT= 12s Alt. = 0° |
| Gam. = -1.2665 Mag. = 0.5064 |

| **Partial** **1808 Oct 19** |
| Saros 111 16:55 TD |
| A.Node |
| ΔT= 12s Alt. = 0° |
| Gam. = -1.4443 Mag. = 0.1688 |

| **Partial** **1808 Nov 18** |
| Saros 149 02:30 TD |
| A.Node |
| ΔT= 12s Alt. = 0° |
| Gam. = 1.1875 Mag. = 0.6564 |

| **Annular** **1809 Apr 14** |
| Saros 116 20:07 TD |
| D.Node |
| ΔT= 12s Alt. = 29° |
| Gam. = 0.8741 Dur. = 04m35s |

| **Total** **1809 Oct 09** |
| Saros 121 07:39 TD |
| A.Node |
| ΔT= 12s Alt. = 37° |
| Gam. = -0.7904 Dur. = 01m02s |

| **Annular** **1810 Apr 04** |
| Saros 126 01:41 TD |
| D.Node |
| ΔT= 12s Alt. = 84° |
| Gam. = 0.1031 Dur. = 00m21s |

| **Annular** **1810 Sep 28** |
| Saros 131 16:37 TD |
| A.Node |
| ΔT= 12s Alt. = 86° |
| Gam. = -0.0697 Dur. = 03m45s |

| **Total** **1811 Mar 24** |
| Saros 136 14:12 TD |
| D.Node |
| ΔT= 12s Alt. = 52° |
| Gam. = -0.6190 Dur. = 03m27s |

| **Annular** **1811 Sep 17** |
| Saros 141 18:44 TD |
| A.Node |
| ΔT= 12s Alt. = 47° |
| Gam. = 0.6798 Dur. = 06m51s |

| **Partial** **1812 Feb 12** |
| Saros 108 20:29 TD |
| D.Node |
| ΔT= 12s Alt. = 0° |
| Gam. = 1.3544 Mag. = 0.3422 |

Plate 063

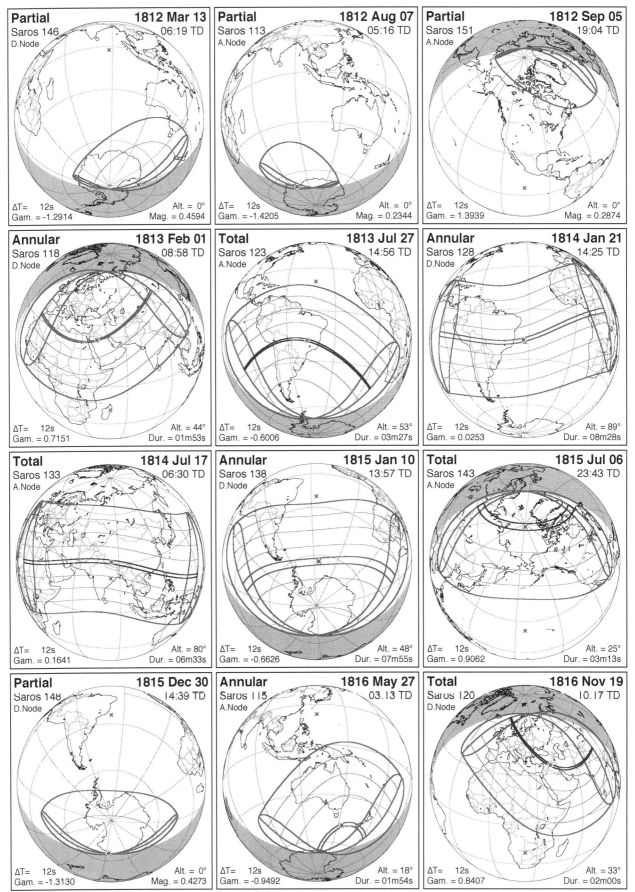

Partial **1812 Mar 13**	**Partial** **1812 Aug 07**	**Partial** **1812 Sep 05**
Saros 146 06:19 TD	Saros 113 05:16 TD	Saros 151 19:04 TD
D.Node	A.Node	A.Node
ΔT= 12s Alt. = 0°	ΔT= 12s Alt. = 0°	ΔT= 12s Alt. = 0°
Gam. = -1.2914 Mag. = 0.4594	Gam. = -1.4205 Mag. = 0.2344	Gam. = 1.3939 Mag. = 0.2874
Annular **1813 Feb 01**	**Total** **1813 Jul 27**	**Annular** **1814 Jan 21**
Saros 118 08:58 TD	Saros 123 14:56 TD	Saros 128 14:25 TD
D.Node	A.Node	D.Node
ΔT= 12s Alt. = 44°	ΔT= 12s Alt. = 53°	ΔT= 12s Alt. = 89°
Gam. = 0.7151 Dur. = 01m53s	Gam. = -0.6006 Dur. = 03m27s	Gam. = 0.0253 Dur. = 08m28s
Total **1814 Jul 17**	**Annular** **1815 Jan 10**	**Total** **1815 Jul 06**
Saros 133 06:30 TD	Saros 138 13:57 TD	Saros 143 23:43 TD
A.Node	D.Node	A.Node
ΔT= 12s Alt. = 80°	ΔT= 12s Alt. = 48°	ΔT= 12s Alt. = 25°
Gam. = 0.1641 Dur. = 06m33s	Gam. = -0.6626 Dur. = 07m55s	Gam. = 0.9062 Dur. = 03m13s
Partial **1815 Dec 30**	**Annular** **1816 May 27**	**Total** **1816 Nov 19**
Saros 148 14:39 TD	Saros 115 03.13 TD	Saros 120 10.17 TD
D.Node	A.Node	D.Node
ΔT= 12s Alt. = 0°	ΔT= 12s Alt. = 18°	ΔT= 12s Alt. = 33°
Gam. = -1.3130 Mag. = 0.4273	Gam. = -0.9492 Dur. = 01m54s	Gam. = 0.8407 Dur. = 02m00s

Plate 064

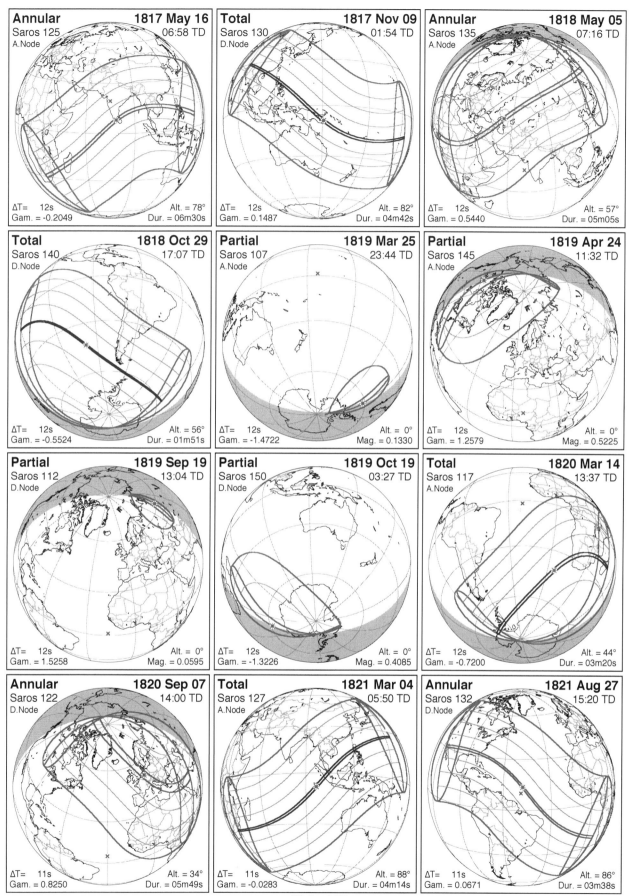

Annular   **1817 May 16**
Saros 125   06:58 TD
A.Node
ΔT= 12s   Alt. = 78°
Gam. = -0.2049   Dur. = 06m30s

Total   **1817 Nov 09**
Saros 130   01:54 TD
D.Node
ΔT= 12s   Alt. = 82°
Gam. = 0.1487   Dur. = 04m42s

Annular   **1818 May 05**
Saros 135   07:16 TD
A.Node
ΔT= 12s   Alt. = 57°
Gam. = 0.5440   Dur. = 05m05s

Total   **1818 Oct 29**
Saros 140   17:07 TD
D.Node
ΔT= 12s   Alt. = 56°
Gam. = -0.5524   Dur. = 01m51s

Partial   **1819 Mar 25**
Saros 107   23:44 TD
A.Node
ΔT= 12s   Alt. = 0°
Gam. = -1.4722   Mag. = 0.1330

Partial   **1819 Apr 24**
Saros 145   11:32 TD
A.Node
ΔT= 12s   Alt. = 0°
Gam. = 1.2579   Mag. = 0.5225

Partial   **1819 Sep 19**
Saros 112   13:04 TD
D.Node
ΔT= 12s   Alt. = 0°
Gam. = 1.5258   Mag. = 0.0595

Partial   **1819 Oct 19**
Saros 150   03:27 TD
D.Node
ΔT= 12s   Alt. = 0°
Gam. = -1.3226   Mag. = 0.4085

Total   **1820 Mar 14**
Saros 117   13:37 TD
A.Node
ΔT= 12s   Alt. = 44°
Gam. = -0.7200   Dur. = 03m20s

Annular   **1820 Sep 07**
Saros 122   14:00 TD
D.Node
ΔT= 11s   Alt. = 34°
Gam. = 0.8250   Dur. = 05m49s

Total   **1821 Mar 04**
Saros 127   05:50 TD
A.Node
ΔT= 11s   Alt. = 88°
Gam. = -0.0283   Dur. = 04m14s

Annular   **1821 Aug 27**
Saros 132   15:20 TD
D.Node
ΔT= 11s   Alt. = 86°
Gam. = 0.0671   Dur. = 03m38s

Plate 065

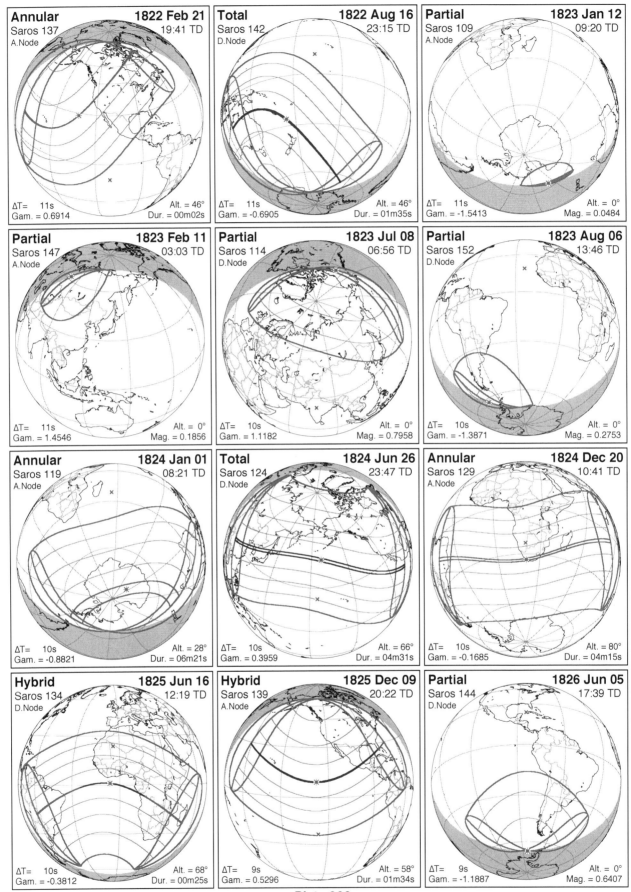

Plate 066

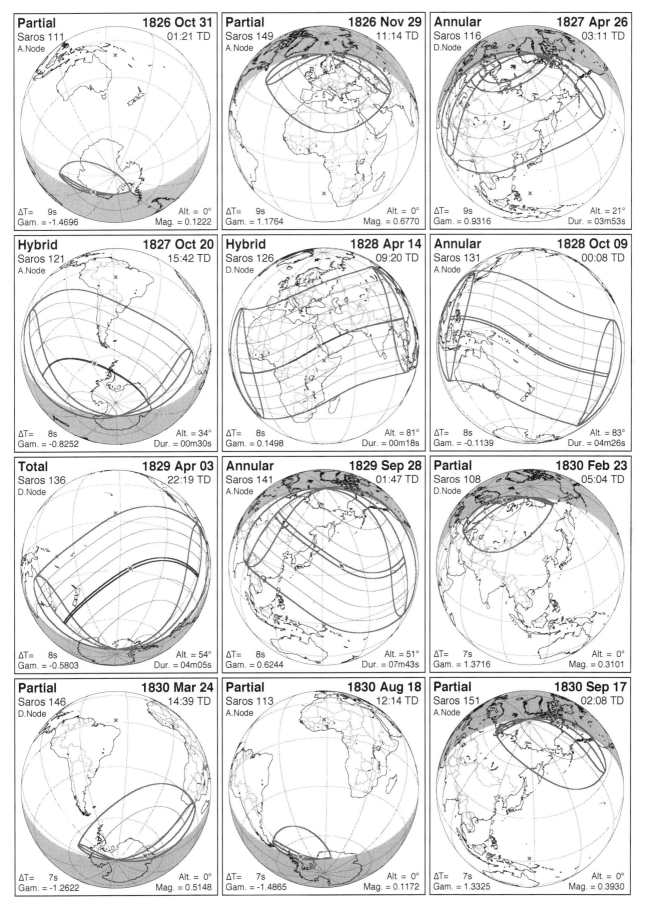

Partial	1826 Oct 31
Saros 111	01:21 TD
A.Node	
ΔT= 9s	Alt. = 0°
Gam. = -1.4696	Mag. = 0.1222

Partial	1826 Nov 29
Saros 149	11:14 TD
A.Node	
ΔT= 9s	Alt. = 0°
Gam. = 1.1764	Mag. = 0.6770

Annular	1827 Apr 26
Saros 116	03:11 TD
D.Node	
ΔT= 9s	Alt. = 21°
Gam. = 0.9316	Dur. = 03m53s

Hybrid	1827 Oct 20
Saros 121	15:42 TD
A.Node	
ΔT= 8s	Alt. = 34°
Gam. = -0.8252	Dur. = 00m30s

Hybrid	1828 Apr 14
Saros 126	09:20 TD
D.Node	
ΔT= 8s	Alt. = 81°
Gam. = 0.1498	Dur. = 00m18s

Annular	1828 Oct 09
Saros 131	00:08 TD
A.Node	
ΔT= 8s	Alt. = 83°
Gam. = -0.1139	Dur. = 04m26s

Total	1829 Apr 03
Saros 136	22:19 TD
D.Node	
ΔT= 8s	Alt. = 54°
Gam. = -0.5803	Dur. = 04m05s

Annular	1829 Sep 28
Saros 141	01:47 TD
A.Node	
ΔT= 8s	Alt. = 51°
Gam. = 0.6244	Dur. = 07m43s

Partial	1830 Feb 23
Saros 108	05:04 TD
D.Node	
ΔT= 7s	Alt. = 0°
Gam. = 1.3716	Mag. = 0.3101

Partial	1830 Mar 24
Saros 146	14:39 TD
D.Node	
ΔT= 7s	Alt. = 0°
Gam. = -1.2622	Mag. = 0.5148

Partial	1830 Aug 18
Saros 113	12:14 TD
A.Node	
ΔT= 7s	Alt. = 0°
Gam. = -1.4865	Mag. = 0.1172

Partial	1830 Sep 17
Saros 151	02:08 TD
A.Node	
ΔT= 7s	Alt. = 0°
Gam. = 1.3325	Mag. = 0.3930

Plate 067

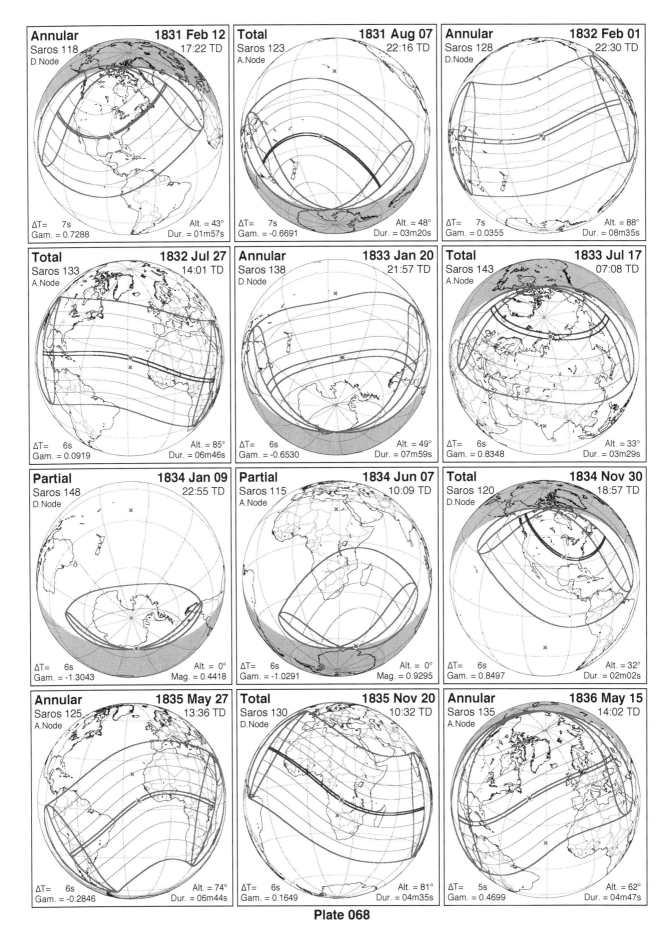

Annular   **1831 Feb 12**
Saros 118   17:22 TD
D.Node
ΔT= 7s   Alt. = 43°
Gam. = 0.7288   Dur. = 01m57s

Total   **1831 Aug 07**
Saros 123   22:16 TD
A.Node
ΔT= 7s   Alt. = 48°
Gam. = -0.6691   Dur. = 03m20s

Annular   **1832 Feb 01**
Saros 128   22:30 TD
D.Node
ΔT= 7s   Alt. = 88°
Gam. = 0.0355   Dur. = 08m35s

Total   **1832 Jul 27**
Saros 133   14:01 TD
A.Node
ΔT= 6s   Alt. = 85°
Gam. = 0.0919   Dur. = 06m46s

Annular   **1833 Jan 20**
Saros 138   21:57 TD
D.Node
ΔT= 6s   Alt. = 49°
Gam. = -0.6530   Dur. = 07m59s

Total   **1833 Jul 17**
Saros 143   07:08 TD
A.Node
ΔT= 6s   Alt. = 33°
Gam. = 0.8348   Dur. = 03m29s

Partial   **1834 Jan 09**
Saros 148   22:55 TD
D.Node
ΔT= 6s   Alt. = 0°
Gam. = -1.3043   Mag. = 0.4418

Partial   **1834 Jun 07**
Saros 115   10:09 TD
A.Node
ΔT= 6s   Alt. = 0°
Gam. = -1.0291   Mag. = 0.9295

Total   **1834 Nov 30**
Saros 120   18:57 TD
D.Node
ΔT= 6s   Alt. = 32°
Gam. = 0.8497   Dur. = 02m02s

Annular   **1835 May 27**
Saros 125   13:36 TD
A.Node
ΔT= 6s   Alt. = 74°
Gam. = -0.2846   Dur. = 06m44s

Total   **1835 Nov 20**
Saros 130   10:32 TD
D.Node
ΔT= 6s   Alt. = 81°
Gam. = 0.1649   Dur. = 04m35s

Annular   **1836 May 15**
Saros 135   14:02 TD
A.Node
ΔT= 5s   Alt. = 62°
Gam. = 0.4699   Dur. = 04m47s

Plate 068

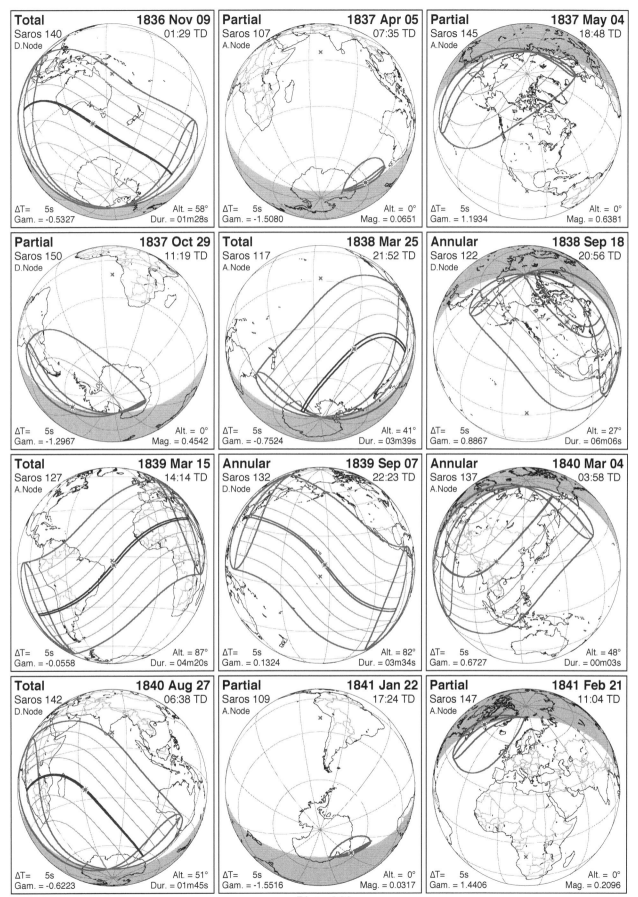

Total	1836 Nov 09
Saros 140	01:29 TD
D.Node	
ΔT= 5s	Alt. = 58°
Gam. = -0.5327	Dur. = 01m28s

Partial	1837 Apr 05
Saros 107	07:35 TD
A.Node	
ΔT= 5s	Alt. = 0°
Gam. = -1.5080	Mag. = 0.0651

Partial	1837 May 04
Saros 145	18:48 TD
A.Node	
ΔT= 5s	Alt. = 0°
Gam. = 1.1934	Mag. = 0.6381

Partial	1837 Oct 29
Saros 150	11:19 TD
D.Node	
ΔT= 5s	Alt. = 0°
Gam. = -1.2967	Mag. = 0.4542

Total	1838 Mar 25
Saros 117	21:52 TD
A.Node	
ΔT= 5s	Alt. = 41°
Gam. = -0.7524	Dur. = 03m39s

Annular	1838 Sep 18
Saros 122	20:56 TD
D.Node	
ΔT= 5s	Alt. = 27°
Gam. = 0.8867	Dur. = 06m06s

Total	1839 Mar 15
Saros 127	14:14 TD
A.Node	
ΔT= 5s	Alt. = 87°
Gam. = -0.0558	Dur. = 04m20s

Annular	1839 Sep 07
Saros 132	22:23 TD
D.Node	
ΔT= 5s	Alt. = 82°
Gam. = 0.1324	Dur. = 03m34s

Annular	1840 Mar 04
Saros 137	03:58 TD
A.Node	
ΔT= 5s	Alt. = 48°
Gam. = 0.6727	Dur. = 00m03s

Total	1840 Aug 27
Saros 142	06:38 TD
D.Node	
ΔT= 5s	Alt. = 51°
Gam. = -0.6223	Dur. = 01m45s

Partial	1841 Jan 22
Saros 109	17:24 TD
A.Node	
ΔT= 5s	Alt. = 0°
Gam. = -1.5516	Mag. = 0.0317

Partial	1841 Feb 21
Saros 147	11:04 TD
A.Node	
ΔT= 5s	Alt. = 0°
Gam. = 1.4406	Mag. = 0.2096

Plate 069

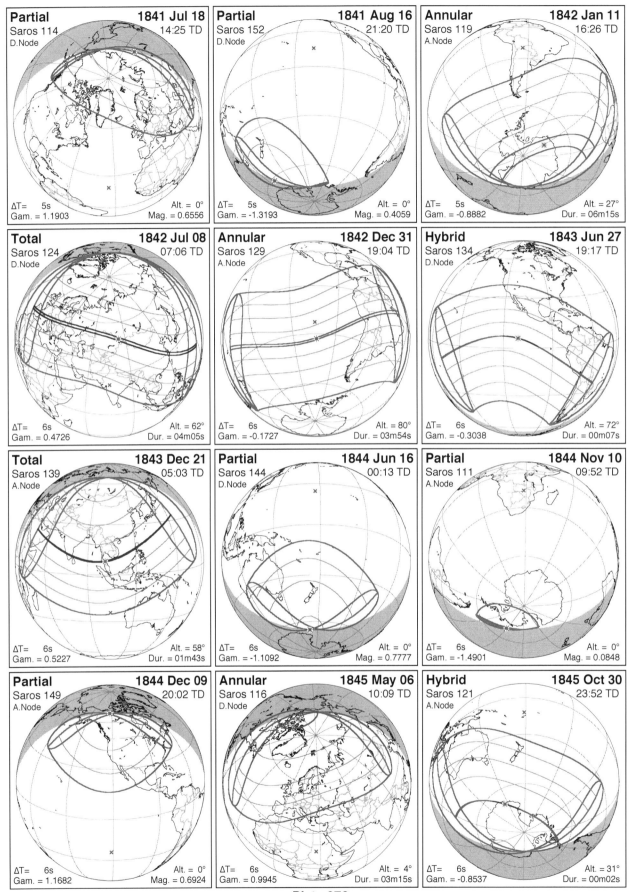

Partial	1841 Jul 18
Saros 114	14:25 TD
D.Node	
ΔT= 5s	Alt. = 0°
Gam. = 1.1903	Mag. = 0.6556

Partial	1841 Aug 16
Saros 152	21:20 TD
D.Node	
ΔT= 5s	Alt. = 0°
Gam. = -1.3193	Mag. = 0.4059

Annular	1842 Jan 11
Saros 119	16:26 TD
A.Node	
ΔT= 5s	Alt. = 27°
Gam. = -0.8882	Dur. = 06m15s

Total	1842 Jul 08
Saros 124	07:06 TD
D.Node	
ΔT= 6s	Alt. = 62°
Gam. = 0.4726	Dur. = 04m05s

Annular	1842 Dec 31
Saros 129	19:04 TD
A.Node	
ΔT= 6s	Alt. = 80°
Gam. = -0.1727	Dur. = 03m54s

Hybrid	1843 Jun 27
Saros 134	19:17 TD
D.Node	
ΔT= 6s	Alt. = 72°
Gam. = -0.3038	Dur. = 00m07s

Total	1843 Dec 21
Saros 139	05:03 TD
A.Node	
ΔT= 6s	Alt. = 58°
Gam. = 0.5227	Dur. = 01m43s

Partial	1844 Jun 16
Saros 144	00:13 TD
D.Node	
ΔT= 6s	Alt. = 0°
Gam. = -1.1092	Mag. = 0.7777

Partial	1844 Nov 10
Saros 111	09:52 TD
A.Node	
ΔT= 6s	Alt. = 0°
Gam. = -1.4901	Mag. = 0.0848

Partial	1844 Dec 09
Saros 149	20:02 TD
A.Node	
ΔT= 6s	Alt. = 0°
Gam. = 1.1682	Mag. = 0.6924

Annular	1845 May 06
Saros 116	10:09 TD
D.Node	
ΔT= 6s	Alt. = 4°
Gam. = 0.9945	Dur. = 03m15s

Hybrid	1845 Oct 30
Saros 121	23:52 TD
A.Node	
ΔT= 6s	Alt. = 31°
Gam. = -0.8537	Dur. = 00m02s

Plate 070

164

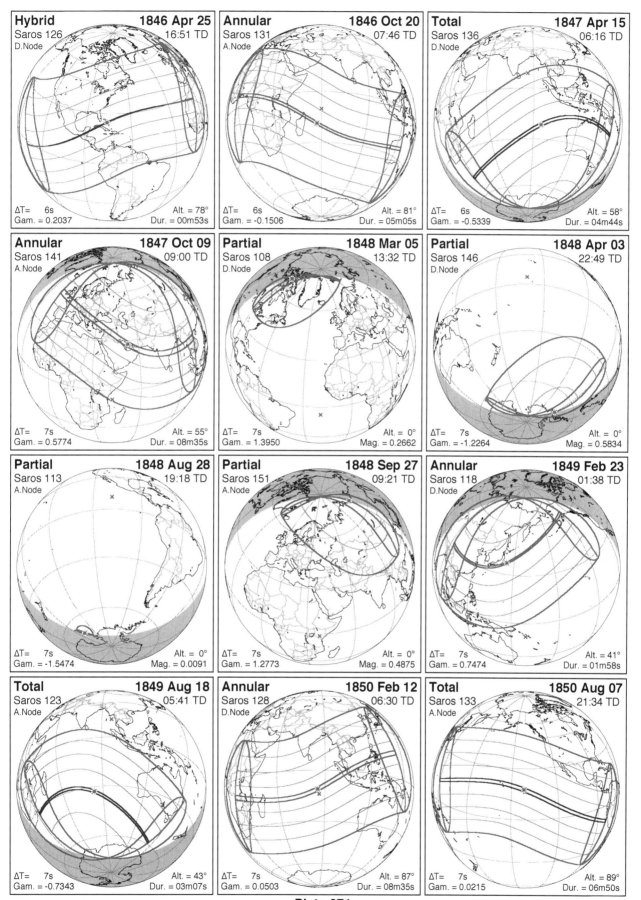

Hybrid	1846 Apr 25
Saros 126	16:51 TD
D.Node	
ΔT= 6s	Alt. = 78°
Gam. = 0.2037	Dur. = 00m53s

Annular	1846 Oct 20
Saros 131	07:46 TD
A.Node	
ΔT= 6s	Alt. = 81°
Gam. = -0.1506	Dur. = 05m05s

Total	1847 Apr 15
Saros 136	06:16 TD
D.Node	
ΔT= 6s	Alt. = 58°
Gam. = -0.5339	Dur. = 04m44s

Annular	1847 Oct 09
Saros 141	09:00 TD
A.Node	
ΔT= 7s	Alt. = 55°
Gam. = 0.5774	Dur. = 08m35s

Partial	1848 Mar 05
Saros 108	13:32 TD
D.Node	
ΔT= 7s	Alt. = 0°
Gam. = 1.3950	Mag. = 0.2662

Partial	1848 Apr 03
Saros 146	22:49 TD
D.Node	
ΔT= 7s	Alt. = 0°
Gam. = -1.2264	Mag. = 0.5834

Partial	1848 Aug 28
Saros 113	19:18 TD
A.Node	
ΔT= 7s	Alt. = 0°
Gam. = -1.5474	Mag. = 0.0091

Partial	1848 Sep 27
Saros 151	09:21 TD
A.Node	
ΔT= 7s	Alt. = 0°
Gam. = 1.2773	Mag. = 0.4875

Annular	1849 Feb 23
Saros 118	01:38 TD
D.Node	
ΔT= 7s	Alt. = 41°
Gam. = 0.7474	Dur. = 01m58s

Total	1849 Aug 18
Saros 123	05:41 TD
A.Node	
ΔT= 7s	Alt. = 43°
Gam. = -0.7343	Dur. = 03m07s

Annular	1850 Feb 12
Saros 128	06:30 TD
D.Node	
ΔT= 7s	Alt. = 87°
Gam. = 0.0503	Dur. = 08m35s

Total	1850 Aug 07
Saros 133	21:34 TD
A.Node	
ΔT= 7s	Alt. = 89°
Gam. = 0.0215	Dur. = 06m50s

Plate 071

165

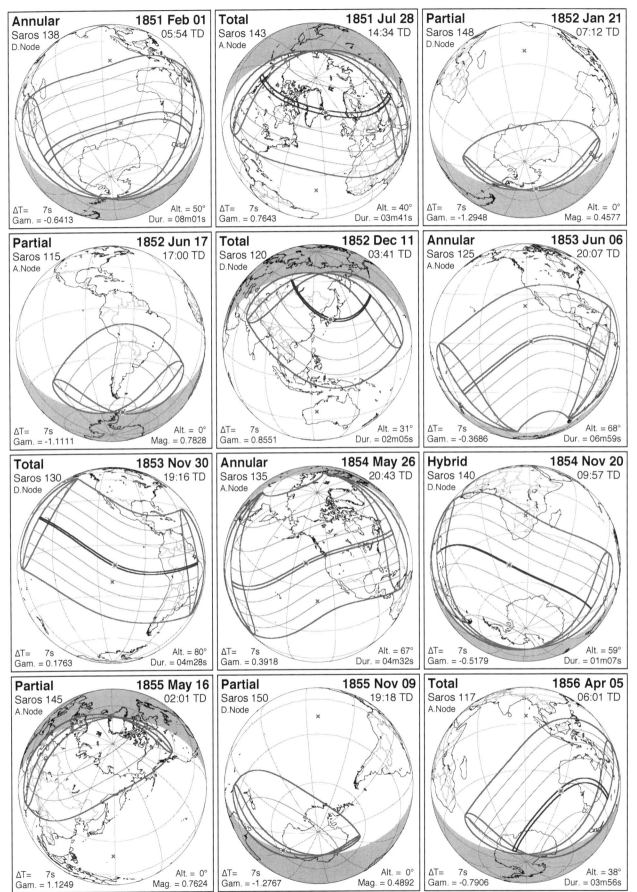

Annular 1851 Feb 01 Saros 138 D.Node 05:54 TD ΔT= 7s Gam. = -0.6413 Alt. = 50° Dur. = 08m01s	**Total** 1851 Jul 28 Saros 143 A.Node 14:34 TD ΔT= 7s Gam. = 0.7643 Alt. = 40° Dur. = 03m41s	**Partial** 1852 Jan 21 Saros 148 D.Node 07:12 TD ΔT= 7s Gam. = -1.2948 Alt. = 0° Mag. = 0.4577
Partial 1852 Jun 17 Saros 115 A.Node 17:00 TD ΔT= 7s Gam. = -1.1111 Alt. = 0° Mag. = 0.7828	**Total** 1852 Dec 11 Saros 120 D.Node 03:41 TD ΔT= 7s Gam. = 0.8551 Alt. = 31° Dur. = 02m05s	**Annular** 1853 Jun 06 Saros 125 A.Node 20:07 TD ΔT= 7s Gam. = -0.3686 Alt. = 68° Dur. = 06m59s
Total 1853 Nov 30 Saros 130 D.Node 19:16 TD ΔT= 7s Gam. = 0.1763 Alt. = 80° Dur. = 04m28s	**Annular** 1854 May 26 Saros 135 A.Node 20:43 TD ΔT= 7s Gam. = 0.3918 Alt. = 67° Dur. = 04m32s	**Hybrid** 1854 Nov 20 Saros 140 D.Node 09:57 TD ΔT= 7s Gam. = -0.5179 Alt. = 59° Dur. = 01m07s
Partial 1855 May 16 Saros 145 A.Node 02:01 TD ΔT= 7s Gam. = 1.1249 Alt. = 0° Mag. = 0.7624	**Partial** 1855 Nov 09 Saros 150 D.Node 19:18 TD ΔT= 7s Gam. = -1.2767 Alt. = 0° Mag. = 0.4892	**Total** 1856 Apr 05 Saros 117 A.Node 06:01 TD ΔT= 7s Gam. = -0.7906 Alt. = 38° Dur. = 03m56s

Plate 072

166

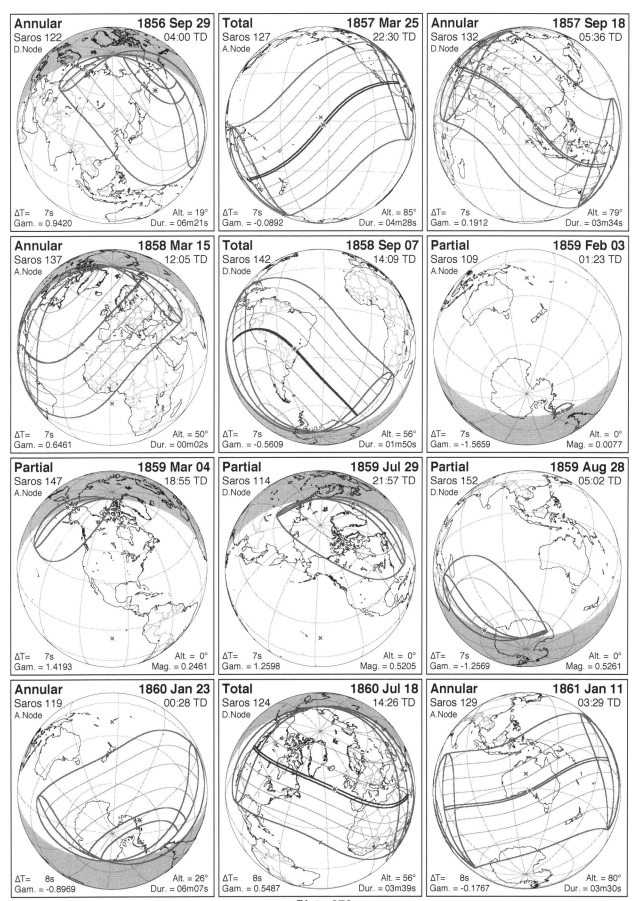

Annular   **1856 Sep 29**
Saros 122   04:00 TD
D.Node
ΔT= 7s   Alt. = 19°
Gam. = 0.9420   Dur. = 06m21s

Total   **1857 Mar 25**
Saros 127   22:30 TD
A.Node
ΔT= 7s   Alt. = 85°
Gam. = -0.0892   Dur. = 04m28s

Annular   **1857 Sep 18**
Saros 132   05:36 TD
D.Node
ΔT= 7s   Alt. = 79°
Gam. = 0.1912   Dur. = 03m34s

Annular   **1858 Mar 15**
Saros 137   12:05 TD
A.Node
ΔT= 7s   Alt. = 50°
Gam. = 0.6461   Dur. = 00m02s

Total   **1858 Sep 07**
Saros 142   14:09 TD
D.Node
ΔT= 7s   Alt. = 56°
Gam. = -0.5609   Dur. = 01m50s

Partial   **1859 Feb 03**
Saros 109   01:23 TD
A.Node
ΔT= 7s   Alt. = 0°
Gam. = -1.5659   Mag. = 0.0077

Partial   **1859 Mar 04**
Saros 147   18:55 TD
A.Node
ΔT= 7s   Alt. = 0°
Gam. = 1.4193   Mag. = 0.2461

Partial   **1859 Jul 29**
Saros 114   21:57 TD
D.Node
ΔT= 7s   Alt. = 0°
Gam. = 1.2598   Mag. = 0.5205

Partial   **1859 Aug 28**
Saros 152   05:02 TD
D.Node
ΔT= 7s   Alt. = 0°
Gam. = -1.2569   Mag. = 0.5261

Annular   **1860 Jan 23**
Saros 119   00:28 TD
A.Node
ΔT= 8s   Alt. = 26°
Gam. = -0.8969   Dur. = 06m07s

Total   **1860 Jul 18**
Saros 124   14:26 TD
D.Node
ΔT= 8s   Alt. = 56°
Gam. = 0.5487   Dur. = 03m39s

Annular   **1861 Jan 11**
Saros 129   03:29 TD
A.Node
ΔT= 8s   Alt. = 80°
Gam. = -0.1767   Dur. = 03m30s

Plate 073

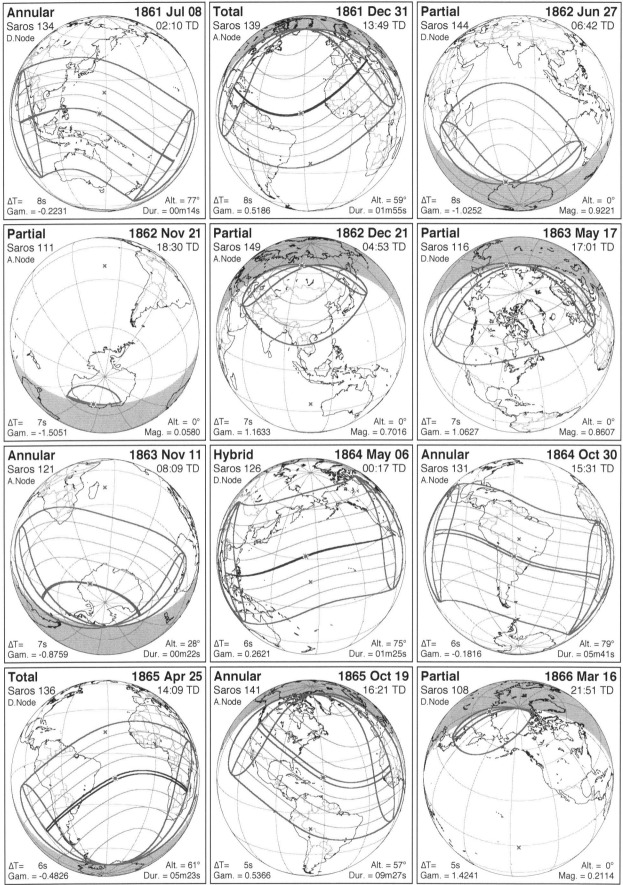

Annular 1861 Jul 08	**Total** 1861 Dec 31	**Partial** 1862 Jun 27
Saros 134 02:10 TD	Saros 139 13:49 TD	Saros 144 06:42 TD
D.Node	A.Node	D.Node
ΔT= 8s Alt. = 77°	ΔT= 8s Alt. = 59°	ΔT= 8s Alt. = 0°
Gam. = -0.2231 Dur. = 00m14s	Gam. = 0.5186 Dur. = 01m55s	Gam. = -1.0252 Mag. = 0.9221
Partial 1862 Nov 21	**Partial** 1862 Dec 21	**Partial** 1863 May 17
Saros 111 18:30 TD	Saros 149 04:53 TD	Saros 116 17:01 TD
A.Node	A.Node	D.Node
ΔT= 7s Alt. = 0°	ΔT= 7s Alt. = 0°	ΔT= 7s Alt. = 0°
Gam. = -1.5051 Mag. = 0.0580	Gam. = 1.1633 Mag. = 0.7016	Gam. = 1.0627 Mag. = 0.8607
Annular 1863 Nov 11	**Hybrid** 1864 May 06	**Annular** 1864 Oct 30
Saros 121 08:09 TD	Saros 126 00:17 TD	Saros 131 15:31 TD
A.Node	D.Node	A.Node
ΔT= 7s Alt. = 28°	ΔT= 6s Alt. = 75°	ΔT= 6s Alt. = 79°
Gam. = -0.8759 Dur. = 00m22s	Gam. = 0.2621 Dur. = 01m25s	Gam. = -0.1816 Dur. = 05m41s
Total 1865 Apr 25	**Annular** 1865 Oct 19	**Partial** 1866 Mar 16
Saros 136 14:09 TD	Saros 141 16:21 TD	Saros 108 21:51 TD
D.Node	A.Node	D.Node
ΔT= 6s Alt. = 61°	ΔT= 5s Alt. = 57°	ΔT= 5s Alt. = 0°
Gam. = -0.4826 Dur. = 05m23s	Gam. = 0.5366 Dur. = 09m27s	Gam. = 1.4241 Mag. = 0.2114

Plate 074

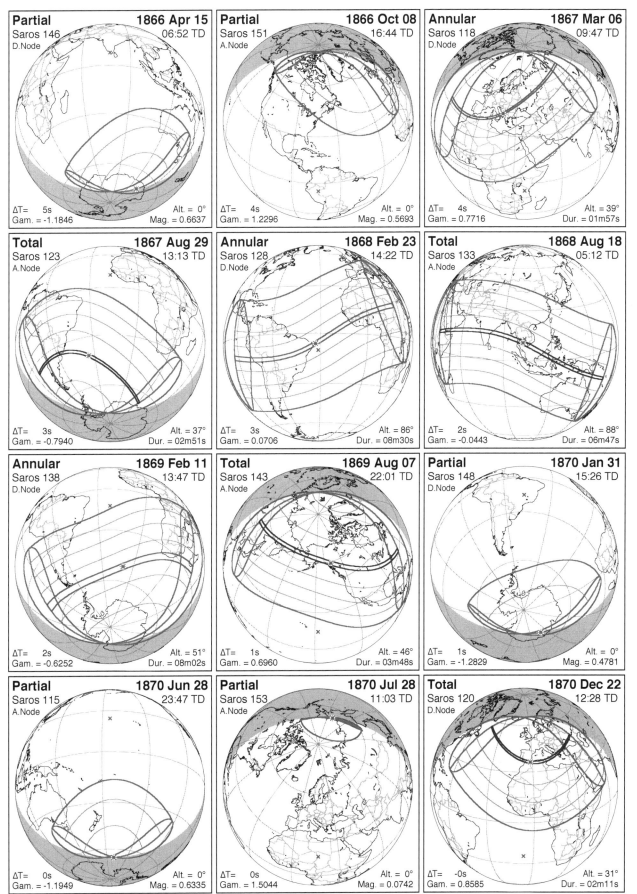

Partial   **1866 Apr 15**
Saros 146   06:52 TD
D.Node
ΔT=   5s   Alt. = 0°
Gam. = -1.1846   Mag. = 0.6637

Partial   **1866 Oct 08**
Saros 151   16:44 TD
A.Node
ΔT=   4s   Alt. = 0°
Gam. = 1.2296   Mag. = 0.5693

Annular   **1867 Mar 06**
Saros 118   09:47 TD
D.Node
ΔT=   4s   Alt. = 39°
Gam. = 0.7716   Dur. = 01m57s

Total   **1867 Aug 29**
Saros 123   13:13 TD
A.Node
ΔT=   3s   Alt. = 37°
Gam. = -0.7940   Dur. = 02m51s

Annular   **1868 Feb 23**
Saros 128   14:22 TD
D.Node
ΔT=   3s   Alt. = 86°
Gam. = 0.0706   Dur. = 08m30s

Total   **1868 Aug 18**
Saros 133   05:12 TD
A.Node
ΔT=   2s   Alt. = 88°
Gam. = -0.0443   Dur. = 06m47s

Annular   **1869 Feb 11**
Saros 138   13:47 TD
D.Node
ΔT=   2s   Alt. = 51°
Gam. = -0.6252   Dur. = 08m02s

Total   **1869 Aug 07**
Saros 143   22:01 TD
A.Node
ΔT=   1s   Alt. = 46°
Gam. = 0.6960   Dur. = 03m48s

Partial   **1870 Jan 31**
Saros 148   15:26 TD
D.Node
ΔT=   1s   Alt. = 0°
Gam. = -1.2829   Mag. = 0.4781

Partial   **1870 Jun 28**
Saros 115   23:47 TD
A.Node
ΔT=   0s   Alt. = 0°
Gam. = -1.1949   Mag. = 0.6335

Partial   **1870 Jul 28**
Saros 153   11:03 TD
A.Node
ΔT=   0s   Alt. = 0°
Gam. = 1.5044   Mag. = 0.0742

Total   **1870 Dec 22**
Saros 120   12:28 TD
D.Node
ΔT=   -0s   Alt. = 31°
Gam. = 0.8585   Dur. = 02m11s

Plate 075

169

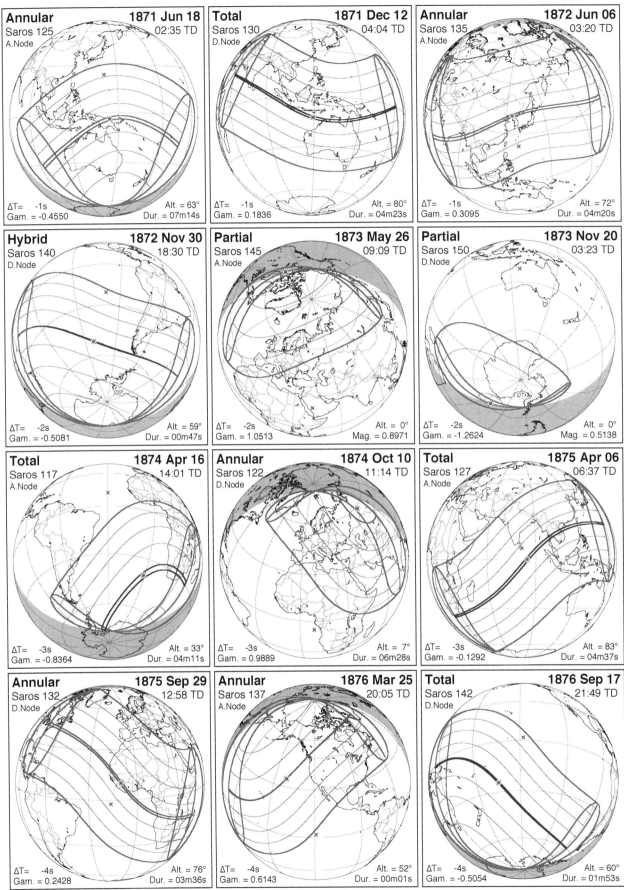

Annular 1871 Jun 18	**Total** 1871 Dec 12	**Annular** 1872 Jun 06
Saros 125 02:35 TD	Saros 130 04:04 TD	Saros 135 03:20 TD
A.Node	D.Node	A.Node
ΔT= -1s Alt. = 63°	ΔT= -1s Alt. = 80°	ΔT= -1s Alt. = 72°
Gam. = -0.4550 Dur. = 07m14s	Gam. = 0.1836 Dur. = 04m23s	Gam. = 0.3095 Dur. = 04m20s
Hybrid 1872 Nov 30	**Partial** 1873 May 26	**Partial** 1873 Nov 20
Saros 140 18:30 TD	Saros 145 09:09 TD	Saros 150 03:23 TD
D.Node	A.Node	D.Node
ΔT= -2s Alt. = 59°	ΔT= -2s Alt. = 0°	ΔT= -2s Alt. = 0°
Gam. = -0.5081 Dur. = 00m47s	Gam. = 1.0513 Mag. = 0.8971	Gam. = -1.2624 Mag. = 0.5138
Total 1874 Apr 16	**Annular** 1874 Oct 10	**Total** 1875 Apr 06
Saros 117 14:01 TD	Saros 122 11:14 TD	Saros 127 06:37 TD
A.Node	D.Node	A.Node
ΔT= -3s Alt. = 33°	ΔT= -3s Alt. = 7°	ΔT= -3s Alt. = 83°
Gam. = -0.8364 Dur. = 04m11s	Gam. = 0.9889 Dur. = 06m28s	Gam. = -0.1292 Dur. = 04m37s
Annular 1875 Sep 29	**Annular** 1876 Mar 25	**Total** 1876 Sep 17
Saros 132 12:58 TD	Saros 137 20:05 TD	Saros 142 21:49 TD
D.Node	A.Node	D.Node
ΔT= -4s Alt. = 76°	ΔT= -4s Alt. = 52°	ΔT= -4s Alt. = 60°
Gam. = 0.2428 Dur. = 03m36s	Gam. = 0.6143 Dur. = 00m01s	Gam. = -0.5054 Dur. = 01m53s

Plate 076

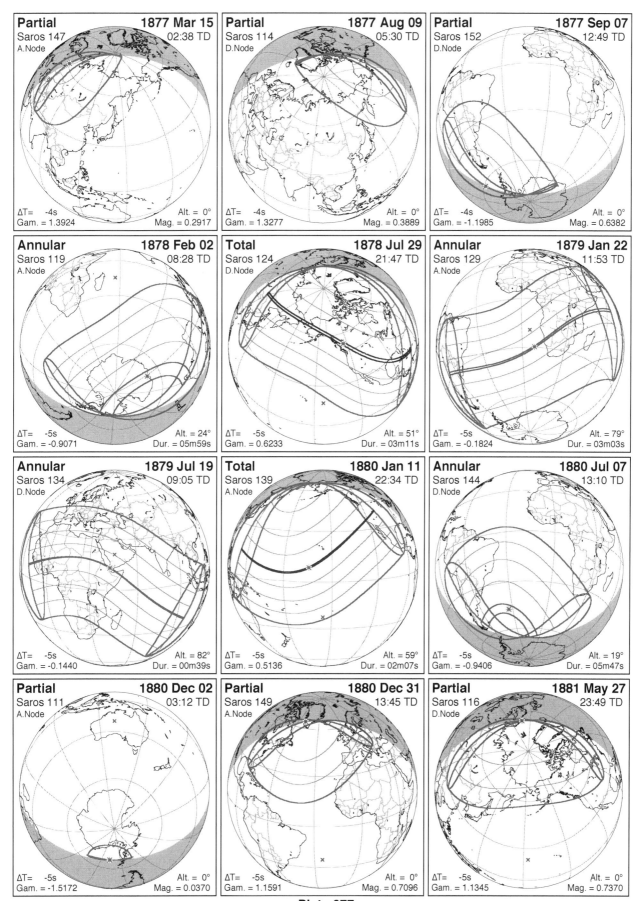

Partial **1877 Mar 15** Saros 147 02:38 TD A.Node ΔT= -4s Alt. = 0° Gam. = 1.3924 Mag. = 0.2917	**Partial** **1877 Aug 09** Saros 114 05:30 TD D.Node ΔT= -4s Alt. = 0° Gam. = 1.3277 Mag. = 0.3889	**Partial** **1877 Sep 07** Saros 152 12:49 TD D.Node ΔT= -4s Alt. = 0° Gam. = -1.1985 Mag. = 0.6382
Annular **1878 Feb 02** Saros 119 08:28 TD A.Node ΔT= -5s Alt. = 24° Gam. = -0.9071 Dur. = 05m59s	**Total** **1878 Jul 29** Saros 124 21:47 TD D.Node ΔT= -5s Alt. = 51° Gam. = 0.6233 Dur. = 03m11s	**Annular** **1879 Jan 22** Saros 129 11:53 TD A.Node ΔT= -5s Alt. = 79° Gam. = -0.1824 Dur. = 03m03s
Annular **1879 Jul 19** Saros 134 09:05 TD D.Node ΔT= -5s Alt. = 82° Gam. = -0.1440 Dur. = 00m39s	**Total** **1880 Jan 11** Saros 139 22:34 TD A.Node ΔT= -5s Alt. = 59° Gam. = 0.5136 Dur. = 02m07s	**Annular** **1880 Jul 07** Saros 144 13:10 TD D.Node ΔT= -5s Alt. = 19° Gam. = -0.9406 Dur. = 05m47s
Partial **1880 Dec 02** Saros 111 03:12 TD A.Node ΔT= -5s Alt. = 0° Gam. = -1.5172 Mag. = 0.0370	**Partial** **1880 Dec 31** Saros 149 13:45 TD A.Node ΔT= -5s Alt. = 0° Gam. = 1.1591 Mag. = 0.7096	**Partial** **1881 May 27** Saros 116 23:49 TD D.Node ΔT= -5s Alt. = 0° Gam. = 1.1345 Mag. = 0.7370

Plate 077

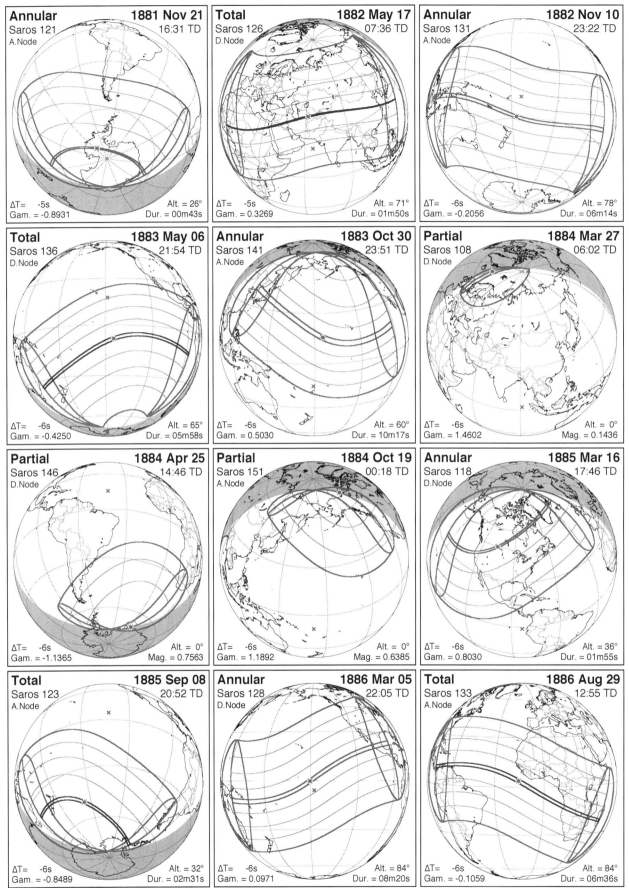

Annular	1881 Nov 21
Saros 121	16:31 TD
A.Node	
ΔT= -5s	Alt. = 26°
Gam. = -0.8931	Dur. = 00m43s

Total	1882 May 17
Saros 126	07:36 TD
D.Node	
ΔT= -5s	Alt. = 71°
Gam. = 0.3269	Dur. = 01m50s

Annular	1882 Nov 10
Saros 131	23:22 TD
A.Node	
ΔT= -6s	Alt. = 78°
Gam. = -0.2056	Dur. = 06m14s

Total	1883 May 06
Saros 136	21:54 TD
D.Node	
ΔT= -6s	Alt. = 65°
Gam. = -0.4250	Dur. = 05m58s

Annular	1883 Oct 30
Saros 141	23:51 TD
A.Node	
ΔT= -6s	Alt. = 60°
Gam. = 0.5030	Dur. = 10m17s

Partial	1884 Mar 27
Saros 108	06:02 TD
D.Node	
ΔT= -6s	Alt. = 0°
Gam. = 1.4602	Mag. = 0.1436

Partial	1884 Apr 25
Saros 146	14:46 TD
D.Node	
ΔT= -6s	Alt. = 0°
Gam. = -1.1365	Mag. = 0.7563

Partial	1884 Oct 19
Saros 151	00:18 TD
A.Node	
ΔT= -6s	Alt. = 0°
Gam. = 1.1892	Mag. = 0.6385

Annular	1885 Mar 16
Saros 118	17:46 TD
D.Node	
ΔT= -6s	Alt. = 36°
Gam. = 0.8030	Dur. = 01m55s

Total	1885 Sep 08
Saros 123	20:52 TD
A.Node	
ΔT= -6s	Alt. = 32°
Gam. = -0.8489	Dur. = 02m31s

Annular	1886 Mar 05
Saros 128	22:05 TD
D.Node	
ΔT= -6s	Alt. = 84°
Gam. = 0.0971	Dur. = 08m20s

Total	1886 Aug 29
Saros 133	12:55 TD
A.Node	
ΔT= -6s	Alt. = 84°
Gam. = -0.1059	Dur. = 06m36s

Plate 078

172

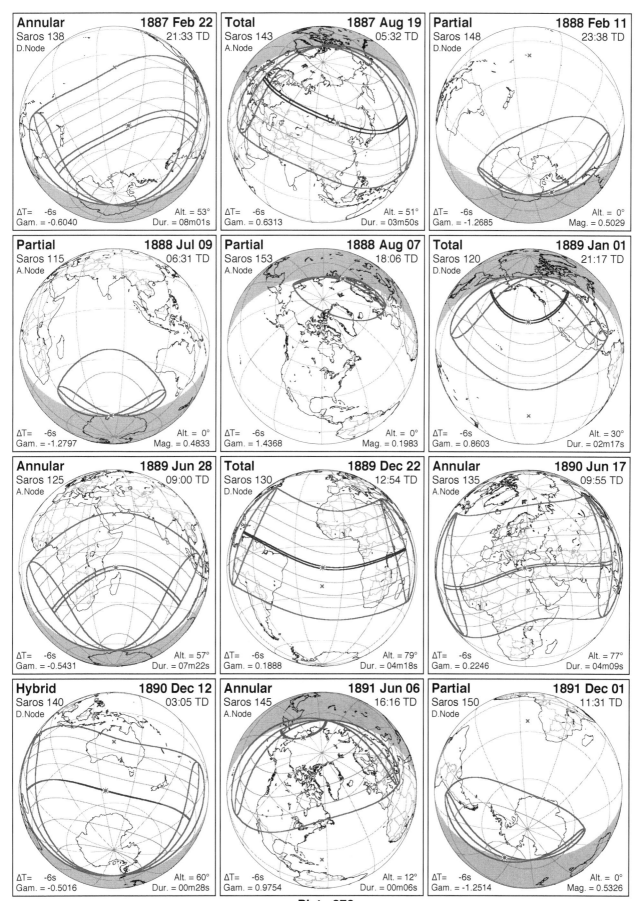

Annular **1887 Feb 22** Saros 138 21:33 TD D.Node	**Total** **1887 Aug 19** Saros 143 05:32 TD A.Node	**Partial** **1888 Feb 11** Saros 148 23:38 TD D.Node
ΔT= -6s Alt. = 53° Gam. = -0.6040 Dur. = 08m01s	ΔT= -6s Alt. = 51° Gam. = 0.6313 Dur. = 03m50s	ΔT= -6s Alt. = 0° Gam. = -1.2685 Mag. = 0.5029
Partial **1888 Jul 09** Saros 115 06:31 TD A.Node	**Partial** **1888 Aug 07** Saros 153 18:06 TD A.Node	**Total** **1889 Jan 01** Saros 120 21:17 TD D.Node
ΔT= -6s Alt. = 0° Gam. = -1.2797 Mag. = 0.4833	ΔT= -6s Alt. = 0° Gam. = 1.4368 Mag. = 0.1983	ΔT= -6s Alt. = 30° Gam. = 0.8603 Dur. = 02m17s
Annular **1889 Jun 28** Saros 125 09:00 TD A.Node	**Total** **1889 Dec 22** Saros 130 12:54 TD D.Node	**Annular** **1890 Jun 17** Saros 135 09:55 TD A.Node
ΔT= -6s Alt. = 57° Gam. = -0.5431 Dur. = 07m22s	ΔT= -6s Alt. = 79° Gam. = 0.1888 Dur. = 04m18s	ΔT= -6s Alt. = 77° Gam. = 0.2246 Dur. = 04m09s
Hybrid **1890 Dec 12** Saros 140 03:05 TD D.Node	**Annular** **1891 Jun 06** Saros 145 16:16 TD A.Node	**Partial** **1891 Dec 01** Saros 150 11:31 TD D.Node
ΔT= -6s Alt. = 60° Gam. = -0.5016 Dur. = 00m28s	ΔT= -6s Alt. = 12° Gam. = 0.9754 Dur. = 00m06s	ΔT= -6s Alt. = 0° Gam. = -1.2514 Mag. = 0.5326

Plate 079

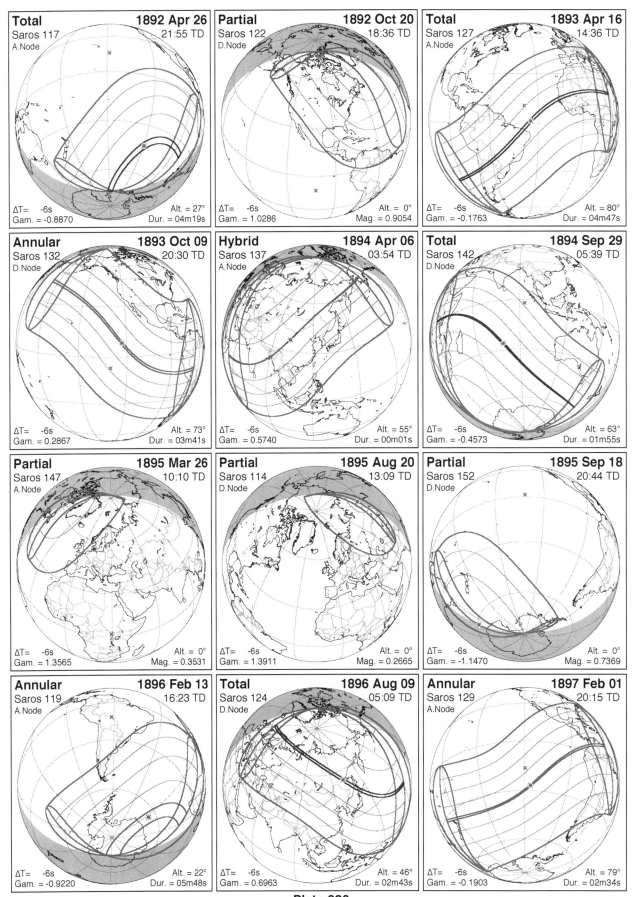

Total   **1892 Apr 26**
Saros 117   21:55 TD
A.Node
ΔT=   -6s   Alt. = 27°
Gam. = -0.8870   Dur. = 04m19s

Partial   **1892 Oct 20**
Saros 122   18:36 TD
D.Node
ΔT=   -6s   Alt. = 0°
Gam. = 1.0286   Mag. = 0.9054

Total   **1893 Apr 16**
Saros 127   14:36 TD
A.Node
ΔT=   -6s   Alt. = 80°
Gam. = -0.1763   Dur. = 04m47s

Annular   **1893 Oct 09**
Saros 132   20:30 TD
D.Node
ΔT=   -6s   Alt. = 73°
Gam. = 0.2867   Dur. = 03m41s

Hybrid   **1894 Apr 06**
Saros 137   03:54 TD
A.Node
ΔT=   -6s   Alt. = 55°
Gam. = 0.5740   Dur. = 00m01s

Total   **1894 Sep 29**
Saros 142   05:39 TD
D.Node
ΔT=   -6s   Alt. = 63°
Gam. = -0.4573   Dur. = 01m55s

Partial   **1895 Mar 26**
Saros 147   10:10 TD
A.Node
ΔT=   -6s   Alt. = 0°
Gam. = 1.3565   Mag. = 0.3531

Partial   **1895 Aug 20**
Saros 114   13:09 TD
D.Node
ΔT=   -6s   Alt. = 0°
Gam. = 1.3911   Mag. = 0.2665

Partial   **1895 Sep 18**
Saros 152   20:44 TD
D.Node
ΔT=   -6s   Alt. = 0°
Gam. = -1.1470   Mag. = 0.7369

Annular   **1896 Feb 13**
Saros 119   16:23 TD
A.Node
ΔT=   -6s   Alt. = 22°
Gam. = -0.9220   Dur. = 05m48s

Total   **1896 Aug 09**
Saros 124   05:09 TD
D.Node
ΔT=   -6s   Alt. = 46°
Gam. = 0.6963   Dur. = 02m43s

Annular   **1897 Feb 01**
Saros 129   20:15 TD
A.Node
ΔT=   -6s   Alt. = 79°
Gam. = -0.1903   Dur. = 02m34s

Plate 080

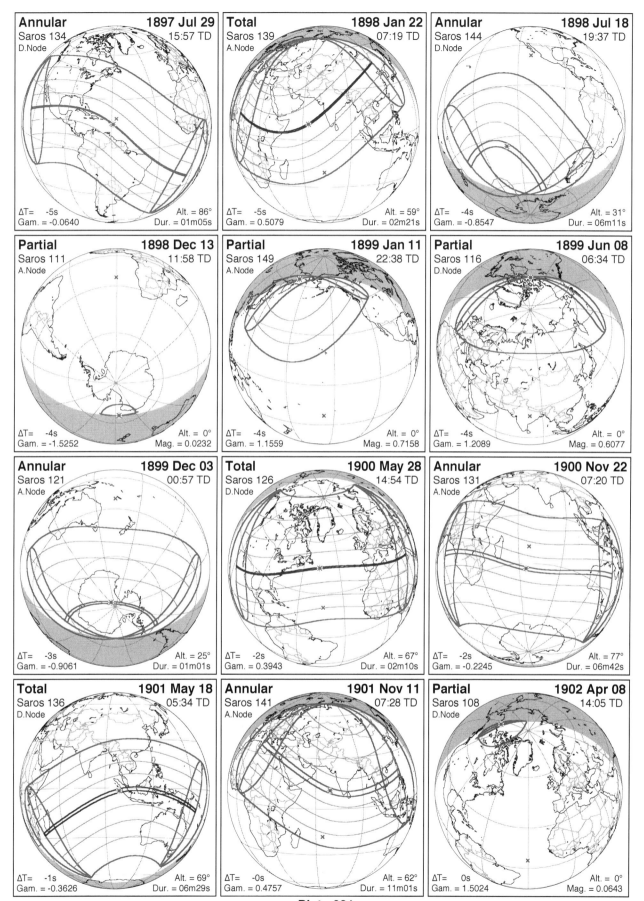

Annular 1897 Jul 29	
Saros 134 15:57 TD	
D.Node	
ΔT= -5s Alt. = 86°	
Gam. = -0.0640 Dur. = 01m05s	

| **Total** 1898 Jan 22 |
| Saros 139 07:19 TD |
| A.Node |
| ΔT= -5s Alt. = 59° |
| Gam. = 0.5079 Dur. = 02m21s |

| **Annular** 1898 Jul 18 |
| Saros 144 19:37 TD |
| D.Node |
| ΔT= -4s Alt. = 31° |
| Gam. = -0.8547 Dur. = 06m11s |

| **Partial** 1898 Dec 13 |
| Saros 111 11:58 TD |
| A.Node |
| ΔT= -4s Alt. = 0° |
| Gam. = -1.5252 Mag. = 0.0232 |

| **Partial** 1899 Jan 11 |
| Saros 149 22:38 TD |
| A.Node |
| ΔT= -4s Alt. = 0° |
| Gam. = 1.1559 Mag. = 0.7158 |

| **Partial** 1899 Jun 08 |
| Saros 116 06:34 TD |
| D.Node |
| ΔT= -4s Alt. = 0° |
| Gam. = 1.2089 Mag. = 0.6077 |

| **Annular** 1899 Dec 03 |
| Saros 121 00:57 TD |
| A.Node |
| ΔT= -3s Alt. = 25° |
| Gam. = -0.9061 Dur. = 01m01s |

| **Total** 1900 May 28 |
| Saros 126 14:54 TD |
| D.Node |
| ΔT= -2s Alt. = 67° |
| Gam. = 0.3943 Dur. = 02m10s |

| **Annular** 1900 Nov 22 |
| Saros 131 07:20 TD |
| A.Node |
| ΔT= -2s Alt. = 77° |
| Gam. = -0.2245 Dur. = 06m42s |

| **Total** 1901 May 18 |
| Saros 136 05:34 TD |
| D.Node |
| ΔT= -1s Alt. = 69° |
| Gam. = -0.3626 Dur. = 06m29s |

| **Annular** 1901 Nov 11 |
| Saros 141 07:28 TD |
| A.Node |
| ΔT= -0s Alt. = 62° |
| Gam. = 0.4757 Dur. = 11m01s |

| **Partial** 1902 Apr 08 |
| Saros 108 14:05 TD |
| D.Node |
| ΔT= 0s Alt. = 0° |
| Gam. = 1.5024 Mag. = 0.0643 |

Plate 081

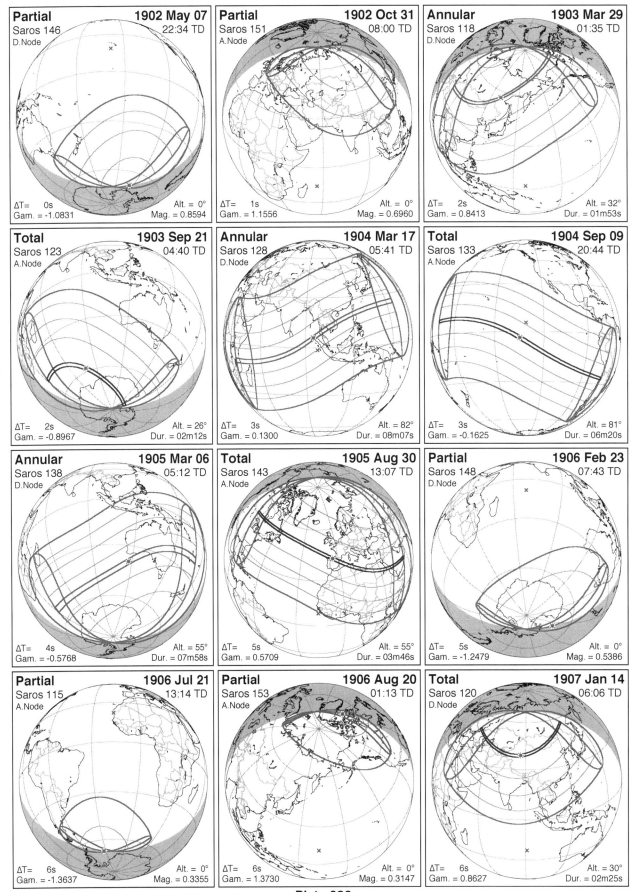

Partial	1902 May 07
Saros 146	22:34 TD
D.Node	
ΔT= 0s	Alt. = 0°
Gam. = -1.0831	Mag. = 0.8594

Partial	1902 Oct 31
Saros 151	08:00 TD
A.Node	
ΔT= 1s	Alt. = 0°
Gam. = 1.1556	Mag. = 0.6960

Annular	1903 Mar 29
Saros 118	01:35 TD
D.Node	
ΔT= 2s	Alt. = 32°
Gam. = 0.8413	Dur. = 01m53s

Total	1903 Sep 21
Saros 123	04:40 TD
A.Node	
ΔT= 2s	Alt. = 26°
Gam. = -0.8967	Dur. = 02m12s

Annular	1904 Mar 17
Saros 128	05:41 TD
D.Node	
ΔT= 3s	Alt. = 82°
Gam. = 0.1300	Dur. = 08m07s

Total	1904 Sep 09
Saros 133	20:44 TD
A.Node	
ΔT= 3s	Alt. = 81°
Gam. = -0.1625	Dur. = 06m20s

Annular	1905 Mar 06
Saros 138	05:12 TD
D.Node	
ΔT= 4s	Alt. = 55°
Gam. = -0.5768	Dur. = 07m58s

Total	1905 Aug 30
Saros 143	13:07 TD
A.Node	
ΔT= 5s	Alt. = 55°
Gam. = 0.5709	Dur. = 03m46s

Partial	1906 Feb 23
Saros 148	07:43 TD
D.Node	
ΔT= 5s	Alt. = 0°
Gam. = -1.2479	Mag. = 0.5386

Partial	1906 Jul 21
Saros 115	13:14 TD
A.Node	
ΔT= 6s	Alt. = 0°
Gam. = -1.3637	Mag. = 0.3355

Partial	1906 Aug 20
Saros 153	01:13 TD
A.Node	
ΔT= 6s	Alt. = 0°
Gam. = 1.3730	Mag. = 0.3147

Total	1907 Jan 14
Saros 120	06:06 TD
D.Node	
ΔT= 6s	Alt. = 30°
Gam. = 0.8627	Dur. = 02m25s

Plate 082

176

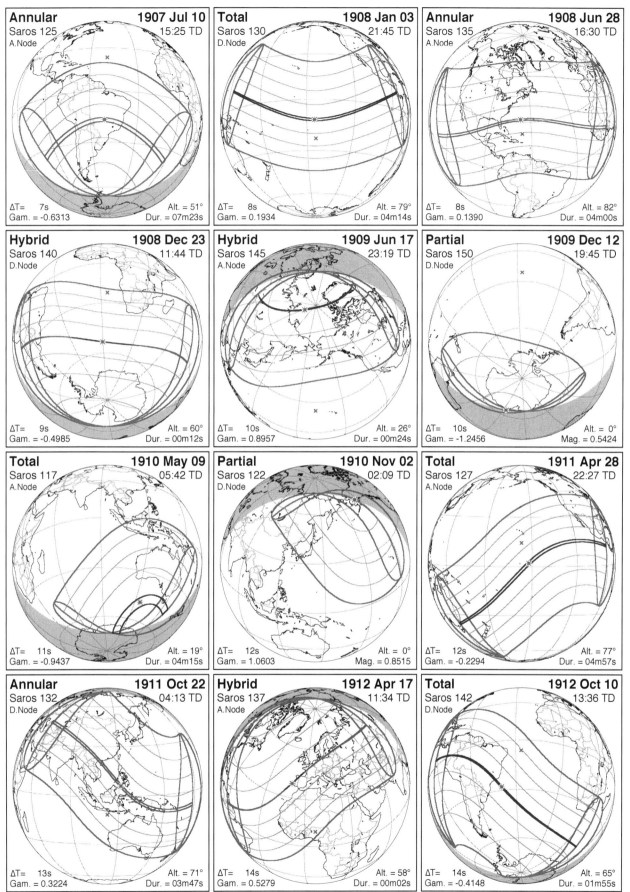

Annular	1907 Jul 10
Saros 125	15:25 TD
A.Node	
ΔT= 7s	Alt. = 51°
Gam. = -0.6313	Dur. = 07m23s

Total	1908 Jan 03
Saros 130	21:45 TD
D.Node	
ΔT= 8s	Alt. = 79°
Gam. = 0.1934	Dur. = 04m14s

Annular	1908 Jun 28
Saros 135	16:30 TD
A.Node	
ΔT= 8s	Alt. = 82°
Gam. = 0.1390	Dur. = 04m00s

Hybrid	1908 Dec 23
Saros 140	11:44 TD
D.Node	
ΔT= 9s	Alt. = 60°
Gam. = -0.4985	Dur. = 00m12s

Hybrid	1909 Jun 17
Saros 145	23:19 TD
A.Node	
ΔT= 10s	Alt. = 26°
Gam. = 0.8957	Dur. = 00m24s

Partial	1909 Dec 12
Saros 150	19:45 TD
D.Node	
ΔT= 10s	Alt. = 0°
Gam. = -1.2456	Mag. = 0.5424

Total	1910 May 09
Saros 117	05:42 TD
A.Node	
ΔT= 11s	Alt. = 19°
Gam. = -0.9437	Dur. = 04m15s

Partial	1910 Nov 02
Saros 122	02:09 TD
D.Node	
ΔT= 12s	Alt. = 0°
Gam. = 1.0603	Mag. = 0.8515

Total	1911 Apr 28
Saros 127	22:27 TD
A.Node	
ΔT= 12s	Alt. = 77°
Gam. = -0.2294	Dur. = 04m57s

Annular	1911 Oct 22
Saros 132	04:13 TD
D.Node	
ΔT= 13s	Alt. = 71°
Gam. = 0.3224	Dur. = 03m47s

Hybrid	1912 Apr 17
Saros 137	11:34 TD
A.Node	
ΔT= 14s	Alt. = 58°
Gam. = 0.5279	Dur. = 00m02s

Total	1912 Oct 10
Saros 142	13:36 TD
D.Node	
ΔT= 14s	Alt. = 65°
Gam. = -0.4148	Dur. = 01m55s

Plate 083

177

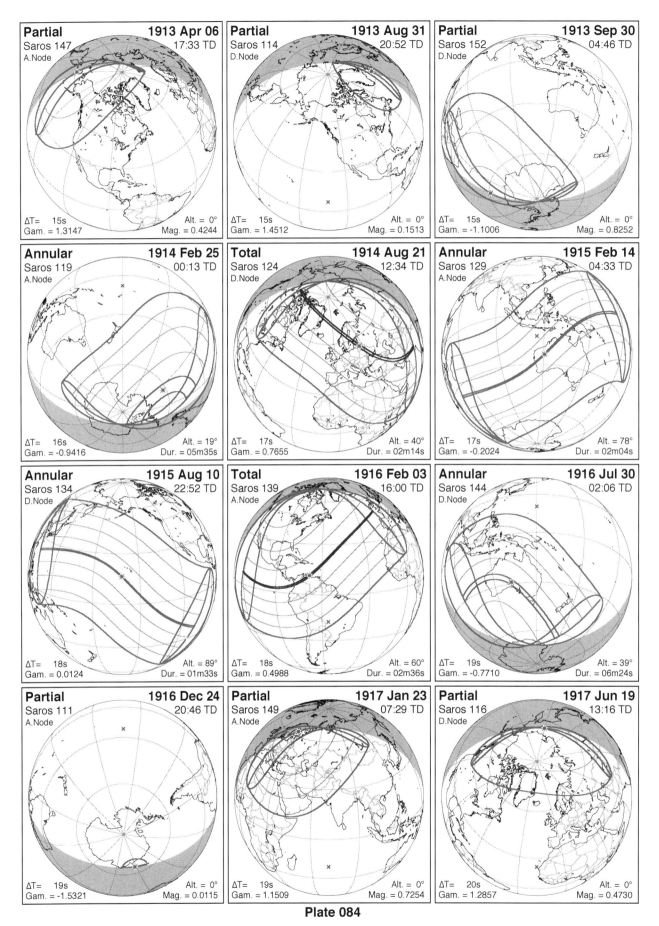

Partial	1913 Apr 06
Saros 147	17:33 TD
A.Node	
ΔT= 15s	Alt. = 0°
Gam. = 1.3147	Mag. = 0.4244

Partial	1913 Aug 31
Saros 114	20:52 TD
D.Node	
ΔT= 15s	Alt. = 0°
Gam. = 1.4512	Mag. = 0.1513

Partial	1913 Sep 30
Saros 152	04:46 TD
D.Node	
ΔT= 15s	Alt. = 0°
Gam. = -1.1006	Mag. = 0.8252

Annular	1914 Feb 25
Saros 119	00:13 TD
A.Node	
ΔT= 16s	Alt. = 19°
Gam. = -0.9416	Dur. = 05m35s

Total	1914 Aug 21
Saros 124	12:34 TD
D.Node	
ΔT= 17s	Alt. = 40°
Gam. = 0.7655	Dur. = 02m14s

Annular	1915 Feb 14
Saros 129	04:33 TD
A.Node	
ΔT= 17s	Alt. = 78°
Gam. = -0.2024	Dur. = 02m04s

Annular	1915 Aug 10
Saros 134	22:52 TD
D.Node	
ΔT= 18s	Alt. = 89°
Gam. = 0.0124	Dur. = 01m33s

Total	1916 Feb 03
Saros 139	16:00 TD
A.Node	
ΔT= 18s	Alt. = 60°
Gam. = 0.4988	Dur. = 02m36s

Annular	1916 Jul 30
Saros 144	02:06 TD
D.Node	
ΔT= 19s	Alt. = 39°
Gam. = -0.7710	Dur. = 06m24s

Partial	1916 Dec 24
Saros 111	20:46 TD
A.Node	
ΔT= 19s	Alt. = 0°
Gam. = -1.5321	Mag. = 0.0115

Partial	1917 Jan 23
Saros 149	07:29 TD
A.Node	
ΔT= 19s	Alt. = 0°
Gam. = 1.1509	Mag. = 0.7254

Partial	1917 Jun 19
Saros 116	13:16 TD
D.Node	
ΔT= 20s	Alt. = 0°
Gam. = 1.2857	Mag. = 0.4730

Plate 084

178

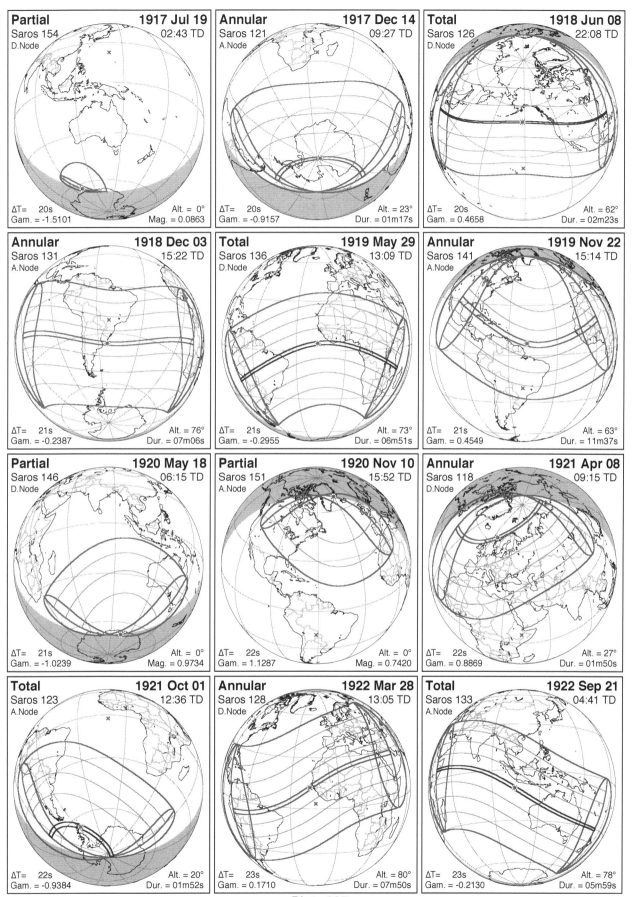

Partial	1917 Jul 19
Saros 154	02:43 TD
D.Node	
ΔT= 20s	Alt. = 0°
Gam. = -1.5101	Mag. = 0.0863

Annular	1917 Dec 14
Saros 121	09:27 TD
A.Node	
ΔT= 20s	Alt. = 23°
Gam. = -0.9157	Dur. = 01m17s

Total	1918 Jun 08
Saros 126	22:08 TD
D.Node	
ΔT= 20s	Alt. = 62°
Gam. = 0.4658	Dur. = 02m23s

Annular	1918 Dec 03
Saros 131	15:22 TD
A.Node	
ΔT= 21s	Alt. = 76°
Gam. = -0.2387	Dur. = 07m06s

Total	1919 May 29
Saros 136	13:09 TD
D.Node	
ΔT= 21s	Alt. = 73°
Gam. = -0.2955	Dur. = 06m51s

Annular	1919 Nov 22
Saros 141	15:14 TD
A.Node	
ΔT= 21s	Alt. = 63°
Gam. = 0.4549	Dur. = 11m37s

Partial	1920 May 18
Saros 146	06:15 TD
D.Node	
ΔT= 21s	Alt. = 0°
Gam. = -1.0239	Mag. = 0.9734

Partial	1920 Nov 10
Saros 151	15:52 TD
A.Node	
ΔT= 22s	Alt. = 0°
Gam. = 1.1287	Mag. = 0.7420

Annular	1921 Apr 08
Saros 118	09:15 TD
D.Node	
ΔT= 22s	Alt. = 27°
Gam. = 0.8869	Dur. = 01m50s

Total	1921 Oct 01
Saros 123	12:36 TD
A.Node	
ΔT= 22s	Alt. = 20°
Gam. = -0.9384	Dur. = 01m52s

Annular	1922 Mar 28
Saros 128	13:05 TD
D.Node	
ΔT= 23s	Alt. = 80°
Gam. = 0.1710	Dur. = 07m50s

Total	1922 Sep 21
Saros 133	04:41 TD
A.Node	
ΔT= 23s	Alt. = 78°
Gam. = -0.2130	Dur. = 05m59s

Plate 085

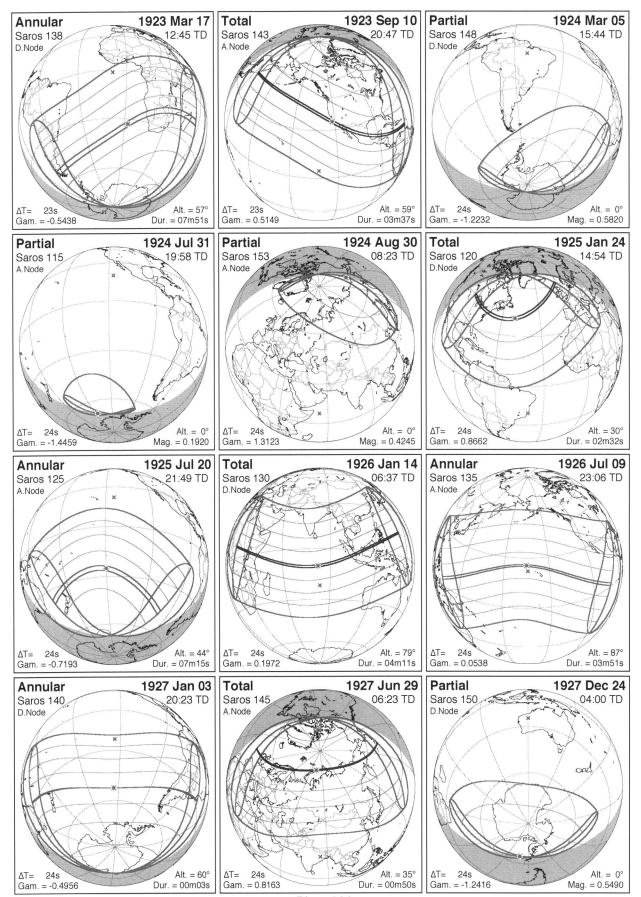

Annular 1923 Mar 17 Saros 138 12:45 TD D.Node ΔT= 23s Alt. = 57° Gam. = -0.5438 Dur. = 07m51s	**Total** 1923 Sep 10 Saros 143 20:47 TD A.Node ΔT= 23s Alt. = 59° Gam. = 0.5149 Dur. = 03m37s	**Partial** 1924 Mar 05 Saros 148 15:44 TD D.Node ΔT= 24s Alt. = 0° Gam. = -1.2232 Mag. = 0.5820
Partial 1924 Jul 31 Saros 115 19:58 TD A.Node ΔT= 24s Alt. = 0° Gam. = -1.4459 Mag. = 0.1920	**Partial** 1924 Aug 30 Saros 153 08:23 TD A.Node ΔT= 24s Alt. = 0° Gam. = 1.3123 Mag. = 0.4245	**Total** 1925 Jan 24 Saros 120 14:54 TD D.Node ΔT= 24s Alt. = 30° Gam. = 0.8662 Dur. = 02m32s
Annular 1925 Jul 20 Saros 125 21:49 TD A.Node ΔT= 24s Alt. = 44° Gam. = -0.7193 Dur. = 07m15s	**Total** 1926 Jan 14 Saros 130 06:37 TD D.Node ΔT= 24s Alt. = 79° Gam. = 0.1972 Dur. = 04m11s	**Annular** 1926 Jul 09 Saros 135 23:06 TD A.Node ΔT= 24s Alt. = 87° Gam. = 0.0538 Dur. = 03m51s
Annular 1927 Jan 03 Saros 140 20:23 TD D.Node ΔT= 24s Alt. = 60° Gam. = -0.4956 Dur. = 00m03s	**Total** 1927 Jun 29 Saros 145 06:23 TD A.Node ΔT= 24s Alt. = 35° Gam. = 0.8163 Dur. = 00m50s	**Partial** 1927 Dec 24 Saros 150 04:00 TD D.Node ΔT= 24s Alt. = 0° Gam. = -1.2416 Mag. = 0.5490

Plate 086

180

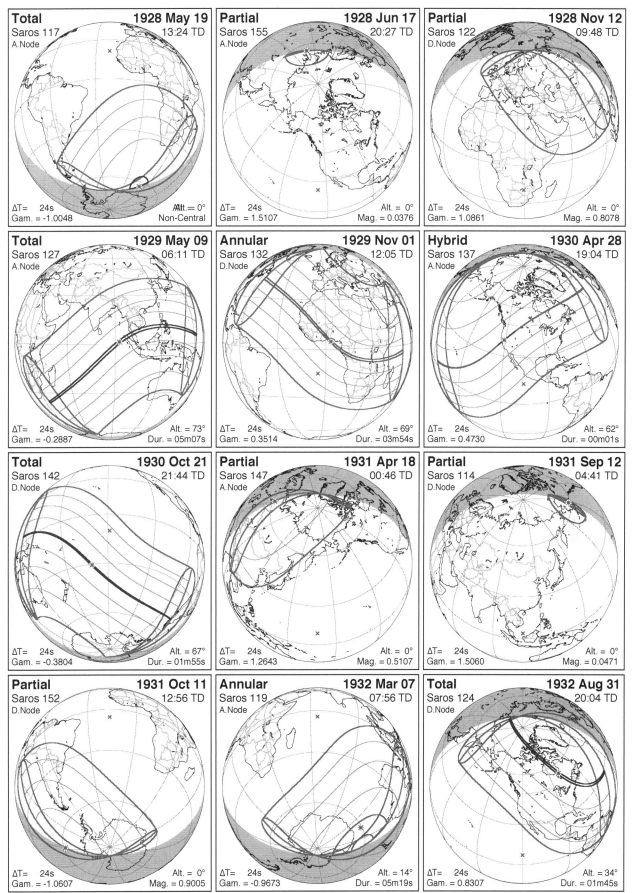

Total **1928 May 19**	
Saros 117 13:24 TD	
A.Node	
ΔT= 24s Alt.= 0°	
Gam. = -1.0048 Non-Central	

Partial   **1928 Jun 17**
Saros 155   20:27 TD
A.Node
ΔT= 24s   Gam. = 1.5107   Mag. = 0.0376

Partial   **1928 Nov 12**
Saros 122   09:48 TD
D.Node
ΔT= 24s   Alt. = 0°   Gam. = 1.0861   Mag. = 0.8078

Total   **1929 May 09** — Saros 127, 06:11 TD, A.Node, ΔT= 24s, Gam. = -0.2887, Alt. = 73°, Dur. = 05m07s

Annular   **1929 Nov 01** — Saros 132, 12:05 TD, D.Node, ΔT= 24s, Gam. = 0.3514, Alt. = 69°, Dur. = 03m54s

Hybrid   **1930 Apr 28** — Saros 137, 19:04 TD, A.Node, ΔT= 24s, Gam. = 0.4730, Alt. = 62°, Dur. = 00m01s

Total   **1930 Oct 21** — Saros 142, 21:44 TD, D.Node, ΔT= 24s, Gam. = -0.3804, Alt. = 67°, Dur. = 01m55s

Partial   **1931 Apr 18** — Saros 147, 00:46 TD, A.Node, ΔT= 24s, Gam. = 1.2643, Alt. = 0°, Mag. = 0.5107

Partial   **1931 Sep 12** — Saros 114, 04:41 TD, D.Node, ΔT= 24s, Gam. = 1.5060, Alt. = 0°, Mag. = 0.0471

Partial   **1931 Oct 11** — Saros 152, 12:56 TD, D.Node, ΔT= 24s, Gam. = -1.0607, Alt. = 0°, Mag. = 0.9005

Annular   **1932 Mar 07** — Saros 119, 07:56 TD, A.Node, ΔT= 24s, Gam. = -0.9673, Alt. = 14°, Dur. = 05m19s

Total   **1932 Aug 31** — Saros 124, 20:04 TD, D.Node, ΔT= 24s, Gam. = 0.8307, Alt. = 34°, Dur. = 01m45s

Plate 087

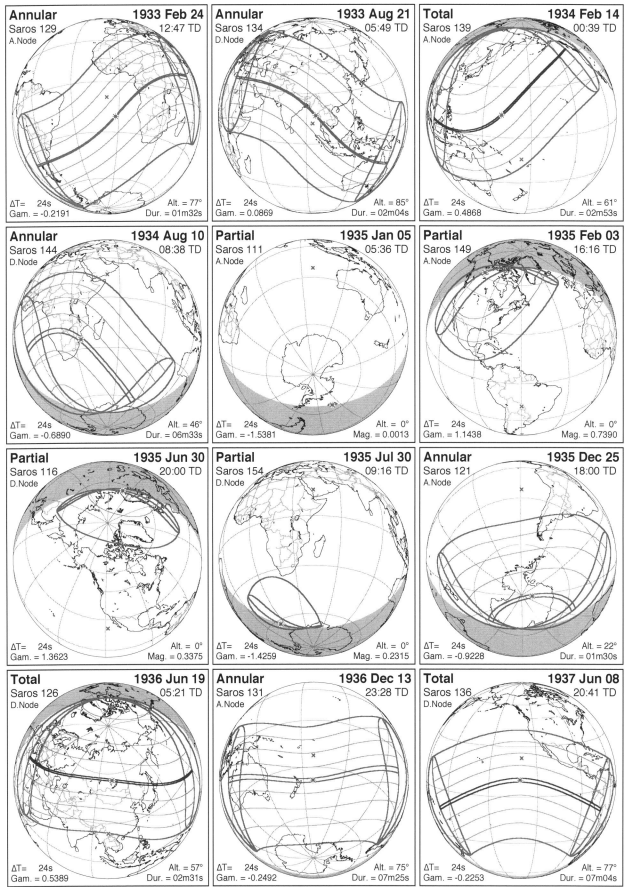

Annular   **1933 Feb 24**
Saros 129   12:47 TD
A.Node
ΔT= 24s   Alt. = 77°
Gam. = -0.2191   Dur. = 01m32s

Annular   **1933 Aug 21**
Saros 134   05:49 TD
D.Node
ΔT= 24s   Alt. = 85°
Gam. = 0.0869   Dur. = 02m04s

Total   **1934 Feb 14**
Saros 139   00:39 TD
A.Node
ΔT= 24s   Alt. = 61°
Gam. = 0.4868   Dur. = 02m53s

Annular   **1934 Aug 10**
Saros 144   08:38 TD
D.Node
ΔT= 24s   Alt. = 46°
Gam. = -0.6890   Dur. = 06m33s

Partial   **1935 Jan 05**
Saros 111   05:36 TD
A.Node
ΔT= 24s   Alt. = 0°
Gam. = -1.5381   Mag. = 0.0013

Partial   **1935 Feb 03**
Saros 149   16:16 TD
A.Node
ΔT= 24s   Alt. = 0°
Gam. = 1.1438   Mag. = 0.7390

Partial   **1935 Jun 30**
Saros 116   20:00 TD
D.Node
ΔT= 24s   Alt. = 0°
Gam. = 1.3623   Mag. = 0.3375

Partial   **1935 Jul 30**
Saros 154   09:16 TD
D.Node
ΔT= 24s   Alt. = 0°
Gam. = -1.4259   Mag. = 0.2315

Annular   **1935 Dec 25**
Saros 121   18:00 TD
A.Node
ΔT= 24s   Alt. = 22°
Gam. = -0.9228   Dur. = 01m30s

Total   **1936 Jun 19**
Saros 126   05:21 TD
D.Node
ΔT= 24s   Alt. = 57°
Gam. = 0.5389   Dur. = 02m31s

Annular   **1936 Dec 13**
Saros 131   23:28 TD
A.Node
ΔT= 24s   Alt. = 75°
Gam. = -0.2492   Dur. = 07m25s

Total   **1937 Jun 08**
Saros 136   20:41 TD
D.Node
ΔT= 24s   Alt. = 77°
Gam. = -0.2253   Dur. = 07m04s

Plate 088

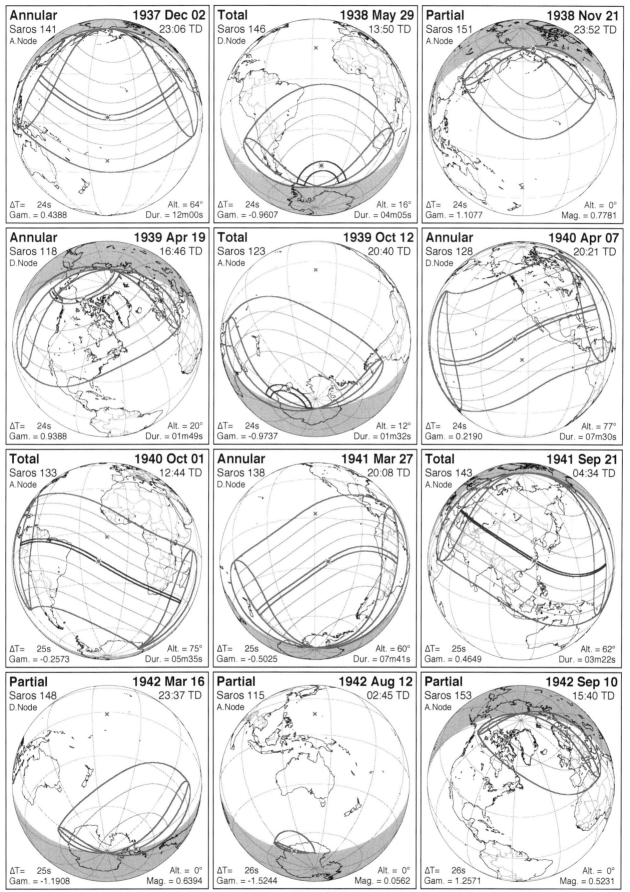

Annular	1937 Dec 02
Saros 141	23:06 TD
A.Node	
ΔT= 24s	Alt. = 64°
Gam. = 0.4388	Dur. = 12m00s

Total	1938 May 29
Saros 146	13:50 TD
D.Node	
ΔT= 24s	Alt. = 16°
Gam. = -0.9607	Dur. = 04m05s

Partial	1938 Nov 21
Saros 151	23:52 TD
A.Node	
ΔT= 24s	Alt. = 0°
Gam. = 1.1077	Mag. = 0.7781

Annular	1939 Apr 19
Saros 118	16:46 TD
D.Node	
ΔT= 24s	Alt. = 20°
Gam. = 0.9388	Dur. = 01m49s

Total	1939 Oct 12
Saros 123	20:40 TD
A.Node	
ΔT= 24s	Alt. = 12°
Gam. = -0.9737	Dur. = 01m32s

Annular	1940 Apr 07
Saros 128	20:21 TD
D.Node	
ΔT= 24s	Alt. = 77°
Gam. = 0.2190	Dur. = 07m30s

Total	1940 Oct 01
Saros 133	12:44 TD
A.Node	
ΔT= 25s	Alt. = 75°
Gam. = -0.2573	Dur. = 05m35s

Annular	1941 Mar 27
Saros 138	20:08 TD
D.Node	
ΔT= 25s	Alt. = 60°
Gam. = -0.5025	Dur. = 07m41s

Total	1941 Sep 21
Saros 143	04:34 TD
A.Node	
ΔT= 25s	Alt. = 62°
Gam. = 0.4649	Dur. = 03m22s

Partial	1942 Mar 16
Saros 148	23:37 TD
D.Node	
ΔT= 25s	Alt. = 0°
Gam. = -1.1908	Mag. = 0.6394

Partial	1942 Aug 12
Saros 115	02:45 TD
A.Node	
ΔT= 26s	Alt. = 0°
Gam. = -1.5244	Mag. = 0.0562

Partial	1942 Sep 10
Saros 153	15:40 TD
A.Node	
ΔT= 26s	Alt. = 0°
Gam. = 1.2571	Mag. = 0.5231

Plate 089

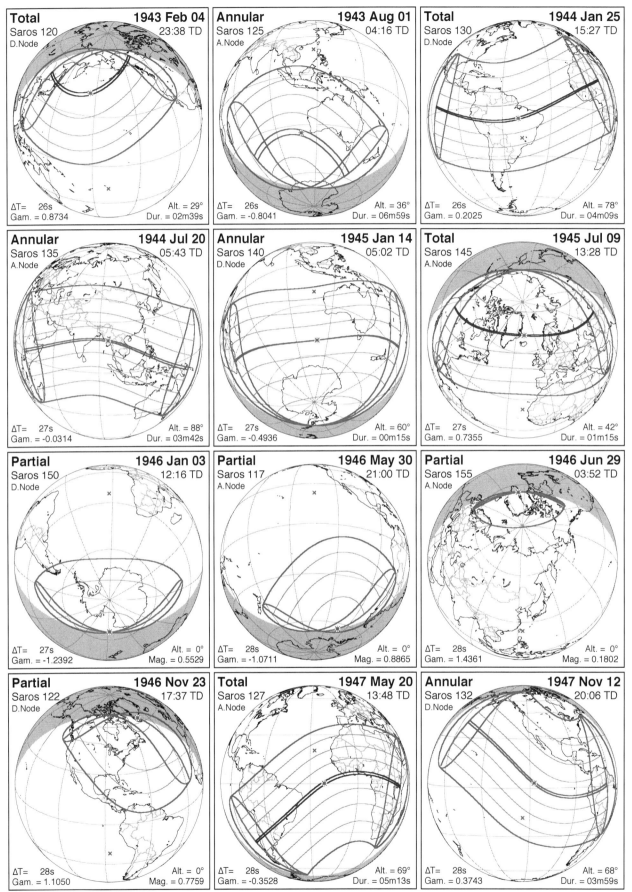

Total 1943 Feb 04 Saros 120 23:38 TD D.Node ΔT= 26s Alt. = 29° Gam. = 0.8734 Dur. = 02m39s	**Annular** 1943 Aug 01 Saros 125 04:16 TD A.Node ΔT= 26s Alt. = 36° Gam. = -0.8041 Dur. = 06m59s	**Total** 1944 Jan 25 Saros 130 15:27 TD D.Node ΔT= 26s Alt. = 78° Gam. = 0.2025 Dur. = 04m09s
Annular 1944 Jul 20 Saros 135 05:43 TD A.Node ΔT= 27s Alt. = 88° Gam. = -0.0314 Dur. = 03m42s	**Annular** 1945 Jan 14 Saros 140 05:02 TD D.Node ΔT= 27s Alt. = 60° Gam. = -0.4936 Dur. = 00m15s	**Total** 1945 Jul 09 Saros 145 13:28 TD A.Node ΔT= 27s Alt. = 42° Gam. = 0.7355 Dur. = 01m15s
Partial 1946 Jan 03 Saros 150 12:16 TD D.Node ΔT= 27s Alt. = 0° Gam. = -1.2392 Mag. = 0.5529	**Partial** 1946 May 30 Saros 117 21:00 TD A.Node ΔT= 28s Alt. = 0° Gam. = -1.0711 Mag. = 0.8865	**Partial** 1946 Jun 29 Saros 155 03:52 TD A.Node ΔT= 28s Alt. = 0° Gam. = 1.4361 Mag. = 0.1802
Partial 1946 Nov 23 Saros 122 17:37 TD D.Node ΔT= 28s Alt. = 0° Gam. = 1.1050 Mag. = 0.7759	**Total** 1947 May 20 Saros 127 13:48 TD A.Node ΔT= 28s Alt. = 69° Gam. = -0.3528 Dur. = 05m13s	**Annular** 1947 Nov 12 Saros 132 20:06 TD D.Node ΔT= 28s Alt. = 68° Gam. = 0.3743 Dur. = 03m59s

Plate 090

184

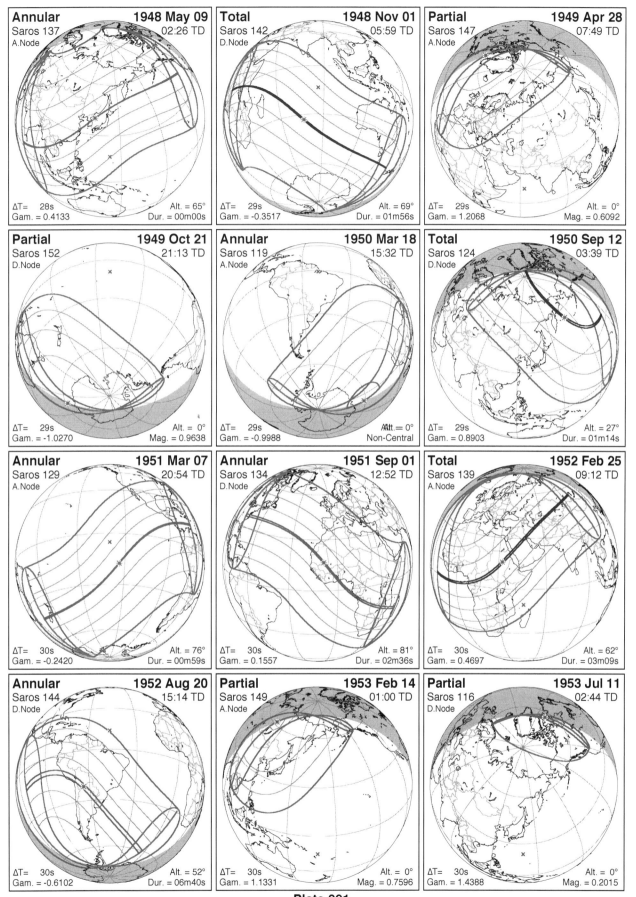

Annular   **1948 May 09**
Saros 137   02:26 TD
A.Node
ΔT= 28s   Alt. = 65°
Gam. = 0.4133   Dur. = 00m00s

Total   **1948 Nov 01**
Saros 142   05:59 TD
D.Node
ΔT= 29s   Alt. = 69°
Gam. = -0.3517   Dur. = 01m56s

Partial   **1949 Apr 28**
Saros 147   07:49 TD
A.Node
ΔT= 29s   Alt. = 0°
Gam. = 1.2068   Mag. = 0.6092

Partial   **1949 Oct 21**
Saros 152   21:13 TD
D.Node
ΔT= 29s   Alt. = 0°
Gam. = -1.0270   Mag. = 0.9638

Annular   **1950 Mar 18**
Saros 119   15:32 TD
A.Node
ΔT= 29s   Alt. = 0°
Gam. = -0.9988   Non-Central

Total   **1950 Sep 12**
Saros 124   03:39 TD
D.Node
ΔT= 29s   Alt. = 27°
Gam. = 0.8903   Dur. = 01m14s

Annular   **1951 Mar 07**
Saros 129   20:54 TD
A.Node
ΔT= 30s   Alt. = 76°
Gam. = -0.2420   Dur. = 00m59s

Annular   **1951 Sep 01**
Saros 134   12:52 TD
D.Node
ΔT= 30s   Alt. = 81°
Gam. = 0.1557   Dur. = 02m36s

Total   **1952 Feb 25**
Saros 139   09:12 TD
A.Node
ΔT= 30s   Alt. = 62°
Gam. = 0.4697   Dur. = 03m09s

Annular   **1952 Aug 20**
Saros 144   15:14 TD
D.Node
ΔT= 30s   Alt. = 52°
Gam. = -0.6102   Dur. = 06m40s

Partial   **1953 Feb 14**
Saros 149   01:00 TD
A.Node
ΔT= 30s   Alt. = 0°
Gam. = 1.1331   Mag. = 0.7596

Partial   **1953 Jul 11**
Saros 116   02:44 TD
D.Node
ΔT= 30s   Alt. = 0°
Gam. = 1.4388   Mag. = 0.2015

Plate 091

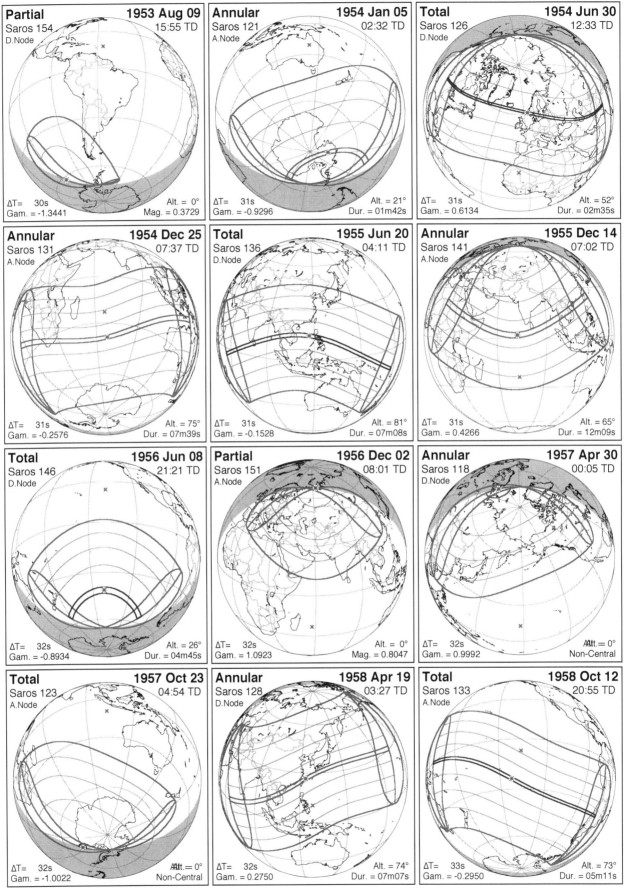

Partial **1953 Aug 09**	**Annular** **1954 Jan 05**	**Total** **1954 Jun 30**
Saros 154 15:55 TD	Saros 121 02:32 TD	Saros 126 12:33 TD
D.Node	A.Node	D.Node
ΔT= 30s Alt. = 0°	ΔT= 31s Alt. = 21°	ΔT= 31s Alt. = 52°
Gam. = -1.3441 Mag. = 0.3729	Gam. = -0.9296 Dur. = 01m42s	Gam. = 0.6134 Dur. = 02m35s
Annular **1954 Dec 25**	**Total** **1955 Jun 20**	**Annular** **1955 Dec 14**
Saros 131 07:37 TD	Saros 136 04:11 TD	Saros 141 07:02 TD
A.Node	D.Node	A.Node
ΔT= 31s Alt. = 75°	ΔT= 31s Alt. = 81°	ΔT= 31s Alt. = 65°
Gam. = -0.2576 Dur. = 07m39s	Gam. = -0.1528 Dur. = 07m08s	Gam. = 0.4266 Dur. = 12m09s
Total **1956 Jun 08**	**Partial** **1956 Dec 02**	**Annular** **1957 Apr 30**
Saros 146 21:21 TD	Saros 151 08:01 TD	Saros 118 00:05 TD
D.Node	A.Node	D.Node
ΔT= 32s Alt. = 26°	ΔT= 32s Alt. = 0°	ΔT= 32s Alt. = 0°
Gam. = -0.8934 Dur. = 04m45s	Gam. = 1.0923 Mag. = 0.8047	Gam. = 0.9992 Non-Central
Total **1957 Oct 23**	**Annular** **1958 Apr 19**	**Total** **1958 Oct 12**
Saros 123 04:54 TD	Saros 128 03:27 TD	Saros 133 20:55 TD
A.Node	D.Node	A.Node
ΔT= 32s Alt. = 0°	ΔT= 32s Alt. = 74°	ΔT= 33s Alt. = 73°
Gam. = -1.0022 Non-Central	Gam. = 0.2750 Dur. = 07m07s	Gam. = -0.2950 Dur. = 05m11s

Plate 092

186

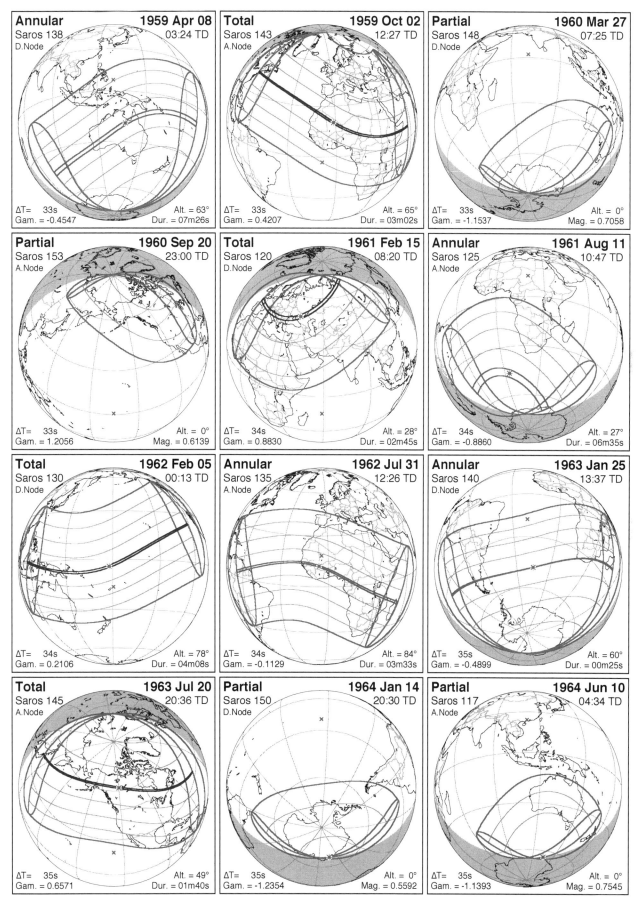

Annular   **1959 Apr 08**
Saros 138   03:24 TD
D.Node
ΔT= 33s   Alt. = 63°
Gam. = -0.4547   Dur. = 07m26s

Total   **1959 Oct 02**
Saros 143   12:27 TD
A.Node
ΔT= 33s   Alt. = 65°
Gam. = 0.4207   Dur. = 03m02s

Partial   **1960 Mar 27**
Saros 148   07:25 TD
D.Node
ΔT= 33s   Alt. = 0°
Gam. = -1.1537   Mag. = 0.7058

Partial   **1960 Sep 20**
Saros 153   23:00 TD
A.Node
ΔT= 33s   Alt. = 0°
Gam. = 1.2056   Mag. = 0.6139

Total   **1961 Feb 15**
Saros 120   08:20 TD
D.Node
ΔT= 34s   Alt. = 28°
Gam. = 0.8830   Dur. = 02m45s

Annular   **1961 Aug 11**
Saros 125   10:47 TD
A.Node
ΔT= 34s   Alt. = 27°
Gam. = -0.8860   Dur. = 06m35s

Total   **1962 Feb 05**
Saros 130   00:13 TD
D.Node
ΔT= 34s   Alt. = 78°
Gam. = 0.2106   Dur. = 04m08s

Annular   **1962 Jul 31**
Saros 135   12:26 TD
A.Node
ΔT= 34s   Alt. = 84°
Gam. = -0.1129   Dur. = 03m33s

Annular   **1963 Jan 25**
Saros 140   13:37 TD
D.Node
ΔT= 35s   Alt. = 60°
Gam. = -0.4899   Dur. = 00m25s

Total   **1963 Jul 20**
Saros 145   20:36 TD
A.Node
ΔT= 35s   Alt. = 49°
Gam. = 0.6571   Dur. = 01m40s

Partial   **1964 Jan 14**
Saros 150   20:30 TD
D.Node
ΔT= 35s   Alt. = 0°
Gam. = -1.2354   Mag. = 0.5592

Partial   **1964 Jun 10**
Saros 117   04:34 TD
A.Node
ΔT= 35s   Alt. = 0°
Gam. = -1.1393   Mag. = 0.7545

Plate 093

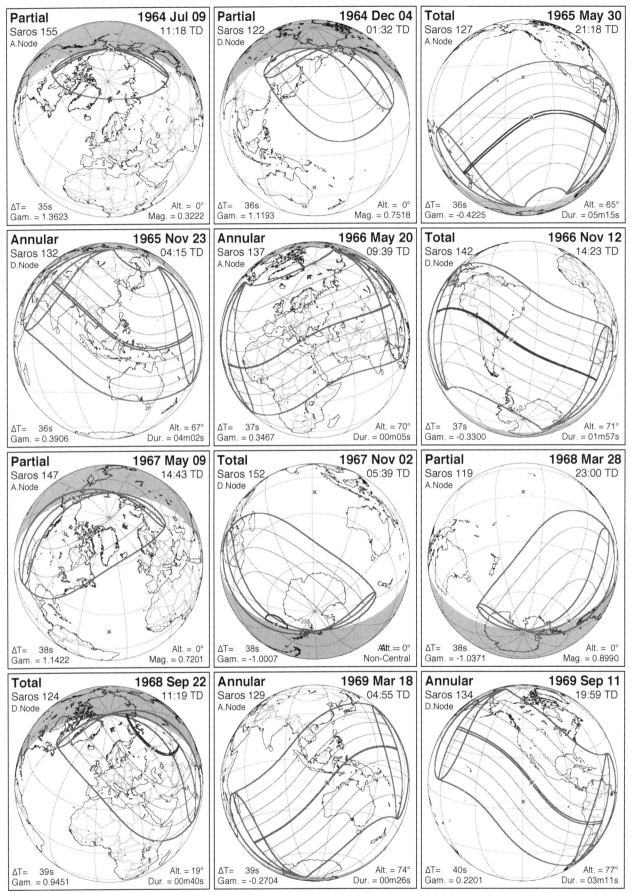

Partial 1964 Jul 09	**Partial** 1964 Dec 04	**Total** 1965 May 30
Saros 155 — 11:18 TD — A.Node	Saros 122 — 01:32 TD — D.Node	Saros 127 — 21:18 TD — A.Node
ΔT= 35s — Alt. = 0°	ΔT= 36s — Alt. = 0°	ΔT= 36s — Alt. = 65°
Gam. = 1.3623 — Mag. = 0.3222	Gam. = 1.1193 — Mag. = 0.7518	Gam. = -0.4225 — Dur. = 05m15s
Annular 1965 Nov 23	**Annular** 1966 May 20	**Total** 1966 Nov 12
Saros 132 — 04:15 TD — D.Node	Saros 137 — 09:39 TD — A.Node	Saros 142 — 14:23 TD — D.Node
ΔT= 36s — Alt. = 67°	ΔT= 37s — Alt. = 70°	ΔT= 37s — Alt. = 71°
Gam. = 0.3906 — Dur. = 04m02s	Gam. = 0.3467 — Dur. = 00m05s	Gam. = -0.3300 — Dur. = 01m57s
Partial 1967 May 09	**Total** 1967 Nov 02	**Partial** 1968 Mar 28
Saros 147 — 14:43 TD — A.Node	Saros 152 — 05:39 TD — D.Node	Saros 119 — 23:00 TD — A.Node
ΔT= 38s — Alt. = 0°	ΔT= 38s — Alt. = 0°	ΔT= 38s — Alt. = 0°
Gam. = 1.1422 — Mag. = 0.7201	Gam. = -1.0007 — Non-Central	Gam. = -1.0371 — Mag. = 0.8990
Total 1968 Sep 22	**Annular** 1969 Mar 18	**Annular** 1969 Sep 11
Saros 124 — 11:19 TD — D.Node	Saros 129 — 04:55 TD — A.Node	Saros 134 — 19:59 TD — D.Node
ΔT= 39s — Alt. = 19°	ΔT= 39s — Alt. = 74°	ΔT= 40s — Alt. = 77°
Gam. = 0.9451 — Dur. = 00m40s	Gam. = -0.2704 — Dur. = 00m26s	Gam. = 0.2201 — Dur. = 03m11s

Plate 094

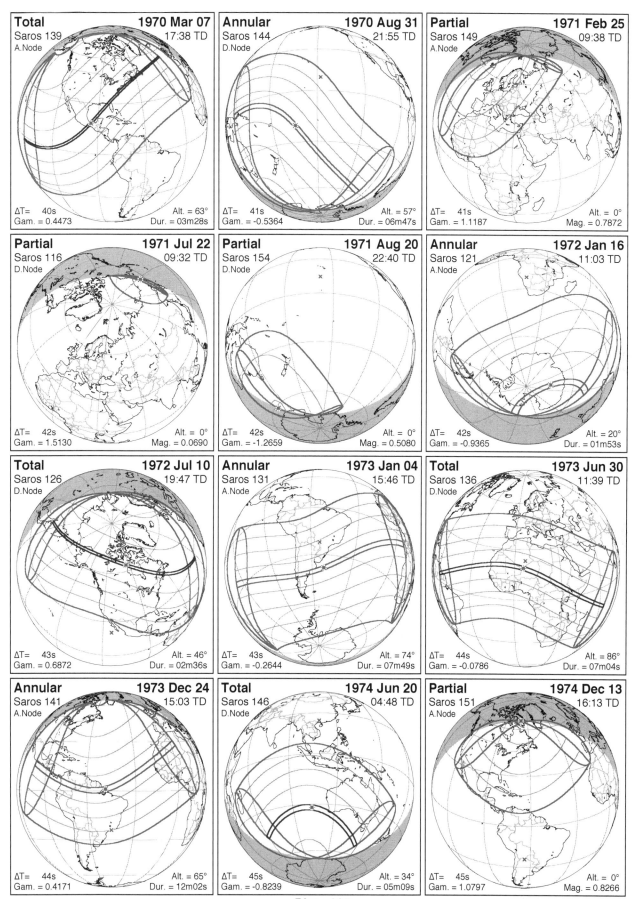

Total	1970 Mar 07
Saros 139	17:38 TD
A.Node	
ΔT= 40s	Alt. = 63°
Gam. = 0.4473	Dur. = 03m28s

Annular	1970 Aug 31
Saros 144	21:55 TD
D.Node	
ΔT= 41s	Alt. = 57°
Gam. = -0.5364	Dur. = 06m47s

Partial	1971 Feb 25
Saros 149	09:38 TD
A.Node	
ΔT= 41s	Alt. = 0°
Gam. = 1.1187	Mag. = 0.7872

Partial	1971 Jul 22
Saros 116	09:32 TD
D.Node	
ΔT= 42s	Alt. = 0°
Gam. = 1.5130	Mag. = 0.0690

Partial	1971 Aug 20
Saros 154	22:40 TD
D.Node	
ΔT= 42s	Alt. = 0°
Gam. = -1.2659	Mag. = 0.5080

Annular	1972 Jan 16
Saros 121	11:03 TD
A.Node	
ΔT= 42s	Alt. = 20°
Gam. = -0.9365	Dur. = 01m53s

Total	1972 Jul 10
Saros 126	19:47 TD
D.Node	
ΔT= 43s	Alt. = 46°
Gam. = 0.6872	Dur. = 02m36s

Annular	1973 Jan 04
Saros 131	15:46 TD
A.Node	
ΔT= 43s	Alt. = 74°
Gam. = -0.2644	Dur. = 07m49s

Total	1973 Jun 30
Saros 136	11:39 TD
D.Node	
ΔT= 44s	Alt. = 86°
Gam. = -0.0786	Dur. = 07m04s

Annular	1973 Dec 24
Saros 141	15:03 TD
A.Node	
ΔT= 44s	Alt. = 65°
Gam. = 0.4171	Dur. = 12m02s

Total	1974 Jun 20
Saros 146	04:48 TD
D.Node	
ΔT= 45s	Alt. = 34°
Gam. = -0.8239	Dur. = 05m09s

Partial	1974 Dec 13
Saros 151	16:13 TD
A.Node	
ΔT= 45s	Alt. = 0°
Gam. = 1.0797	Mag. = 0.8266

Plate 095

189

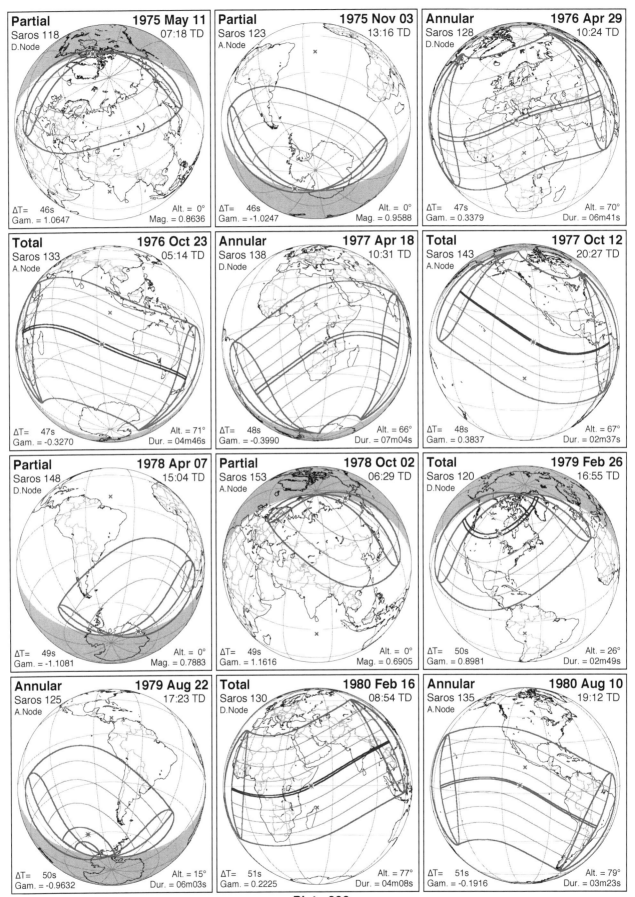

Partial   **1975 May 11**
Saros 118   07:18 TD
D.Node
ΔT= 46s   Alt. = 0°
Gam. = 1.0647   Mag. = 0.8636

Partial   **1975 Nov 03**
Saros 123   13:16 TD
A.Node
ΔT= 46s   Alt. = 0°
Gam. = -1.0247   Mag. = 0.9588

Annular   **1976 Apr 29**
Saros 128   10:24 TD
D.Node
ΔT= 47s   Alt. = 70°
Gam. = 0.3379   Dur. = 06m41s

Total   **1976 Oct 23**
Saros 133   05:14 TD
A.Node
ΔT= 47s   Alt. = 71°
Gam. = -0.3270   Dur. = 04m46s

Annular   **1977 Apr 18**
Saros 138   10:31 TD
D.Node
ΔT= 48s   Alt. = 66°
Gam. = -0.3990   Dur. = 07m04s

Total   **1977 Oct 12**
Saros 143   20:27 TD
A.Node
ΔT= 48s   Alt. = 67°
Gam. = 0.3837   Dur. = 02m37s

Partial   **1978 Apr 07**
Saros 148   15:04 TD
D.Node
ΔT= 49s   Alt. = 0°
Gam. = -1.1081   Mag. = 0.7883

Partial   **1978 Oct 02**
Saros 153   06:29 TD
A.Node
ΔT= 49s   Alt. = 0°
Gam. = 1.1616   Mag. = 0.6905

Total   **1979 Feb 26**
Saros 120   16:55 TD
D.Node
ΔT= 50s   Alt. = 26°
Gam. = 0.8981   Dur. = 02m49s

Annular   **1979 Aug 22**
Saros 125   17:23 TD
A.Node
ΔT= 50s   Alt. = 15°
Gam. = -0.9632   Dur. = 06m03s

Total   **1980 Feb 16**
Saros 130   08:54 TD
D.Node
ΔT= 51s   Alt. = 77°
Gam. = 0.2225   Dur. = 04m08s

Annular   **1980 Aug 10**
Saros 135   19:12 TD
A.Node
ΔT= 51s   Alt. = 79°
Gam. = -0.1916   Dur. = 03m23s

Plate 096

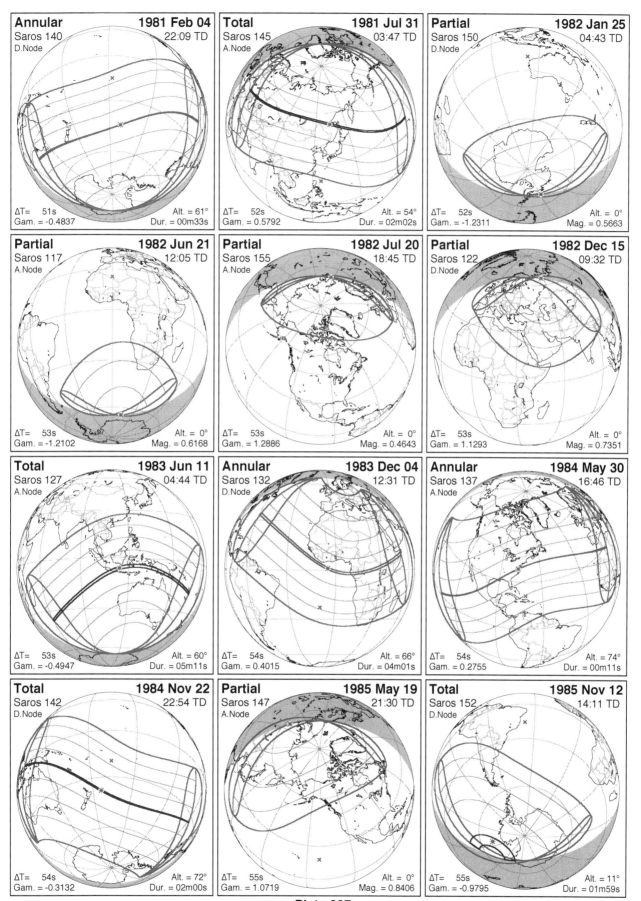

Annular **1981 Feb 04**	**Total** **1981 Jul 31**	**Partial** **1982 Jan 25**
Saros 140 22:09 TD	Saros 145 03:47 TD	Saros 150 04:43 TD
D.Node	A.Node	D.Node
ΔT= 51s Alt. = 61°	ΔT= 52s Alt. = 54°	ΔT= 52s Alt. = 0°
Gam. = -0.4837 Dur. = 00m33s	Gam. = 0.5792 Dur. = 02m02s	Gam. = -1.2311 Mag. = 0.5663
Partial **1982 Jun 21**	**Partial** **1982 Jul 20**	**Partial** **1982 Dec 15**
Saros 117 12:05 TD	Saros 155 18:45 TD	Saros 122 09:32 TD
A.Node	A.Node	D.Node
ΔT= 53s Alt. = 0°	ΔT= 53s Alt. = 0°	ΔT= 53s Alt. = 0°
Gam. = -1.2102 Mag. = 0.6168	Gam. = 1.2886 Mag. = 0.4643	Gam. = 1.1293 Mag. = 0.7351
Total **1983 Jun 11**	**Annular** **1983 Dec 04**	**Annular** **1984 May 30**
Saros 127 04:44 TD	Saros 132 12:31 TD	Saros 137 16:46 TD
A.Node	D.Node	A.Node
ΔT= 53s Alt. = 60°	ΔT= 54s Alt. = 66°	ΔT= 54s Alt. = 74°
Gam. = -0.4947 Dur. = 05m11s	Gam. = 0.4015 Dur. = 04m01s	Gam. = 0.2755 Dur. = 00m11s
Total **1984 Nov 22**	**Partial** **1985 May 19**	**Total** **1985 Nov 12**
Saros 142 22:54 TD	Saros 147 21:30 TD	Saros 152 14:11 TD
D.Node	A.Node	D.Node
ΔT= 54s Alt. = 72°	ΔT= 55s Alt. = 0°	ΔT= 55s Alt. = 11°
Gam. = -0.3132 Dur. = 02m00s	Gam. = 1.0719 Mag. = 0.8406	Gam. = -0.9795 Dur. = 01m59s

Plate 097

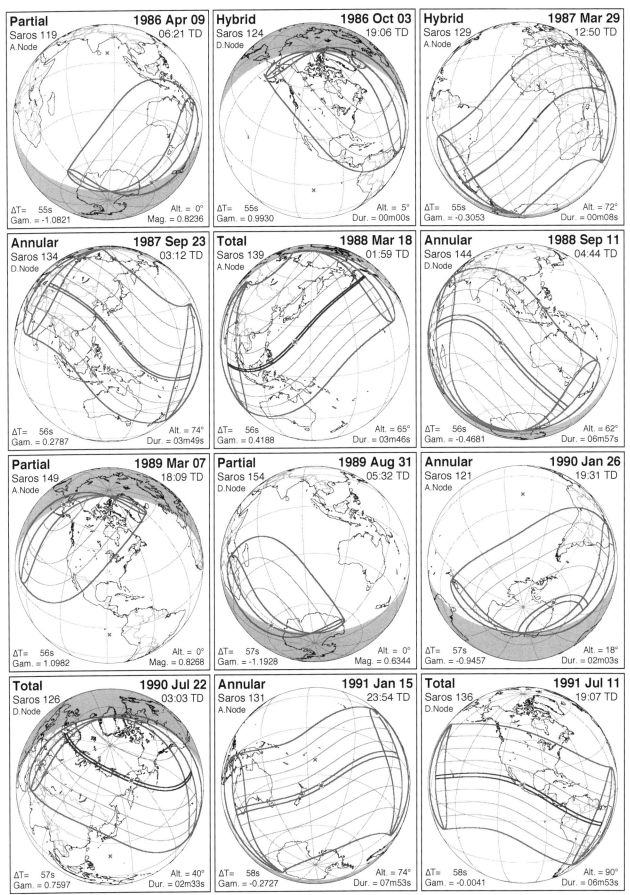

Partial — **1986 Apr 09**
Saros 119 — 06:21 TD
A.Node
ΔT= 55s — Alt. = 0°
Gam. = -1.0821 — Mag. = 0.8236

Hybrid — **1986 Oct 03**
Saros 124 — 19:06 TD
D.Node
ΔT= 55s — Alt. = 5°
Gam. = 0.9930 — Dur. = 00m00s

Hybrid — **1987 Mar 29**
Saros 129 — 12:50 TD
A.Node
ΔT= 55s — Alt. = 72°
Gam. = -0.3053 — Dur. = 00m08s

Annular — **1987 Sep 23**
Saros 134 — 03:12 TD
D.Node
ΔT= 56s — Alt. = 74°
Gam. = 0.2787 — Dur. = 03m49s

Total — **1988 Mar 18**
Saros 139 — 01:59 TD
A.Node
ΔT= 56s — Alt. = 65°
Gam. = 0.4188 — Dur. = 03m46s

Annular — **1988 Sep 11**
Saros 144 — 04:44 TD
D.Node
ΔT= 56s — Alt. = 62°
Gam. = -0.4681 — Dur. = 06m57s

Partial — **1989 Mar 07**
Saros 149 — 18:09 TD
A.Node
ΔT= 56s — Alt. = 0°
Gam. = 1.0982 — Mag. = 0.8268

Partial — **1989 Aug 31**
Saros 154 — 05:32 TD
D.Node
ΔT= 57s — Alt. = 0°
Gam. = -1.1928 — Mag. = 0.6344

Annular — **1990 Jan 26**
Saros 121 — 19:31 TD
A.Node
ΔT= 57s — Alt. = 18°
Gam. = -0.9457 — Dur. = 02m03s

Total — **1990 Jul 22**
Saros 126 — 03:03 TD
D.Node
ΔT= 57s — Alt. = 40°
Gam. = 0.7597 — Dur. = 02m33s

Annular — **1991 Jan 15**
Saros 131 — 23:54 TD
A.Node
ΔT= 58s — Alt. = 74°
Gam. = -0.2727 — Dur. = 07m53s

Total — **1991 Jul 11**
Saros 136 — 19:07 TD
D.Node
ΔT= 58s — Alt. = 90°
Gam. = -0.0041 — Dur. = 06m53s

Plate 098

192

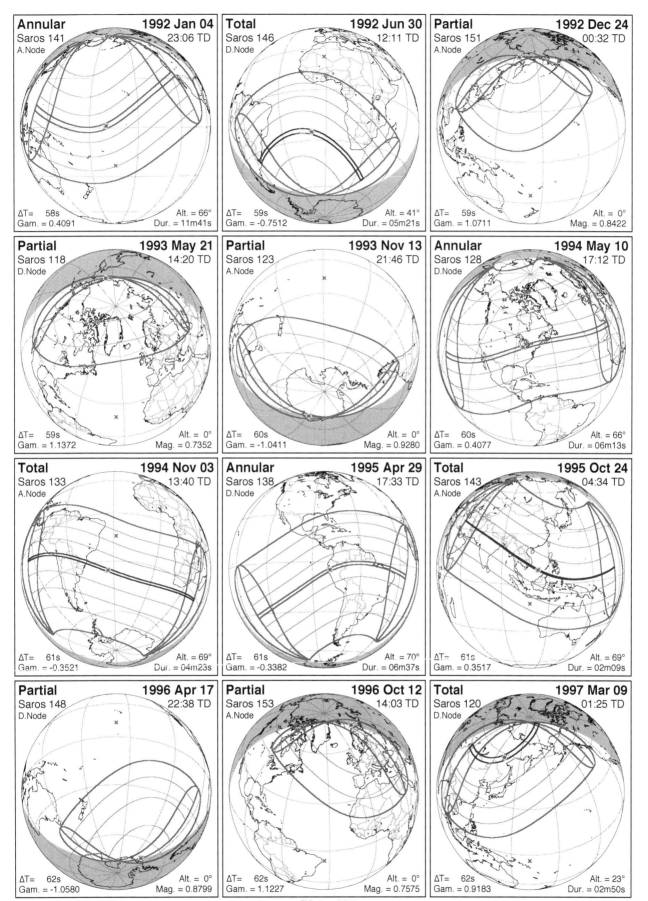

Annular 1992 Jan 04	**Total** 1992 Jun 30	**Partial** 1992 Dec 24
Saros 141 23:06 TD	Saros 146 12:11 TD	Saros 151 00:32 TD
A.Node	D.Node	A.Node
ΔT= 58s Alt. = 66°	ΔT= 59s Alt. = 41°	ΔT= 59s Alt. = 0°
Gam. = 0.4091 Dur. = 11m41s	Gam. = -0.7512 Dur. = 05m21s	Gam. = 1.0711 Mag. = 0.8422
Partial 1993 May 21	**Partial** 1993 Nov 13	**Annular** 1994 May 10
Saros 118 14:20 TD	Saros 123 21:46 TD	Saros 128 17:12 TD
D.Node	A.Node	D.Node
ΔT= 59s Alt. = 0°	ΔT= 60s Alt. = 0°	ΔT= 60s Alt. = 66°
Gam. = 1.1372 Mag. = 0.7352	Gam. = -1.0411 Mag. = 0.9280	Gam. = 0.4077 Dur. = 06m13s
Total 1994 Nov 03	**Annular** 1995 Apr 29	**Total** 1995 Oct 24
Saros 133 13:40 TD	Saros 138 17:33 TD	Saros 143 04:34 TD
A.Node	D.Node	A.Node
ΔT= 61s Alt. = 69°	ΔT= 61s Alt. = 70°	ΔT= 61s Alt. = 69°
Gam. = -0.3521 Dur. = 04m23s	Gam. = -0.3382 Dur. = 06m37s	Gam. = 0.3517 Dur. = 02m09s
Partial 1996 Apr 17	**Partial** 1996 Oct 12	**Total** 1997 Mar 09
Saros 148 22:38 TD	Saros 153 14:03 TD	Saros 120 01:25 TD
D.Node	A.Node	D.Node
ΔT= 62s Alt. = 0°	ΔT= 62s Alt. = 0°	ΔT= 62s Alt. = 23°
Gam. = -1.0580 Mag. = 0.8799	Gam. = 1.1227 Mag. = 0.7575	Gam. = 0.9183 Dur. = 02m50s

Plate 099

193

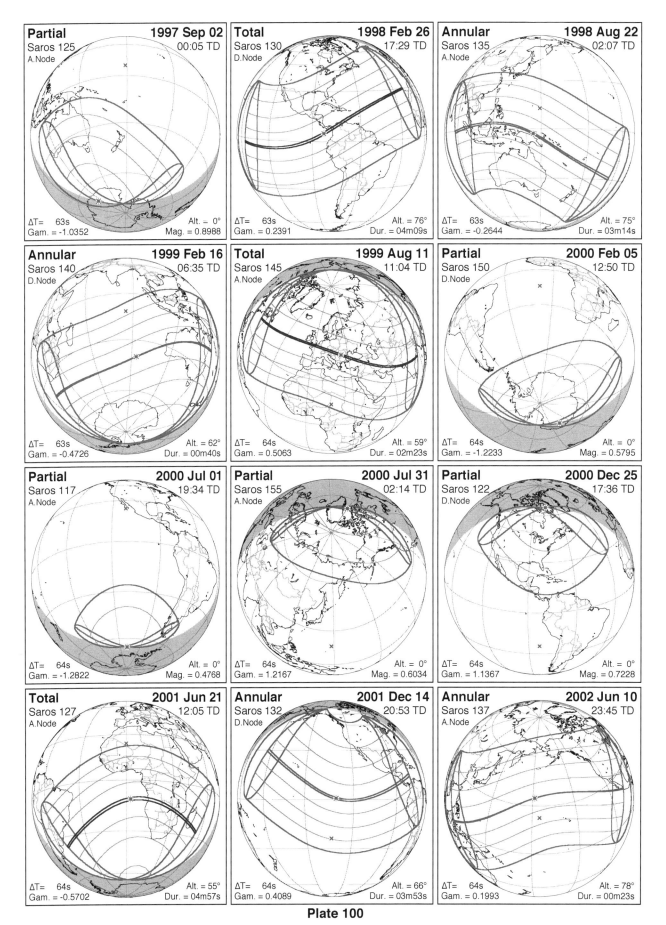

Partial	1997 Sep 02
Saros 125	00:05 TD
A.Node	
ΔT= 63s	Alt. = 0°
Gam. = -1.0352	Mag. = 0.8988

Total	1998 Feb 26
Saros 130	17:29 TD
D.Node	
ΔT= 63s	Alt. = 76°
Gam. = 0.2391	Dur. = 04m09s

Annular	1998 Aug 22
Saros 135	02:07 TD
A.Node	
ΔT= 63s	Alt. = 75°
Gam. = -0.2644	Dur. = 03m14s

Annular	1999 Feb 16
Saros 140	06:35 TD
D.Node	
ΔT= 63s	Alt. = 62°
Gam. = -0.4726	Dur. = 00m40s

Total	1999 Aug 11
Saros 145	11:04 TD
A.Node	
ΔT= 64s	Alt. = 59°
Gam. = 0.5063	Dur. = 02m23s

Partial	2000 Feb 05
Saros 150	12:50 TD
D.Node	
ΔT= 64s	Alt. = 0°
Gam. = -1.2233	Mag. = 0.5795

Partial	2000 Jul 01
Saros 117	19:34 TD
A.Node	
ΔT= 64s	Alt. = 0°
Gam. = -1.2822	Mag. = 0.4768

Partial	2000 Jul 31
Saros 155	02:14 TD
A.Node	
ΔT= 64s	Alt. = 0°
Gam. = 1.2167	Mag. = 0.6034

Partial	2000 Dec 25
Saros 122	17:36 TD
D.Node	
ΔT= 64s	Alt. = 0°
Gam. = 1.1367	Mag. = 0.7228

Total	2001 Jun 21
Saros 127	12:05 TD
A.Node	
ΔT= 64s	Alt. = 55°
Gam. = -0.5702	Dur. = 04m57s

Annular	2001 Dec 14
Saros 132	20:53 TD
D.Node	
ΔT= 64s	Alt. = 66°
Gam. = 0.4089	Dur. = 03m53s

Annular	2002 Jun 10
Saros 137	23:45 TD
A.Node	
ΔT= 64s	Alt. = 78°
Gam. = 0.1993	Dur. = 00m23s

Plate 100

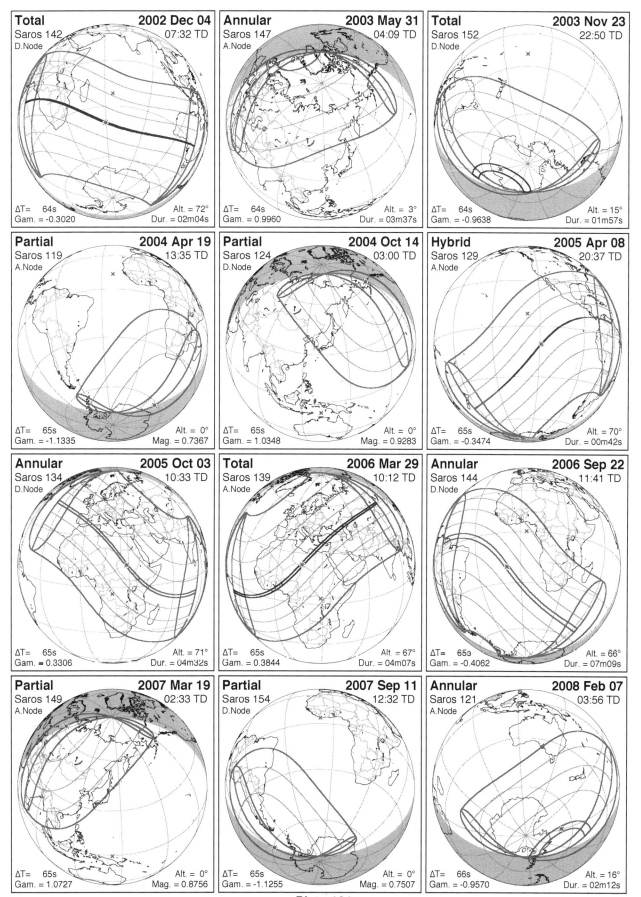

Total 2002 Dec 04	**Annular** 2003 May 31	**Total** 2003 Nov 23
Saros 142 07:32 TD	Saros 147 04:09 TD	Saros 152 22:50 TD
D.Node	A.Node	D.Node
ΔT= 64s Alt. = 72°	ΔT= 64s Alt. = 3°	ΔT= 64s Alt. = 15°
Gam. = -0.3020 Dur. = 02m04s	Gam. = 0.9960 Dur. = 03m37s	Gam. = -0.9638 Dur. = 01m57s
Partial 2004 Apr 19	**Partial** 2004 Oct 14	**Hybrid** 2005 Apr 08
Saros 119 13:35 TD	Saros 124 03:00 TD	Saros 129 20:37 TD
A.Node	D.Node	A.Node
ΔT= 65s Alt. = 0°	ΔT= 65s Alt. = 0°	ΔT= 65s Alt. = 70°
Gam. = -1.1335 Mag. = 0.7367	Gam. = 1.0348 Mag. = 0.9283	Gam. = -0.3474 Dur. = 00m42s
Annular 2005 Oct 03	**Total** 2006 Mar 29	**Annular** 2006 Sep 22
Saros 134 10:33 TD	Saros 139 10:12 TD	Saros 144 11:41 TD
D.Node	A.Node	D.Node
ΔT= 65s Alt. = 71°	ΔT= 65s Alt. = 67°	ΔT= 65s Alt. = 66°
Gam. = 0.3306 Dur. = 04m32s	Gam. = 0.3844 Dur. = 04m07s	Gam. = -0.4062 Dur. = 07m09s
Partial 2007 Mar 19	**Partial** 2007 Sep 11	**Annular** 2008 Feb 07
Saros 149 02:33 TD	Saros 154 12:32 TD	Saros 121 03:56 TD
A.Node	D.Node	A.Node
ΔT= 65s Alt. = 0°	ΔT= 65s Alt. = 0°	ΔT= 66s Alt. = 16°
Gam. = 1.0727 Mag. = 0.8756	Gam. = -1.1255 Mag. = 0.7507	Gam. = -0.9570 Dur. = 02m12s

Plate 101

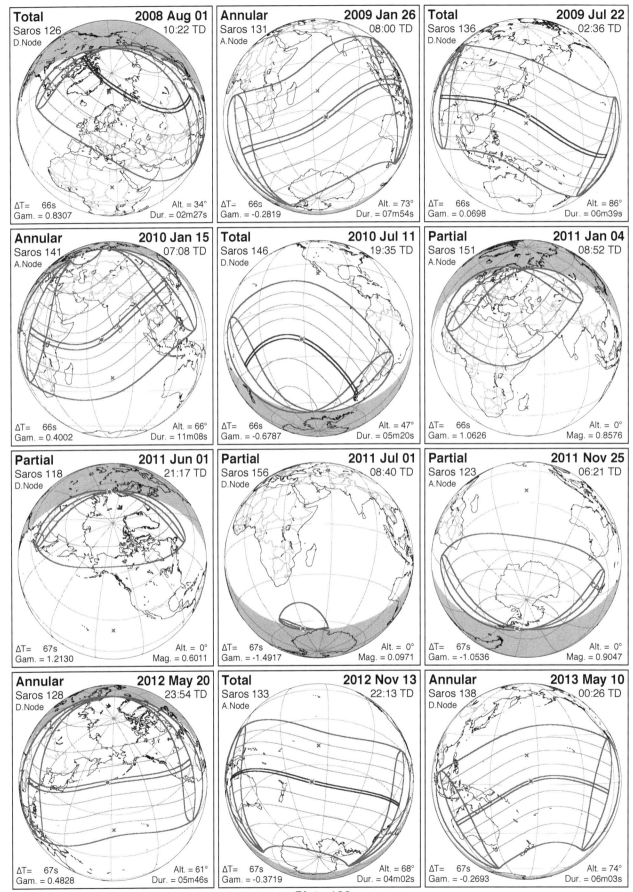

Plate 102

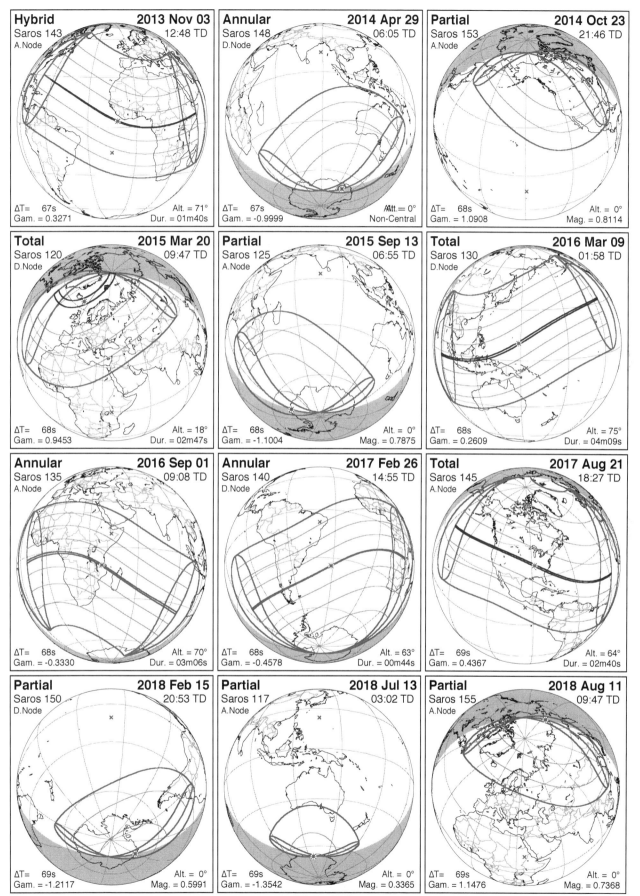

Hybrid   **2013 Nov 03**
Saros 143   12:48 TD
A.Node
ΔT= 67s   Alt. = 71°
Gam. = 0.3271   Dur. = 01m40s

Annular   **2014 Apr 29**
Saros 148   06:05 TD
D.Node
ΔT= 67s   Alt. = 0°
Gam. = -0.9999   Non-Central

Partial   **2014 Oct 23**
Saros 153   21:46 TD
A.Node
ΔT= 68s   Alt. = 0°
Gam. = 1.0908   Mag. = 0.8114

Total   **2015 Mar 20**
Saros 120   09:47 TD
D.Node
ΔT= 68s   Alt. = 18°
Gam. = 0.9453   Dur. = 02m47s

Partial   **2015 Sep 13**
Saros 125   06:55 TD
A.Node
ΔT= 68s   Alt. = 0°
Gam. = -1.1004   Mag. = 0.7875

Total   **2016 Mar 09**
Saros 130   01:58 TD
D.Node
ΔT= 68s   Alt. = 75°
Gam. = 0.2609   Dur. = 04m09s

Annular   **2016 Sep 01**
Saros 135   09:08 TD
A.Node
ΔT= 68s   Alt. = 70°
Gam. = -0.3330   Dur. = 03m06s

Annular   **2017 Feb 26**
Saros 140   14:55 TD
D.Node
ΔT= 68s   Alt. = 63°
Gam. = -0.4578   Dur. = 00m44s

Total   **2017 Aug 21**
Saros 145   18:27 TD
A.Node
ΔT= 69s   Alt. = 64°
Gam. = 0.4367   Dur. = 02m40s

Partial   **2018 Feb 15**
Saros 150   20:53 TD
D.Node
ΔT= 69s   Alt. = 0°
Gam. = -1.2117   Mag. = 0.5991

Partial   **2018 Jul 13**
Saros 117   03:02 TD
A.Node
ΔT= 69s   Alt. = 0°
Gam. = -1.3542   Mag. = 0.3365

Partial   **2018 Aug 11**
Saros 155   09:47 TD
A.Node
ΔT= 69s   Alt. = 0°
Gam. = 1.1476   Mag. = 0.7368

Plate 103

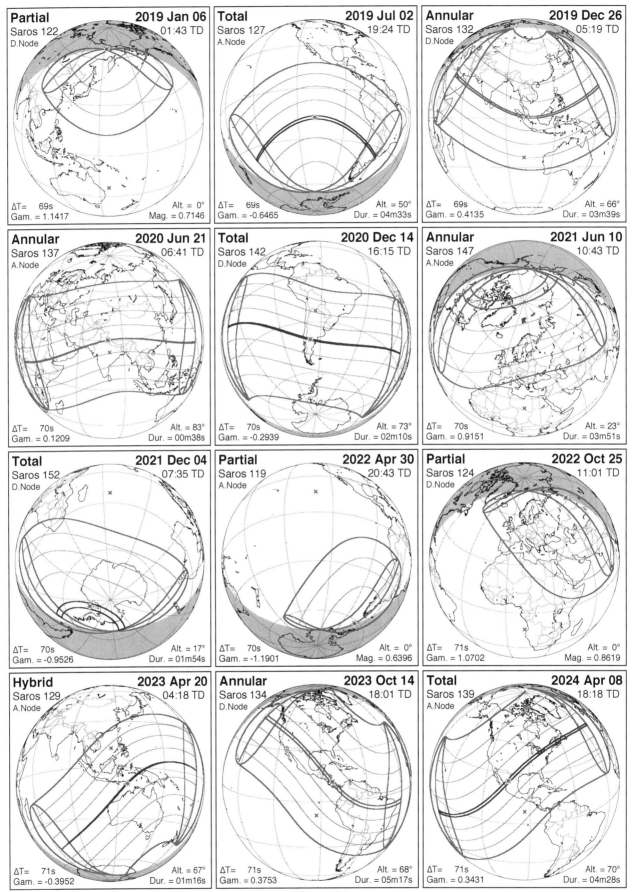

Partial	2019 Jan 06
Saros 122	01:43 TD
D.Node	
ΔT= 69s	Alt. = 0°
Gam. = 1.1417	Mag. = 0.7146

Total	2019 Jul 02
Saros 127	19:24 TD
A.Node	
ΔT= 69s	Alt. = 50°
Gam. = -0.6465	Dur. = 04m33s

Annular	2019 Dec 26
Saros 132	05:19 TD
D.Node	
ΔT= 69s	Alt. = 66°
Gam. = 0.4135	Dur. = 03m39s

Annular	2020 Jun 21
Saros 137	06:41 TD
A.Node	
ΔT= 70s	Alt. = 83°
Gam. = 0.1209	Dur. = 00m38s

Total	2020 Dec 14
Saros 142	16:15 TD
D.Node	
ΔT= 70s	Alt. = 73°
Gam. = -0.2939	Dur. = 02m10s

Annular	2021 Jun 10
Saros 147	10:43 TD
A.Node	
ΔT= 70s	Alt. = 23°
Gam. = 0.9151	Dur. = 03m51s

Total	2021 Dec 04
Saros 152	07:35 TD
D.Node	
ΔT= 70s	Alt. = 17°
Gam. = -0.9526	Dur. = 01m54s

Partial	2022 Apr 30
Saros 119	20:43 TD
A.Node	
ΔT= 70s	Alt. = 0°
Gam. = -1.1901	Mag. = 0.6396

Partial	2022 Oct 25
Saros 124	11:01 TD
D.Node	
ΔT= 71s	Alt. = 0°
Gam. = 1.0702	Mag. = 0.8619

Hybrid	2023 Apr 20
Saros 129	04:18 TD
A.Node	
ΔT= 71s	Alt. = 67°
Gam. = -0.3952	Dur. = 01m16s

Annular	2023 Oct 14
Saros 134	18:01 TD
D.Node	
ΔT= 71s	Alt. = 68°
Gam. = 0.3753	Dur. = 05m17s

Total	2024 Apr 08
Saros 139	18:18 TD
A.Node	
ΔT= 71s	Alt. = 70°
Gam. = 0.3431	Dur. = 04m28s

Plate 104

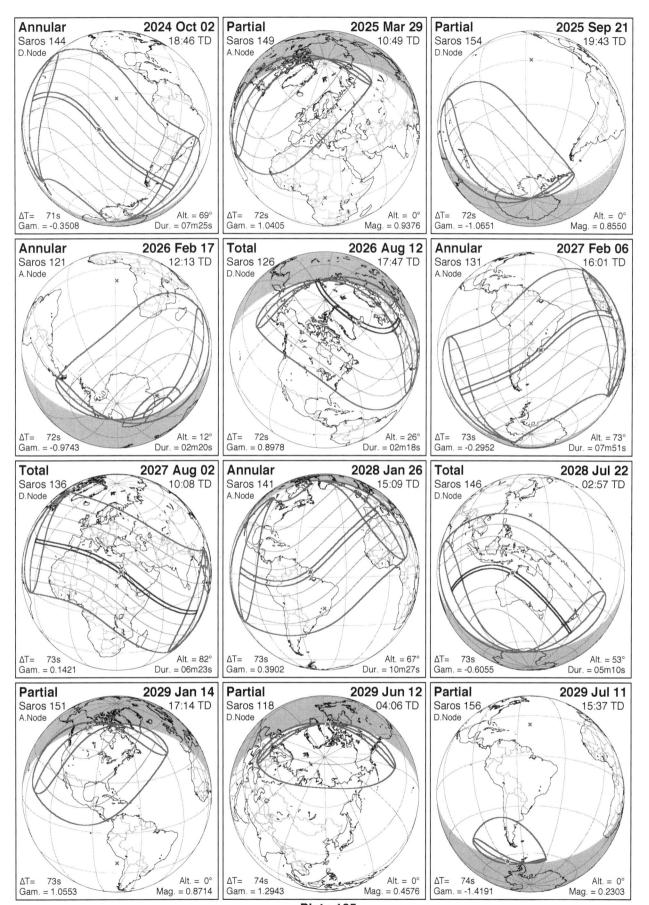

Annular **2024 Oct 02**	
Saros 144 18:46 TD	
D.Node	
ΔT= 71s Alt. = 69°	
Gam. = -0.3508 Dur. = 07m25s	

Partial **2025 Mar 29**	
Saros 149 10:49 TD	
A.Node	
ΔT= 72s Alt. = 0°	
Gam. = 1.0405 Mag. = 0.9376	

Partial **2025 Sep 21**	
Saros 154 19:43 TD	
D.Node	
ΔT= 72s Alt. = 0°	
Gam. = -1.0651 Mag. = 0.8550	

Annular **2026 Feb 17**	
Saros 121 12:13 TD	
A.Node	
ΔT= 72s Alt. = 12°	
Gam. = -0.9743 Dur. = 02m20s	

Total **2026 Aug 12**	
Saros 126 17:47 TD	
D.Node	
ΔT= 72s Alt. = 26°	
Gam. = 0.8978 Dur. = 02m18s	

Annular **2027 Feb 06**	
Saros 131 16:01 TD	
A.Node	
ΔT= 73s Alt. = 73°	
Gam. = -0.2952 Dur. = 07m51s	

Total **2027 Aug 02**	
Saros 136 10:08 TD	
D.Node	
ΔT= 73s Alt. = 82°	
Gam. = 0.1421 Dur. = 06m23s	

Annular **2028 Jan 26**	
Saros 141 15:09 TD	
A.Node	
ΔT= 73s Alt. = 67°	
Gam. = 0.3902 Dur. = 10m27s	

Total **2028 Jul 22**	
Saros 146 02:57 TD	
D.Node	
ΔT= 73s Alt. = 53°	
Gam. = -0.6055 Dur. = 05m10s	

Partial **2029 Jan 14**	
Saros 151 17:14 TD	
A.Node	
ΔT= 73s Alt. = 0°	
Gam. = 1.0553 Mag. = 0.8714	

Partial **2029 Jun 12**	
Saros 118 04:06 TD	
D.Node	
ΔT= 74s Alt. = 0°	
Gam. = 1.2943 Mag. = 0.4576	

Partial **2029 Jul 11**	
Saros 156 15:37 TD	
D.Node	
ΔT= 74s Alt. = 0°	
Gam. = -1.4191 Mag. = 0.2303	

Plate 105

199

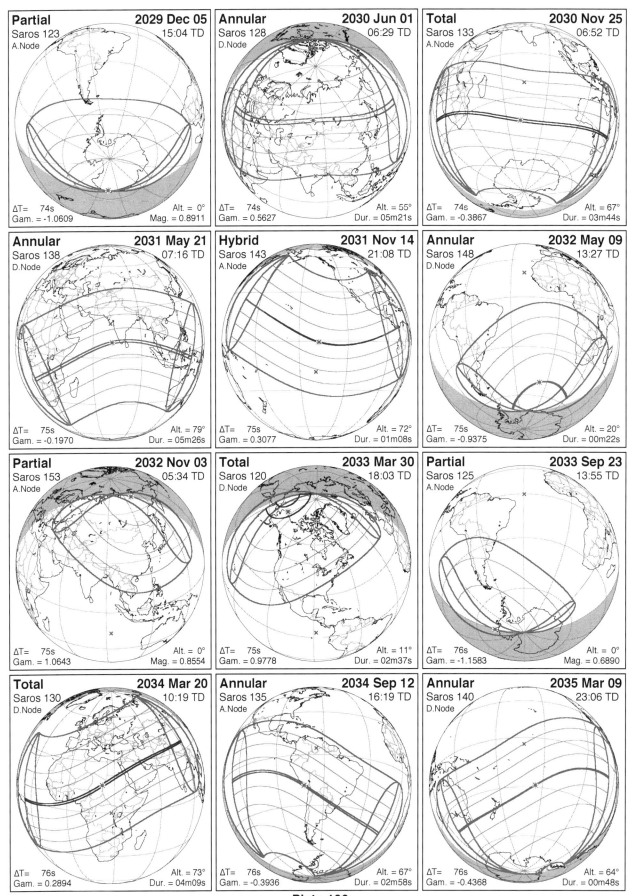

Partial **2029 Dec 05** Saros 123 15:04 TD A.Node ΔT= 74s Alt. = 0° Gam. = -1.0609 Mag. = 0.8911	**Annular** **2030 Jun 01** Saros 128 06:29 TD D.Node ΔT= 74s Alt. = 55° Gam. = 0.5627 Dur. = 05m21s	**Total** **2030 Nov 25** Saros 133 06:52 TD A.Node ΔT= 74s Alt. = 67° Gam. = -0.3867 Dur. = 03m44s
Annular **2031 May 21** Saros 138 07:16 TD D.Node ΔT= 75s Alt. = 79° Gam. = -0.1970 Dur. = 05m26s	**Hybrid** **2031 Nov 14** Saros 143 21:08 TD A.Node ΔT= 75s Alt. = 72° Gam. = 0.3077 Dur. = 01m08s	**Annular** **2032 May 09** Saros 148 13:27 TD D.Node ΔT= 75s Alt. = 20° Gam. = -0.9375 Dur. = 00m22s
Partial **2032 Nov 03** Saros 153 05:34 TD A.Node ΔT= 75s Alt. = 0° Gam. = 1.0643 Mag. = 0.8554	**Total** **2033 Mar 30** Saros 120 18:03 TD D.Node ΔT= 75s Alt. = 11° Gam. = 0.9778 Dur. = 02m37s	**Partial** **2033 Sep 23** Saros 125 13:55 TD A.Node ΔT= 76s Alt. = 0° Gam. = -1.1583 Mag. = 0.6890
Total **2034 Mar 20** Saros 130 10:19 TD D.Node ΔT= 76s Alt. = 73° Gam. = 0.2894 Dur. = 04m09s	**Annular** **2034 Sep 12** Saros 135 16:19 TD A.Node ΔT= 76s Alt. = 67° Gam. = -0.3936 Dur. = 02m58s	**Annular** **2035 Mar 09** Saros 140 23:06 TD D.Node ΔT= 76s Alt. = 64° Gam. = -0.4368 Dur. = 00m48s

Plate 106

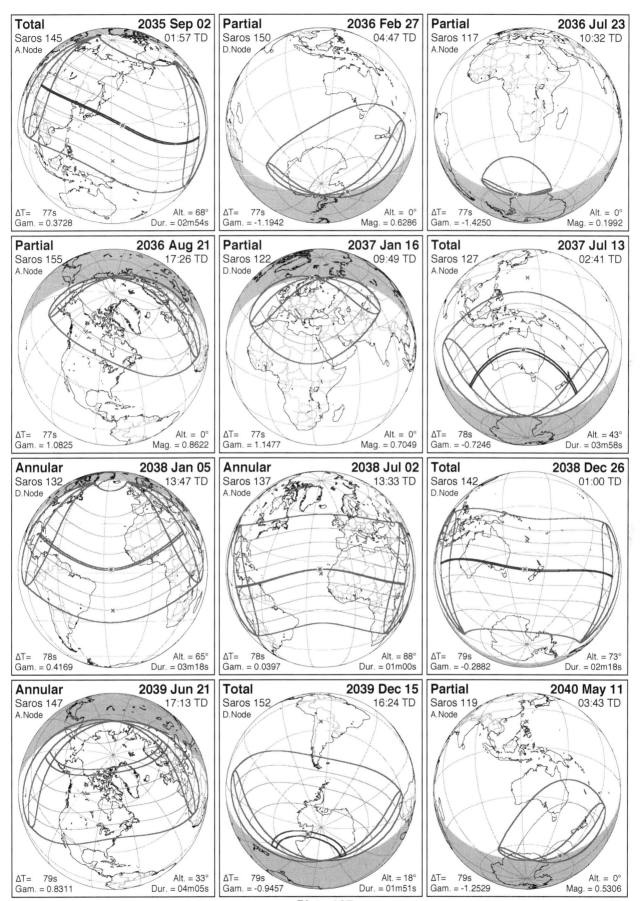

Plate 107

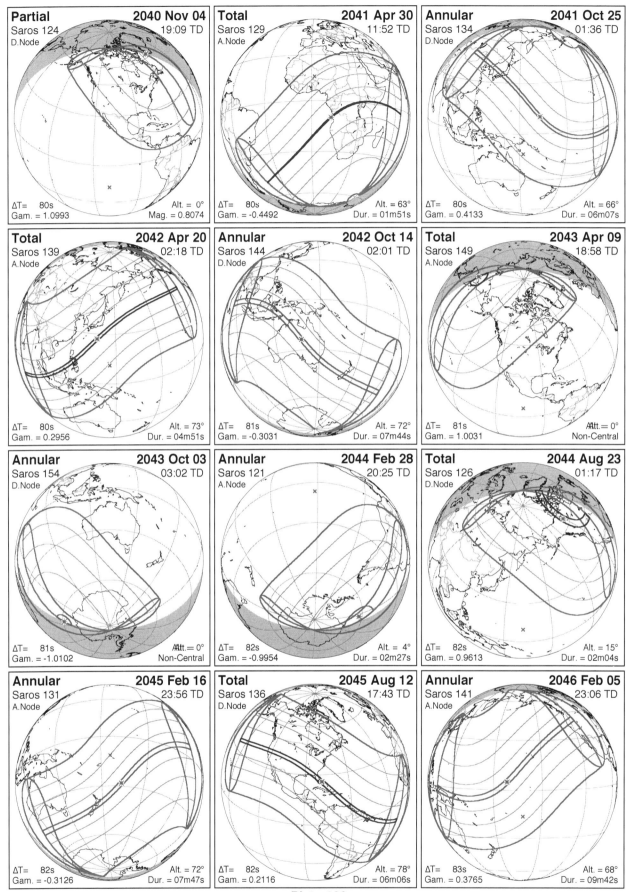

Partial	2040 Nov 04
Saros 124	19:09 TD
D.Node	
ΔT= 80s	Alt. = 0°
Gam. = 1.0993	Mag. = 0.8074

Total	2041 Apr 30
Saros 129	11:52 TD
A.Node	
ΔT= 80s	Alt. = 63°
Gam. = -0.4492	Dur. = 01m51s

Annular	2041 Oct 25
Saros 134	01:36 TD
D.Node	
ΔT= 80s	Alt. = 66°
Gam. = 0.4133	Dur. = 06m07s

Total	2042 Apr 20
Saros 139	02:18 TD
A.Node	
ΔT= 80s	Alt. = 73°
Gam. = 0.2956	Dur. = 04m51s

Annular	2042 Oct 14
Saros 144	02:01 TD
D.Node	
ΔT= 81s	Alt. = 72°
Gam. = -0.3031	Dur. = 07m44s

Total	2043 Apr 09
Saros 149	18:58 TD
A.Node	
ΔT= 81s	Alt. = 0°
Gam. = 1.0031	Non-Central

Annular	2043 Oct 03
Saros 154	03:02 TD
D.Node	
ΔT= 81s	Alt. = 0°
Gam. = -1.0102	Non-Central

Annular	2044 Feb 28
Saros 121	20:25 TD
A.Node	
ΔT= 82s	Alt. = 4°
Gam. = -0.9954	Dur. = 02m27s

Total	2044 Aug 23
Saros 126	01:17 TD
D.Node	
ΔT= 82s	Alt. = 15°
Gam. = 0.9613	Dur. = 02m04s

Annular	2045 Feb 16
Saros 131	23:56 TD
A.Node	
ΔT= 82s	Alt. = 72°
Gam. = -0.3126	Dur. = 07m47s

Total	2045 Aug 12
Saros 136	17:43 TD
D.Node	
ΔT= 82s	Alt. = 78°
Gam. = 0.2116	Dur. = 06m06s

Annular	2046 Feb 05
Saros 141	23:06 TD
A.Node	
ΔT= 83s	Alt. = 68°
Gam. = 0.3765	Dur. = 09m42s

Plate 108

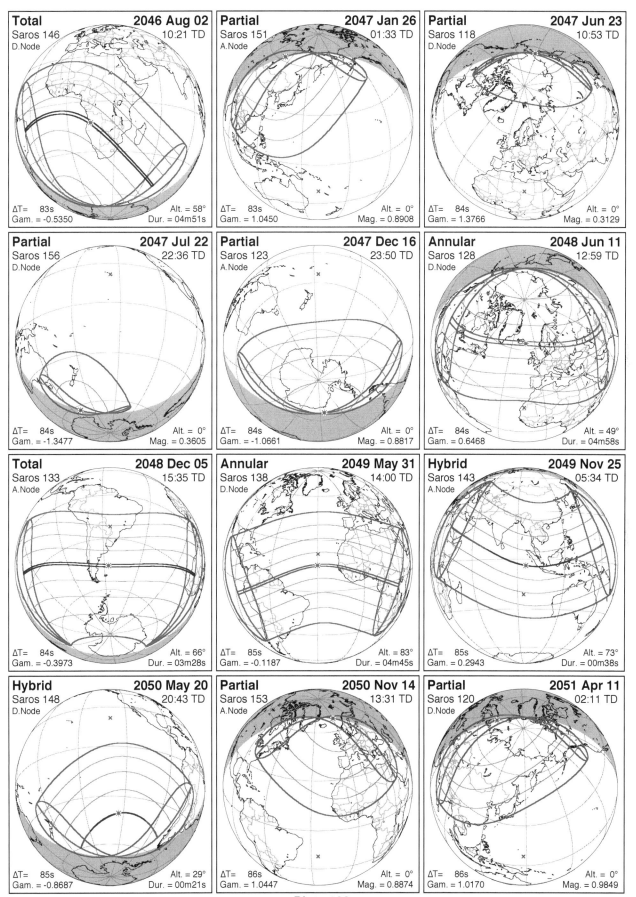

Total	2046 Aug 02
Saros 146	10:21 TD
D.Node	
ΔT= 83s	Alt. = 58°
Gam. = -0.5350	Dur. = 04m51s

Partial	2047 Jan 26
Saros 151	01:33 TD
A.Node	
ΔT= 83s	Alt. = 0°
Gam. = 1.0450	Mag. = 0.8908

Partial	2047 Jun 23
Saros 118	10:53 TD
D.Node	
ΔT= 84s	Alt. = 0°
Gam. = 1.3766	Mag. = 0.3129

Partial	2047 Jul 22
Saros 156	22:36 TD
D.Node	
ΔT= 84s	Alt. = 0°
Gam. = -1.3477	Mag. = 0.3605

Partial	2047 Dec 16
Saros 123	23:50 TD
A.Node	
ΔT= 84s	Alt. = 0°
Gam. = -1.0661	Mag. = 0.8817

Annular	2048 Jun 11
Saros 128	12:59 TD
D.Node	
ΔT= 84s	Alt. = 49°
Gam. = 0.6468	Dur. = 04m58s

Total	2048 Dec 05
Saros 133	15:35 TD
A.Node	
ΔT= 84s	Alt. = 66°
Gam. = -0.3973	Dur. = 03m28s

Annular	2049 May 31
Saros 138	14:00 TD
D.Node	
ΔT= 85s	Alt. = 83°
Gam. = -0.1187	Dur. = 04m45s

Hybrid	2049 Nov 25
Saros 143	05:34 TD
A.Node	
ΔT= 85s	Alt. = 73°
Gam. = 0.2943	Dur. = 00m38s

Hybrid	2050 May 20
Saros 148	20:43 TD
D.Node	
ΔT= 85s	Alt. = 29°
Gam. = -0.8687	Dur. = 00m21s

Partial	2050 Nov 14
Saros 153	13:31 TD
A.Node	
ΔT= 86s	Alt. = 0°
Gam. = 1.0447	Mag. = 0.8874

Partial	2051 Apr 11
Saros 120	02:11 TD
D.Node	
ΔT= 86s	Alt. = 0°
Gam. = 1.0170	Mag. = 0.9849

Plate 109

203

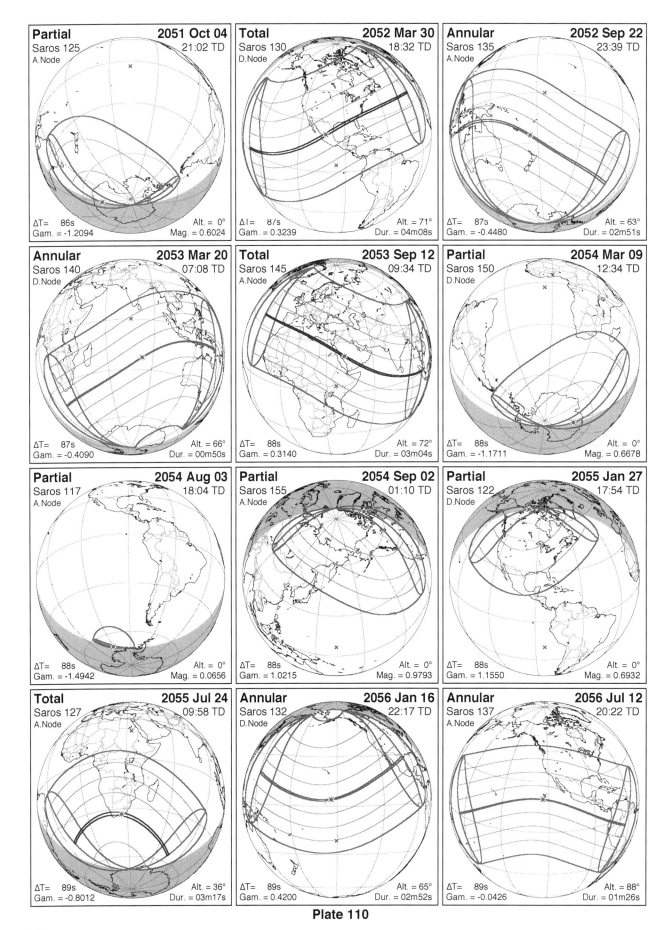

Plate 110

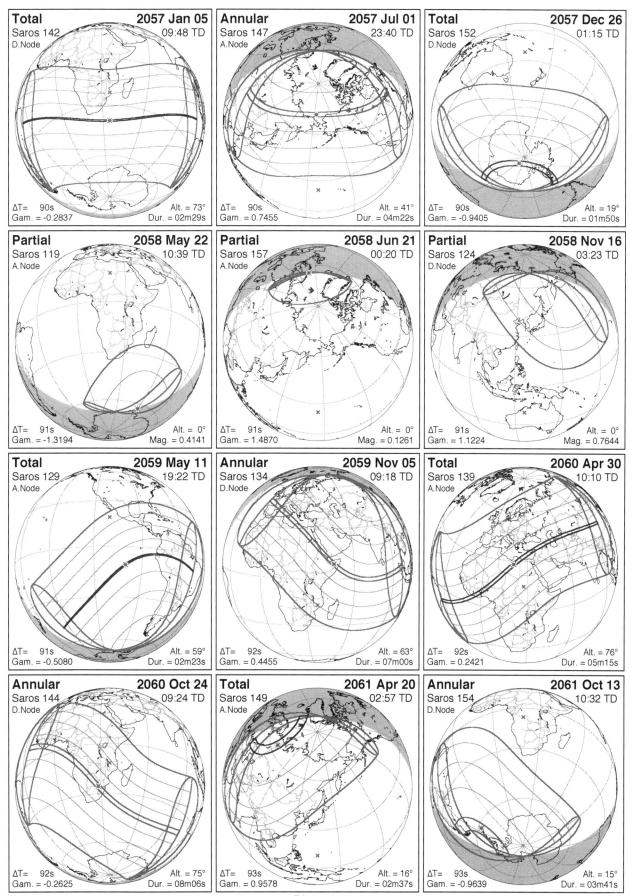

Total **2057 Jan 05**	**Annular** **2057 Jul 01**	**Total** **2057 Dec 26**
Saros 142 09:48 TD	Saros 147 23:40 TD	Saros 152 01:15 TD
D.Node	A.Node	D.Node
ΔT= 90s Alt. = 73°	ΔT= 90s Alt. = 41°	ΔT= 90s Alt. = 19°
Gam. = -0.2837 Dur. = 02m29s	Gam. = 0.7455 Dur. = 04m22s	Gam. = -0.9405 Dur. = 01m50s
Partial **2058 May 22**	**Partial** **2058 Jun 21**	**Partial** **2058 Nov 16**
Saros 119 10:39 TD	Saros 157 00:20 TD	Saros 124 03:23 TD
A.Node	A.Node	D.Node
ΔT= 91s Alt. = 0°	ΔT= 91s Alt. = 0°	ΔT= 91s Alt. = 0°
Gam. = -1.3194 Mag. = 0.4141	Gam. = 1.4870 Mag. = 0.1261	Gam. = 1.1224 Mag. = 0.7644
Total **2059 May 11**	**Annular** **2059 Nov 05**	**Total** **2060 Apr 30**
Saros 129 19:22 TD	Saros 134 09:18 TD	Saros 139 10:10 TD
A.Node	D.Node	A.Node
ΔT= 91s Alt. = 59°	ΔT= 92s Alt. = 63°	ΔT= 92s Alt. = 76°
Gam. = -0.5080 Dur. = 02m23s	Gam. = 0.4455 Dur. = 07m00s	Gam. = 0.2421 Dur. = 05m15s
Annular **2060 Oct 24**	**Total** **2061 Apr 20**	**Annular** **2061 Oct 13**
Saros 144 09:24 TD	Saros 149 02:57 TD	Saros 154 10:32 TD
D.Node	A.Node	D.Node
ΔT= 92s Alt. = 75°	ΔT= 93s Alt. = 16°	ΔT= 93s Alt. = 15°
Gam. = -0.2625 Dur. = 08m06s	Gam. = 0.9578 Dur. = 02m37s	Gam. = -0.9639 Dur. = 03m41s

Plate 111

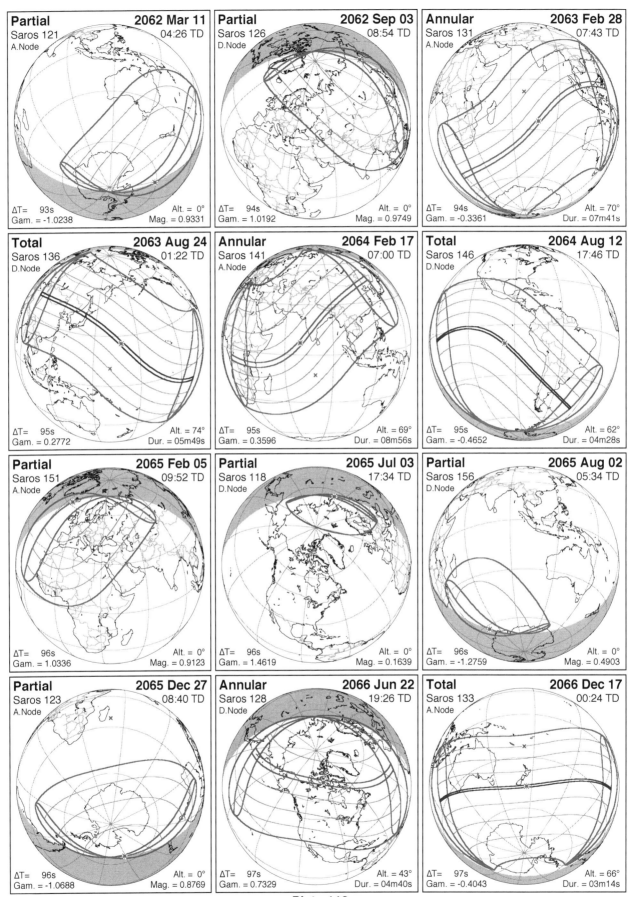

Partial **2062 Mar 11** Saros 121 04:26 TD A.Node ΔT= 93s Alt. = 0° Gam. = -1.0238 Mag. = 0.9331	**Partial** **2062 Sep 03** Saros 126 08:54 TD D.Node ΔT= 94s Alt. = 0° Gam. = 1.0192 Mag. = 0.9749	**Annular** **2063 Feb 28** Saros 131 07:43 TD A.Node ΔT= 94s Alt. = 70° Gam. = -0.3361 Dur. = 07m41s
Total **2063 Aug 24** Saros 136 01:22 TD D.Node ΔT= 95s Alt. = 74° Gam. = 0.2772 Dur. = 05m49s	**Annular** **2064 Feb 17** Saros 141 07:00 TD A.Node ΔT= 95s Alt. = 69° Gam. = 0.3596 Dur. = 08m56s	**Total** **2064 Aug 12** Saros 146 17:46 TD D.Node ΔT= 95s Alt. = 62° Gam. = -0.4652 Dur. = 04m28s
Partial **2065 Feb 05** Saros 151 09:52 TD A.Node ΔT= 96s Alt. = 0° Gam. = 1.0336 Mag. = 0.9123	**Partial** **2065 Jul 03** Saros 118 17:34 TD D.Node ΔT= 96s Alt. = 0° Gam. = 1.4619 Mag. = 0.1639	**Partial** **2065 Aug 02** Saros 156 05:34 TD D.Node ΔT= 96s Alt. = 0° Gam. = -1.2759 Mag. = 0.4903
Partial **2065 Dec 27** Saros 123 08:40 TD A.Node ΔT= 96s Alt. = 0° Gam. = -1.0688 Mag. = 0.8769	**Annular** **2066 Jun 22** Saros 128 19:26 TD D.Node ΔT= 97s Alt. = 43° Gam. = 0.7329 Dur. = 04m40s	**Total** **2066 Dec 17** Saros 133 00:24 TD A.Node ΔT= 97s Alt. = 66° Gam. = -0.4043 Dur. = 03m14s

Plate 112

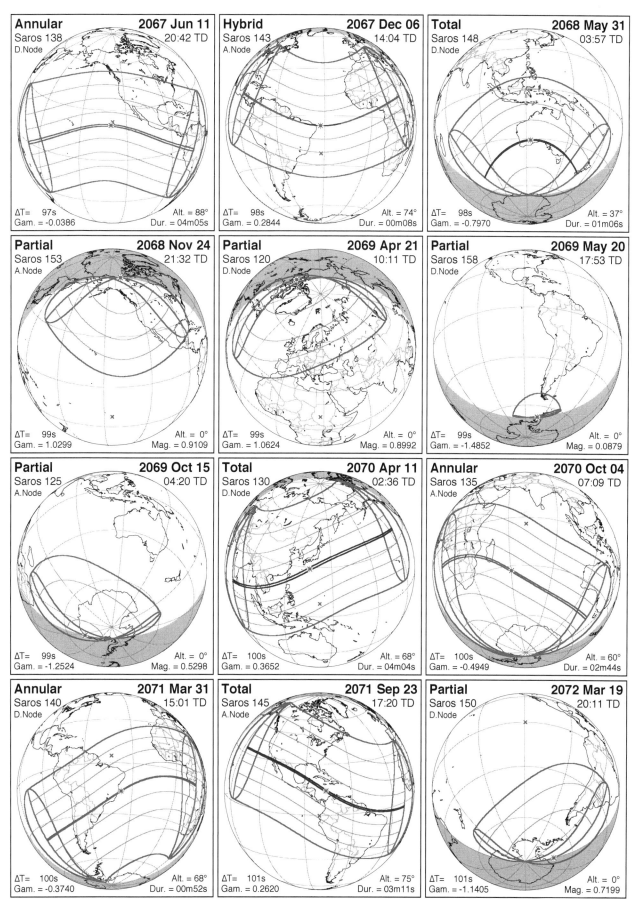

Annular 2067 Jun 11 Saros 138 20:42 TD D.Node ΔT= 97s Gam. = -0.0386 Alt. = 88° Dur. = 04m05s	**Hybrid** 2067 Dec 06 Saros 143 14:04 TD A.Node ΔT= 98s Gam. = 0.2844 Alt. = 74° Dur. = 00m08s	**Total** 2068 May 31 Saros 148 03:57 TD D.Node ΔT= 98s Gam. = -0.7970 Alt. = 37° Dur. = 01m06s
Partial 2068 Nov 24 Saros 153 21:32 TD A.Node ΔT= 99s Gam. = 1.0299 Alt. = 0° Mag. = 0.9109	**Partial** 2069 Apr 21 Saros 120 10:11 TD D.Node ΔT= 99s Gam. = 1.0624 Alt. = 0° Mag. = 0.8992	**Partial** 2069 May 20 Saros 158 17:53 TD D.Node ΔT= 99s Gam. = -1.4852 Alt. = 0° Mag. = 0.0879
Partial 2069 Oct 15 Saros 125 04:20 TD A.Node ΔT= 99s Gam. = -1.2524 Alt. = 0° Mag. = 0.5298	**Total** 2070 Apr 11 Saros 130 02:36 TD D.Node ΔT= 100s Gam. = 0.3652 Alt. = 68° Dur. = 04m04s	**Annular** 2070 Oct 04 Saros 135 07:09 TD A.Node ΔT= 100s Gam. = -0.4949 Alt. = 60° Dur. = 02m44s
Annular 2071 Mar 31 Saros 140 15:01 TD D.Node ΔT= 100s Gam. = -0.3740 Alt. = 68° Dur. = 00m52s	**Total** 2071 Sep 23 Saros 145 17:20 TD A.Node ΔT= 101s Gam. = 0.2620 Alt. = 75° Dur. = 03m11s	**Partial** 2072 Mar 19 Saros 150 20:11 TD D.Node ΔT= 101s Gam. = -1.1405 Alt. = 0° Mag. = 0.7199

Plate 113

207

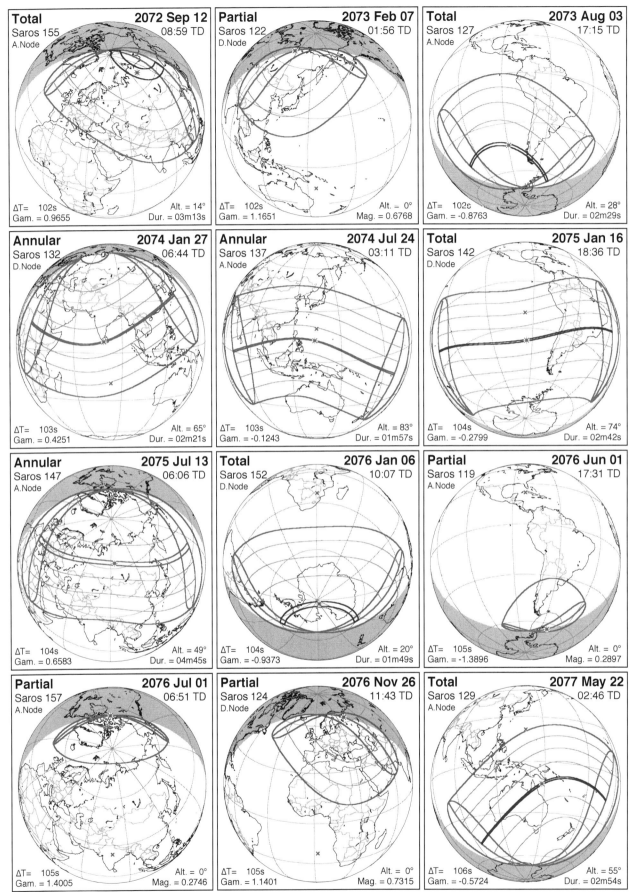

Total 2072 Sep 12	**Partial** 2073 Feb 07	**Total** 2073 Aug 03
Saros 155 08:59 TD	Saros 122 01:56 TD	Saros 127 17:15 TD
A.Node	D.Node	A.Node
ΔT= 102s Alt. = 14°	ΔT= 102s Alt. = 0°	ΔT= 102s Alt. = 28°
Gam. = 0.9655 Dur. = 03m13s	Gam. = 1.1651 Mag. = 0.6768	Gam. = -0.8763 Dur. = 02m29s
Annular 2074 Jan 27	**Annular** 2074 Jul 24	**Total** 2075 Jan 16
Saros 132 06:44 TD	Saros 137 03:11 TD	Saros 142 18:36 TD
D.Node	A.Node	D.Node
ΔT= 103s Alt. = 65°	ΔT= 103s Alt. = 83°	ΔT= 104s Alt. = 74°
Gam. = 0.4251 Dur. = 02m21s	Gam. = -0.1243 Dur. = 01m57s	Gam. = -0.2799 Dur. = 02m42s
Annular 2075 Jul 13	**Total** 2076 Jan 06	**Partial** 2076 Jun 01
Saros 147 06:06 TD	Saros 152 10:07 TD	Saros 119 17:31 TD
A.Node	D.Node	A.Node
ΔT= 104s Alt. = 49°	ΔT= 104s Alt. = 20°	ΔT= 105s Alt. = 0°
Gam. = 0.6583 Dur. = 04m45s	Gam. = -0.9373 Dur. = 01m49s	Gam. = -1.3896 Mag. = 0.2897
Partial 2076 Jul 01	**Partial** 2076 Nov 26	**Total** 2077 May 22
Saros 157 06:51 TD	Saros 124 11:43 TD	Saros 129 02:46 TD
A.Node	D.Node	A.Node
ΔT= 105s Alt. = 0°	ΔT= 105s Alt. = 0°	ΔT= 106s Alt. = 55°
Gam. = 1.4005 Mag. = 0.2746	Gam. = 1.1401 Mag. = 0.7315	Gam. = -0.5724 Dur. = 02m54s

Plate 114

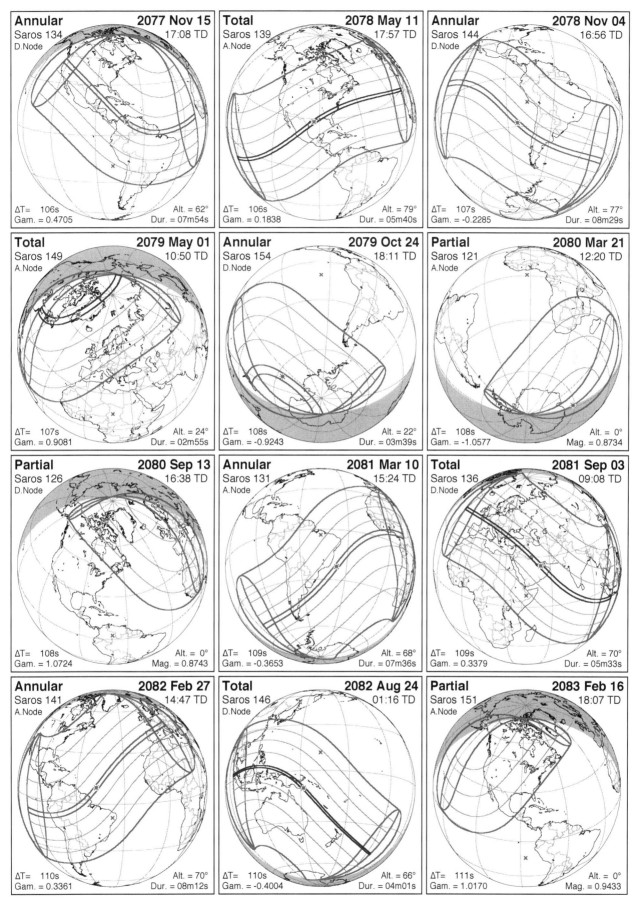

Annular 2077 Nov 15	
Saros 134 17:08 TD	
D.Node	
ΔT= 106s	Alt. = 62°
Gam. = 0.4705	Dur. = 07m54s

Total 2078 May 11	
Saros 139 17:57 TD	
A.Node	
ΔT= 106s	Alt. = 79°
Gam. = 0.1838	Dur. = 05m40s

Annular 2078 Nov 04	
Saros 144 16:56 TD	
D.Node	
ΔT= 107s	Alt. = 77°
Gam. = -0.2285	Dur. = 08m29s

Total 2079 May 01	
Saros 149 10:50 TD	
A.Node	
ΔT= 107s	Alt. = 24°
Gam. = 0.9081	Dur. = 02m55s

Annular 2079 Oct 24	
Saros 154 18:11 TD	
D.Node	
ΔT= 108s	Alt. = 22°
Gam. = -0.9243	Dur. = 03m39s

Partial 2080 Mar 21	
Saros 121 12:20 TD	
A.Node	
ΔT= 108s	Alt. = 0°
Gam. = -1.0577	Mag. = 0.8734

Partial 2080 Sep 13	
Saros 126 16:38 TD	
D.Node	
ΔT= 108s	Alt. = 0°
Gam. = 1.0724	Mag. = 0.8743

Annular 2081 Mar 10	
Saros 131 15:24 TD	
A.Node	
ΔT= 109s	Alt. = 68°
Gam. = -0.3653	Dur. = 07m36s

Total 2081 Sep 03	
Saros 136 09:08 TD	
D.Node	
ΔT= 109s	Alt. = 70°
Gam. = 0.3379	Dur. = 05m33s

Annular 2082 Feb 27	
Saros 141 14:47 TD	
A.Node	
ΔT= 110s	Alt. = 70°
Gam. = 0.3361	Dur. = 08m12s

Total 2082 Aug 24	
Saros 146 01:16 TD	
D.Node	
ΔT= 110s	Alt. = 66°
Gam. = -0.4004	Dur. = 04m01s

Partial 2083 Feb 16	
Saros 151 18:07 TD	
A.Node	
ΔT= 111s	Alt. = 0°
Gam. = 1.0170	Mag. = 0.9433

Plate 115

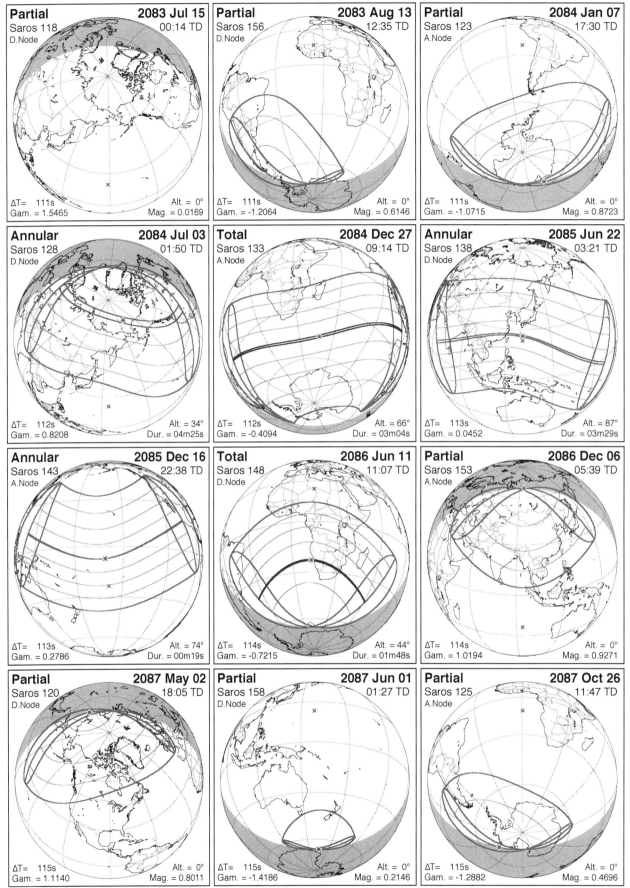

Partial	2083 Jul 15
Saros 118	00:14 TD
D.Node	
ΔT= 111s	Alt. = 0°
Gam. = 1.5465	Mag. = 0.0169

Partial	2083 Aug 13
Saros 156	12:35 TD
D.Node	
ΔT= 111s	Alt. = 0°
Gam. = -1.2064	Mag. = 0.6146

Partial	2084 Jan 07
Saros 123	17:30 TD
A.Node	
ΔT= 111s	Alt. = 0°
Gam. = -1.0715	Mag. = 0.8723

Annular	2084 Jul 03
Saros 128	01:50 TD
D.Node	
ΔT= 112s	Alt. = 34°
Gam. = 0.8208	Dur. = 04m25s

Total	2084 Dec 27
Saros 133	09:14 TD
A.Node	
ΔT= 112s	Alt. = 66°
Gam. = -0.4094	Dur. = 03m04s

Annular	2085 Jun 22
Saros 138	03:21 TD
D.Node	
ΔT= 113s	Alt. = 87°
Gam. = 0.0452	Dur. = 03m29s

Annular	2085 Dec 16
Saros 143	22:38 TD
A.Node	
ΔT= 113s	Alt. = 74°
Gam. = 0.2786	Dur. = 00m19s

Total	2086 Jun 11
Saros 148	11:07 TD
D.Node	
ΔT= 114s	Alt. = 44°
Gam. = -0.7215	Dur. = 01m48s

Partial	2086 Dec 06
Saros 153	05:39 TD
A.Node	
ΔT= 114s	Alt. = 0°
Gam. = 1.0194	Mag. = 0.9271

Partial	2087 May 02
Saros 120	18:05 TD
D.Node	
ΔT= 115s	Alt. = 0°
Gam. = 1.1140	Mag. = 0.8011

Partial	2087 Jun 01
Saros 158	01:27 TD
D.Node	
ΔT= 115s	Alt. = 0°
Gam. = -1.4186	Mag. = 0.2146

Partial	2087 Oct 26
Saros 125	11:47 TD
A.Node	
ΔT= 115s	Alt. = 0°
Gam. = -1.2882	Mag. = 0.4696

Plate 116

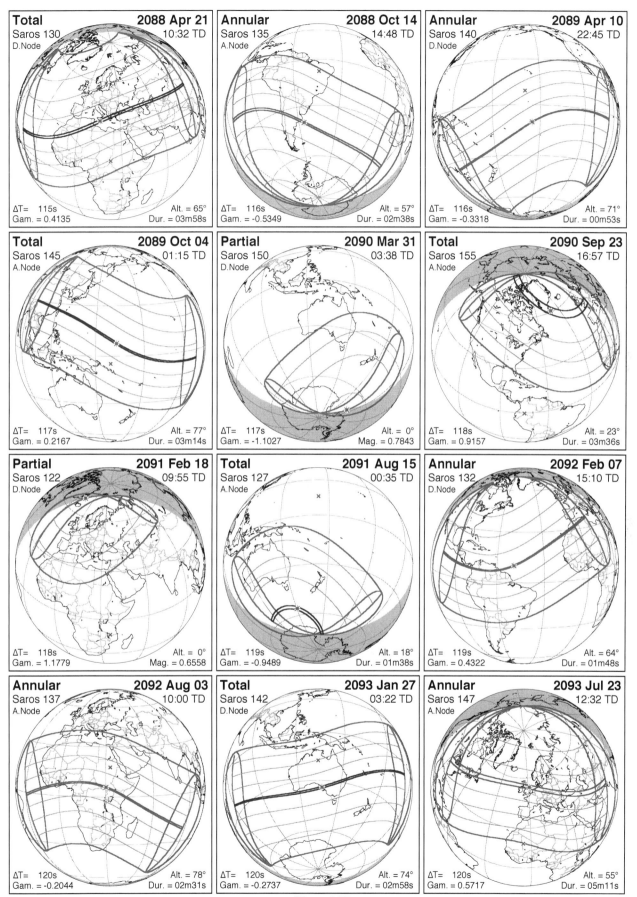

Total	2088 Apr 21
Saros 130	10:32 TD
D.Node	
ΔT= 115s	Alt. = 65°
Gam. = 0.4135	Dur. = 03m58s

Annular	2088 Oct 14
Saros 135	14:48 TD
A.Node	
ΔT= 116s	Alt. = 57°
Gam. = -0.5349	Dur. = 02m38s

Annular	2089 Apr 10
Saros 140	22:45 TD
D.Node	
ΔT= 116s	Alt. = 71°
Gam. = -0.3318	Dur. = 00m53s

Total	2089 Oct 04
Saros 145	01:15 TD
A.Node	
ΔT= 117s	Alt. = 77°
Gam. = 0.2167	Dur. = 03m14s

Partial	2090 Mar 31
Saros 150	03:38 TD
D.Node	
ΔT= 117s	Alt. = 0°
Gam. = -1.1027	Mag. = 0.7843

Total	2090 Sep 23
Saros 155	16:57 TD
A.Node	
ΔT= 118s	Alt. = 23°
Gam. = 0.9157	Dur. = 03m36s

Partial	2091 Feb 18
Saros 122	09:55 TD
D.Node	
ΔT= 118s	Alt. = 0°
Gam. = 1.1779	Mag. = 0.6558

Total	2091 Aug 15
Saros 127	00:35 TD
A.Node	
ΔT= 119s	Alt. = 18°
Gam. = -0.9489	Dur. = 01m38s

Annular	2092 Feb 07
Saros 132	15:10 TD
D.Node	
ΔT= 119s	Alt. = 64°
Gam. = 0.4322	Dur. = 01m48s

Annular	2092 Aug 03
Saros 137	10:00 TD
A.Node	
ΔT= 120s	Alt. = 78°
Gam. = -0.2044	Dur. = 02m31s

Total	2093 Jan 27
Saros 142	03:22 TD
D.Node	
ΔT= 120s	Alt. = 74°
Gam. = -0.2737	Dur. = 02m58s

Annular	2093 Jul 23
Saros 147	12:32 TD
A.Node	
ΔT= 120s	Alt. = 55°
Gam. = 0.5717	Dur. = 05m11s

Plate 117

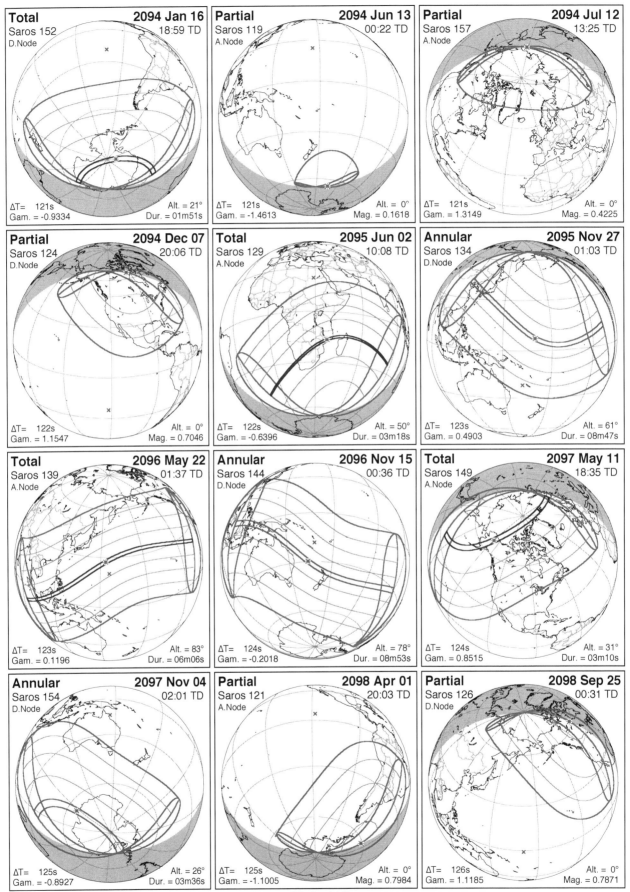

Total 2094 Jan 16	**Partial** 2094 Jun 13	**Partial** 2094 Jul 12
Saros 152 18:59 TD	Saros 119 00:22 TD	Saros 157 13:25 TD
D.Node	A.Node	A.Node
ΔT= 121s Alt. = 21°	ΔT= 121s Alt. = 0°	ΔT= 121s Alt. = 0°
Gam. = -0.9334 Dur. = 01m51s	Gam. = -1.4613 Mag. = 0.1618	Gam. = 1.3149 Mag. = 0.4225
Partial 2094 Dec 07	**Total** 2095 Jun 02	**Annular** 2095 Nov 27
Saros 124 20:06 TD	Saros 129 10:08 TD	Saros 134 01:03 TD
D.Node	A.Node	D.Node
ΔT= 122s Alt. = 0°	ΔT= 122s Alt. = 50°	ΔT= 123s Alt. = 61°
Gam. = 1.1547 Mag. = 0.7046	Gam. = -0.6396 Dur. = 03m18s	Gam. = 0.4903 Dur. = 08m47s
Total 2096 May 22	**Annular** 2096 Nov 15	**Total** 2097 May 11
Saros 139 01:37 TD	Saros 144 00:36 TD	Saros 149 18:35 TD
A.Node	D.Node	A.Node
ΔT= 123s Alt. = 83°	ΔT= 124s Alt. = 78°	ΔT= 124s Alt. = 31°
Gam. = 0.1196 Dur. = 06m06s	Gam. = -0.2018 Dur. = 08m53s	Gam. = 0.8515 Dur. = 03m10s
Annular 2097 Nov 04	**Partial** 2098 Apr 01	**Partial** 2098 Sep 25
Saros 154 02:01 TD	Saros 121 20:03 TD	Saros 126 00:31 TD
D.Node	A.Node	D.Node
ΔT= 125s Alt. = 26°	ΔT= 125s Alt. = 0°	ΔT= 126s Alt. = 0°
Gam. = -0.8927 Dur. = 03m36s	Gam. = -1.1005 Mag. = 0.7984	Gam. = 1.1185 Mag. = 0.7871

Plate 118

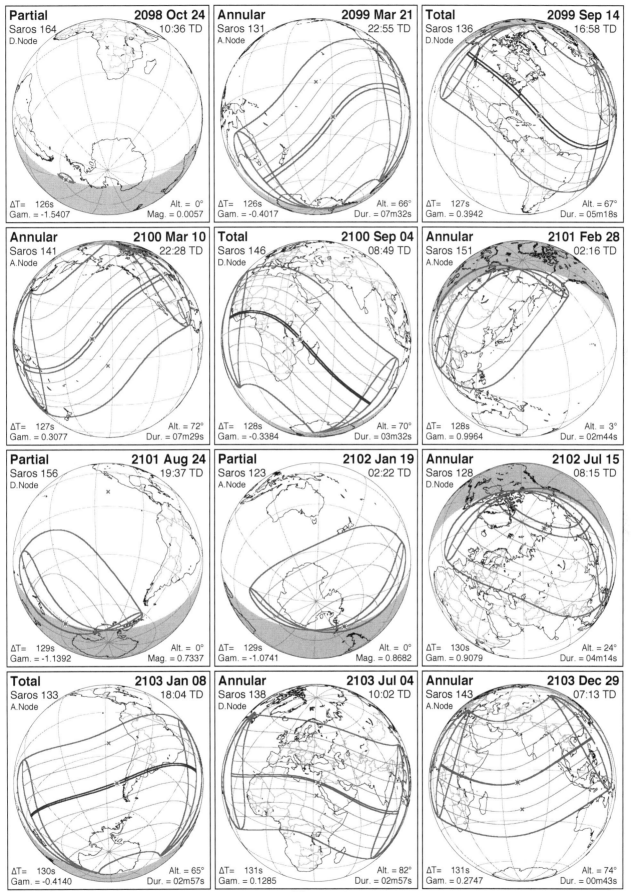

Partial	2098 Oct 24
Saros 164	10:36 TD
D.Node	
ΔT= 126s	Alt. = 0°
Gam. = -1.5407	Mag. = 0.0057

Annular	2099 Mar 21
Saros 131	22:55 TD
A.Node	
ΔT= 126s	Alt. = 66°
Gam. = -0.4017	Dur. = 07m32s

Total	2099 Sep 14
Saros 136	16:58 TD
D.Node	
ΔT= 127s	Alt. = 67°
Gam. = 0.3942	Dur. = 05m18s

Annular	2100 Mar 10
Saros 141	22:28 TD
A.Node	
ΔT= 127s	Alt. = 72°
Gam. = 0.3077	Dur. = 07m29s

Total	2100 Sep 04
Saros 146	08:49 TD
D.Node	
ΔT= 128s	Alt. = 70°
Gam. = -0.3384	Dur. = 03m32s

Annular	2101 Feb 28
Saros 151	02:16 TD
A.Node	
ΔT= 128s	Alt. = 3°
Gam. = 0.9964	Dur. = 02m44s

Partial	2101 Aug 24
Saros 156	19:37 TD
D.Node	
ΔT= 129s	Alt. = 0°
Gam. = -1.1392	Mag. = 0.7337

Partial	2102 Jan 19
Saros 123	02:22 TD
A.Node	
ΔT= 129s	Alt. = 0°
Gam. = -1.0741	Mag. = 0.8682

Annular	2102 Jul 15
Saros 128	08:15 TD
D.Node	
ΔT= 130s	Alt. = 24°
Gam. = 0.9079	Dur. = 04m14s

Total	2103 Jan 08
Saros 133	18:04 TD
A.Node	
ΔT= 130s	Alt. = 65°
Gam. = -0.4140	Dur. = 02m57s

Annular	2103 Jul 04
Saros 138	10:02 TD
D.Node	
ΔT= 131s	Alt. = 82°
Gam. = 0.1285	Dur. = 02m57s

Annular	2103 Dec 29
Saros 143	07:13 TD
A.Node	
ΔT= 131s	Alt. = 74°
Gam. = 0.2747	Dur. = 00m43s

Plate 119

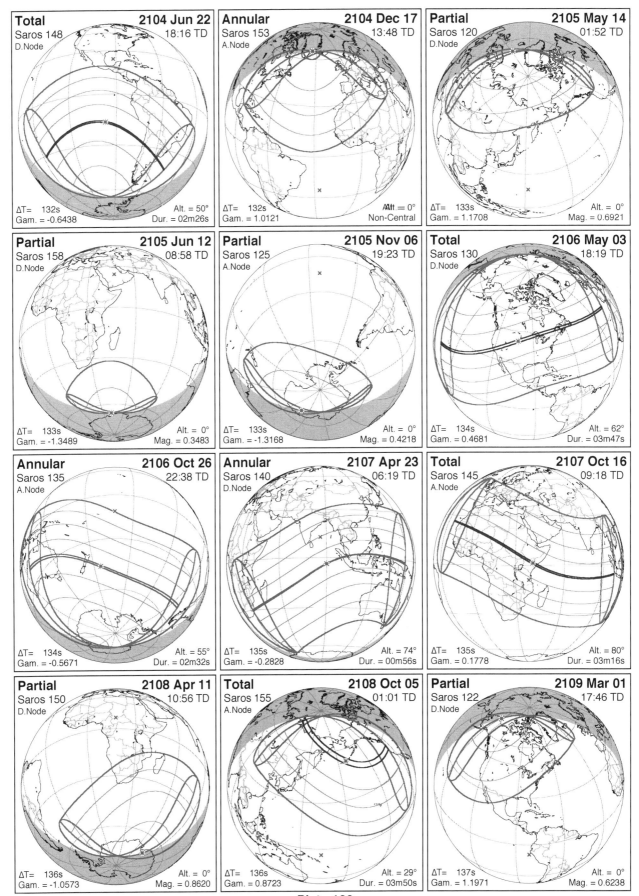

Total 2104 Jun 22	
Saros 148 18:16 TD	
D.Node	
ΔT= 132s Alt. = 50°	
Gam. = -0.6438 Dur. = 02m26s	

Annular 2104 Dec 17
Saros 153 13:48 TD
A.Node
ΔT= 132s Alt. = 0°
Gam. = 1.0121 Non-Central

Partial 2105 May 14
Saros 120 01:52 TD
D.Node
ΔT= 133s Alt. = 0°
Gam. = 1.1708 Mag. = 0.6921

Partial 2105 Jun 12
Saros 158 08:58 TD
D.Node
ΔT= 133s Alt. = 0°
Gam. = -1.3489 Mag. = 0.3483

Partial 2105 Nov 06
Saros 125 19:23 TD
A.Node
ΔT= 133s Alt. = 0°
Gam. = -1.3168 Mag. = 0.4218

Total 2106 May 03
Saros 130 18:19 TD
D.Node
ΔT= 134s Alt. = 62°
Gam. = 0.4681 Dur. = 03m47s

Annular 2106 Oct 26
Saros 135 22:38 TD
A.Node
ΔT= 134s Alt. = 55°
Gam. = -0.5671 Dur. = 02m32s

Annular 2107 Apr 23
Saros 140 06:19 TD
D.Node
ΔT= 135s Alt. = 74°
Gam. = -0.2828 Dur. = 00m56s

Total 2107 Oct 16
Saros 145 09:18 TD
A.Node
ΔT= 135s Alt. = 80°
Gam. = 0.1778 Dur. = 03m16s

Partial 2108 Apr 11
Saros 150 10:56 TD
D.Node
ΔT= 136s Alt. = 0°
Gam. = -1.0573 Mag. = 0.8620

Total 2108 Oct 05
Saros 155 01:01 TD
A.Node
ΔT= 136s Alt. = 29°
Gam. = 0.8723 Dur. = 03m50s

Partial 2109 Mar 01
Saros 122 17:46 TD
D.Node
ΔT= 137s Alt. = 0°
Gam. = 1.1971 Mag. = 0.6238

Plate 120

214

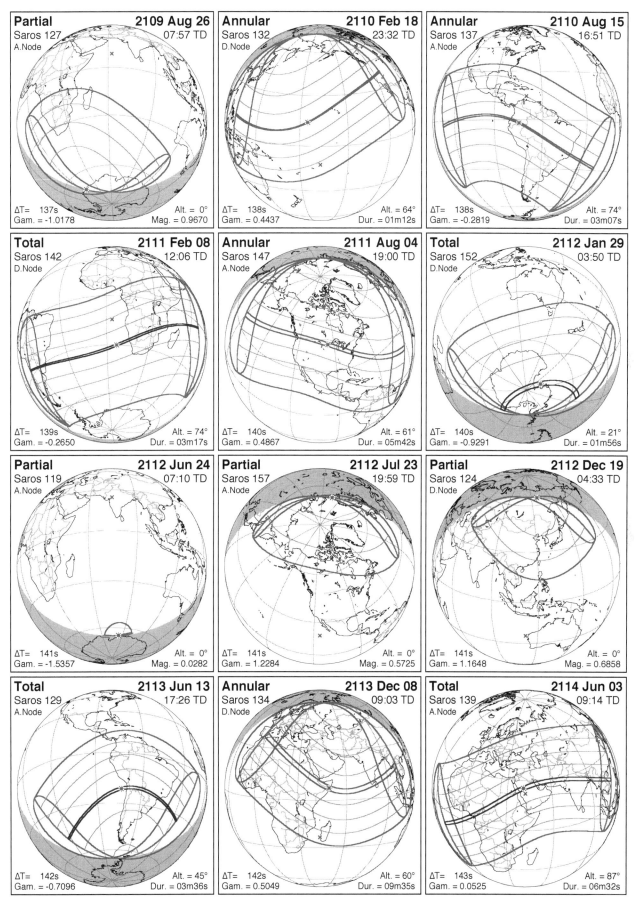

Partial	2109 Aug 26
Saros 127	07:57 TD
A.Node	
ΔT= 137s	Alt. = 0°
Gam. = -1.0178	Mag. = 0.9670

Annular	2110 Feb 18
Saros 132	23:32 TD
D.Node	
ΔT= 138s	Alt. = 64°
Gam. = 0.4437	Dur. = 01m12s

Annular	2110 Aug 15
Saros 137	16:51 TD
A.Node	
ΔT= 138s	Alt. = 74°
Gam. = -0.2819	Dur. = 03m07s

Total	2111 Feb 08
Saros 142	12:06 TD
D.Node	
ΔT= 139s	Alt. = 74°
Gam. = -0.2650	Dur. = 03m17s

Annular	2111 Aug 04
Saros 147	19:00 TD
A.Node	
ΔT= 140s	Alt. = 61°
Gam. = 0.4867	Dur. = 05m42s

Total	2112 Jan 29
Saros 152	03:50 TD
D.Node	
ΔT= 140s	Alt. = 21°
Gam. = -0.9291	Dur. = 01m56s

Partial	2112 Jun 24
Saros 119	07:10 TD
A.Node	
ΔT= 141s	Alt. = 0°
Gam. = -1.5357	Mag. = 0.0282

Partial	2112 Jul 23
Saros 157	19:59 TD
A.Node	
ΔT= 141s	Alt. = 0°
Gam. = 1.2284	Mag. = 0.5725

Partial	2112 Dec 19
Saros 124	04:33 TD
D.Node	
ΔT= 141s	Alt. = 0°
Gam. = 1.1648	Mag. = 0.6858

Total	2113 Jun 13
Saros 129	17:26 TD
A.Node	
ΔT= 142s	Alt. = 45°
Gam. = -0.7096	Dur. = 03m36s

Annular	2113 Dec 08
Saros 134	09:03 TD
D.Node	
ΔT= 142s	Alt. = 60°
Gam. = 0.5049	Dur. = 09m35s

Total	2114 Jun 03
Saros 139	09:14 TD
A.Node	
ΔT= 143s	Alt. = 87°
Gam. = 0.0525	Dur. = 06m32s

Plate 121

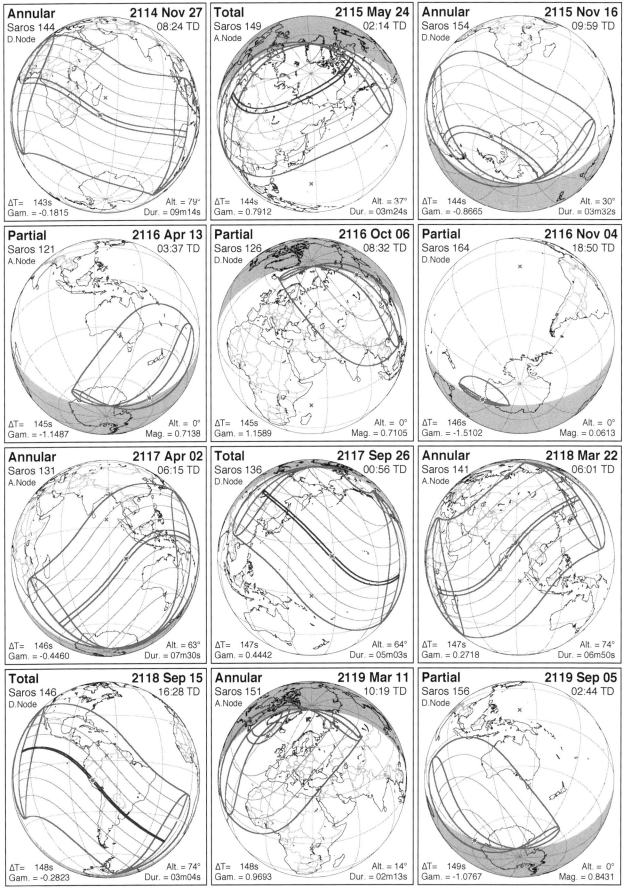

Annular   **2114 Nov 27**
Saros 144   08:24 TD
D.Node
ΔT= 143s   Alt. = 79°
Gam. = -0.1815   Dur. = 09m14s

Total   **2115 May 24**
Saros 149   02:14 TD
A.Node
ΔT= 144s   Alt. = 37°
Gam. = 0.7912   Dur. = 03m24s

Annular   **2115 Nov 16**
Saros 154   09:59 TD
D.Node
ΔT= 144s   Alt. = 30°
Gam. = -0.8665   Dur. = 03m32s

Partial   **2116 Apr 13**
Saros 121   03:37 TD
A.Node
ΔT= 145s   Alt. = 0°
Gam. = -1.1487   Mag. = 0.7138

Partial   **2116 Oct 06**
Saros 126   08:32 TD
D.Node
ΔT= 145s   Alt. = 0°
Gam. = 1.1589   Mag. = 0.7105

Partial   **2116 Nov 04**
Saros 164   18:50 TD
D.Node
ΔT= 146s   Alt. = 0°
Gam. = -1.5102   Mag. = 0.0613

Annular   **2117 Apr 02**
Saros 131   06:15 TD
A.Node
ΔT= 146s   Alt. = 63°
Gam. = -0.4460   Dur. = 07m30s

Total   **2117 Sep 26**
Saros 136   00:56 TD
D.Node
ΔT= 147s   Alt. = 64°
Gam. = 0.4442   Dur. = 05m03s

Annular   **2118 Mar 22**
Saros 141   06:01 TD
A.Node
ΔT= 147s   Alt. = 74°
Gam. = 0.2718   Dur. = 06m50s

Total   **2118 Sep 15**
Saros 146   16:28 TD
D.Node
ΔT= 148s   Alt. = 74°
Gam. = -0.2823   Dur. = 03m04s

Annular   **2119 Mar 11**
Saros 151   10:19 TD
A.Node
ΔT= 148s   Alt. = 14°
Gam. = 0.9693   Dur. = 02m13s

Partial   **2119 Sep 05**
Saros 156   02:44 TD
D.Node
ΔT= 149s   Alt. = 0°
Gam. = -1.0767   Mag. = 0.8431

Plate 122

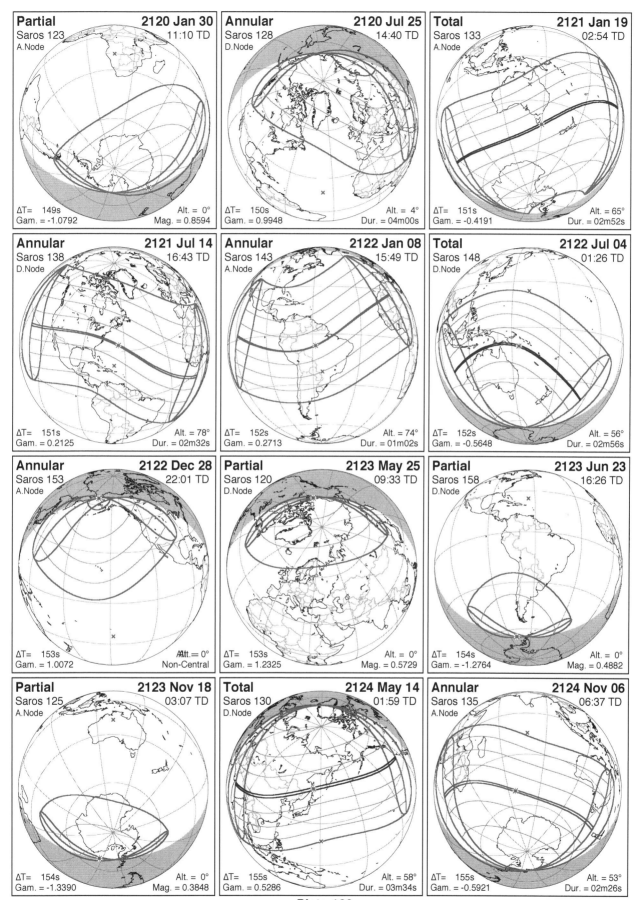

Partial 2120 Jan 30 Saros 123 11:10 TD A.Node ΔT= 149s Alt. = 0° Gam. = -1.0792 Mag. = 0.8594	**Annular** 2120 Jul 25 Saros 128 14:40 TD D.Node ΔT= 150s Alt. = 4° Gam. = 0.9948 Dur. = 04m00s	**Total** 2121 Jan 19 Saros 133 02:54 TD A.Node ΔT= 151s Alt. = 65° Gam. = -0.4191 Dur. = 02m52s
Annular 2121 Jul 14 Saros 138 16:43 TD D.Node ΔT= 151s Alt. = 78° Gam. = 0.2125 Dur. = 02m32s	**Annular** 2122 Jan 08 Saros 143 15:49 TD A.Node ΔT= 152s Alt. = 74° Gam. = 0.2713 Dur. = 01m02s	**Total** 2122 Jul 04 Saros 148 01:26 TD D.Node ΔT= 152s Alt. = 56° Gam. = -0.5648 Dur. = 02m56s
Annular 2122 Dec 28 Saros 153 22:01 TD A.Node ΔT= 153s Alt. = 0° Gam. = 1.0072 Non-Central	**Partial** 2123 May 25 Saros 120 09:33 TD D.Node ΔT= 153s Alt. = 0° Gam. = 1.2325 Mag. = 0.5729	**Partial** 2123 Jun 23 Saros 158 16:26 TD D.Node ΔT= 154s Alt. = 0° Gam. = -1.2764 Mag. = 0.4882
Partial 2123 Nov 18 Saros 125 03:07 TD A.Node ΔT= 154s Alt. = 0° Gam. = -1.3390 Mag. = 0.3848	**Total** 2124 May 14 Saros 130 01:59 TD D.Node ΔT= 155s Alt. = 58° Gam. = 0.5286 Dur. = 03m34s	**Annular** 2124 Nov 06 Saros 135 06:37 TD A.Node ΔT= 155s Alt. = 53° Gam. = -0.5921 Dur. = 02m26s

Plate 123

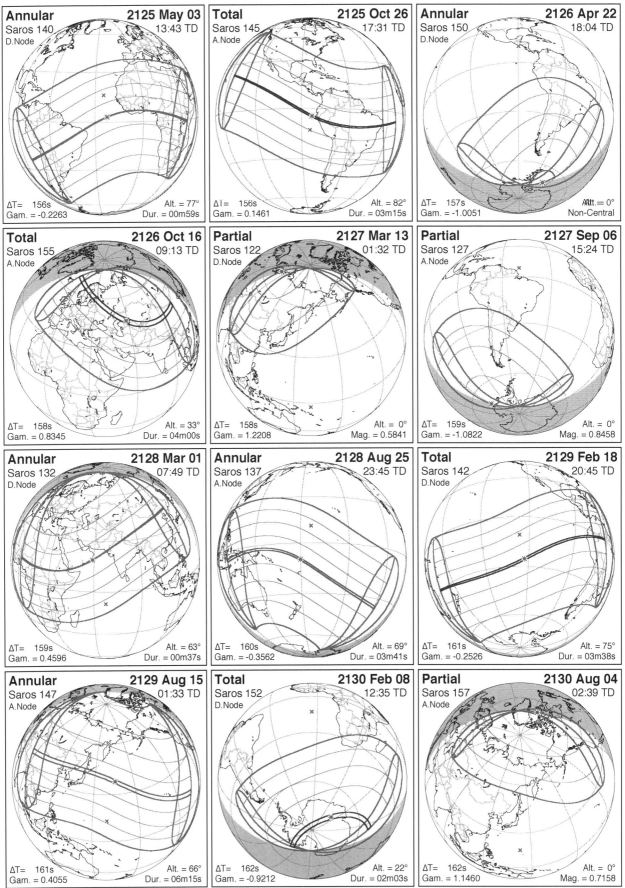

Annular 2125 May 03	**Total** 2125 Oct 26	**Annular** 2126 Apr 22
Saros 140 13:43 TD	Saros 145 17:31 TD	Saros 150 18:04 TD
D.Node	A.Node	D.Node
ΔT= 156s Alt.= 77°	ΔT= 156s Alt.= 82°	ΔT= 157s Alt.= 0°
Gam. = -0.2263 Dur. = 00m59s	Gam. = 0.1461 Dur. = 03m15s	Gam. = -1.0051 Non-Central
Total 2126 Oct 16	**Partial** 2127 Mar 13	**Partial** 2127 Sep 06
Saros 155 09:13 TD	Saros 122 01:32 TD	Saros 127 15:24 TD
A.Node	D.Node	A.Node
ΔT= 158s Alt. = 33°	ΔT= 158s Alt. = 0°	ΔT= 159s Alt. = 0°
Gam. = 0.8345 Dur. = 04m00s	Gam. = 1.2208 Mag. = 0.5841	Gam. = -1.0822 Mag. = 0.8458
Annular 2128 Mar 01	**Annular** 2128 Aug 25	**Total** 2129 Feb 18
Saros 132 07:49 TD	Saros 137 23:45 TD	Saros 142 20:45 TD
D.Node	A.Node	D.Node
ΔT= 159s Alt. = 63°	ΔT= 160s Alt. = 69°	ΔT= 161s Alt. = 75°
Gam. = 0.4596 Dur. = 00m37s	Gam. = -0.3562 Dur. = 03m41s	Gam. = -0.2526 Dur. = 03m38s
Annular 2129 Aug 15	**Total** 2130 Feb 08	**Partial** 2130 Aug 04
Saros 147 01:33 TD	Saros 152 12:35 TD	Saros 157 02:39 TD
A.Node	D.Node	A.Node
ΔT= 161s Alt. = 66°	ΔT= 162s Alt. = 22°	ΔT= 162s Alt. = 0°
Gam. = 0.4055 Dur. = 06m15s	Gam. = -0.9212 Dur. = 02m03s	Gam. = 1.1460 Mag. = 0.7158

Plate 124

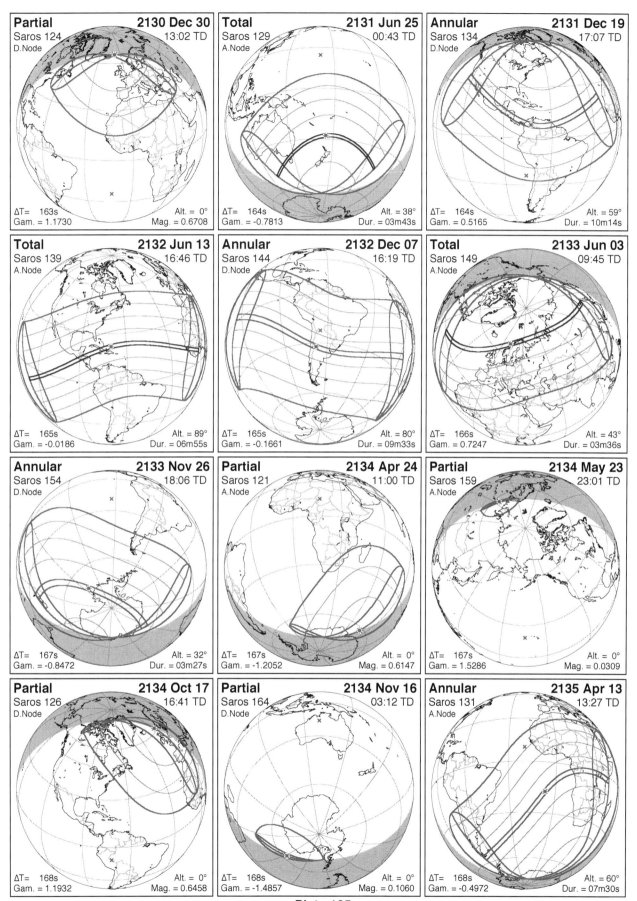

Partial   **2130 Dec 30**
Saros 124   13:02 TD
D.Node
ΔT= 163s   Alt. = 0°
Gam. = 1.1730   Mag. = 0.6708

Total   **2131 Jun 25**
Saros 129   00:43 TD
A.Node
ΔT= 164s   Alt. = 38°
Gam. = -0.7813   Dur. = 03m43s

Annular   **2131 Dec 19**
Saros 134   17:07 TD
D.Node
ΔT= 164s   Alt. = 59°
Gam. = 0.5165   Dur. = 10m14s

Total   **2132 Jun 13**
Saros 139   16:46 TD
A.Node
ΔT= 165s   Alt. = 89°
Gam. = -0.0186   Dur. = 06m55s

Annular   **2132 Dec 07**
Saros 144   16:19 TD
D.Node
ΔT= 165s   Alt. = 80°
Gam. = -0.1661   Dur. = 09m33s

Total   **2133 Jun 03**
Saros 149   09:45 TD
A.Node
ΔT= 166s   Alt. = 43°
Gam. = 0.7247   Dur. = 03m36s

Annular   **2133 Nov 26**
Saros 154   18:06 TD
D.Node
ΔT= 167s   Alt. = 32°
Gam. = -0.8472   Dur. = 03m27s

Partial   **2134 Apr 24**
Saros 121   11:00 TD
A.Node
ΔT= 167s   Alt. = 0°
Gam. = -1.2052   Mag. = 0.6147

Partial   **2134 May 23**
Saros 159   23:01 TD
A.Node
ΔT= 167s   Alt. = 0°
Gam. = 1.5286   Mag. = 0.0309

Partial   **2134 Oct 17**
Saros 126   16:41 TD
D.Node
ΔT= 168s   Alt. = 0°
Gam. = 1.1932   Mag. = 0.6458

Partial   **2134 Nov 16**
Saros 164   03:12 TD
D.Node
ΔT= 168s   Alt. = 0°
Gam. = -1.4857   Mag. = 0.1060

Annular   **2135 Apr 13**
Saros 131   13:27 TD
A.Node
ΔT= 168s   Alt. = 60°
Gam. = -0.4972   Dur. = 07m30s

Plate 125

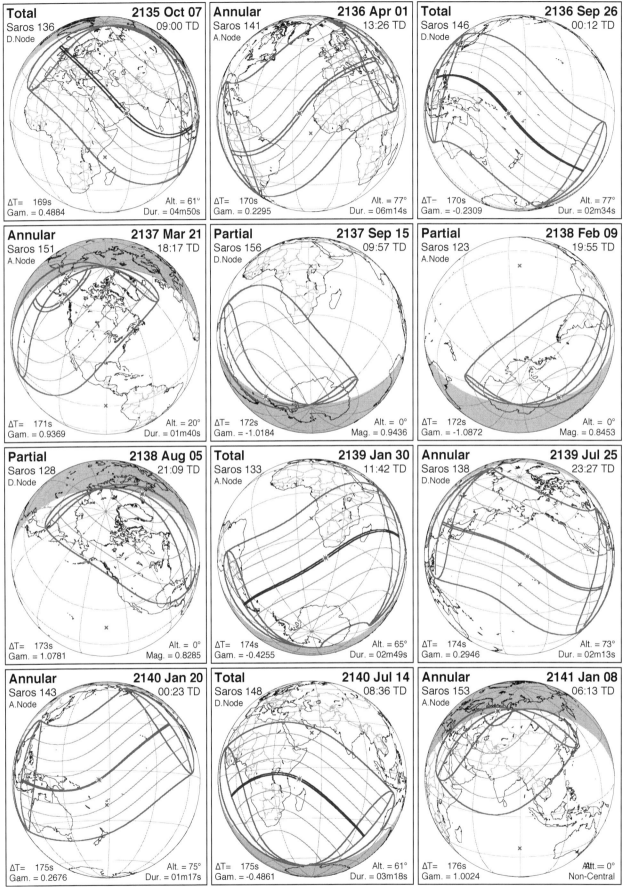

Total 2135 Oct 07 Saros 136 09:00 TD D.Node ΔT= 169s Alt. = 61° Gam. = 0.4884 Dur. = 04m50s	**Annular** 2136 Apr 01 Saros 141 13:26 TD A.Node ΔT= 170s Alt. = 77° Gam. = 0.2295 Dur. = 06m14s	**Total** 2136 Sep 26 Saros 146 00:12 TD D.Node ΔT− 170s Alt. = 77° Gam. = -0.2309 Dur. = 02m34s
Annular 2137 Mar 21 Saros 151 18:17 TD A.Node ΔT= 171s Alt. = 20° Gam. = 0.9369 Dur. = 01m40s	**Partial** 2137 Sep 15 Saros 156 09:57 TD D.Node ΔT= 172s Alt. = 0° Gam. = -1.0184 Mag. = 0.9436	**Partial** 2138 Feb 09 Saros 123 19:55 TD A.Node ΔT= 172s Alt. = 0° Gam. = -1.0872 Mag. = 0.8453
Partial 2138 Aug 05 Saros 128 21:09 TD D.Node ΔT= 173s Alt. = 0° Gam. = 1.0781 Mag. = 0.8285	**Total** 2139 Jan 30 Saros 133 11:42 TD A.Node ΔT= 174s Alt. = 65° Gam. = -0.4255 Dur. = 02m49s	**Annular** 2139 Jul 25 Saros 138 23:27 TD D.Node ΔT= 174s Alt. = 73° Gam. = 0.2946 Dur. = 02m13s
Annular 2140 Jan 20 Saros 143 00:23 TD A.Node ΔT= 175s Alt. = 75° Gam. = 0.2676 Dur. = 01m17s	**Total** 2140 Jul 14 Saros 148 08:36 TD D.Node ΔT= 175s Alt. = 61° Gam. = -0.4861 Dur. = 03m18s	**Annular** 2141 Jan 08 Saros 153 06:13 TD A.Node ΔT= 176s Alt. = 0° Gam. = 1.0024 Non-Central

Plate 126

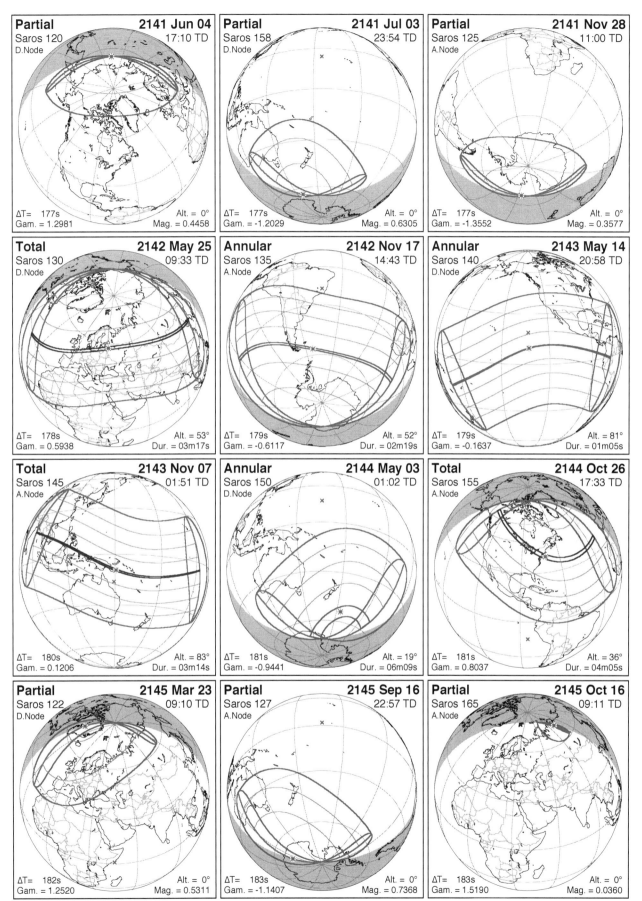

Partial	2141 Jun 04
Saros 120	17:10 TD
D.Node	
ΔT= 177s	Alt. = 0°
Gam. = 1.2981	Mag. = 0.4458

Partial	2141 Jul 03
Saros 158	23:54 TD
D.Node	
ΔT= 177s	Alt. = 0°
Gam. = -1.2029	Mag. = 0.6305

Partial	2141 Nov 28
Saros 125	11:00 TD
A.Node	
ΔT= 177s	Alt. = 0°
Gam. = -1.3552	Mag. = 0.3577

Total	2142 May 25
Saros 130	09:33 TD
D.Node	
ΔT= 178s	Alt. = 53°
Gam. = 0.5938	Dur. = 03m17s

Annular	2142 Nov 17
Saros 135	14:43 TD
A.Node	
ΔT= 179s	Alt. = 52°
Gam. = -0.6117	Dur. = 02m19s

Annular	2143 May 14
Saros 140	20:58 TD
D.Node	
ΔT= 179s	Alt. = 81°
Gam. = -0.1637	Dur. = 01m05s

Total	2143 Nov 07
Saros 145	01:51 TD
A.Node	
ΔT= 180s	Alt. = 83°
Gam. = 0.1206	Dur. = 03m14s

Annular	2144 May 03
Saros 150	01:02 TD
D.Node	
ΔT= 181s	Alt. = 19°
Gam. = -0.9441	Dur. = 06m09s

Total	2144 Oct 26
Saros 155	17:33 TD
A.Node	
ΔT= 181s	Alt. = 36°
Gam. = 0.8037	Dur. = 04m05s

Partial	2145 Mar 23
Saros 122	09:10 TD
D.Node	
ΔT= 182s	Alt. = 0°
Gam. = 1.2520	Mag. = 0.5311

Partial	2145 Sep 16
Saros 127	22:57 TD
A.Node	
ΔT= 183s	Alt. = 0°
Gam. = -1.1407	Mag. = 0.7368

Partial	2145 Oct 16
Saros 165	09:11 TD
A.Node	
ΔT= 183s	Alt. = 0°
Gam. = 1.5190	Mag. = 0.0360

Plate 127

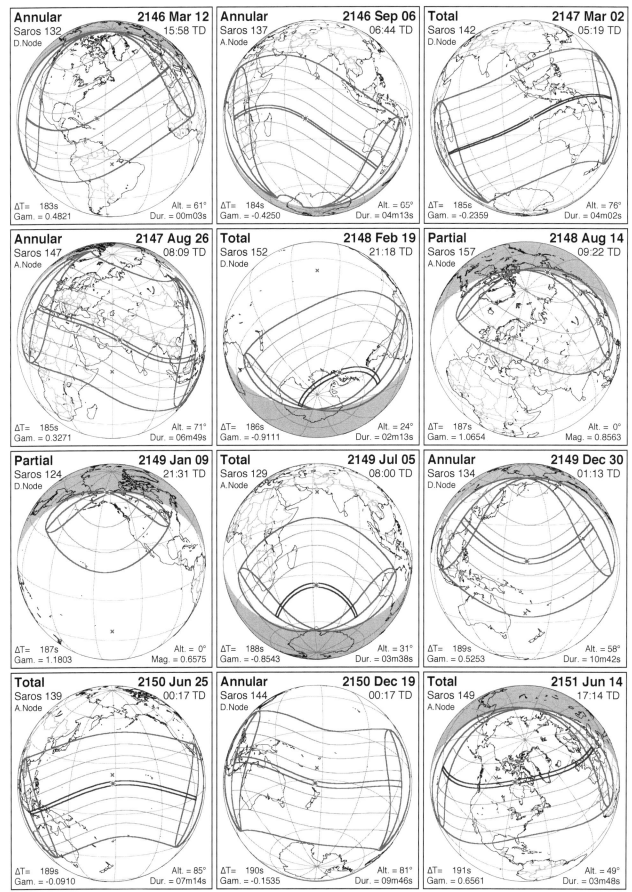

Annular	**2146 Mar 12**
Saros 132	15:58 TD
D.Node	
ΔT= 183s	Alt. = 61°
Gam. = 0.4821	Dur. = 00m03s

Annular	**2146 Sep 06**
Saros 137	06:44 TD
A.Node	
ΔT= 184s	Alt. = 65°
Gam. = -0.4250	Dur. = 04m13s

Total	**2147 Mar 02**
Saros 142	05:19 TD
D.Node	
ΔT= 185s	Alt. = 76°
Gam. = -0.2359	Dur. = 04m02s

Annular	**2147 Aug 26**
Saros 147	08:09 TD
A.Node	
ΔT= 185s	Alt. = 71°
Gam. = 0.3271	Dur. = 06m49s

Total	**2148 Feb 19**
Saros 152	21:18 TD
D.Node	
ΔT= 186s	Alt. = 24°
Gam. = -0.9111	Dur. = 02m13s

Partial	**2148 Aug 14**
Saros 157	09:22 TD
A.Node	
ΔT= 187s	Alt. = 0°
Gam. = 1.0654	Mag. = 0.8563

Partial	**2149 Jan 09**
Saros 124	21:31 TD
D.Node	
ΔT= 187s	Alt. = 0°
Gam. = 1.1803	Mag. = 0.6575

Total	**2149 Jul 05**
Saros 129	08:00 TD
A.Node	
ΔT= 188s	Alt. = 31°
Gam. = -0.8543	Dur. = 03m38s

Annular	**2149 Dec 30**
Saros 134	01:13 TD
D.Node	
ΔT= 189s	Alt. = 58°
Gam. = 0.5253	Dur. = 10m42s

Total	**2150 Jun 25**
Saros 139	00:17 TD
A.Node	
ΔT= 189s	Alt. = 85°
Gam. = -0.0910	Dur. = 07m14s

Annular	**2150 Dec 19**
Saros 144	00:17 TD
D.Node	
ΔT= 190s	Alt. = 81°
Gam. = -0.1535	Dur. = 09m46s

Total	**2151 Jun 14**
Saros 149	17:14 TD
A.Node	
ΔT= 191s	Alt. = 49°
Gam. = 0.6561	Dur. = 03m48s

Plate 128

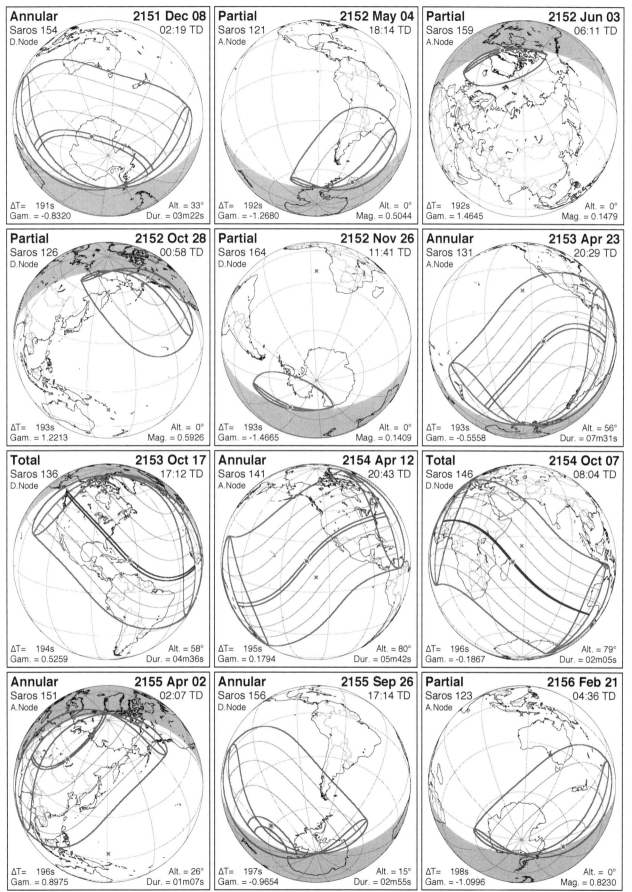

Annular	2151 Dec 08
Saros 154	02:19 TD
D.Node	
ΔT= 191s	Alt. = 33°
Gam. = -0.8320	Dur. = 03m22s

Partial	2152 May 04
Saros 121	18:14 TD
A.Node	
ΔT= 192s	Alt. = 0°
Gam. = -1.2680	Mag. = 0.5044

Partial	2152 Jun 03
Saros 159	06:11 TD
A.Node	
ΔT= 192s	Alt. = 0°
Gam. = 1.4645	Mag. = 0.1479

Partial	2152 Oct 28
Saros 126	00:58 TD
D.Node	
ΔT= 193s	Alt. = 0°
Gam. = 1.2213	Mag. = 0.5926

Partial	2152 Nov 26
Saros 164	11:41 TD
D.Node	
ΔT= 193s	Alt. = 0°
Gam. = -1.4665	Mag. = 0.1409

Annular	2153 Apr 23
Saros 131	20:29 TD
A.Node	
ΔT= 193s	Alt. = 56°
Gam. = -0.5558	Dur. = 07m31s

Total	2153 Oct 17
Saros 136	17:12 TD
D.Node	
ΔT= 194s	Alt. = 58°
Gam. = 0.5259	Dur. = 04m36s

Annular	2154 Apr 12
Saros 141	20:43 TD
A.Node	
ΔT= 195s	Alt. = 80°
Gam. = 0.1794	Dur. = 05m42s

Total	2154 Oct 07
Saros 146	08:04 TD
D.Node	
ΔT= 196s	Alt. = 79°
Gam. = -0.1867	Dur. = 02m05s

Annular	2155 Apr 02
Saros 151	02:07 TD
A.Node	
ΔT= 196s	Alt. = 26°
Gam. = 0.8975	Dur. = 01m07s

Annular	2155 Sep 26
Saros 156	17:14 TD
D.Node	
ΔT= 197s	Alt. = 15°
Gam. = -0.9654	Dur. = 02m55s

Partial	2156 Feb 21
Saros 123	04:36 TD
A.Node	
ΔT= 198s	Alt. = 0°
Gam. = -1.0996	Mag. = 0.8230

Plate 129

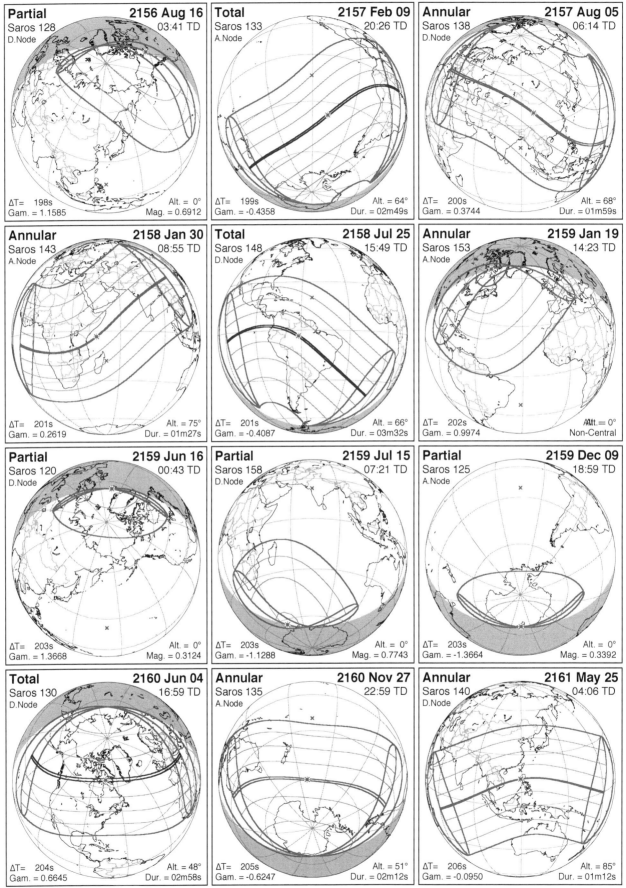

Partial   **2156 Aug 16**
Saros 128   03:41 TD
D.Node
ΔT= 198s   Alt. = 0°
Gam. = 1.1585   Mag. = 0.6912

Total   **2157 Feb 09**
Saros 133   20:26 TD
A.Node
ΔT= 199s   Alt. = 64°
Gam. = -0.4358   Dur. = 02m49s

Annular   **2157 Aug 05**
Saros 138   06:14 TD
D.Node
ΔT= 200s   Alt. = 68°
Gam. = 0.3744   Dur. = 01m59s

Annular   **2158 Jan 30**
Saros 143   08:55 TD
A.Node
ΔT= 201s   Alt. = 75°
Gam. = 0.2619   Dur. = 01m27s

Total   **2158 Jul 25**
Saros 148   15:49 TD
D.Node
ΔT= 201s   Alt. = 66°
Gam. = -0.4087   Dur. = 03m32s

Annular   **2159 Jan 19**
Saros 153   14:23 TD
A.Node
ΔT= 202s   Alt. = 0°
Gam. = 0.9974   Non-Central

Partial   **2159 Jun 16**
Saros 120   00:43 TD
D.Node
ΔT= 203s   Alt. = 0°
Gam. = 1.3668   Mag. = 0.3124

Partial   **2159 Jul 15**
Saros 158   07:21 TD
D.Node
ΔT= 203s   Alt. = 0°
Gam. = -1.1288   Mag. = 0.7743

Partial   **2159 Dec 09**
Saros 125   18:59 TD
A.Node
ΔT= 203s   Alt. = 0°
Gam. = -1.3664   Mag. = 0.3392

Total   **2160 Jun 04**
Saros 130   16:59 TD
D.Node
ΔT= 204s   Alt. = 48°
Gam. = 0.6645   Dur. = 02m58s

Annular   **2160 Nov 27**
Saros 135   22:59 TD
A.Node
ΔT= 205s   Alt. = 51°
Gam. = -0.6247   Dur. = 02m12s

Annular   **2161 May 25**
Saros 140   04:06 TD
D.Node
ΔT= 206s   Alt. = 85°
Gam. = -0.0950   Dur. = 01m12s

Plate 130

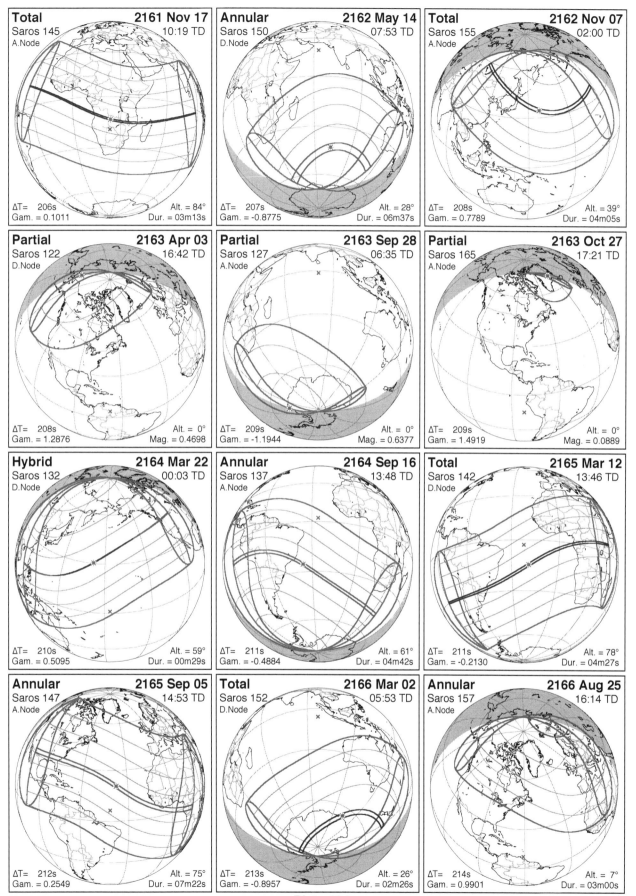

Total **2161 Nov 17** Saros 145 10:19 TD A.Node ΔT= 206s Alt. = 84° Gam. = 0.1011 Dur. = 03m13s	**Annular** **2162 May 14** Saros 150 07:53 TD D.Node ΔT= 207s Alt. = 28° Gam. = -0.8775 Dur. = 06m37s	**Total** **2162 Nov 07** Saros 155 02:00 TD A.Node ΔT= 208s Alt. = 39° Gam. = 0.7789 Dur. = 04m05s
Partial **2163 Apr 03** Saros 122 16:42 TD D.Node ΔT= 208s Alt. = 0° Gam. = 1.2876 Mag. = 0.4698	**Partial** **2163 Sep 28** Saros 127 06:35 TD A.Node ΔT= 209s Alt. = 0° Gam. = -1.1944 Mag. = 0.6377	**Partial** **2163 Oct 27** Saros 165 17:21 TD A.Node ΔT= 209s Alt. = 0° Gam. = 1.4919 Mag. = 0.0889
Hybrid **2164 Mar 22** Saros 132 00:03 TD D.Node ΔT= 210s Alt. = 59° Gam. = 0.5095 Dur. = 00m29s	**Annular** **2164 Sep 16** Saros 137 13:48 TD A.Node ΔT= 211s Alt. = 61° Gam. = -0.4884 Dur. = 04m42s	**Total** **2165 Mar 12** Saros 142 13:46 TD D.Node ΔT= 211s Alt. = 78° Gam. = -0.2130 Dur. = 04m27s
Annular **2165 Sep 05** Saros 147 14:53 TD A.Node ΔT= 212s Alt. = 75° Gam. = 0.2549 Dur. = 07m22s	**Total** **2166 Mar 02** Saros 152 05:53 TD D.Node ΔT= 213s Alt. = 26° Gam. = -0.8957 Dur. = 02m26s	**Annular** **2166 Aug 25** Saros 157 16:14 TD A.Node ΔT= 214s Alt. = 7° Gam. = 0.9901 Dur. = 03m00s

Plate 131

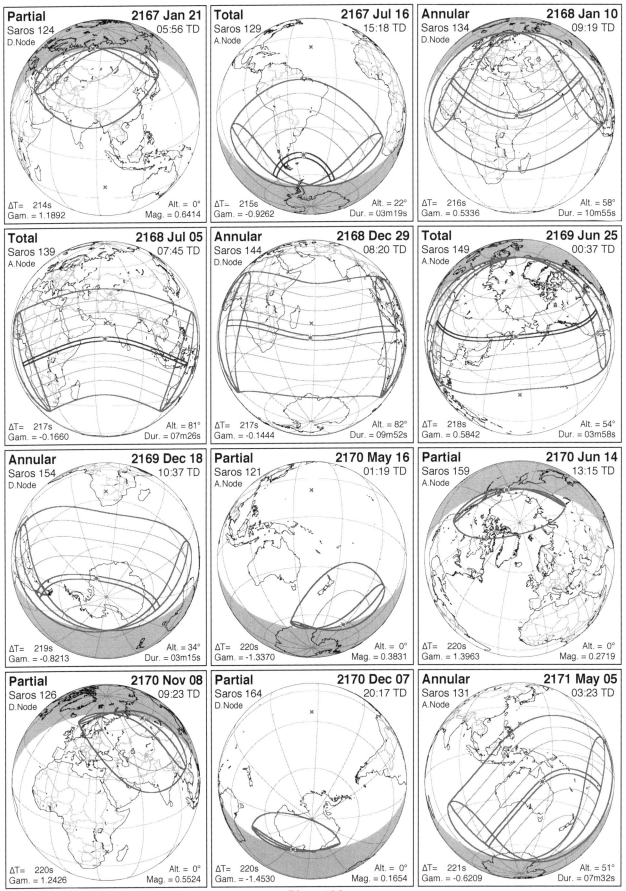

Partial   **2167 Jan 21**
Saros 124   05:56 TD
D.Node
ΔT= 214s   Alt. = 0°
Gam. = 1.1892   Mag. = 0.6414

Total   **2167 Jul 16**
Saros 129   15:18 TD
A.Node
ΔT= 215s   Alt. = 22°
Gam. = -0.9262   Dur. = 03m19s

Annular   **2168 Jan 10**
Saros 134   09:19 TD
D.Node
ΔT= 216s   Alt. = 58°
Gam. = 0.5336   Dur. = 10m55s

Total   **2168 Jul 05**
Saros 139   07:45 TD
A.Node
ΔT= 217s   Alt. = 81°
Gam. = -0.1660   Dur. = 07m26s

Annular   **2168 Dec 29**
Saros 144   08:20 TD
D.Node
ΔT= 217s   Alt. = 82°
Gam. = -0.1444   Dur. = 09m52s

Total   **2169 Jun 25**
Saros 149   00:37 TD
A.Node
ΔT= 218s   Alt. = 54°
Gam. = 0.5842   Dur. = 03m58s

Annular   **2169 Dec 18**
Saros 154   10:37 TD
D.Node
ΔT= 219s   Alt. = 34°
Gam. = -0.8213   Dur. = 03m15s

Partial   **2170 May 16**
Saros 121   01:19 TD
A.Node
ΔT= 220s   Alt. = 0°
Gam. = -1.3370   Mag. = 0.3831

Partial   **2170 Jun 14**
Saros 159   13:15 TD
A.Node
ΔT= 220s   Alt. = 0°
Gam. = 1.3963   Mag. = 0.2719

Partial   **2170 Nov 08**
Saros 126   09:23 TD
D.Node
ΔT= 220s   Alt. = 0°
Gam. = 1.2426   Mag. = 0.5524

Partial   **2170 Dec 07**
Saros 164   20:17 TD
D.Node
ΔT= 220s   Alt. = 0°
Gam. = -1.4530   Mag. = 0.1654

Annular   **2171 May 05**
Saros 131   03:23 TD
A.Node
ΔT= 221s   Alt. = 51°
Gam. = -0.6209   Dur. = 07m32s

Plate 132

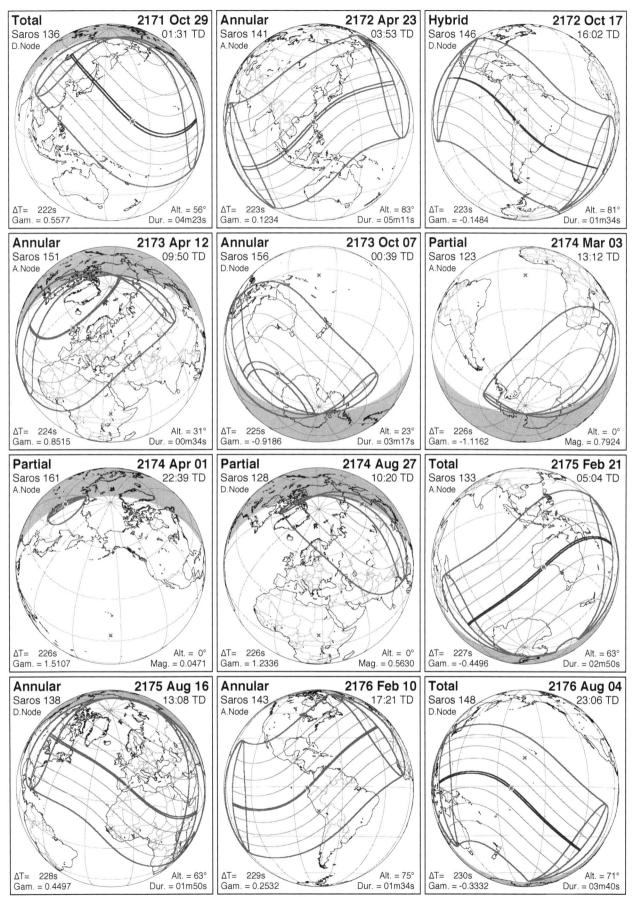

Total	2171 Oct 29
Saros 136	01:31 TD
D.Node	
ΔT= 222s	Alt. = 56°
Gam. = 0.5577	Dur. = 04m23s

Annular	2172 Apr 23
Saros 141	03:53 TD
A.Node	
ΔT= 223s	Alt. = 83°
Gam. = 0.1234	Dur. = 05m11s

Hybrid	2172 Oct 17
Saros 146	16:02 TD
D.Node	
ΔT= 223s	Alt. = 81°
Gam. = -0.1484	Dur. = 01m34s

Annular	2173 Apr 12
Saros 151	09:50 TD
A.Node	
ΔT= 224s	Alt. = 31°
Gam. = 0.8515	Dur. = 00m34s

Annular	2173 Oct 07
Saros 156	00:39 TD
D.Node	
ΔT= 225s	Alt. = 23°
Gam. = -0.9186	Dur. = 03m17s

Partial	2174 Mar 03
Saros 123	13:12 TD
A.Node	
ΔT= 226s	Alt. = 0°
Gam. = -1.1162	Mag. = 0.7924

Partial	2174 Apr 01
Saros 161	22:39 TD
A.Node	
ΔT= 226s	Alt. = 0°
Gam. = 1.5107	Mag. = 0.0471

Partial	2174 Aug 27
Saros 128	10:20 TD
D.Node	
ΔT= 226s	Alt. = 0°
Gam. = 1.2336	Mag. = 0.5630

Total	2175 Feb 21
Saros 133	05:04 TD
A.Node	
ΔT= 227s	Alt. = 63°
Gam. = -0.4496	Dur. = 02m50s

Annular	2175 Aug 16
Saros 138	13:08 TD
D.Node	
ΔT= 228s	Alt. = 63°
Gam. = 0.4497	Dur. = 01m50s

Annular	2176 Feb 10
Saros 143	17:21 TD
A.Node	
ΔT= 229s	Alt. = 75°
Gam. = 0.2532	Dur. = 01m34s

Total	2176 Aug 04
Saros 148	23:06 TD
D.Node	
ΔT= 230s	Alt. = 71°
Gam. = -0.3332	Dur. = 03m40s

Plate 133

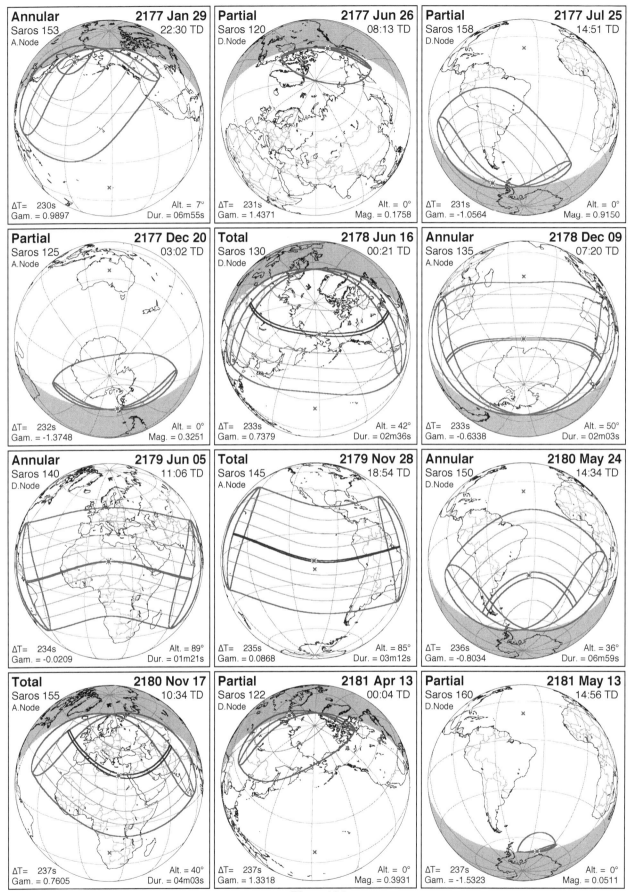

Annular	2177 Jan 29
Saros 153	22:30 TD
A.Node	
ΔT= 230s	Alt. = 7°
Gam. = 0.9897	Dur. = 06m55s

Partial	2177 Jun 26
Saros 120	08:13 TD
D.Node	
ΔT= 231s	Alt. = 0°
Gam. = 1.4371	Mag. = 0.1758

Partial	2177 Jul 25
Saros 158	14:51 TD
D.Node	
ΔT= 231s	Alt. = 0°
Gam. = -1.0564	Mag. = 0.9150

Partial	2177 Dec 20
Saros 125	03:02 TD
A.Node	
ΔT= 232s	Alt. = 0°
Gam. = -1.3748	Mag. = 0.3251

Total	2178 Jun 16
Saros 130	00:21 TD
D.Node	
ΔT= 233s	Alt. = 42°
Gam. = 0.7379	Dur. = 02m36s

Annular	2178 Dec 09
Saros 135	07:20 TD
A.Node	
ΔT= 233s	Alt. = 50°
Gam. = -0.6338	Dur. = 02m03s

Annular	2179 Jun 05
Saros 140	11:06 TD
D.Node	
ΔT= 234s	Alt. = 89°
Gam. = -0.0209	Dur. = 01m21s

Total	2179 Nov 28
Saros 145	18:54 TD
A.Node	
ΔT= 235s	Alt. = 85°
Gam. = 0.0868	Dur. = 03m12s

Annular	2180 May 24
Saros 150	14:34 TD
D.Node	
ΔT= 236s	Alt. = 36°
Gam. = -0.8034	Dur. = 06m59s

Total	2180 Nov 17
Saros 155	10:34 TD
A.Node	
ΔT= 237s	Alt. = 40°
Gam. = 0.7605	Dur. = 04m03s

Partial	2181 Apr 13
Saros 122	00:04 TD
D.Node	
ΔT= 237s	Alt. = 0°
Gam. = 1.3318	Mag. = 0.3931

Partial	2181 May 13
Saros 160	14:56 TD
D.Node	
ΔT= 237s	Alt. = 0°
Gam. = -1.5323	Mag. = 0.0511

Plate 134

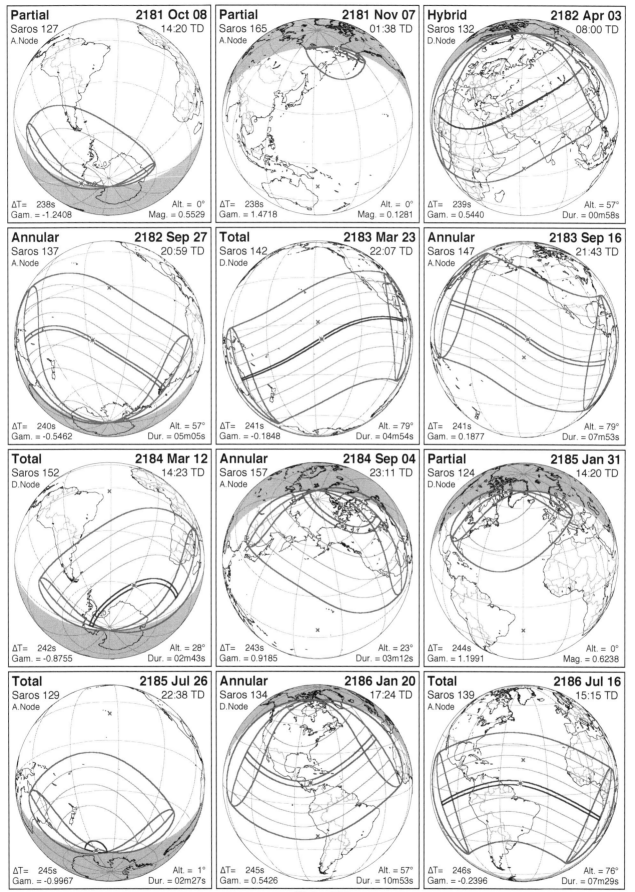

Partial	2181 Oct 08
Saros 127	14:20 TD
A.Node	
ΔT= 238s	Alt. = 0°
Gam. = -1.2408	Mag. = 0.5529

Partial	2181 Nov 07
Saros 165	01:38 TD
A.Node	
ΔT= 238s	Alt. = 0°
Gam. = 1.4718	Mag. = 0.1281

Hybrid	2182 Apr 03
Saros 132	08:00 TD
D.Node	
ΔT= 239s	Alt. = 57°
Gam. = 0.5440	Dur. = 00m58s

Annular	2182 Sep 27
Saros 137	20:59 TD
A.Node	
ΔT= 240s	Alt. = 57°
Gam. = -0.5462	Dur. = 05m05s

Total	2183 Mar 23
Saros 142	22:07 TD
D.Node	
ΔT= 241s	Alt. = 79°
Gam. = -0.1848	Dur. = 04m54s

Annular	2183 Sep 16
Saros 147	21:43 TD
A.Node	
ΔT= 241s	Alt. = 79°
Gam. = 0.1877	Dur. = 07m53s

Total	2184 Mar 12
Saros 152	14:23 TD
D.Node	
ΔT= 242s	Alt. = 28°
Gam. = -0.8755	Dur. = 02m43s

Annular	2184 Sep 04
Saros 157	23:11 TD
A.Node	
ΔT= 243s	Alt. = 23°
Gam. = 0.9185	Dur. = 03m12s

Partial	2185 Jan 31
Saros 124	14:20 TD
D.Node	
ΔT= 244s	Alt. = 0°
Gam. = 1.1991	Mag. = 0.6238

Total	2185 Jul 26
Saros 129	22:38 TD
A.Node	
ΔT= 245s	Alt. = 1°
Gam. = -0.9967	Dur. = 02m27s

Annular	2186 Jan 20
Saros 134	17:24 TD
D.Node	
ΔT= 245s	Alt. = 57°
Gam. = 0.5426	Dur. = 10m53s

Total	2186 Jul 16
Saros 139	15:15 TD
A.Node	
ΔT= 246s	Alt. = 76°
Gam. = -0.2396	Dur. = 07m29s

Plate 135

229

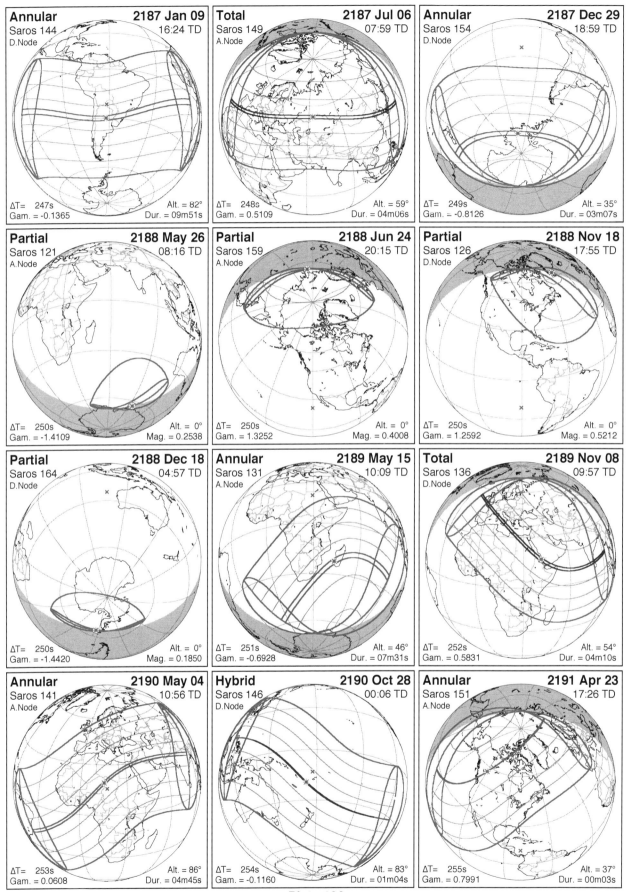

Annular	2187 Jan 09
Saros 144	16:24 TD
D.Node	
ΔT= 247s	Alt. = 82°
Gam. = -0.1365	Dur. = 09m51s

Total	2187 Jul 06
Saros 149	07:59 TD
A.Node	
ΔT= 248s	Alt. = 59°
Gam. = 0.5109	Dur. = 04m06s

Annular	2187 Dec 29
Saros 154	18:59 TD
D.Node	
ΔT= 249s	Alt. = 35°
Gam. = -0.8126	Dur. = 03m07s

Partial	2188 May 26
Saros 121	08:16 TD
A.Node	
ΔT= 250s	Alt. = 0°
Gam. = -1.4109	Mag. = 0.2538

Partial	2188 Jun 24
Saros 159	20:15 TD
A.Node	
ΔT= 250s	Alt. = 0°
Gam. = 1.3252	Mag. = 0.4008

Partial	2188 Nov 18
Saros 126	17:55 TD
D.Node	
ΔT= 250s	Alt. = 0°
Gam. = 1.2592	Mag. = 0.5212

Partial	2188 Dec 18
Saros 164	04:57 TD
D.Node	
ΔT= 250s	Alt. = 0°
Gam. = -1.4420	Mag. = 0.1850

Annular	2189 May 15
Saros 131	10:09 TD
A.Node	
ΔT= 251s	Alt. = 46°
Gam. = -0.6928	Dur. = 07m31s

Total	2189 Nov 08
Saros 136	09:57 TD
D.Node	
ΔT= 252s	Alt. = 54°
Gam. = 0.5831	Dur. = 04m10s

Annular	2190 May 04
Saros 141	10:56 TD
A.Node	
ΔT= 253s	Alt. = 86°
Gam. = 0.0608	Dur. = 04m45s

Hybrid	2190 Oct 28
Saros 146	00:06 TD
D.Node	
ΔT= 254s	Alt. = 83°
Gam. = -0.1160	Dur. = 01m04s

Annular	2191 Apr 23
Saros 151	17:26 TD
A.Node	
ΔT= 255s	Alt. = 37°
Gam. = 0.7991	Dur. = 00m03s

Plate 136

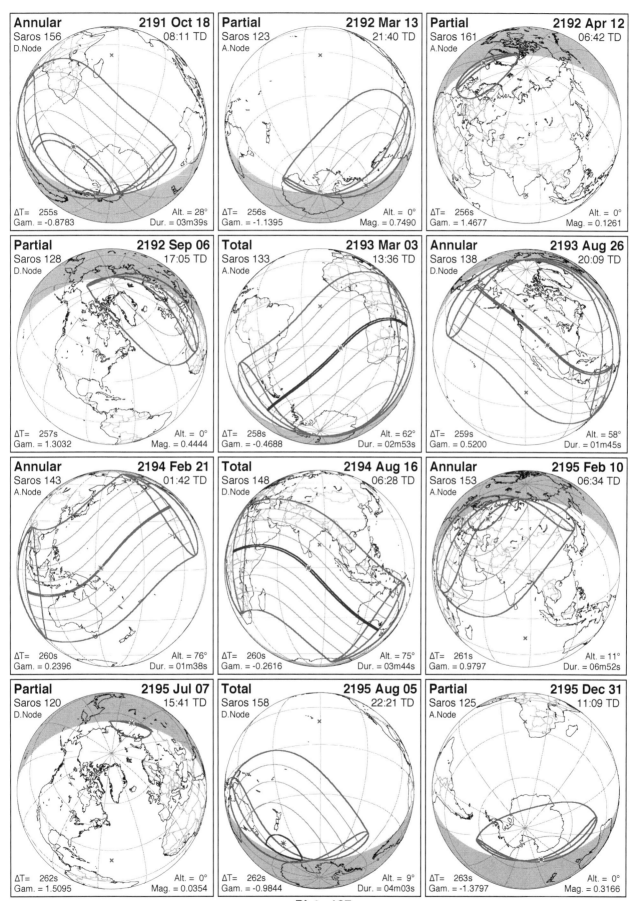

Annular 2191 Oct 18	**Partial** 2192 Mar 13	**Partial** 2192 Apr 12
Saros 156 08:11 TD	Saros 123 21:40 TD	Saros 161 06:42 TD
D.Node	A.Node	A.Node
ΔT= 255s Alt. = 28°	ΔT= 256s Alt. = 0°	ΔT= 256s Alt. = 0°
Gam. = -0.8783 Dur. = 03m39s	Gam. = -1.1395 Mag. = 0.7490	Gam. = 1.4677 Mag. = 0.1261
Partial 2192 Sep 06	**Total** 2193 Mar 03	**Annular** 2193 Aug 26
Saros 128 17:05 TD	Saros 133 13:36 TD	Saros 138 20:09 TD
D.Node	A.Node	D.Node
ΔT= 257s Alt. = 0°	ΔT= 258s Alt. = 62°	ΔT= 259s Alt. = 58°
Gam. = 1.3032 Mag. = 0.4444	Gam. = -0.4688 Dur. = 02m53s	Gam. = 0.5200 Dur. = 01m45s
Annular 2194 Feb 21	**Total** 2194 Aug 16	**Annular** 2195 Feb 10
Saros 143 01:42 TD	Saros 148 06:28 TD	Saros 153 06:34 TD
A.Node	D.Node	A.Node
ΔT= 260s Alt. = 76°	ΔT= 260s Alt. = 75°	ΔT= 261s Alt. = 11°
Gam. = 0.2396 Dur. = 01m38s	Gam. = -0.2616 Dur. = 03m44s	Gam. = 0.9797 Dur. = 06m52s
Partial 2195 Jul 07	**Total** 2195 Aug 05	**Partial** 2195 Dec 31
Saros 120 15:41 TD	Saros 158 22:21 TD	Saros 125 11:09 TD
D.Node	D.Node	A.Node
ΔT= 262s Alt. = 0°	ΔT= 262s Alt. = 9°	ΔT= 263s Alt. = 0°
Gam. = 1.5095 Mag. = 0.0354	Gam. = -0.9844 Dur. = 04m03s	Gam. = -1.3797 Mag. = 0.3166

Plate 137

231

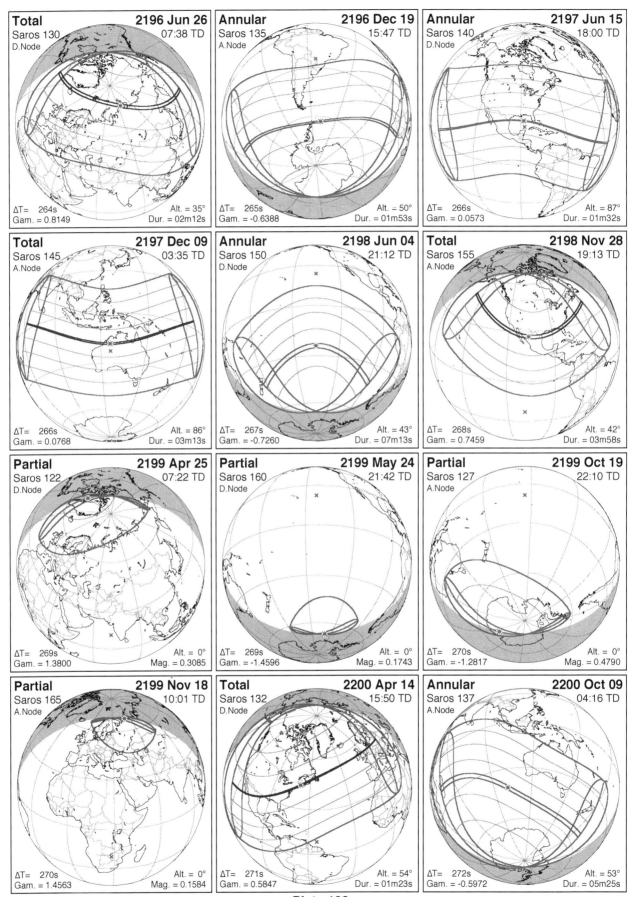

Plate 138

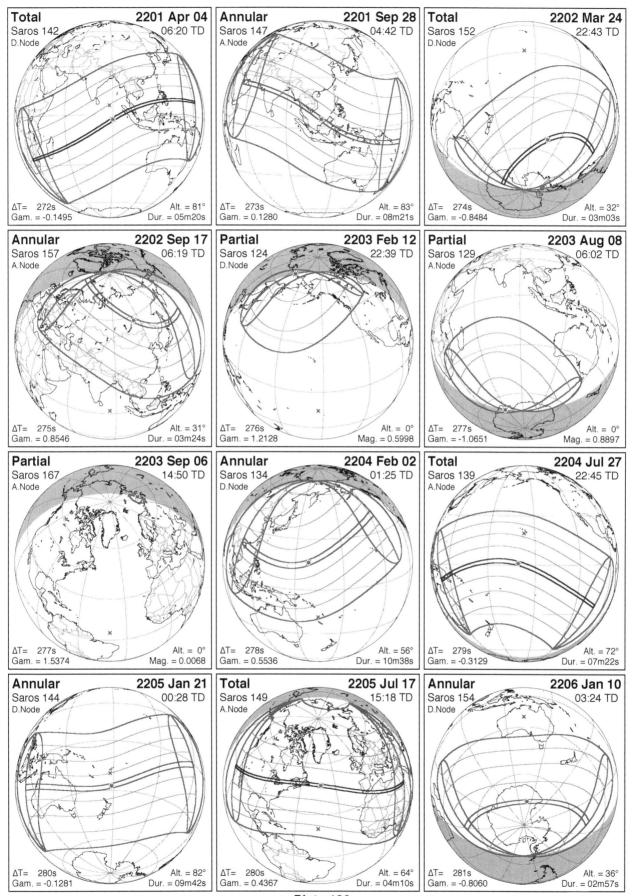

Total 2201 Apr 04	**Annular** 2201 Sep 28	**Total** 2202 Mar 24
Saros 142 06:20 TD	Saros 147 04:42 TD	Saros 152 22:43 TD
D.Node	A.Node	D.Node
ΔT= 272s Alt. = 81°	ΔT= 273s Alt. = 83°	ΔT= 274s Alt. = 32°
Gam. = -0.1495 Dur. = 05m20s	Gam. = 0.1280 Dur. = 08m21s	Gam. = -0.8484 Dur. = 03m03s
Annular 2202 Sep 17	**Partial** 2203 Feb 12	**Partial** 2203 Aug 08
Saros 157 06:19 TD	Saros 124 22:39 TD	Saros 129 06:02 TD
A.Node	D.Node	A.Node
ΔT= 275s Alt. = 31°	ΔT= 276s Alt. = 0°	ΔT= 277s Alt. = 0°
Gam. = 0.8546 Dur. = 03m24s	Gam. = 1.2128 Mag. = 0.5998	Gam. = -1.0651 Mag. = 0.8897
Partial 2203 Sep 06	**Annular** 2204 Feb 02	**Total** 2204 Jul 27
Saros 167 14:50 TD	Saros 134 01:25 TD	Saros 139 22:45 TD
A.Node	D.Node	A.Node
ΔT= 277s Alt. = 0°	ΔT= 278s Alt. = 56°	ΔT= 279s Alt. = 72°
Gam. = 1.5374 Mag. = 0.0068	Gam. = 0.5536 Dur. = 10m38s	Gam. = -0.3129 Dur. = 07m22s
Annular 2205 Jan 21	**Total** 2205 Jul 17	**Annular** 2206 Jan 10
Saros 144 00:28 TD	Saros 149 15:18 TD	Saros 154 03:24 TD
D.Node	A.Node	D.Node
ΔT= 280s Alt. = 82°	ΔT= 280s Alt. = 64°	ΔT= 281s Alt. = 36°
Gam. = -0.1281 Dur. = 09m42s	Gam. = 0.4367 Dur. = 04m10s	Gam. = -0.8060 Dur. = 02m57s

Plate 139

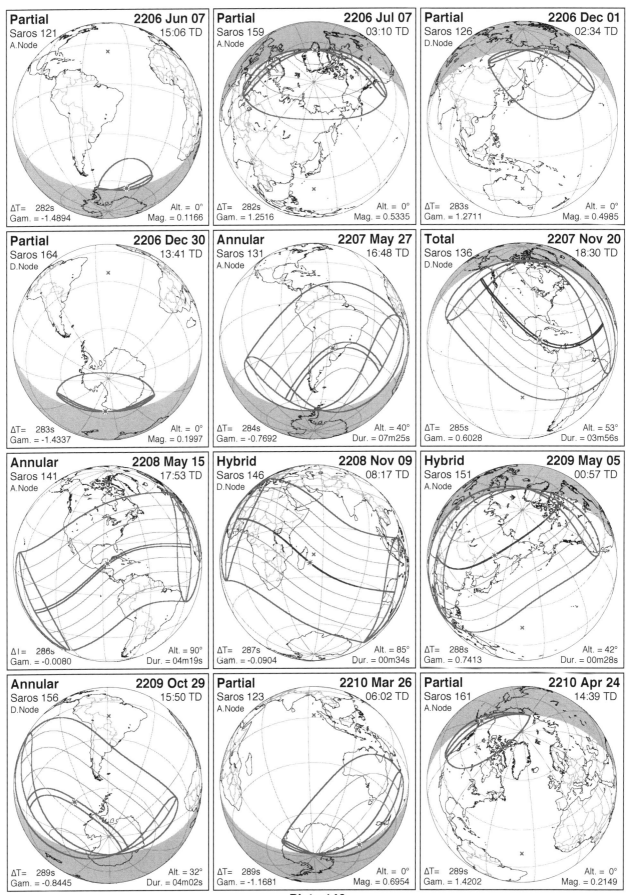

Partial	2206 Jun 07
Saros 121	15:06 TD
A.Node	
ΔT= 282s	Alt. = 0°
Gam. = -1.4894	Mag. = 0.1166

Partial	2206 Jul 07
Saros 159	03:10 TD
A.Node	
ΔT= 282s	Alt. = 0°
Gam. = 1.2516	Mag. = 0.5335

Partial	2206 Dec 01
Saros 126	02:34 TD
D.Node	
ΔT= 283s	Alt. = 0°
Gam. = 1.2711	Mag. = 0.4985

Partial	2206 Dec 30
Saros 164	13:41 TD
D.Node	
ΔT= 283s	Alt. = 0°
Gam. = -1.4337	Mag. = 0.1997

Annular	2207 May 27
Saros 131	16:48 TD
A.Node	
ΔT= 284s	Alt. = 40°
Gam. = -0.7692	Dur. = 07m25s

Total	2207 Nov 20
Saros 136	18:30 TD
D.Node	
ΔT= 285s	Alt. = 53°
Gam. = 0.6028	Dur. = 03m56s

Annular	2208 May 15
Saros 141	17:53 TD
A.Node	
ΔI = 286s	Alt. = 90°
Gam. = -0.0080	Dur. = 04m19s

Hybrid	2208 Nov 09
Saros 146	08:17 TD
D.Node	
ΔT= 287s	Alt. = 85°
Gam. = -0.0904	Dur. = 00m34s

Hybrid	2209 May 05
Saros 151	00:57 TD
A.Node	
ΔT= 288s	Alt. = 42°
Gam. = 0.7413	Dur. = 00m28s

Annular	2209 Oct 29
Saros 156	15:50 TD
D.Node	
ΔT= 289s	Alt. = 32°
Gam. = -0.8445	Dur. = 04m02s

Partial	2210 Mar 26
Saros 123	06:02 TD
A.Node	
ΔT= 289s	Alt. = 0°
Gam. = -1.1681	Mag. = 0.6954

Partial	2210 Apr 24
Saros 161	14:39 TD
A.Node	
ΔT= 289s	Alt. = 0°
Gam. = 1.4202	Mag. = 0.2149

Plate 140

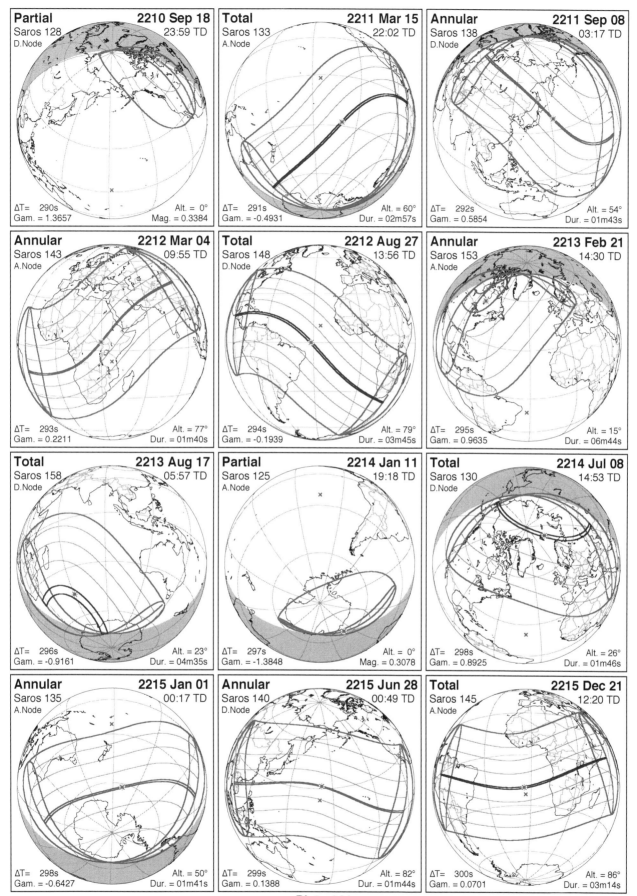

Partial	2210 Sep 18
Saros 128	23:59 TD
D.Node	
ΔT= 290s	Alt. = 0°
Gam. = 1.3657	Mag. = 0.3384

Total	2211 Mar 15
Saros 133	22:02 TD
A.Node	
ΔT= 291s	Alt. = 60°
Gam. = -0.4931	Dur. = 02m57s

Annular	2211 Sep 08
Saros 138	03:17 TD
D.Node	
ΔT= 292s	Alt. = 54°
Gam. = 0.5854	Dur. = 01m43s

Annular	2212 Mar 04
Saros 143	09:55 TD
A.Node	
ΔT= 293s	Alt. = 77°
Gam. = 0.2211	Dur. = 01m40s

Total	2212 Aug 27
Saros 148	13:56 TD
D.Node	
ΔT= 294s	Alt. = 79°
Gam. = -0.1939	Dur. = 03m45s

Annular	2213 Feb 21
Saros 153	14:30 TD
A.Node	
ΔT= 295s	Alt. = 15°
Gam. = 0.9635	Dur. = 06m44s

Total	2213 Aug 17
Saros 158	05:57 TD
D.Node	
ΔT= 296s	Alt. = 23°
Gam. = -0.9161	Dur. = 04m35s

Partial	2214 Jan 11
Saros 125	19:18 TD
A.Node	
ΔT= 297s	Alt. = 0°
Gam. = -1.3848	Mag. = 0.3078

Total	2214 Jul 08
Saros 130	14:53 TD
D.Node	
ΔT= 298s	Alt. = 26°
Gam. = 0.8925	Dur. = 01m46s

Annular	2215 Jan 01
Saros 135	00:17 TD
A.Node	
ΔT= 298s	Alt. = 50°
Gam. = -0.6427	Dur. = 01m41s

Annular	2215 Jun 28
Saros 140	00:49 TD
D.Node	
ΔT= 299s	Alt. = 82°
Gam. = 0.1388	Dur. = 01m44s

Total	2215 Dec 21
Saros 145	12:20 TD
A.Node	
ΔT= 300s	Alt. = 86°
Gam. = 0.0701	Dur. = 03m14s

Plate 141

235

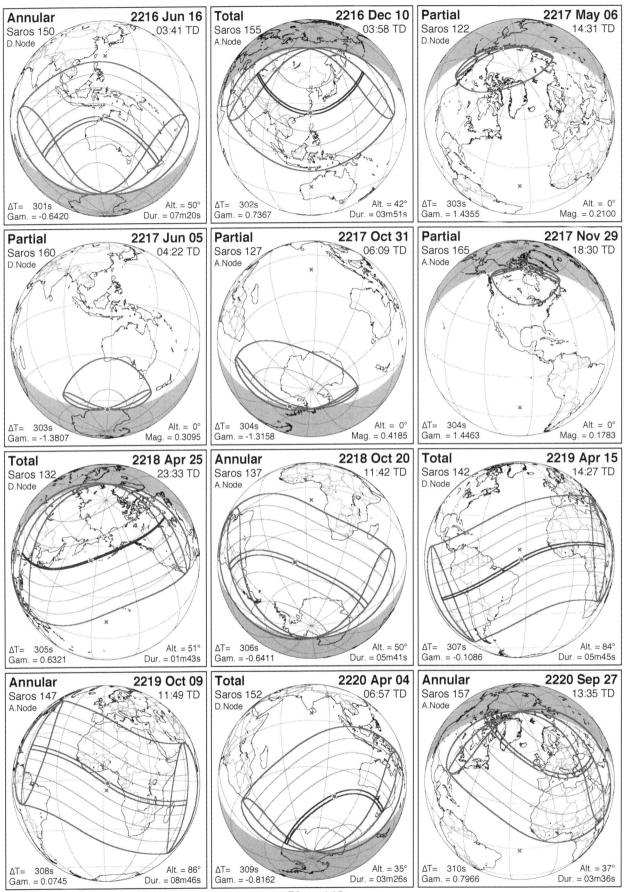

Annular **2216 Jun 16** Saros 150 03:41 TD D.Node ΔT= 301s Alt. = 50° Gam. = -0.6420 Dur. = 07m20s	**Total** **2216 Dec 10** Saros 155 03:58 TD A.Node ΔT= 302s Alt. = 42° Gam. = 0.7367 Dur. = 03m51s	**Partial** **2217 May 06** Saros 122 14:31 TD D.Node ΔT= 303s Alt. = 0° Gam. = 1.4355 Mag. = 0.2100
Partial **2217 Jun 05** Saros 160 04:22 TD D.Node ΔT= 303s Alt. = 0° Gam. = -1.3807 Mag. = 0.3095	**Partial** **2217 Oct 31** Saros 127 06:09 TD A.Node ΔT= 304s Alt. = 0° Gam. = -1.3158 Mag. = 0.4185	**Partial** **2217 Nov 29** Saros 165 18:30 TD A.Node ΔT= 304s Alt. = 0° Gam. = 1.4463 Mag. = 0.1783
Total **2218 Apr 25** Saros 132 23:33 TD D.Node ΔT= 305s Alt. = 51° Gam. = 0.6321 Dur. = 01m43s	**Annular** **2218 Oct 20** Saros 137 11:42 TD A.Node ΔT= 306s Alt. = 50° Gam. = -0.6411 Dur. = 05m41s	**Total** **2219 Apr 15** Saros 142 14:27 TD D.Node ΔT= 307s Alt. = 84° Gam. = -0.1086 Dur. = 05m45s
Annular **2219 Oct 09** Saros 147 11:49 TD A.Node ΔT= 308s Alt. = 86° Gam. = 0.0745 Dur. = 08m46s	**Total** **2220 Apr 04** Saros 152 06:57 TD D.Node ΔT= 309s Alt. = 35° Gam. = -0.8162 Dur. = 03m26s	**Annular** **2220 Sep 27** Saros 157 13:35 TD A.Node ΔT= 310s Alt. = 37° Gam. = 0.7966 Dur. = 03m36s

Plate 142

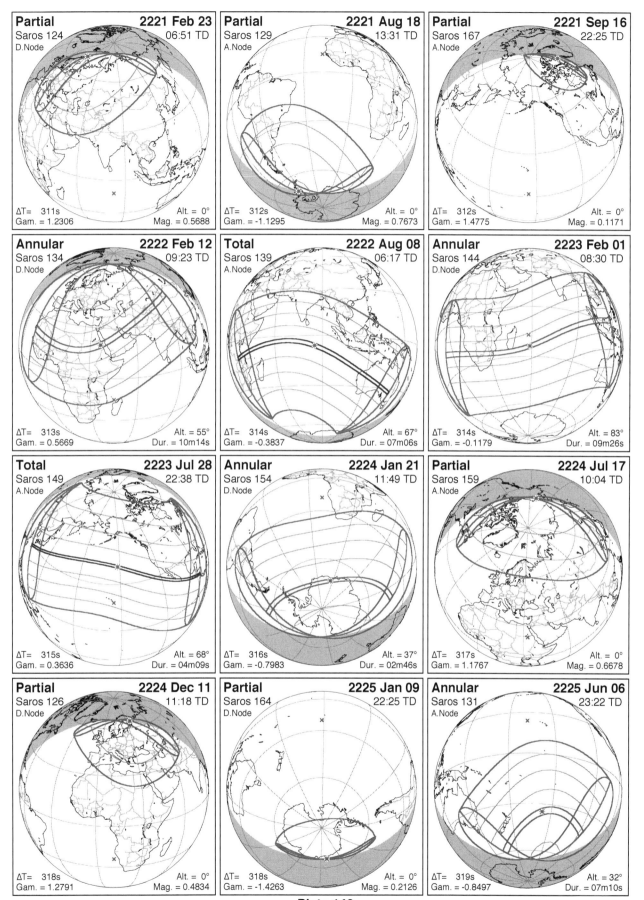

Partial 2221 Feb 23 Saros 124 06:51 TD D.Node ΔT= 311s Alt. = 0° Gam. = 1.2306 Mag. = 0.5688	**Partial** 2221 Aug 18 Saros 129 13:31 TD A.Node ΔT= 312s Alt. = 0° Gam. = -1.1295 Mag. = 0.7673	**Partial** 2221 Sep 16 Saros 167 22:25 TD A.Node ΔT= 312s Alt. = 0° Gam. = 1.4775 Mag. = 0.1171
Annular 2222 Feb 12 Saros 134 09:23 TD D.Node ΔT= 313s Alt. = 55° Gam. = 0.5669 Dur. = 10m14s	**Total** 2222 Aug 08 Saros 139 06:17 TD A.Node ΔT= 314s Alt. = 67° Gam. = -0.3837 Dur. = 07m06s	**Annular** 2223 Feb 01 Saros 144 08:30 TD D.Node ΔT= 314s Alt. = 83° Gam. = -0.1179 Dur. = 09m26s
Total 2223 Jul 28 Saros 149 22:38 TD A.Node ΔT= 315s Alt. = 68° Gam. = 0.3636 Dur. = 04m09s	**Annular** 2224 Jan 21 Saros 154 11:49 TD D.Node ΔT= 316s Alt. = 37° Gam. = -0.7983 Dur. = 02m46s	**Partial** 2224 Jul 17 Saros 159 10:04 TD A.Node ΔT= 317s Alt. = 0° Gam. = 1.1767 Mag. = 0.6678
Partial 2224 Dec 11 Saros 126 11:18 TD D.Node ΔT= 318s Alt. = 0° Gam. = 1.2791 Mag. = 0.4834	**Partial** 2225 Jan 09 Saros 164 22:25 TD D.Node ΔT= 318s Alt. = 0° Gam. = -1.4263 Mag. = 0.2126	**Annular** 2225 Jun 06 Saros 131 23:22 TD A.Node ΔT= 319s Alt. = 32° Gam. = -0.8497 Dur. = 07m10s

Plate 143

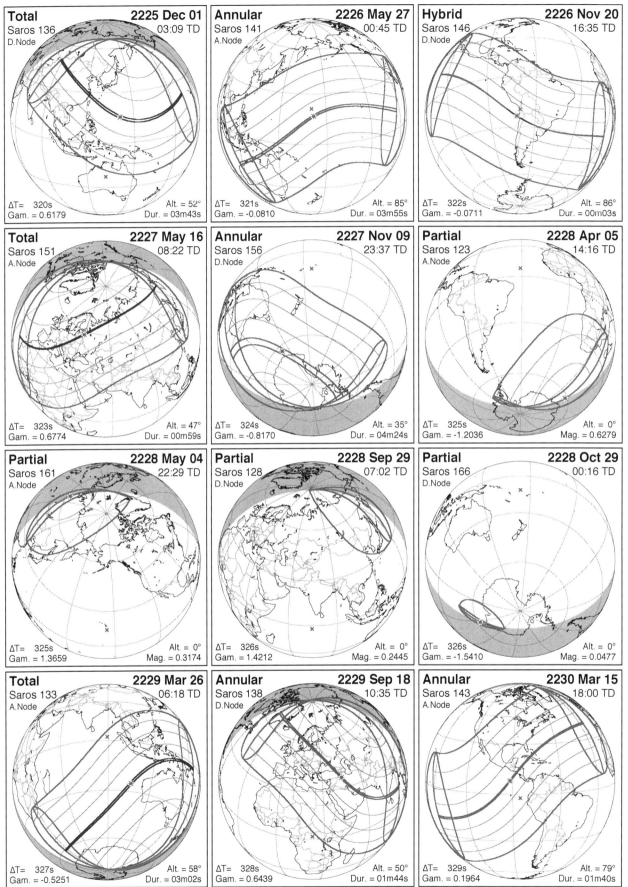

Total **2225 Dec 01** Saros 136 03:09 TD D.Node ΔT= 320s Alt. = 52° Gam. = 0.6179 Dur. = 03m43s	**Annular** **2226 May 27** Saros 141 00:45 TD A.Node ΔT= 321s Alt. = 85° Gam. = -0.0810 Dur. = 03m55s	**Hybrid** **2226 Nov 20** Saros 146 16:35 TD D.Node ΔT= 322s Alt. = 86° Gam. = -0.0711 Dur. = 00m03s
Total **2227 May 16** Saros 151 08:22 TD A.Node ΔT= 323s Alt. = 47° Gam. = 0.6774 Dur. = 00m59s	**Annular** **2227 Nov 09** Saros 156 23:37 TD D.Node ΔT= 324s Alt. = 35° Gam. = -0.8170 Dur. = 04m24s	**Partial** **2228 Apr 05** Saros 123 14:16 TD A.Node ΔT= 325s Alt. = 0° Gam. = -1.2036 Mag. = 0.6279
Partial **2228 May 04** Saros 161 22:29 TD A.Node ΔT= 325s Alt. = 0° Gam. = 1.3659 Mag. = 0.3174	**Partial** **2228 Sep 29** Saros 128 07:02 TD D.Node ΔT= 326s Alt. = 0° Gam. = 1.4212 Mag. = 0.2445	**Partial** **2228 Oct 29** Saros 166 00:16 TD D.Node ΔT= 326s Alt. = 0° Gam. = -1.5410 Mag. = 0.0477
Total **2229 Mar 26** Saros 133 06:18 TD A.Node ΔT= 327s Alt. = 58° Gam. = -0.5251 Dur. = 03m02s	**Annular** **2229 Sep 18** Saros 138 10:35 TD D.Node ΔT= 328s Alt. = 50° Gam. = 0.6439 Dur. = 01m44s	**Annular** **2230 Mar 15** Saros 143 18:00 TD A.Node ΔT= 329s Alt. = 79° Gam. = 0.1964 Dur. = 01m40s

Plate 144

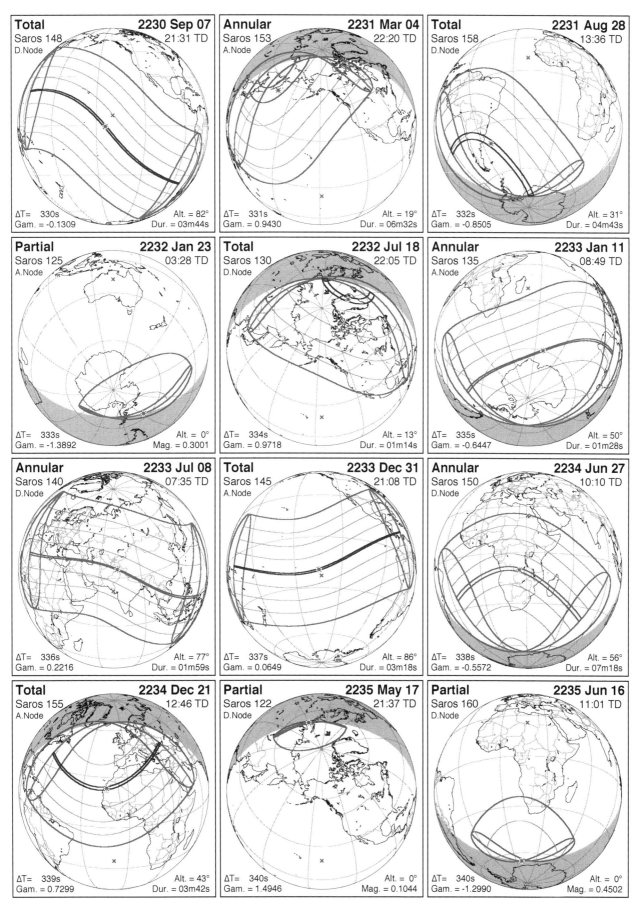

Total	2230 Sep 07
Saros 148	21:31 TD
D.Node	
ΔT= 330s	Alt. = 82°
Gam. = -0.1309	Dur. = 03m44s

Annular	2231 Mar 04
Saros 153	22:20 TD
A.Node	
ΔT= 331s	Alt. = 19°
Gam. = 0.9430	Dur. = 06m32s

Total	2231 Aug 28
Saros 158	13:36 TD
D.Node	
ΔT= 332s	Alt. = 31°
Gam. = -0.8505	Dur. = 04m43s

Partial	2232 Jan 23
Saros 125	03:28 TD
A.Node	
ΔT= 333s	Alt. = 0°
Gam. = -1.3892	Mag. = 0.3001

Total	2232 Jul 18
Saros 130	22:05 TD
D.Node	
ΔT= 334s	Alt. = 13°
Gam. = 0.9718	Dur. = 01m14s

Annular	2233 Jan 11
Saros 135	08:49 TD
A.Node	
ΔT= 335s	Alt. = 50°
Gam. = -0.6447	Dur. = 01m28s

Annular	2233 Jul 08
Saros 140	07:35 TD
D.Node	
ΔT= 336s	Alt. = 77°
Gam. = 0.2216	Dur. = 01m59s

Total	2233 Dec 31
Saros 145	21:08 TD
A.Node	
ΔT= 337s	Alt. = 86°
Gam. = 0.0649	Dur. = 03m18s

Annular	2234 Jun 27
Saros 150	10:10 TD
D.Node	
ΔT= 338s	Alt. = 56°
Gam. = -0.5572	Dur. = 07m18s

Total	2234 Dec 21
Saros 155	12:46 TD
A.Node	
ΔT= 339s	Alt. = 43°
Gam. = 0.7299	Dur. = 03m42s

Partial	2235 May 17
Saros 122	21:37 TD
D.Node	
ΔT= 340s	Alt. = 0°
Gam. = 1.4946	Mag. = 0.1044

Partial	2235 Jun 16
Saros 160	11:01 TD
D.Node	
ΔT= 340s	Alt. = 0°
Gam. = -1.2990	Mag. = 0.4502

Plate 145

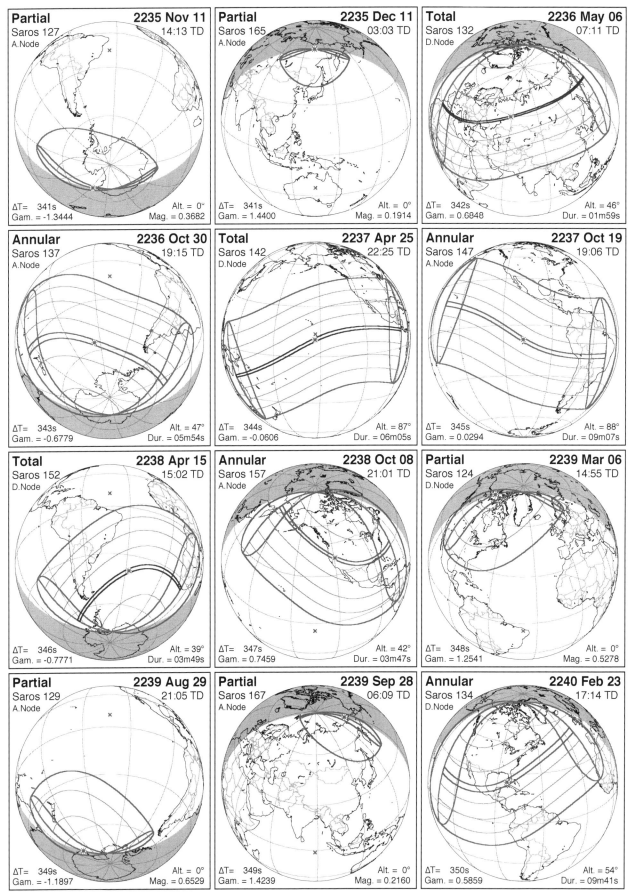

Partial	2235 Nov 11
Saros 127	14:13 TD
A.Node	
ΔT= 341s	Alt. = 0°
Gam. = -1.3444	Mag. = 0.3682

Partial	2235 Dec 11
Saros 165	03:03 TD
A.Node	
ΔT= 341s	Alt. = 0°
Gam. = 1.4400	Mag. = 0.1914

Total	2236 May 06
Saros 132	07:11 TD
D.Node	
ΔT= 342s	Alt. = 46°
Gam. = 0.6848	Dur. = 01m59s

Annular	2236 Oct 30
Saros 137	19:15 TD
A.Node	
ΔT= 343s	Alt. = 47°
Gam. = -0.6779	Dur. = 05m54s

Total	2237 Apr 25
Saros 142	22:25 TD
D.Node	
ΔT= 344s	Alt. = 87°
Gam. = -0.0606	Dur. = 06m05s

Annular	2237 Oct 19
Saros 147	19:06 TD
A.Node	
ΔT= 345s	Alt. = 88°
Gam. = 0.0294	Dur. = 09m07s

Total	2238 Apr 15
Saros 152	15:02 TD
D.Node	
ΔT= 346s	Alt. = 39°
Gam. = -0.7771	Dur. = 03m49s

Annular	2238 Oct 08
Saros 157	21:01 TD
A.Node	
ΔT= 347s	Alt. = 42°
Gam. = 0.7459	Dur. = 03m47s

Partial	2239 Mar 06
Saros 124	14:55 TD
D.Node	
ΔT= 348s	Alt. = 0°
Gam. = 1.2541	Mag. = 0.5278

Partial	2239 Aug 29
Saros 129	21:05 TD
A.Node	
ΔT= 349s	Alt. = 0°
Gam. = -1.1897	Mag. = 0.6529

Partial	2239 Sep 28
Saros 167	06:09 TD
A.Node	
ΔT= 349s	Alt. = 0°
Gam. = 1.4239	Mag. = 0.2160

Annular	2240 Feb 23
Saros 134	17:14 TD
D.Node	
ΔT= 350s	Alt. = 54°
Gam. = 0.5859	Dur. = 09m41s

Plate 146

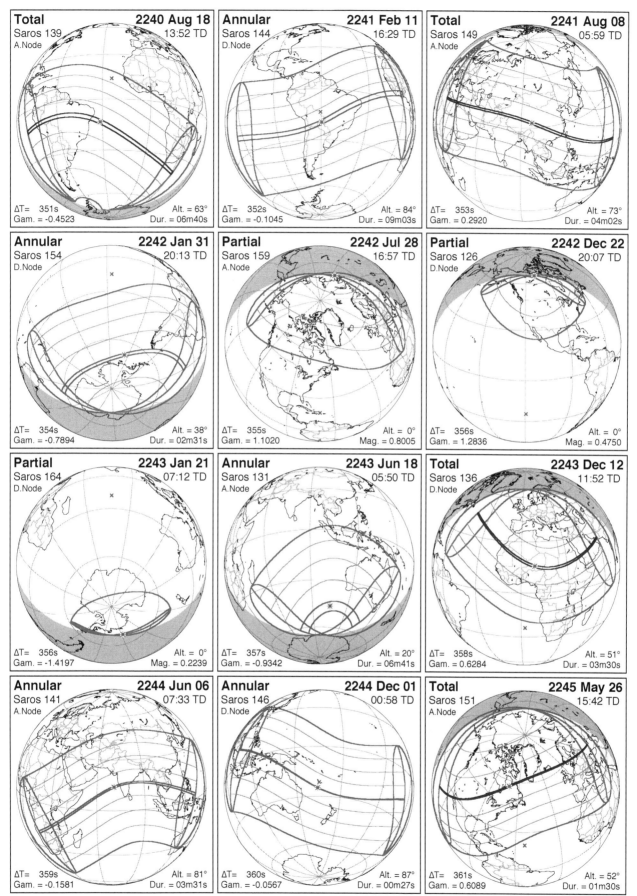

Total	2240 Aug 18
Saros 139	13:52 TD
A.Node	
ΔT = 351s	Alt. = 63°
Gam. = -0.4523	Dur. = 06m40s

Annular	2241 Feb 11
Saros 144	16:29 TD
D.Node	
ΔT = 352s	Alt. = 84°
Gam. = -0.1045	Dur. = 09m03s

Total	2241 Aug 08
Saros 149	05:59 TD
A.Node	
ΔT = 353s	Alt. = 73°
Gam. = 0.2920	Dur. = 04m02s

Annular	2242 Jan 31
Saros 154	20:13 TD
D.Node	
ΔT = 354s	Alt. = 38°
Gam. = -0.7894	Dur. = 02m31s

Partial	2242 Jul 28
Saros 159	16:57 TD
A.Node	
ΔT = 355s	Alt. = 0°
Gam. = 1.1020	Mag. = 0.8005

Partial	2242 Dec 22
Saros 126	20:07 TD
D.Node	
ΔT = 356s	Alt. = 0°
Gam. = 1.2836	Mag. = 0.4750

Partial	2243 Jan 21
Saros 164	07:12 TD
D.Node	
ΔT = 356s	Alt. = 0°
Gam. = -1.4197	Mag. = 0.2239

Annular	2243 Jun 18
Saros 131	05:50 TD
A.Node	
ΔT = 357s	Alt. = 20°
Gam. = -0.9342	Dur. = 06m41s

Total	2243 Dec 12
Saros 136	11:52 TD
D.Node	
ΔT = 358s	Alt. = 51°
Gam. = 0.6284	Dur. = 03m30s

Annular	2244 Jun 06
Saros 141	07:33 TD
A.Node	
ΔT = 359s	Alt. = 81°
Gam. = -0.1581	Dur. = 03m31s

Annular	2244 Dec 01
Saros 146	00:58 TD
D.Node	
ΔT = 360s	Alt. = 87°
Gam. = -0.0567	Dur. = 00m27s

Total	2245 May 26
Saros 151	15:42 TD
A.Node	
ΔT = 361s	Alt. = 52°
Gam. = 0.6089	Dur. = 01m30s

Plate 147

241

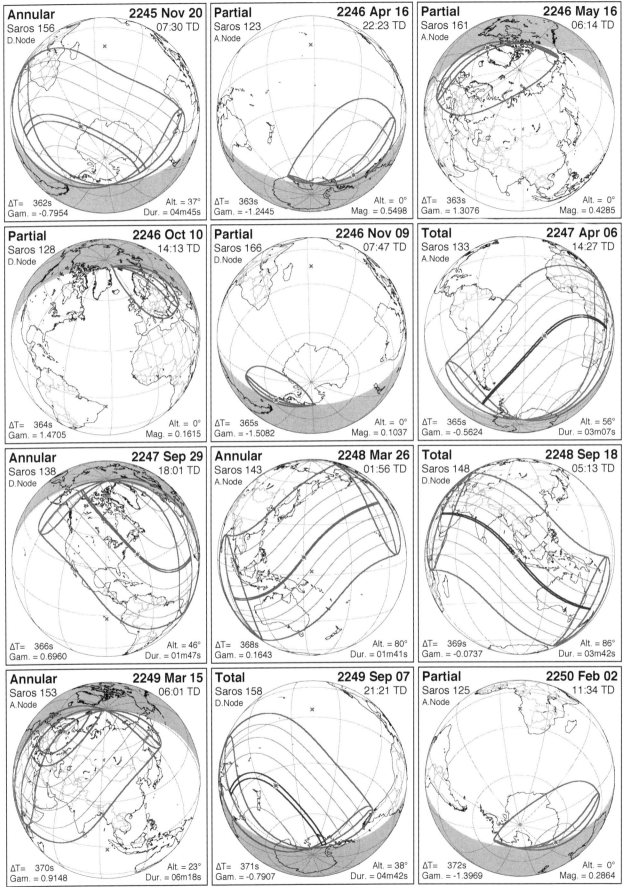

Plate 148

242

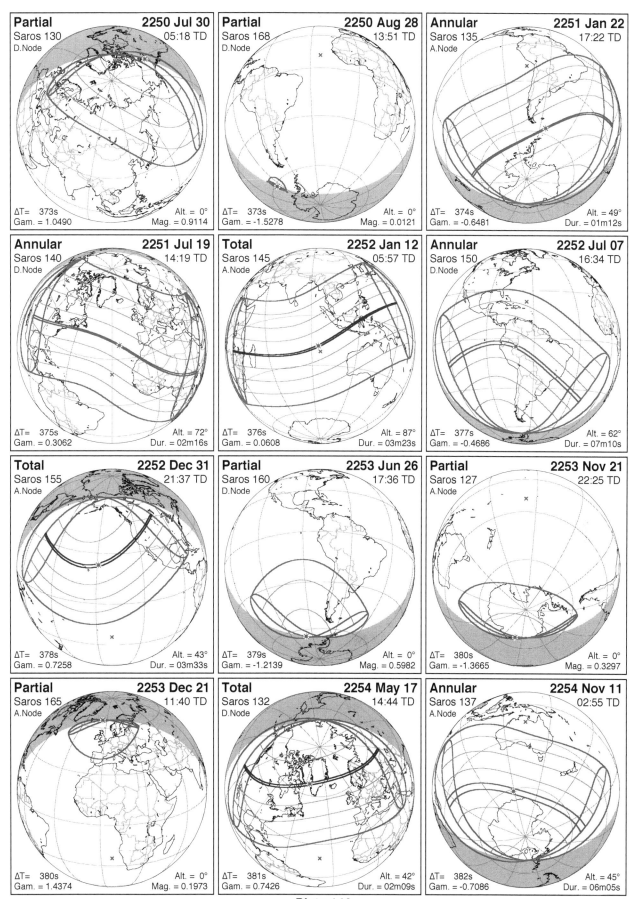

Partial 2250 Jul 30 Saros 130 05:18 TD D.Node	**Partial** 2250 Aug 28 Saros 168 13:51 TD D.Node	**Annular** 2251 Jan 22 Saros 135 17:22 TD A.Node
ΔT= 373s Alt. = 0° Gam. = 1.0490 Mag. = 0.9114	ΔT= 373s Alt. = 0° Gam. = -1.5278 Mag. = 0.0121	ΔT= 374s Alt. = 49° Gam. = -0.6481 Dur. = 01m12s
Annular 2251 Jul 19 Saros 140 14:19 TD D.Node	**Total** 2252 Jan 12 Saros 145 05:57 TD A.Node	**Annular** 2252 Jul 07 Saros 150 16:34 TD D.Node
ΔT= 375s Alt. = 72° Gam. = 0.3062 Dur. = 02m16s	ΔT= 376s Alt. = 87° Gam. = 0.0608 Dur. = 03m23s	ΔT= 377s Alt. = 62° Gam. = -0.4686 Dur. = 07m10s
Total 2252 Dec 31 Saros 155 21:37 TD A.Node	**Partial** 2253 Jun 26 Saros 160 17:36 TD D.Node	**Partial** 2253 Nov 21 Saros 127 22:25 TD A.Node
ΔT= 378s Alt. = 43° Gam. = 0.7258 Dur. = 03m33s	ΔT= 379s Alt. = 0° Gam. = -1.2139 Mag. = 0.5982	ΔT= 380s Alt. = 0° Gam. = -1.3665 Mag. = 0.3297
Partial 2253 Dec 21 Saros 165 11:40 TD A.Node	**Total** 2254 May 17 Saros 132 14:44 TD D.Node	**Annular** 2254 Nov 11 Saros 137 02:55 TD A.Node
ΔT= 380s Alt. = 0° Gam. = 1.4374 Mag. = 0.1973	ΔT= 381s Alt. = 42° Gam. = 0.7426 Dur. = 02m09s	ΔT= 382s Alt. = 45° Gam. = -0.7086 Dur. = 06m05s

Plate 149

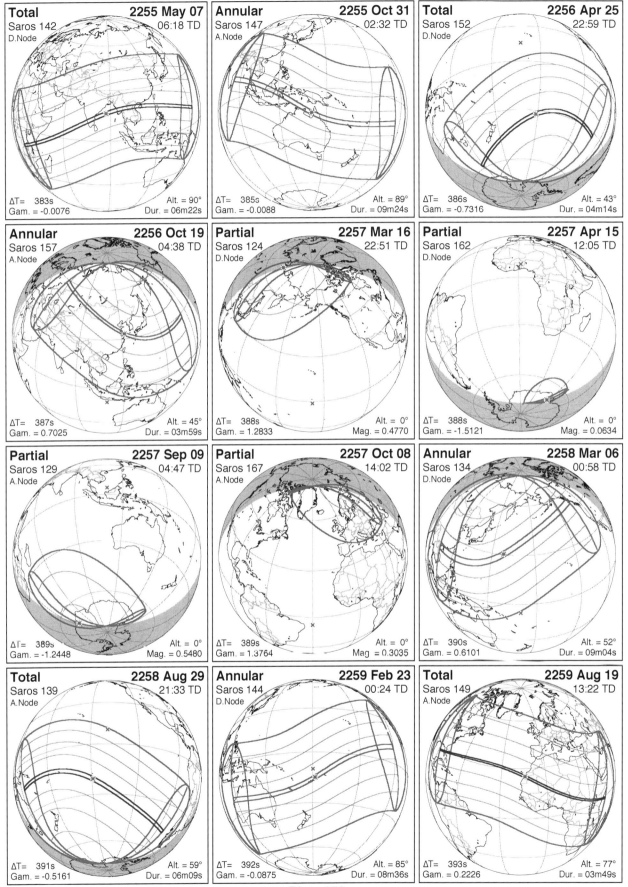

Total **2255 May 07** Saros 142 06:18 TD D.Node ΔT= 383s Alt. = 90° Gam. = -0.0076 Dur. = 06m22s	**Annular** **2255 Oct 31** Saros 147 02:32 TD A.Node ΔT= 385s Alt. = 89° Gam. = -0.0088 Dur. = 09m24s	**Total** **2256 Apr 25** Saros 152 22:59 TD D.Node ΔT= 386s Alt. = 43° Gam. = -0.7316 Dur. = 04m14s
Annular **2256 Oct 19** Saros 157 04:38 TD A.Node ΔT= 387s Alt. = 45° Gam. = 0.7025 Dur. = 03m59s	**Partial** **2257 Mar 16** Saros 124 22:51 TD D.Node ΔT= 388s Alt. = 0° Gam. = 1.2833 Mag. = 0.4770	**Partial** **2257 Apr 15** Saros 162 12:05 TD D.Node ΔT= 388s Alt. = 0° Gam. = -1.5121 Mag. = 0.0634
Partial **2257 Sep 09** Saros 129 04:47 TD A.Node ΔT= 389s Alt. = 0° Gam. = -1.2448 Mag. = 0.5480	**Partial** **2257 Oct 08** Saros 167 14:02 TD A.Node ΔT= 389s Alt. = 0° Gam. = 1.3764 Mag. = 0.3035	**Annular** **2258 Mar 06** Saros 134 00:58 TD D.Node ΔT= 390s Alt. = 52° Gam. = 0.6101 Dur. = 09m04s
Total **2258 Aug 29** Saros 139 21:33 TD A.Node ΔT= 391s Alt. = 59° Gam. = -0.5161 Dur. = 06m09s	**Annular** **2259 Feb 23** Saros 144 00:24 TD D.Node ΔT= 392s Alt. = 85° Gam. = -0.0875 Dur. = 08m36s	**Total** **2259 Aug 19** Saros 149 13:22 TD A.Node ΔT= 393s Alt. = 77° Gam. = 0.2226 Dur. = 03m49s

Plate 150

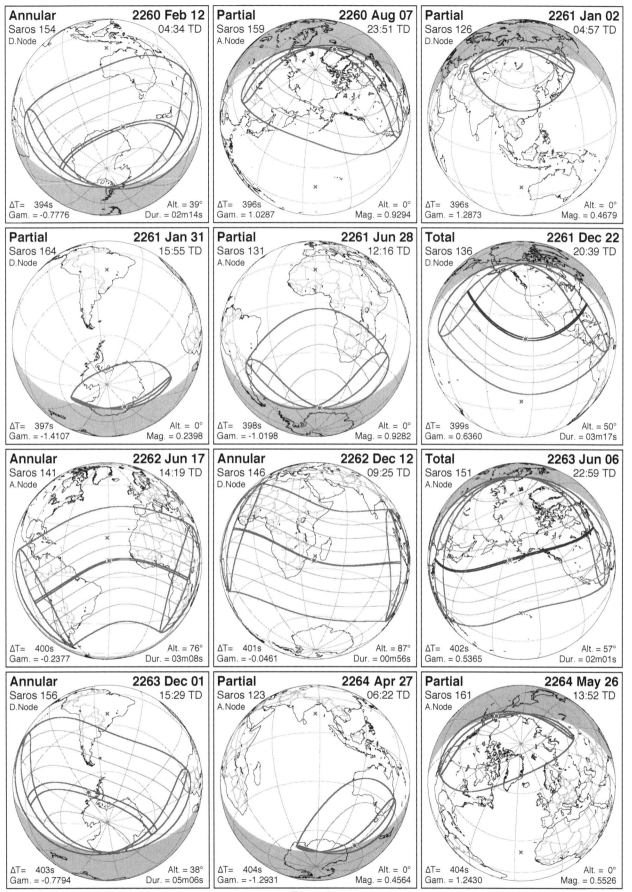

Annular 2260 Feb 12 Saros 154 04:34 TD D.Node	**Partial** 2260 Aug 07 Saros 159 23:51 TD A.Node	**Partial** 2261 Jan 02 Saros 126 04:57 TD D.Node
ΔT= 394s Alt. = 39° Gam. = -0.7776 Dur. = 02m14s	ΔT= 396s Alt. = 0° Gam. = 1.0287 Mag. = 0.9294	ΔT= 396s Alt. = 0° Gam. = 1.2873 Mag. = 0.4679
Partial 2261 Jan 31 Saros 164 15:55 TD D.Node	**Partial** 2261 Jun 28 Saros 131 12:16 TD A.Node	**Total** 2261 Dec 22 Saros 136 20:39 TD D.Node
ΔT= 397s Alt. = 0° Gam. = -1.4107 Mag. = 0.2398	ΔT= 398s Alt. = 0° Gam. = -1.0198 Mag. = 0.9282	ΔT= 399s Alt. = 50° Gam. = 0.6360 Dur. = 03m17s
Annular 2262 Jun 17 Saros 141 14:19 TD A.Node	**Annular** 2262 Dec 12 Saros 146 09:25 TD D.Node	**Total** 2263 Jun 06 Saros 151 22:59 TD A.Node
ΔT= 400s Alt. = 76° Gam. = -0.2377 Dur. = 03m08s	ΔT= 401s Alt. = 87° Gam. = -0.0461 Dur. = 00m56s	ΔT= 402s Alt. = 57° Gam. = 0.5365 Dur. = 02m01s
Annular 2263 Dec 01 Saros 156 15:29 TD D.Node	**Partial** 2264 Apr 27 Saros 123 06:22 TD A.Node	**Partial** 2264 May 26 Saros 161 13:52 TD A.Node
ΔT= 403s Alt. = 38° Gam. = -0.7794 Dur. = 05m06s	ΔT= 404s Alt. = 0° Gam. = -1.2931 Mag. = 0.4564	ΔT= 404s Alt. = 0° Gam. = 1.2430 Mag. = 0.5526

Plate 151

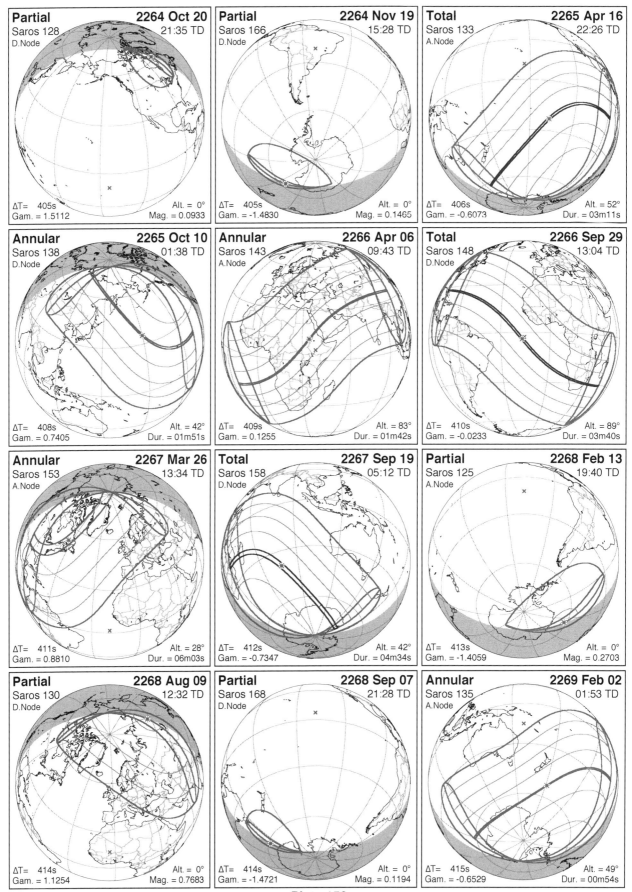

Partial	2264 Oct 20
Saros 128	21:35 TD
D.Node	
ΔT= 405s	Alt. = 0°
Gam. = 1.5112	Mag. = 0.0933

Partial	2264 Nov 19
Saros 166	15:28 TD
D.Node	
ΔT= 405s	Alt. = 0°
Gam. = -1.4830	Mag. = 0.1465

Total	2265 Apr 16
Saros 133	22:26 TD
A.Node	
ΔT= 406s	Alt. = 52°
Gam. = -0.6073	Dur. = 03m11s

Annular	2265 Oct 10
Saros 138	01:38 TD
D.Node	
ΔT= 408s	Alt. = 42°
Gam. = 0.7405	Dur. = 01m51s

Annular	2266 Apr 06
Saros 143	09:43 TD
A.Node	
ΔT= 409s	Alt. = 83°
Gam. = 0.1255	Dur. = 01m42s

Total	2266 Sep 29
Saros 148	13:04 TD
D.Node	
ΔT= 410s	Alt. = 89°
Gam. = -0.0233	Dur. = 03m40s

Annular	2267 Mar 26
Saros 153	13:34 TD
A.Node	
ΔT= 411s	Alt. = 28°
Gam. = 0.8810	Dur. = 06m03s

Total	2267 Sep 19
Saros 158	05:12 TD
D.Node	
ΔT= 412s	Alt. = 42°
Gam. = -0.7347	Dur. = 04m34s

Partial	2268 Feb 13
Saros 125	19:40 TD
A.Node	
ΔT= 413s	Alt. = 0°
Gam. = -1.4059	Mag. = 0.2703

Partial	2268 Aug 09
Saros 130	12:32 TD
D.Node	
ΔT= 414s	Alt. = 0°
Gam. = 1.1254	Mag. = 0.7683

Partial	2268 Sep 07
Saros 168	21:28 TD
D.Node	
ΔT= 414s	Alt. = 0°
Gam. = -1.4721	Mag. = 0.1194

Annular	2269 Feb 02
Saros 135	01:53 TD
A.Node	
ΔT= 415s	Alt. = 49°
Gam. = -0.6529	Dur. = 00m54s

Plate 152

246

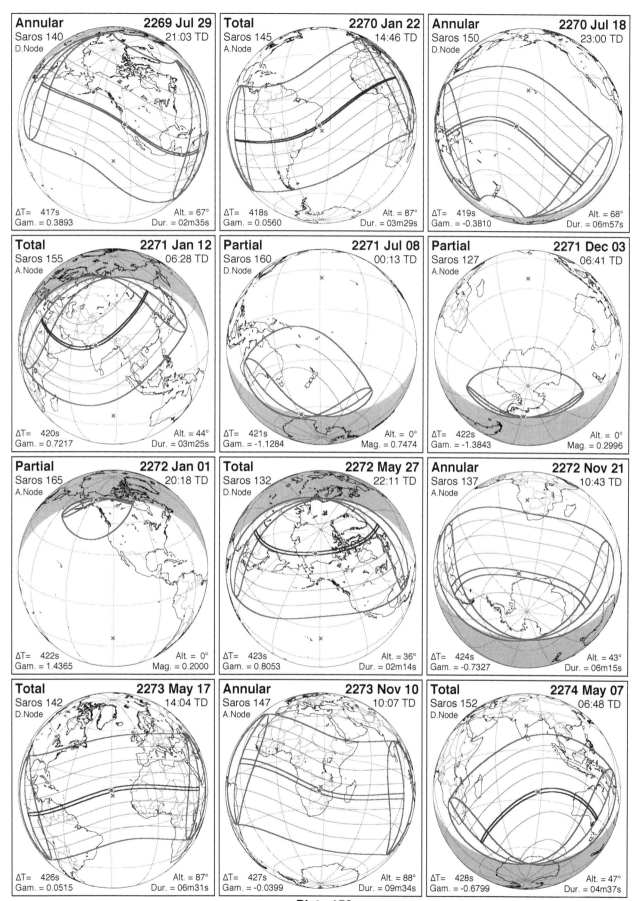

Annular **2269 Jul 29**	**Total** **2270 Jan 22**	**Annular** **2270 Jul 18**
Saros 140 21:03 TD	Saros 145 14:46 TD	Saros 150 23:00 TD
D.Node	A.Node	D.Node
ΔT= 417s Alt. = 67°	ΔT= 418s Alt. = 87°	ΔT= 419s Alt. = 68°
Gam. = 0.3893 Dur. = 02m35s	Gam. = 0.0560 Dur. = 03m29s	Gam. = -0.3810 Dur. = 06m57s
Total **2271 Jan 12**	**Partial** **2271 Jul 08**	**Partial** **2271 Dec 03**
Saros 155 06:28 TD	Saros 160 00:13 TD	Saros 127 06:41 TD
A.Node	D.Node	A.Node
ΔT= 420s Alt. = 44°	ΔT= 421s Alt. = 0°	ΔT= 422s Alt. = 0°
Gam. = 0.7217 Dur. = 03m25s	Gam. = -1.1284 Mag. = 0.7474	Gam. = -1.3843 Mag. = 0.2996
Partial **2272 Jan 01**	**Total** **2272 May 27**	**Annular** **2272 Nov 21**
Saros 165 20:18 TD	Saros 132 22:11 TD	Saros 137 10:43 TD
A.Node	D.Node	A.Node
ΔT= 422s Alt. = 0°	ΔT= 423s Alt. = 36°	ΔT= 424s Alt. = 43°
Gam. = 1.4365 Mag. = 0.2000	Gam. = 0.8053 Dur. = 02m14s	Gam. = -0.7327 Dur. = 06m15s
Total **2273 May 17**	**Annular** **2273 Nov 10**	**Total** **2274 May 07**
Saros 142 14:04 TD	Saros 147 10:07 TD	Saros 152 06:48 TD
D.Node	A.Node	D.Node
ΔT= 426s Alt. = 87°	ΔT= 427s Alt. = 88°	ΔT= 428s Alt. = 47°
Gam. = 0.0515 Dur. = 06m31s	Gam. = -0.0399 Dur. = 09m34s	Gam. = -0.6799 Dur. = 04m37s

Plate 153

247

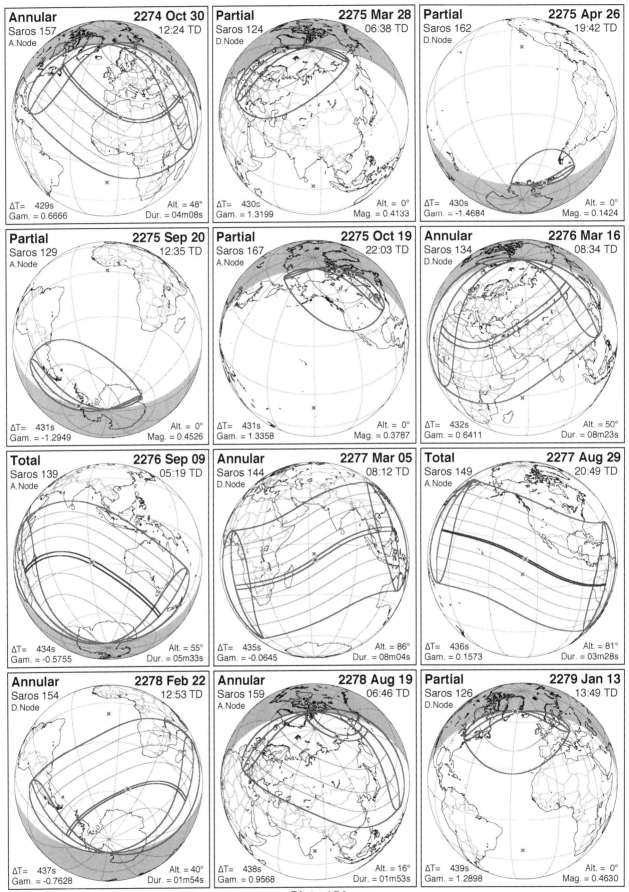

Annular 2274 Oct 30 Saros 157 12:24 TD A.Node ΔT= 429s Alt. = 48° Gam. = 0.6666 Dur. = 04m08s	**Partial** 2275 Mar 28 Saros 124 06:38 TD D.Node ΔT= 430s Alt. = 0° Gam. = 1.3199 Mag. = 0.4133	**Partial** 2275 Apr 26 Saros 162 19:42 TD D.Node ΔT= 430s Alt. = 0° Gam. = -1.4684 Mag. = 0.1424
Partial 2275 Sep 20 Saros 129 12:35 TD A.Node ΔT= 431s Alt. = 0° Gam. = -1.2949 Mag. = 0.4526	**Partial** 2275 Oct 19 Saros 167 22:03 TD A.Node ΔT= 431s Alt. = 0° Gam. = 1.3358 Mag. = 0.3787	**Annular** 2276 Mar 16 Saros 134 08:34 TD D.Node ΔT= 432s Alt. = 50° Gam. = 0.6411 Dur. = 08m23s
Total 2276 Sep 09 Saros 139 05:19 TD A.Node ΔT= 434s Alt. = 55° Gam. = -0.5755 Dur. = 05m33s	**Annular** 2277 Mar 05 Saros 144 08:12 TD D.Node ΔT= 435s Alt. = 86° Gam. = -0.0645 Dur. = 08m04s	**Total** 2277 Aug 29 Saros 149 20:49 TD A.Node ΔT= 436s Alt. = 81° Gam. = 0.1573 Dur. = 03m28s
Annular 2278 Feb 22 Saros 154 12:53 TD D.Node ΔT= 437s Alt. = 40° Gam. = -0.7628 Dur. = 01m54s	**Annular** 2278 Aug 19 Saros 159 06:46 TD A.Node ΔT= 438s Alt. = 16° Gam. = 0.9568 Dur. = 01m53s	**Partial** 2279 Jan 13 Saros 126 13:49 TD D.Node ΔT= 439s Alt. = 0° Gam. = 1.2898 Mag. = 0.4630

Plate 154

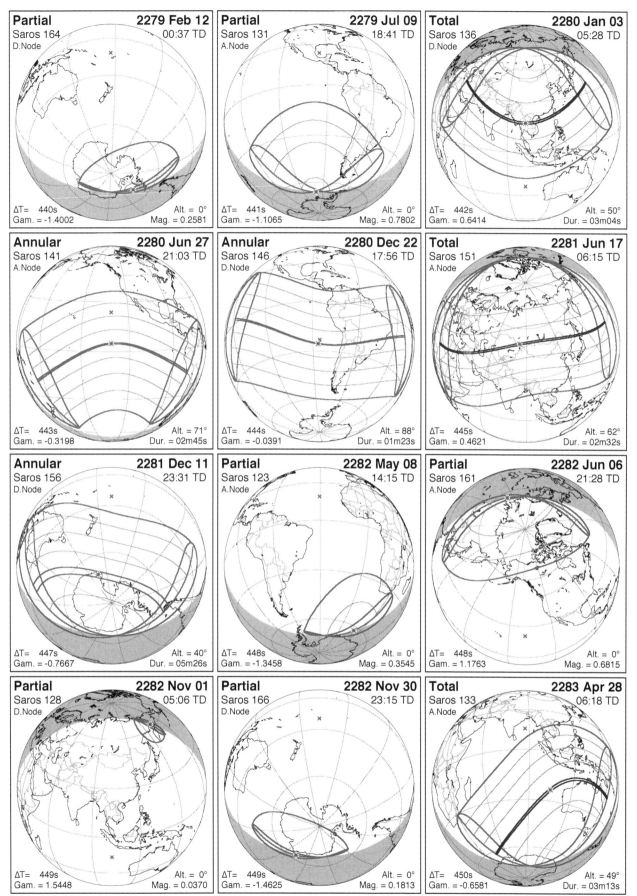

Partial 2279 Feb 12	**Partial** 2279 Jul 09	**Total** 2280 Jan 03
Saros 164 00:37 TD	Saros 131 18:41 TD	Saros 136 05:28 TD
D.Node	A.Node	D.Node
ΔT= 440s Alt. = 0°	ΔT= 441s Alt. = 0°	ΔT= 442s Alt. = 50°
Gam. = -1.4002 Mag. = 0.2581	Gam. = -1.1065 Mag. = 0.7802	Gam. = 0.6414 Dur. = 03m04s
Annular 2280 Jun 27	**Annular** 2280 Dec 22	**Total** 2281 Jun 17
Saros 141 21:03 TD	Saros 146 17:56 TD	Saros 151 06:15 TD
A.Node	D.Node	A.Node
ΔT= 443s Alt. = 71°	ΔT= 444s Alt. = 88°	ΔT= 445s Alt. = 62°
Gam. = -0.3198 Dur. = 02m45s	Gam. = -0.0391 Dur. = 01m23s	Gam. = 0.4621 Dur. = 02m32s
Annular 2281 Dec 11	**Partial** 2282 May 08	**Partial** 2282 Jun 06
Saros 156 23:31 TD	Saros 123 14:15 TD	Saros 161 21:28 TD
D.Node	A.Node	A.Node
ΔT= 447s Alt. = 40°	ΔT= 448s Alt. = 0°	ΔT= 448s Alt. = 0°
Gam. = -0.7667 Dur. = 05m26s	Gam. = -1.3458 Mag. = 0.3545	Gam. = 1.1763 Mag. = 0.6815
Partial 2282 Nov 01	**Partial** 2282 Nov 30	**Total** 2283 Apr 28
Saros 128 05:06 TD	Saros 166 23:15 TD	Saros 133 06:18 TD
D.Node	D.Node	A.Node
ΔT= 449s Alt. = 0°	ΔT= 449s Alt. = 0°	ΔT= 450s Alt. = 49°
Gam. = 1.5448 Mag. = 0.0370	Gam. = -1.4625 Mag. = 0.1813	Gam. = -0.6581 Dur. = 03m13s

Plate 155

249

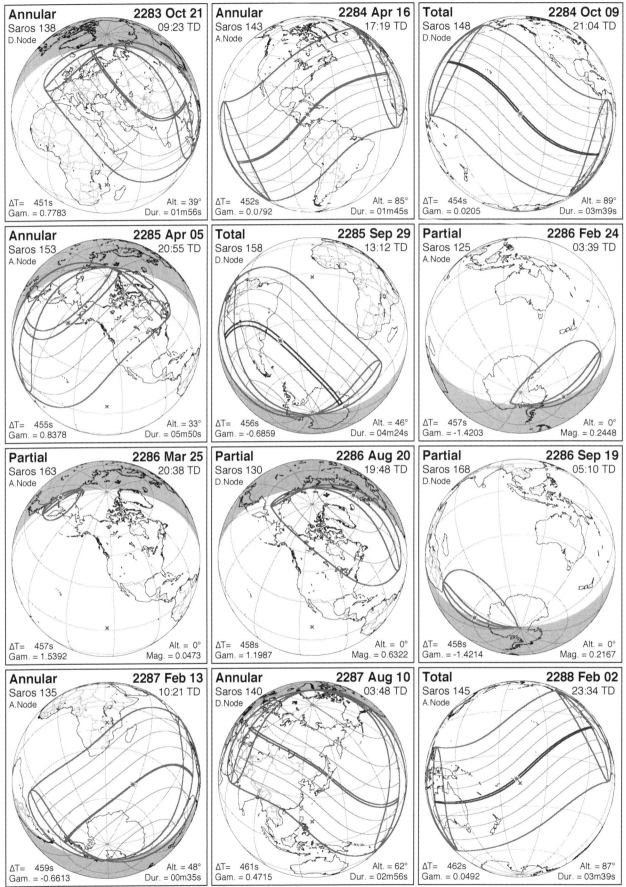

Annular   **2283 Oct 21**
Saros 138   09:23 TD
D.Node
ΔT= 451s   Alt. = 39°
Gam. = 0.7783   Dur. = 01m56s

Annular   **2284 Apr 16**
Saros 143   17:19 TD
A.Node
ΔT= 452s   Alt. = 85°
Gam. = 0.0792   Dur. = 01m45s

Total   **2284 Oct 09**
Saros 148   21:04 TD
D.Node
ΔT= 454s   Alt. = 89°
Gam. = 0.0205   Dur. = 03m39s

Annular   **2285 Apr 05**
Saros 153   20:55 TD
A.Node
ΔT= 455s   Alt. = 33°
Gam. = 0.8378   Dur. = 05m50s

Total   **2285 Sep 29**
Saros 158   13:12 TD
D.Node
ΔT= 456s   Alt. = 46°
Gam. = -0.6859   Dur. = 04m24s

Partial   **2286 Feb 24**
Saros 125   03:39 TD
A.Node
ΔT= 457s   Alt. = 0°
Gam. = -1.4203   Mag. = 0.2448

Partial   **2286 Mar 25**
Saros 163   20:38 TD
A.Node
ΔT= 457s   Alt. = 0°
Gam. = 1.5392   Mag. = 0.0473

Partial   **2286 Aug 20**
Saros 130   19:48 TD
D.Node
ΔT= 458s   Alt. = 0°
Gam. = 1.1987   Mag. = 0.6322

Partial   **2286 Sep 19**
Saros 168   05:10 TD
D.Node
ΔT= 458s   Alt. = 0°
Gam. = -1.4214   Mag. = 0.2167

Annular   **2287 Feb 13**
Saros 135   10:21 TD
A.Node
ΔT= 459s   Alt. = 48°
Gam. = -0.6613   Dur. = 00m35s

Annular   **2287 Aug 10**
Saros 140   03:48 TD
D.Node
ΔT= 461s   Alt. = 62°
Gam. = 0.4715   Dur. = 02m56s

Total   **2288 Feb 02**
Saros 145   23:34 TD
A.Node
ΔT= 462s   Alt. = 87°
Gam. = 0.0492   Dur. = 03m39s

Plate 156

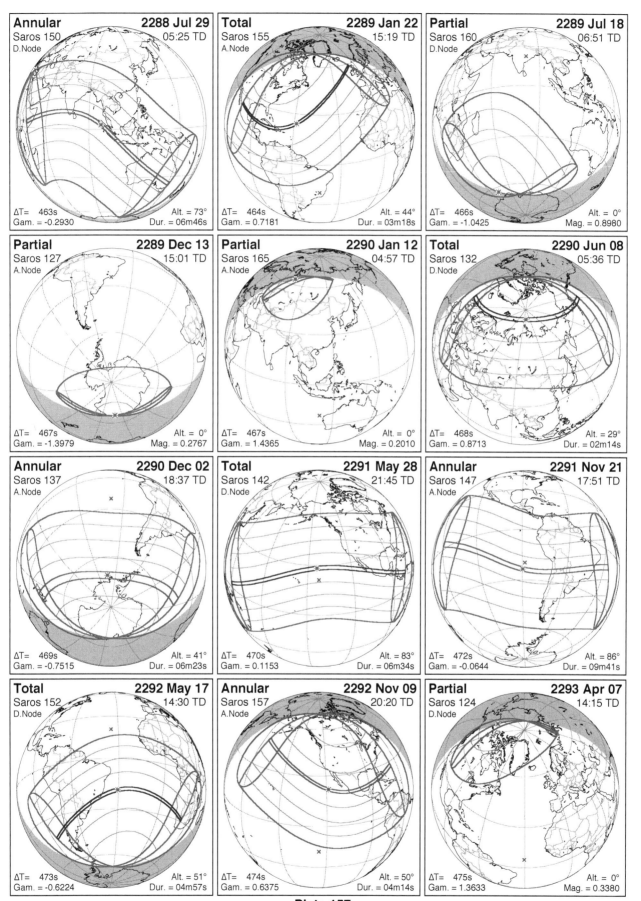

Annular **2288 Jul 29** Saros 150 05:25 TD D.Node ΔT= 463s Alt. = 73° Gam. = -0.2930 Dur. = 06m46s	**Total** **2289 Jan 22** Saros 155 15:19 TD A.Node ΔT= 464s Alt. = 44° Gam. = 0.7181 Dur. = 03m18s	**Partial** **2289 Jul 18** Saros 160 06:51 TD D.Node ΔT= 466s Alt. = 0° Gam. = -1.0425 Mag. = 0.8980
Partial **2289 Dec 13** Saros 127 15:01 TD A.Node ΔT= 467s Alt. = 0° Gam. = -1.3979 Mag. = 0.2767	**Partial** **2290 Jan 12** Saros 165 04:57 TD A.Node ΔT= 467s Alt. = 0° Gam. = 1.4365 Mag. = 0.2010	**Total** **2290 Jun 08** Saros 132 05:36 TD D.Node ΔT= 468s Alt. = 29° Gam. = 0.8713 Dur. = 02m14s
Annular **2290 Dec 02** Saros 137 18:37 TD A.Node ΔT= 469s Alt. = 41° Gam. = -0.7515 Dur. = 06m23s	**Total** **2291 May 28** Saros 142 21:45 TD D.Node ΔT= 470s Alt. = 83° Gam. = 0.1153 Dur. = 06m34s	**Annular** **2291 Nov 21** Saros 147 17:51 TD A.Node ΔT= 472s Alt. = 86° Gam. = -0.0644 Dur. = 09m41s
Total **2292 May 17** Saros 152 14:30 TD D.Node ΔT= 473s Alt. = 51° Gam. = -0.6224 Dur. = 04m57s	**Annular** **2292 Nov 09** Saros 157 20:20 TD A.Node ΔT= 474s Alt. = 50° Gam. = 0.6375 Dur. = 04m14s	**Partial** **2293 Apr 07** Saros 124 14:15 TD D.Node ΔT= 475s Alt. = 0° Gam. = 1.3633 Mag. = 0.3380

Plate 157

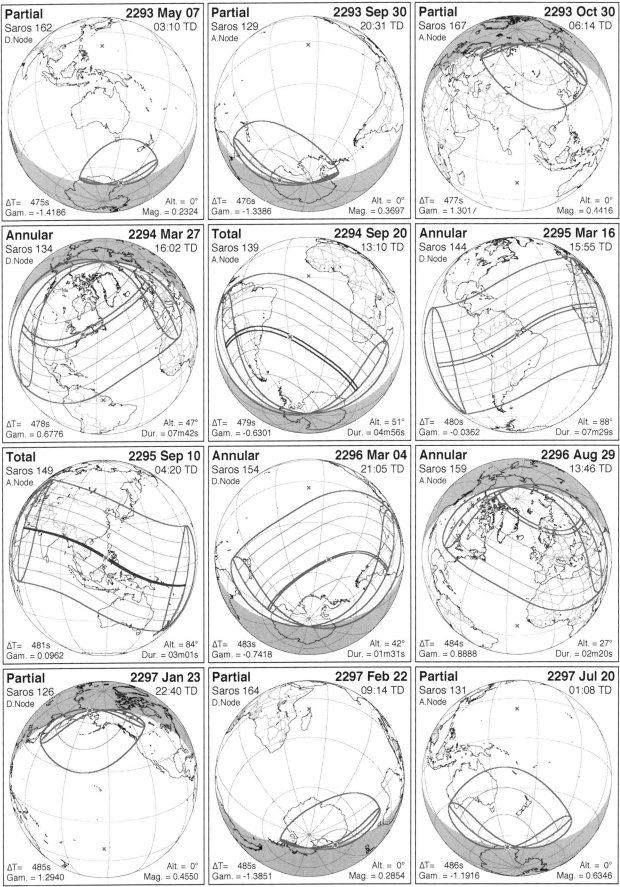

Plate 158

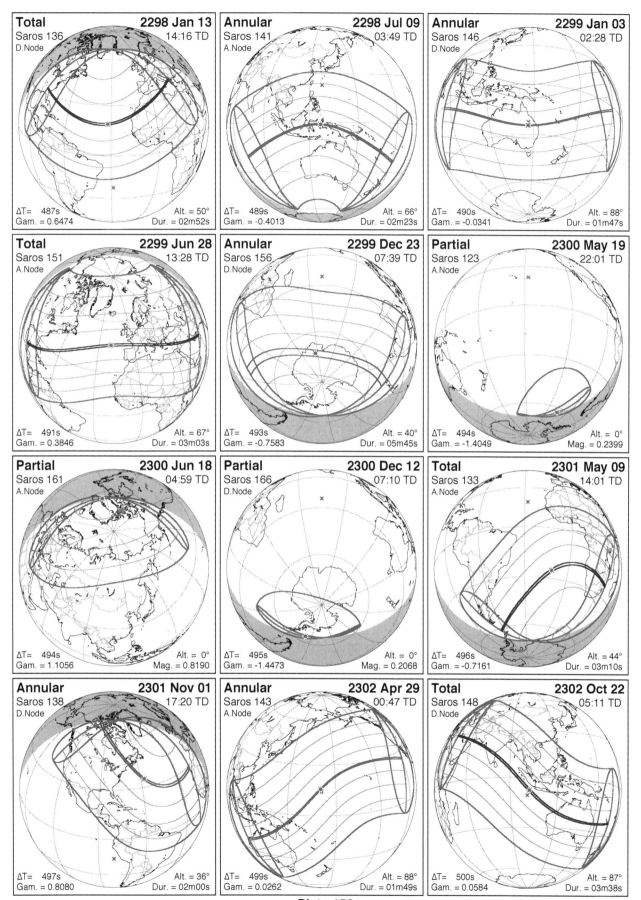

Total 2298 Jan 13	**Annular** 2298 Jul 09	**Annular** 2299 Jan 03
Saros 136 14:16 TD	Saros 141 03:49 TD	Saros 146 02:28 TD
D.Node	A.Node	D.Node
ΔT= 487s Alt. = 50°	ΔT= 489s Alt. = 66°	ΔT= 490s Alt. = 88°
Gam. = 0.6474 Dur. = 02m52s	Gam. = -0.4013 Dur. = 02m23s	Gam. = -0.0341 Dur. = 01m47s
Total 2299 Jun 28	**Annular** 2299 Dec 23	**Partial** 2300 May 19
Saros 151 13:28 TD	Saros 156 07:39 TD	Saros 123 22:01 TD
A.Node	D.Node	A.Node
ΔT= 491s Alt. = 67°	ΔT= 493s Alt. = 40°	ΔT= 494s Alt. = 0°
Gam. = 0.3846 Dur. = 03m03s	Gam. = -0.7583 Dur. = 05m45s	Gam. = -1.4049 Mag. = 0.2399
Partial 2300 Jun 18	**Partial** 2300 Dec 12	**Total** 2301 May 09
Saros 161 04:59 TD	Saros 166 07:10 TD	Saros 133 14:01 TD
A.Node	D.Node	A.Node
ΔT= 494s Alt. = 0°	ΔT= 495s Alt. = 0°	ΔT= 496s Alt. = 44°
Gam. = 1.1056 Mag. = 0.8190	Gam. = -1.4473 Mag. = 0.2068	Gam. = -0.7161 Dur. = 03m10s
Annular 2301 Nov 01	**Annular** 2302 Apr 29	**Total** 2302 Oct 22
Saros 138 17:20 TD	Saros 143 00:47 TD	Saros 148 05:11 TD
D.Node	A.Node	D.Node
ΔT= 497s Alt. = 36°	ΔT= 499s Alt. = 88°	ΔT= 500s Alt. = 87°
Gam. = 0.8080 Dur. = 02m00s	Gam. = 0.0262 Dur. = 01m49s	Gam. = 0.0584 Dur. = 03m38s

Plate 159

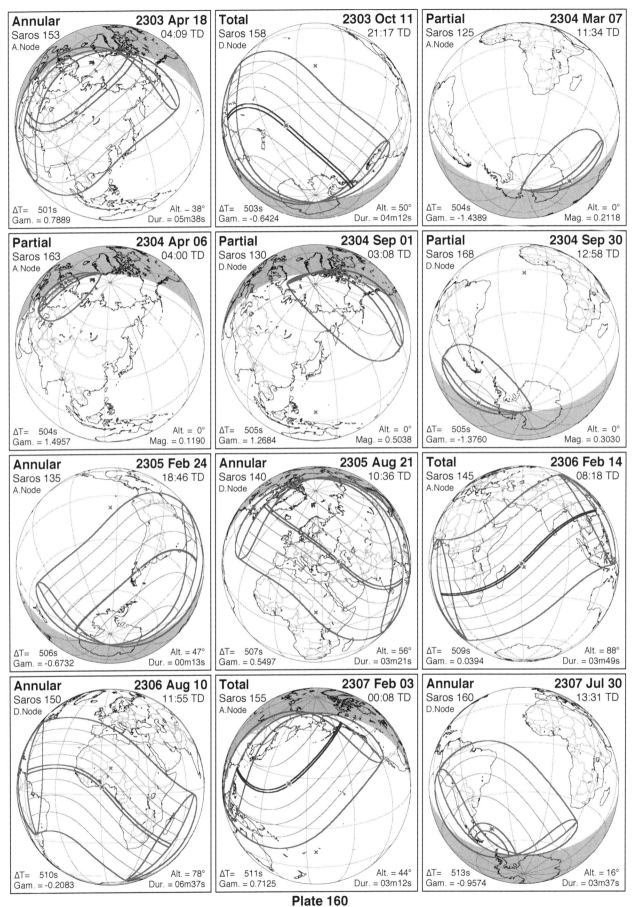

Annular 2303 Apr 18 Saros 153 A.Node 04:09 TD ΔT= 501s Alt. – 38° Gam. = 0.7889 Dur. = 05m38s	**Total** 2303 Oct 11 Saros 158 D.Node 21:17 TD ΔT= 503s Alt. = 50° Gam. = -0.6424 Dur. = 04m12s	**Partial** 2304 Mar 07 Saros 125 A.Node 11:34 TD ΔT= 504s Alt. = 0° Gam. = -1.4389 Mag. = 0.2118
Partial 2304 Apr 06 Saros 163 A.Node 04:00 TD ΔT= 504s Alt. = 0° Gam. = 1.4957 Mag. = 0.1190	**Partial** 2304 Sep 01 Saros 130 D.Node 03:08 TD ΔT= 505s Alt. = 0° Gam. = 1.2684 Mag. = 0.5038	**Partial** 2304 Sep 30 Saros 168 D.Node 12:58 TD ΔT= 505s Alt. = 0° Gam. = -1.3760 Mag. = 0.3030
Annular 2305 Feb 24 Saros 135 A.Node 18:46 TD ΔT= 506s Alt. = 47° Gam. = -0.6732 Dur. = 00m13s	**Annular** 2305 Aug 21 Saros 140 D.Node 10:36 TD ΔT= 507s Alt. = 56° Gam. = 0.5497 Dur. = 03m21s	**Total** 2306 Feb 14 Saros 145 A.Node 08:18 TD ΔT= 509s Alt. = 88° Gam. = 0.0394 Dur. = 03m49s
Annular 2306 Aug 10 Saros 150 D.Node 11:55 TD ΔT= 510s Alt. = 78° Gam. = -0.2083 Dur. = 06m37s	**Total** 2307 Feb 03 Saros 155 A.Node 00:08 TD ΔT= 511s Alt. = 44° Gam. = 0.7125 Dur. = 03m12s	**Annular** 2307 Jul 30 Saros 160 D.Node 13:31 TD ΔT= 513s Alt. = 16° Gam. = -0.9574 Dur. = 03m37s

Plate 160

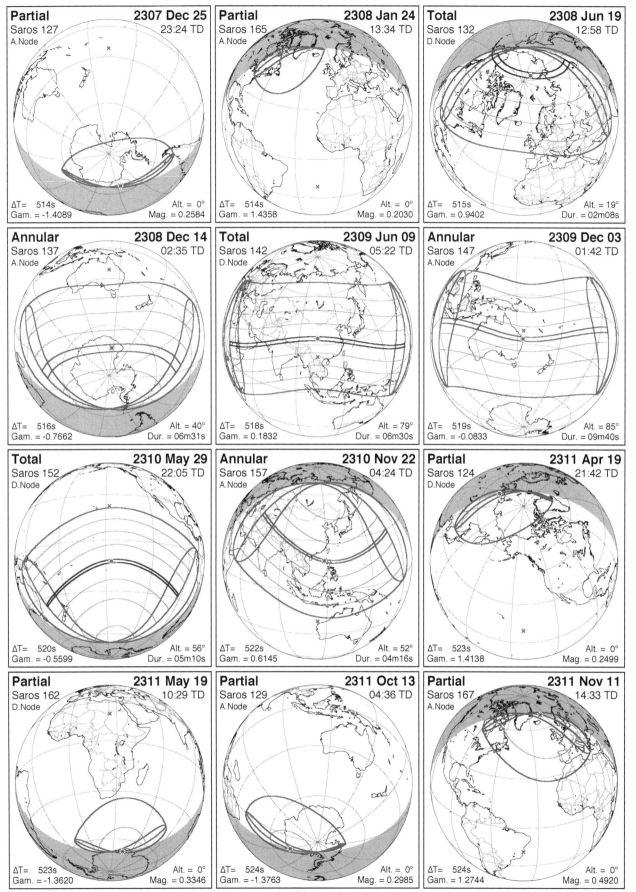

Partial **2307 Dec 25**	
Saros 127 23:24 TD	
A.Node	
ΔT= 514s Alt. = 0°	
Gam. = -1.4089 Mag. = 0.2584	

Plate 161

255

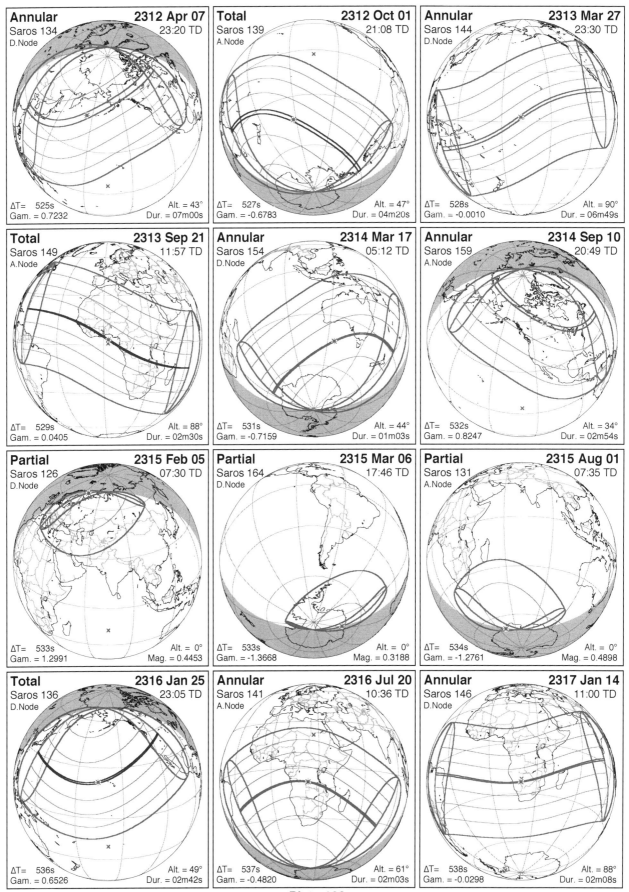

Annular	**2312 Apr 07**
Saros 134	23:20 TD
D.Node	
ΔT= 525s	Alt. = 43°
Gam. = 0.7232	Dur. = 07m00s

Total	**2312 Oct 01**
Saros 139	21:08 TD
A.Node	
ΔT= 527s	Alt. = 47°
Gam. = -0.6783	Dur. = 04m20s

Annular	**2313 Mar 27**
Saros 144	23:30 TD
D.Node	
ΔT= 528s	Alt. = 90°
Gam. = -0.0010	Dur. = 06m49s

Total	**2313 Sep 21**
Saros 149	11:57 TD
A.Node	
ΔT= 529s	Alt. = 88°
Gam. = 0.0405	Dur. = 02m30s

Annular	**2314 Mar 17**
Saros 154	05:12 TD
D.Node	
ΔT= 531s	Alt. = 44°
Gam. = -0.7159	Dur. = 01m03s

Annular	**2314 Sep 10**
Saros 159	20:49 TD
A.Node	
ΔT= 532s	Alt. = 34°
Gam. = 0.8247	Dur. = 02m54s

Partial	**2315 Feb 05**
Saros 126	07:30 TD
D.Node	
ΔT= 533s	Alt. = 0°
Gam. = 1.2991	Mag. = 0.4453

Partial	**2315 Mar 06**
Saros 164	17:46 TD
D.Node	
ΔT= 533s	Alt. = 0°
Gam. = -1.3668	Mag. = 0.3188

Partial	**2315 Aug 01**
Saros 131	07:35 TD
A.Node	
ΔT= 534s	Alt. = 0°
Gam. = -1.2761	Mag. = 0.4898

Total	**2316 Jan 25**
Saros 136	23:05 TD
D.Node	
ΔT= 536s	Alt. = 49°
Gam. = 0.6526	Dur. = 02m42s

Annular	**2316 Jul 20**
Saros 141	10:36 TD
A.Node	
ΔT= 537s	Alt. = 61°
Gam. = -0.4820	Dur. = 02m03s

Annular	**2317 Jan 14**
Saros 146	11:00 TD
D.Node	
ΔT= 538s	Alt. = 88°
Gam. = -0.0298	Dur. = 02m08s

Plate 162

256

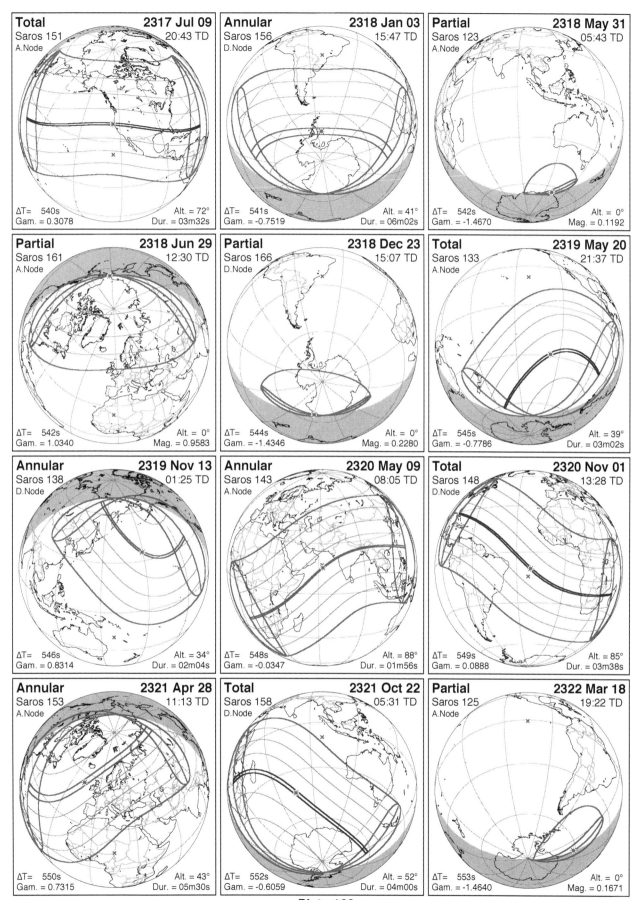

Total	**2317 Jul 09**
Saros 151	20:43 TD
A.Node	
ΔT= 540s	Alt. = 72°
Gam. = 0.3078	Dur. = 03m32s

Annular	**2318 Jan 03**
Saros 156	15:47 TD
D.Node	
ΔT= 541s	Alt. = 41°
Gam. = -0.7519	Dur. = 06m02s

Partial	**2318 May 31**
Saros 123	05:43 TD
A.Node	
ΔT= 542s	Alt. = 0°
Gam. = -1.4670	Mag. = 0.1192

Partial	**2318 Jun 29**
Saros 161	12:30 TD
A.Node	
ΔT= 542s	Alt. = 0°
Gam. = 1.0340	Mag. = 0.9583

Partial	**2318 Dec 23**
Saros 166	15:07 TD
D.Node	
ΔT= 544s	Alt. = 0°
Gam. = -1.4346	Mag. = 0.2280

Total	**2319 May 20**
Saros 133	21:37 TD
A.Node	
ΔT= 545s	Alt. = 39°
Gam. = -0.7786	Dur. = 03m02s

Annular	**2319 Nov 13**
Saros 138	01:25 TD
D.Node	
ΔT= 546s	Alt. = 34°
Gam. = 0.8314	Dur. = 02m04s

Annular	**2320 May 09**
Saros 143	08:05 TD
A.Node	
ΔT= 548s	Alt. = 88°
Gam. = -0.0347	Dur. = 01m56s

Total	**2320 Nov 01**
Saros 148	13:28 TD
D.Node	
ΔT= 549s	Alt. = 85°
Gam. = 0.0888	Dur. = 03m38s

Annular	**2321 Apr 28**
Saros 153	11:13 TD
A.Node	
ΔT= 550s	Alt. = 43°
Gam. = 0.7315	Dur. = 05m30s

Total	**2321 Oct 22**
Saros 158	05:31 TD
D.Node	
ΔT= 552s	Alt. = 52°
Gam. = -0.6059	Dur. = 04m00s

Partial	**2322 Mar 18**
Saros 125	19:22 TD
A.Node	
ΔT= 553s	Alt. = 0°
Gam. = -1.4640	Mag. = 0.1671

Plate 163

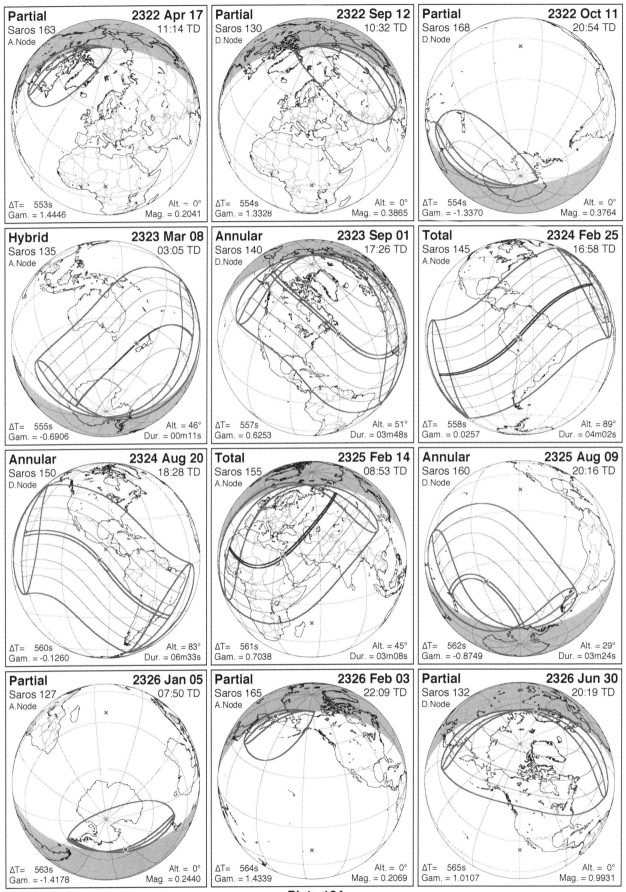

Partial **2322 Apr 17**	
Saros 163 11:14 TD	
A.Node	
ΔT= 553s Alt. = 0°	
Gam. = 1.4446 Mag. = 0.2041	

Partial **2322 Sep 12**	
Saros 130 10:32 TD	
D.Node	
ΔT= 554s Alt. = 0°	
Gam. = 1.3328 Mag. = 0.3865	

Partial **2322 Oct 11**	
Saros 168 20:54 TD	
D.Node	
ΔT= 554s Alt. = 0°	
Gam. = -1.3370 Mag. = 0.3764	

Hybrid **2323 Mar 08**	
Saros 135 03:05 TD	
A.Node	
ΔT= 555s Alt. = 46°	
Gam. = -0.6906 Dur. = 00m11s	

Annular **2323 Sep 01**	
Saros 140 17:26 TD	
D.Node	
ΔT= 557s Alt. = 51°	
Gam. = 0.6253 Dur. = 03m48s	

Total **2324 Feb 25**	
Saros 145 16:58 TD	
A.Node	
ΔT= 558s Alt. = 89°	
Gam. = 0.0257 Dur. = 04m02s	

Annular **2324 Aug 20**	
Saros 150 18:28 TD	
D.Node	
ΔT= 560s Alt. = 83°	
Gam. = -0.1260 Dur. = 06m33s	

Total **2325 Feb 14**	
Saros 155 08:53 TD	
A.Node	
ΔT= 561s Alt. = 45°	
Gam. = 0.7038 Dur. = 03m08s	

Annular **2325 Aug 09**	
Saros 160 20:16 TD	
D.Node	
ΔT= 562s Alt. = 29°	
Gam. = -0.8749 Dur. = 03m24s	

Partial **2326 Jan 05**	
Saros 127 07:50 TD	
A.Node	
ΔT= 563s Alt. = 0°	
Gam. = -1.4178 Mag. = 0.2440	

Partial **2326 Feb 03**	
Saros 165 22:09 TD	
A.Node	
ΔT= 564s Alt. = 0°	
Gam. = 1.4339 Mag. = 0.2069	

Partial **2326 Jun 30**	
Saros 132 20:19 TD	
D.Node	
ΔT= 565s Alt. = 0°	
Gam. = 1.0107 Mag. = 0.9931	

Plate 164

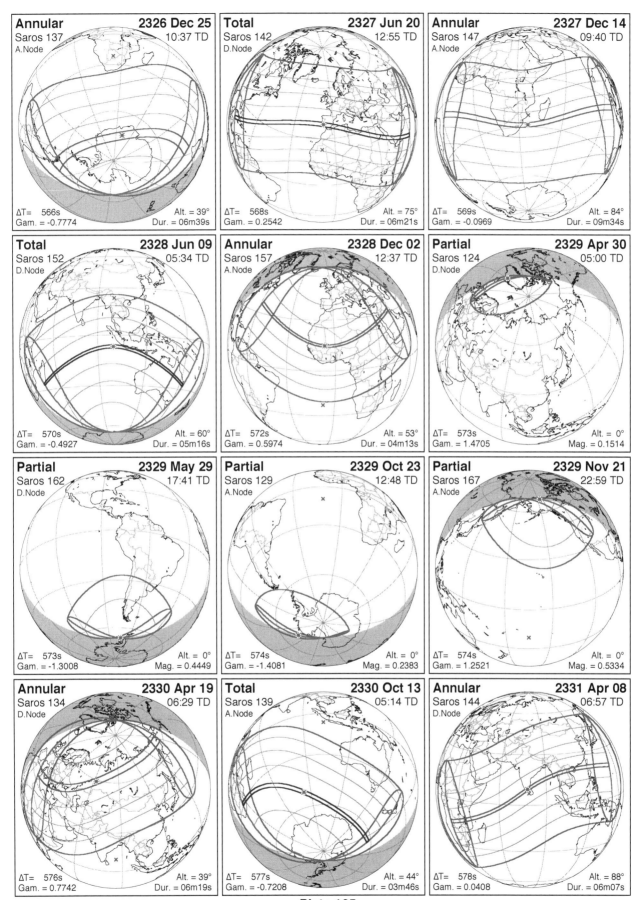

Annular **2326 Dec 25** Saros 137 10:37 TD A.Node	**Total** **2327 Jun 20** Saros 142 12:55 TD D.Node	**Annular** **2327 Dec 14** Saros 147 09:40 TD A.Node
ΔT= 566s Alt. = 39° Gam. = -0.7774 Dur. = 06m39s	ΔT= 568s Alt. = 75° Gam. = 0.2542 Dur. = 06m21s	ΔT= 569s Alt. = 84° Gam. = -0.0969 Dur. = 09m34s
Total **2328 Jun 09** Saros 152 05:34 TD D.Node	**Annular** **2328 Dec 02** Saros 157 12:37 TD A.Node	**Partial** **2329 Apr 30** Saros 124 05:00 TD D.Node
ΔT= 570s Alt. = 60° Gam. = -0.4927 Dur. = 05m16s	ΔT= 572s Alt. = 53° Gam. = 0.5974 Dur. = 04m13s	ΔT= 573s Alt. = 0° Gam. = 1.4705 Mag. = 0.1514
Partial **2329 May 29** Saros 162 17:41 TD D.Node	**Partial** **2329 Oct 23** Saros 129 12:48 TD A.Node	**Partial** **2329 Nov 21** Saros 167 22:59 TD A.Node
ΔT= 573s Alt. = 0° Gam. = -1.3008 Mag. = 0.4449	ΔT= 574s Alt. = 0° Gam. = -1.4081 Mag. = 0.2383	ΔT= 574s Alt. = 0° Gam. = 1.2521 Mag. = 0.5334
Annular **2330 Apr 19** Saros 134 06:29 TD D.Node	**Total** **2330 Oct 13** Saros 139 05:14 TD A.Node	**Annular** **2331 Apr 08** Saros 144 06:57 TD D.Node
ΔT= 576s Alt. = 39° Gam. = 0.7742 Dur. = 06m19s	ΔT= 577s Alt. = 44° Gam. = -0.7208 Dur. = 03m46s	ΔT= 578s Alt. = 88° Gam. = 0.0408 Dur. = 06m07s

Plate 165

259

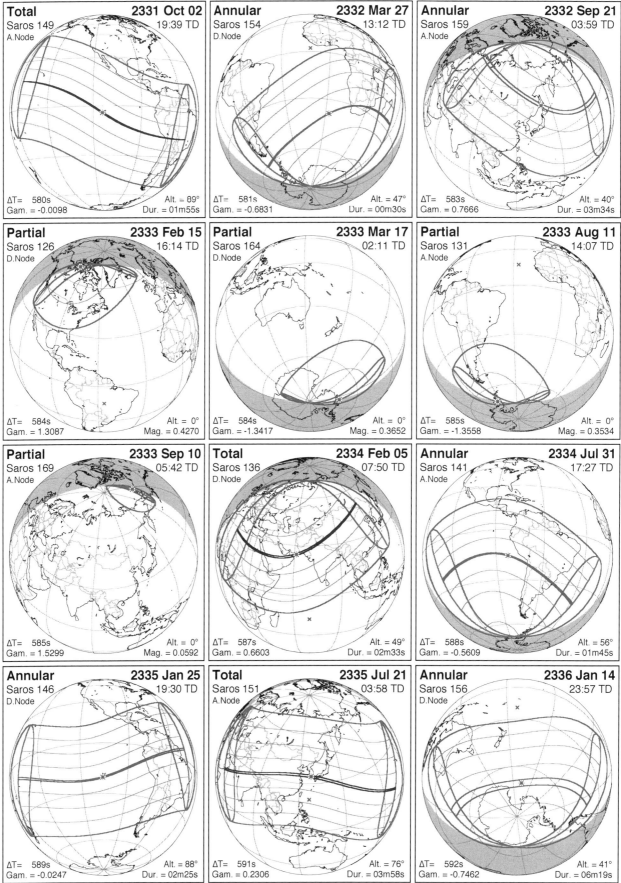

Total 2331 Oct 02 Saros 149 19:39 TD A.Node ΔT= 580s Alt. = 89° Gam. = -0.0098 Dur. = 01m55s	**Annular** 2332 Mar 27 Saros 154 13:12 TD D.Node ΔT= 581s Alt. = 47° Gam. = -0.6831 Dur. = 00m30s	**Annular** 2332 Sep 21 Saros 159 03:59 TD A.Node ΔT= 583s Alt. = 40° Gam. = 0.7666 Dur. = 03m34s
Partial 2333 Feb 15 Saros 126 16:14 TD D.Node ΔT= 584s Alt. = 0° Gam. = 1.3087 Mag. = 0.4270	**Partial** 2333 Mar 17 Saros 164 02:11 TD D.Node ΔT= 584s Alt. = 0° Gam. = -1.3417 Mag. = 0.3652	**Partial** 2333 Aug 11 Saros 131 14:07 TD A.Node ΔT= 585s Alt. = 0° Gam. = -1.3558 Mag. = 0.3534
Partial 2333 Sep 10 Saros 169 05:42 TD A.Node ΔT= 585s Alt. = 0° Gam. = 1.5299 Mag. = 0.0592	**Total** 2334 Feb 05 Saros 136 07:50 TD D.Node ΔT= 587s Alt. = 49° Gam. = 0.6603 Dur. = 02m33s	**Annular** 2334 Jul 31 Saros 141 17:27 TD A.Node ΔT= 588s Alt. = 56° Gam. = -0.5609 Dur. = 01m45s
Annular 2335 Jan 25 Saros 146 19:30 TD D.Node ΔT= 589s Alt. = 88° Gam. = -0.0247 Dur. = 02m25s	**Total** 2335 Jul 21 Saros 151 03:58 TD A.Node ΔT= 591s Alt. = 76° Gam. = 0.2306 Dur. = 03m58s	**Annular** 2336 Jan 14 Saros 156 23:57 TD D.Node ΔT= 592s Alt. = 41° Gam. = -0.7462 Dur. = 06m19s

Plate 166

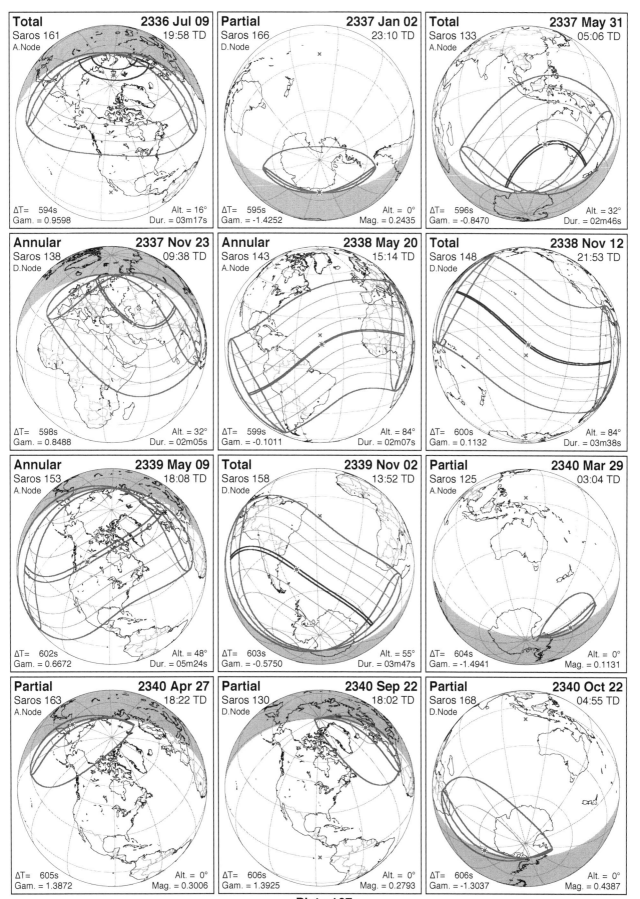

Total	2336 Jul 09
Saros 161	19:58 TD
A.Node	
ΔT= 594s	Alt. = 16°
Gam. = 0.9598	Dur. = 03m17s

Partial	2337 Jan 02
Saros 166	23:10 TD
D.Node	
ΔT= 595s	Alt. = 0°
Gam. = -1.4252	Mag. = 0.2435

Total	2337 May 31
Saros 133	05:06 TD
A.Node	
ΔT= 596s	Alt. = 32°
Gam. = -0.8470	Dur. = 02m46s

Annular	2337 Nov 23
Saros 138	09:38 TD
D.Node	
ΔT= 598s	Alt. = 32°
Gam. = 0.8488	Dur. = 02m05s

Annular	2338 May 20
Saros 143	15:14 TD
A.Node	
ΔT= 599s	Alt. = 84°
Gam. = -0.1011	Dur. = 02m07s

Total	2338 Nov 12
Saros 148	21:53 TD
D.Node	
ΔT= 600s	Alt. = 84°
Gam. = 0.1132	Dur. = 03m38s

Annular	2339 May 09
Saros 153	18:08 TD
A.Node	
ΔT= 602s	Alt. = 48°
Gam. = 0.6672	Dur. = 05m24s

Total	2339 Nov 02
Saros 158	13:52 TD
D.Node	
ΔT= 603s	Alt. = 55°
Gam. = -0.5750	Dur. = 03m47s

Partial	2340 Mar 29
Saros 125	03:04 TD
A.Node	
ΔT= 604s	Alt. = 0°
Gam. = -1.4941	Mag. = 0.1131

Partial	2340 Apr 27
Saros 163	18:22 TD
A.Node	
ΔT= 605s	Alt. = 0°
Gam. = 1.3872	Mag. = 0.3006

Partial	2340 Sep 22
Saros 130	18:02 TD
D.Node	
ΔT= 606s	Alt. = 0°
Gam. = 1.3925	Mag. = 0.2793

Partial	2340 Oct 22
Saros 168	04:55 TD
D.Node	
ΔT= 606s	Alt. = 0°
Gam. = -1.3037	Mag. = 0.4387

Plate 167

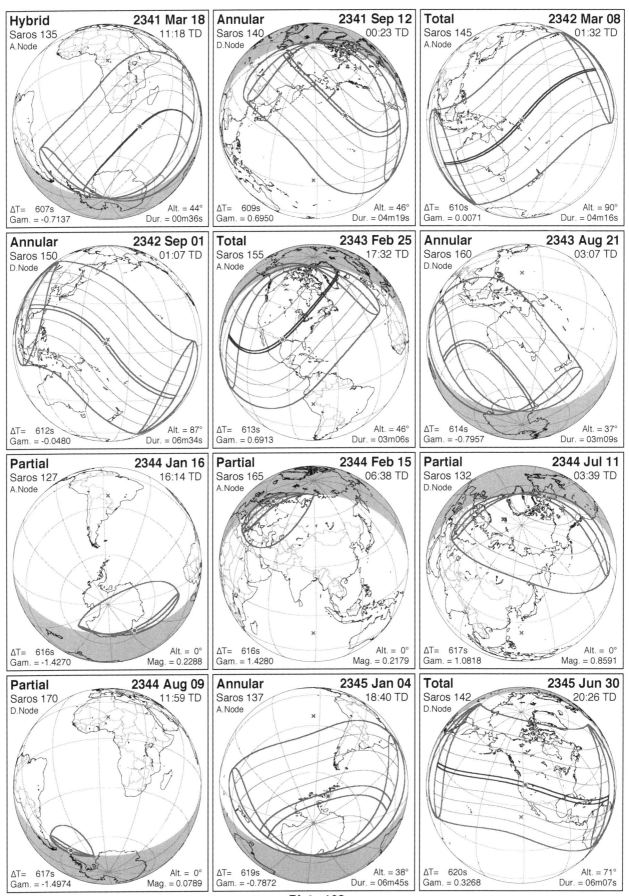

Hybrid 2341 Mar 18	Saros 135, A.Node, 11:18 TD, ΔT= 607s, Gam. = -0.7137, Alt. = 44°, Dur. = 00m36s
Annular 2341 Sep 12	Saros 140, D.Node, 00:23 TD, ΔT= 609s, Gam. = 0.6950, Alt. = 46°, Dur. = 04m19s
Total 2342 Mar 08	Saros 145, A.Node, 01:32 TD, ΔT= 610s, Gam. = 0.0071, Alt. = 90°, Dur. = 04m16s
Annular 2342 Sep 01	Saros 150, D.Node, 01:07 TD, ΔT= 612s, Gam. = -0.0480, Alt. = 87°, Dur. = 06m34s
Total 2343 Feb 25	Saros 155, A.Node, 17:32 TD, ΔT= 613s, Gam. = 0.6913, Alt. = 46°, Dur. = 03m06s
Annular 2343 Aug 21	Saros 160, D.Node, 03:07 TD, ΔT= 614s, Gam. = -0.7957, Alt. = 37°, Dur. = 03m09s
Partial 2344 Jan 16	Saros 127, A.Node, 16:14 TD, ΔT= 616s, Gam. = -1.4270, Alt. = 0°, Mag. = 0.2288
Partial 2344 Feb 15	Saros 165, A.Node, 06:38 TD, ΔT= 616s, Gam. = 1.4280, Alt. = 0°, Mag. = 0.2179
Partial 2344 Jul 11	Saros 132, D.Node, 03:39 TD, ΔT= 617s, Gam. = 1.0818, Alt. = 0°, Mag. = 0.8591
Partial 2344 Aug 09	Saros 170, D.Node, 11:59 TD, ΔT= 617s, Gam. = -1.4974, Alt. = 0°, Mag. = 0.0789
Annular 2345 Jan 04	Saros 137, A.Node, 18:40 TD, ΔT= 619s, Gam. = -0.7872, Alt. = 38°, Dur. = 06m45s
Total 2345 Jun 30	Saros 142, D.Node, 20:26 TD, ΔT= 620s, Gam. = 0.3268, Alt. = 71°, Dur. = 06m07s

Plate 168

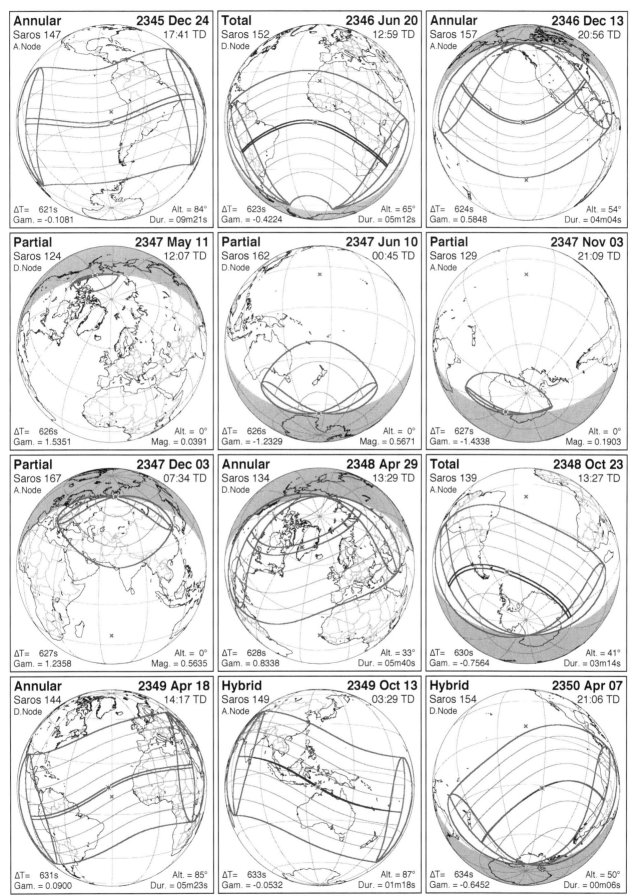

Annular **2345 Dec 24**	
Saros 147 17:41 TD	
A.Node	
ΔT= 621s Alt. = 84°	
Gam. = -0.1081 Dur. = 09m21s	

Plate 169

263

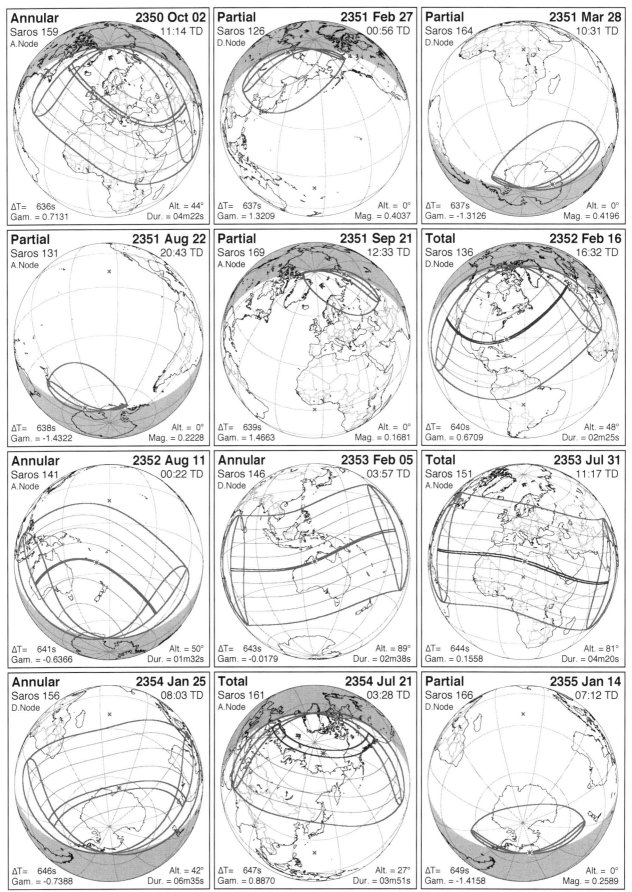

Annular 2350 Oct 02	**Partial** 2351 Feb 27	**Partial** 2351 Mar 28
Saros 159 11:14 TD	Saros 126 00:56 TD	Saros 164 10:31 TD
A.Node	D.Node	D.Node
ΔT= 636s Alt. = 44°	ΔT= 637s Alt. = 0°	ΔT= 637s Alt. = 0°
Gam. = 0.7131 Dur. = 04m22s	Gam. = 1.3209 Mag. = 0.4037	Gam. = -1.3126 Mag. = 0.4196
Partial 2351 Aug 22	**Partial** 2351 Sep 21	**Total** 2352 Feb 16
Saros 131 20:43 TD	Saros 169 12:33 TD	Saros 136 16:32 TD
A.Node	A.Node	D.Node
ΔT= 638s Alt. = 0°	ΔT= 639s Alt. = 0°	ΔT= 640s Alt. = 48°
Gam. = -1.4322 Mag. = 0.2228	Gam. = 1.4663 Mag. = 0.1681	Gam. = 0.6709 Dur. = 02m25s
Annular 2352 Aug 11	**Annular** 2353 Feb 05	**Total** 2353 Jul 31
Saros 141 00:22 TD	Saros 146 03:57 TD	Saros 151 11:17 TD
A.Node	D.Node	A.Node
ΔT= 641s Alt. = 50°	ΔT= 643s Alt. = 89°	ΔT= 644s Alt. = 81°
Gam. = -0.6366 Dur. = 01m32s	Gam. = -0.0179 Dur. = 02m38s	Gam. = 0.1558 Dur. = 04m20s
Annular 2354 Jan 25	**Total** 2354 Jul 21	**Partial** 2355 Jan 14
Saros 156 08:03 TD	Saros 161 03:28 TD	Saros 166 07:12 TD
D.Node	A.Node	D.Node
ΔT= 646s Alt. = 42°	ΔT= 647s Alt. = 27°	ΔT= 649s Alt. = 0°
Gam. = -0.7388 Dur. = 06m35s	Gam. = 0.8870 Dur. = 03m51s	Gam. = -1.4158 Mag. = 0.2589

Plate 170

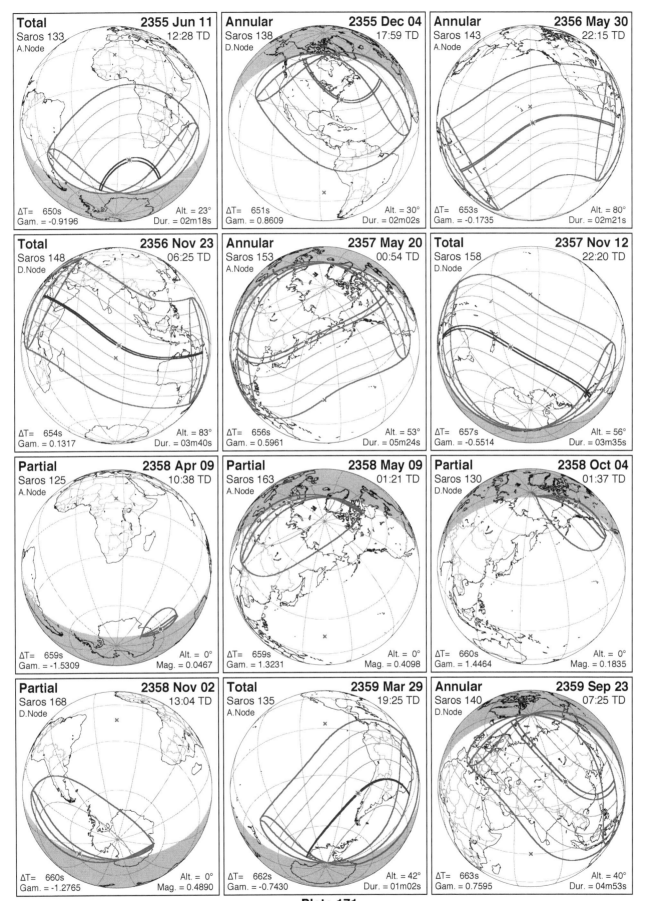

Total 2355 Jun 11	
Saros 133 12:28 TD	
A.Node	
ΔT= 650s Alt. = 23°	
Gam. = -0.9196 Dur. = 02m18s	

Annular 2355 Dec 04	
Saros 138 17:59 TD	
D.Node	
ΔT= 651s Alt. = 30°	
Gam. = 0.8609 Dur. = 02m02s	

Annular 2356 May 30	
Saros 143 22:15 TD	
A.Node	
ΔT= 653s Alt. = 80°	
Gam. = -0.1735 Dur. = 02m21s	

Total 2356 Nov 23	
Saros 148 06:25 TD	
D.Node	
ΔT= 654s Alt. = 83°	
Gam. = 0.1317 Dur. = 03m40s	

Annular 2357 May 20	
Saros 153 00:54 TD	
A.Node	
ΔT= 656s Alt. = 53°	
Gam. = 0.5961 Dur. = 05m24s	

Total 2357 Nov 12	
Saros 158 22:20 TD	
D.Node	
ΔT= 657s Alt. = 56°	
Gam. = -0.5514 Dur. = 03m35s	

Partial 2358 Apr 09	
Saros 125 10:38 TD	
A.Node	
ΔT= 659s Alt. = 0°	
Gam. = -1.5309 Mag. = 0.0467	

Partial 2358 May 09	
Saros 163 01:21 TD	
A.Node	
ΔT= 659s Alt. = 0°	
Gam. = 1.3231 Mag. = 0.4098	

Partial 2358 Oct 04	
Saros 130 01:37 TD	
D.Node	
ΔT= 660s Alt. = 0°	
Gam. = 1.4464 Mag. = 0.1835	

Partial 2358 Nov 02	
Saros 168 13:04 TD	
D.Node	
ΔT= 660s Alt. = 0°	
Gam. = -1.2765 Mag. = 0.4890	

Total 2359 Mar 29	
Saros 135 19:25 TD	
A.Node	
ΔT= 662s Alt. = 42°	
Gam. = -0.7430 Dur. = 01m02s	

Annular 2359 Sep 23	
Saros 140 07:25 TD	
D.Node	
ΔT= 663s Alt. = 40°	
Gam. = 0.7595 Dur. = 04m53s	

Plate 171

265

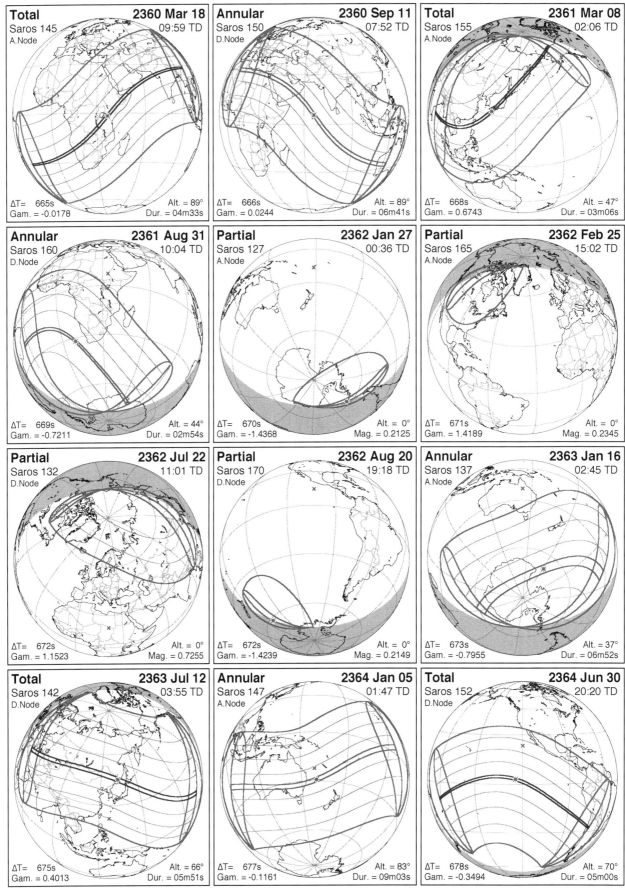

Total 2360 Mar 18 Saros 145 09:59 TD A.Node ΔT= 665s Alt. = 89° Gam. = -0.0178 Dur. = 04m33s	**Annular** 2360 Sep 11 Saros 150 07:52 TD D.Node ΔT= 666s Alt. = 89° Gam. = 0.0244 Dur. = 06m41s	**Total** 2361 Mar 08 Saros 155 02:06 TD A.Node ΔT= 668s Alt. = 47° Gam. = 0.6743 Dur. = 03m06s
Annular 2361 Aug 31 Saros 160 10:04 TD D.Node ΔT= 669s Alt. = 44° Gam. = -0.7211 Dur. = 02m54s	**Partial** 2362 Jan 27 Saros 127 00:36 TD A.Node ΔT= 670s Alt. = 0° Gam. = -1.4368 Mag. = 0.2125	**Partial** 2362 Feb 25 Saros 165 15:02 TD A.Node ΔT= 671s Alt. = 0° Gam. = 1.4189 Mag. = 0.2345
Partial 2362 Jul 22 Saros 132 11:01 TD D.Node ΔT= 672s Alt. = 0° Gam. = 1.1523 Mag. = 0.7255	**Partial** 2362 Aug 20 Saros 170 19:18 TD D.Node ΔT= 672s Alt. = 0° Gam. = -1.4239 Mag. = 0.2149	**Annular** 2363 Jan 16 Saros 137 02:45 TD A.Node ΔT= 673s Alt. = 37° Gam. = -0.7955 Dur. = 06m52s
Total 2363 Jul 12 Saros 142 03:55 TD D.Node ΔT= 675s Alt. = 66° Gam. = 0.4013 Dur. = 05m51s	**Annular** 2364 Jan 05 Saros 147 01:47 TD A.Node ΔT= 677s Alt. = 83° Gam. = -0.1161 Dur. = 09m03s	**Total** 2364 Jun 30 Saros 152 20:20 TD D.Node ΔT= 678s Alt. = 70° Gam. = -0.3494 Dur. = 05m00s

Plate 172

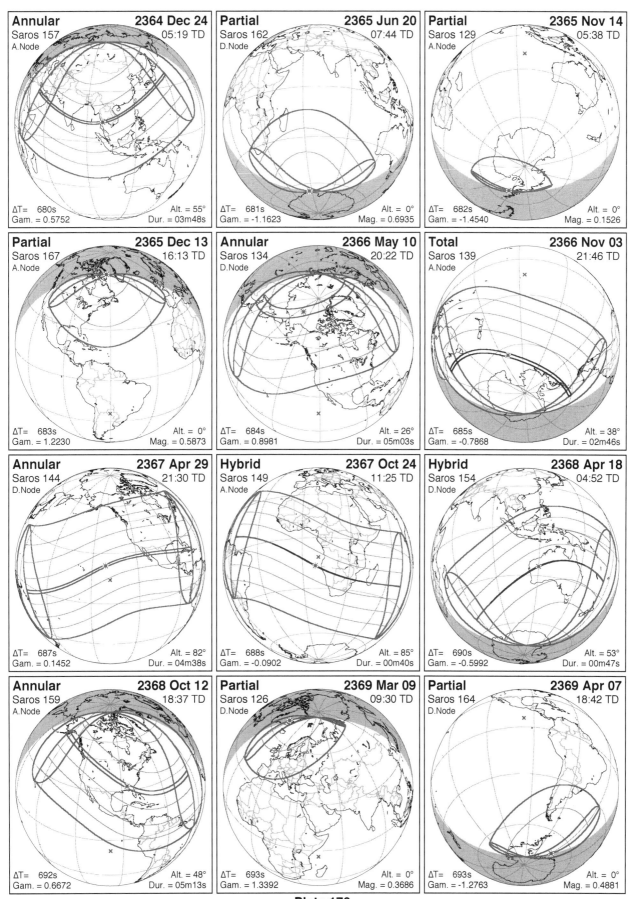

Annular 　　　　　 **2364 Dec 24**	**Partial** 　　　　　 **2365 Jun 20**	**Partial** 　　　　　 **2365 Nov 14**
Saros 157 　　　　　 05:19 TD	Saros 162 　　　　　 07:44 TD	Saros 129 　　　　　 05:38 TD
A.Node	D.Node	A.Node
ΔT= 680s 　　　 Alt. = 55°	ΔT= 681s 　　　 Alt. = 0°	ΔT= 682s 　　　 Alt. = 0°
Gam. = 0.5752 　 Dur. = 03m48s	Gam. = -1.1623 　 Mag. = 0.6935	Gam. = -1.4540 　 Mag. = 0.1526
Partial 　　　　　 **2365 Dec 13**	**Annular** 　　　　　 **2366 May 10**	**Total** 　　　　　 **2366 Nov 03**
Saros 167 　　　　　 16:13 TD	Saros 134 　　　　　 20:22 TD	Saros 139 　　　　　 21:46 TD
A.Node	D.Node	A.Node
ΔT= 683s 　　　 Alt. = 0°	ΔT= 684s 　　　 Alt. = 26°	ΔT= 685s 　　　 Alt. = 38°
Gam. = 1.2230 　 Mag. = 0.5873	Gam. = 0.8981 　 Dur. = 05m03s	Gam. = -0.7868 　 Dur. = 02m46s
Annular 　　　　　 **2367 Apr 29**	**Hybrid** 　　　　　 **2367 Oct 24**	**Hybrid** 　　　　　 **2368 Apr 18**
Saros 144 　　　　　 21:30 TD	Saros 149 　　　　　 11:25 TD	Saros 154 　　　　　 04:52 TD
D.Node	A.Node	D.Node
ΔT= 687s 　　　 Alt. = 82°	ΔT= 688s 　　　 Alt. = 85°	ΔT= 690s 　　　 Alt. = 53°
Gam. = 0.1452 　 Dur. = 04m38s	Gam. = -0.0902 　 Dur. = 00m40s	Gam. = -0.5992 　 Dur. = 00m47s
Annular 　　　　　 **2368 Oct 12**	**Partial** 　　　　　 **2369 Mar 09**	**Partial** 　　　　　 **2369 Apr 07**
Saros 159 　　　　　 18:37 TD	Saros 126 　　　　　 09:30 TD	Saros 164 　　　　　 18:42 TD
A.Node	D.Node	D.Node
ΔT= 692s 　　　 Alt. = 48°	ΔT= 693s 　　　 Alt. = 0°	ΔT= 693s 　　　 Alt. = 0°
Gam. = 0.6672 　 Dur. = 05m13s	Gam. = 1.3392 　 Mag. = 0.3686	Gam. = -1.2763 　 Mag. = 0.4881

Plate 173

267

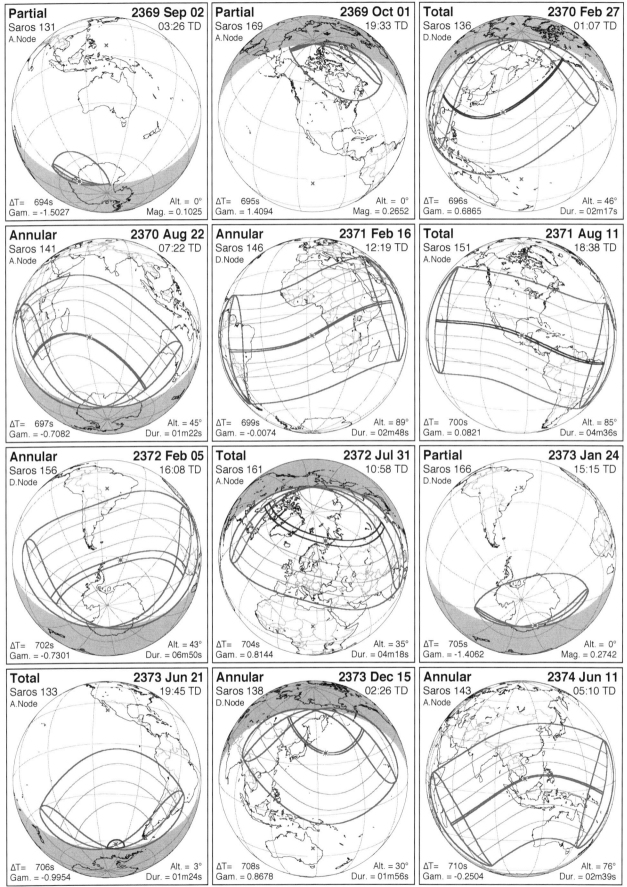

Partial **2369 Sep 02**	
Saros 131 03:26 TD	
A.Node	
ΔT= 694s Alt. = 0°	
Gam. = -1.5027 Mag. = 0.1025	

Partial   **2369 Oct 01**
Saros 169   19:33 TD
A.Node
ΔT= 695s   Alt. = 0°
Gam. = 1.4094   Mag. = 0.2652

Total   **2370 Feb 27**
Saros 136   01:07 TD
D.Node
ΔT= 696s   Alt. = 46°
Gam. = 0.6865   Dur. = 02m17s

Annular   **2370 Aug 22**
Saros 141   07:22 TD
A.Node
ΔT= 697s   Alt. = 45°
Gam. = -0.7082   Dur. = 01m22s

Annular   **2371 Feb 16**
Saros 146   12:19 TD
D.Node
ΔT= 699s   Alt. = 89°
Gam. = -0.0074   Dur. = 02m48s

Total   **2371 Aug 11**
Saros 151   18:38 TD
A.Node
ΔT= 700s   Alt. = 85°
Gam. = 0.0821   Dur. = 04m36s

Annular   **2372 Feb 05**
Saros 156   16:08 TD
D.Node
ΔT= 702s   Alt. = 43°
Gam. = -0.7301   Dur. = 06m50s

Total   **2372 Jul 31**
Saros 161   10:58 TD
A.Node
ΔT= 704s   Alt. = 35°
Gam. = 0.8144   Dur. = 04m18s

Partial   **2373 Jan 24**
Saros 166   15:15 TD
D.Node
ΔT= 705s   Alt. = 0°
Gam. = -1.4062   Mag. = 0.2742

Total   **2373 Jun 21**
Saros 133   19:45 TD
A.Node
ΔT= 706s   Alt. = 3°
Gam. = -0.9954   Dur. = 01m24s

Annular   **2373 Dec 15**
Saros 138   02:26 TD
D.Node
ΔT= 708s   Alt. = 30°
Gam. = 0.8678   Dur. = 01m56s

Annular   **2374 Jun 11**
Saros 143   05:10 TD
A.Node
ΔT= 710s   Alt. = 76°
Gam. = -0.2504   Dur. = 02m39s

Plate 174

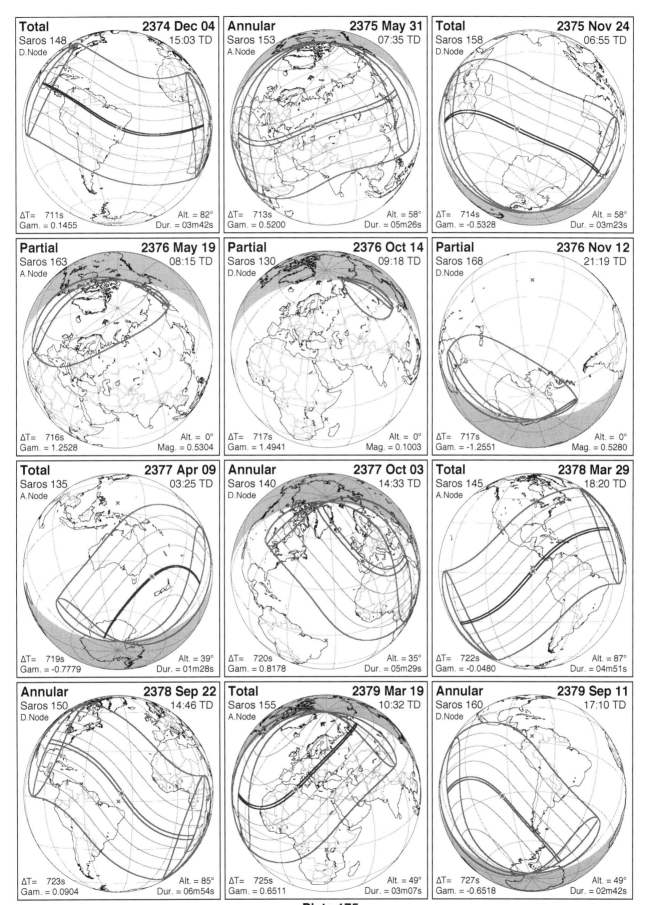

Total	2374 Dec 04
Saros 148	15:03 TD
D.Node	
ΔT= 711s	Alt. = 82°
Gam. = 0.1455	Dur. = 03m42s

Annular	2375 May 31
Saros 153	07:35 TD
A.Node	
ΔT= 713s	Alt. = 58°
Gam. = 0.5200	Dur. = 05m26s

Total	2375 Nov 24
Saros 158	06:55 TD
D.Node	
ΔT= 714s	Alt. = 58°
Gam. = -0.5328	Dur. = 03m23s

Partial	2376 May 19
Saros 163	08:15 TD
A.Node	
ΔT= 716s	Alt. = 0°
Gam. = 1.2528	Mag. = 0.5304

Partial	2376 Oct 14
Saros 130	09:18 TD
D.Node	
ΔT= 717s	Alt. = 0°
Gam. = 1.4941	Mag. = 0.1003

Partial	2376 Nov 12
Saros 168	21:19 TD
D.Node	
ΔT= 717s	Alt. = 0°
Gam. = -1.2551	Mag. = 0.5280

Total	2377 Apr 09
Saros 135	03:25 TD
A.Node	
ΔT= 719s	Alt. = 39°
Gam. = -0.7779	Dur. = 01m28s

Annular	2377 Oct 03
Saros 140	14:33 TD
D.Node	
ΔT= 720s	Alt. = 35°
Gam. = 0.8178	Dur. = 05m29s

Total	2378 Mar 29
Saros 145	18:20 TD
A.Node	
ΔT= 722s	Alt. = 87°
Gam. = -0.0480	Dur. = 04m51s

Annular	2378 Sep 22
Saros 150	14:46 TD
D.Node	
ΔT= 723s	Alt. = 85°
Gam. = 0.0904	Dur. = 06m54s

Total	2379 Mar 19
Saros 155	10:32 TD
A.Node	
ΔT= 725s	Alt. = 49°
Gam. = 0.6511	Dur. = 03m07s

Annular	2379 Sep 11
Saros 160	17:10 TD
D.Node	
ΔT= 727s	Alt. = 49°
Gam. = -0.6518	Dur. = 02m42s

Plate 175

269

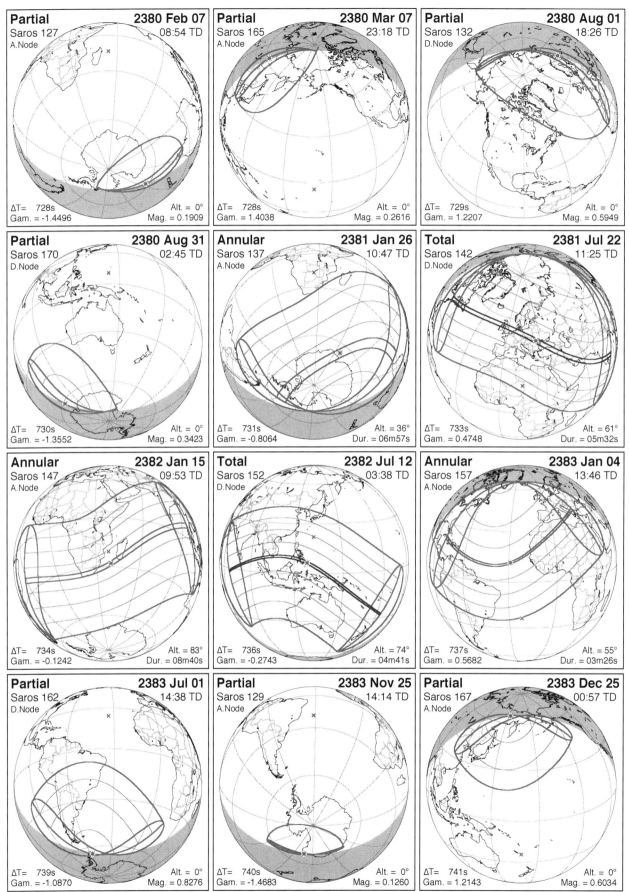

Partial **2380 Feb 07**	
Saros 127 08:54 TD	
A.Node	
$\Delta T = $ 728s Alt. = 0°	
Gam. = -1.4496 Mag. = 0.1909	

| **Partial**   **2380 Mar 07** |
| Saros 165   23:18 TD |
| A.Node |
| $\Delta T = $ 728s   Alt. = 0° |
| Gam. = 1.4038   Mag. = 0.2616 |

| **Partial**   **2380 Aug 01** |
| Saros 132   18:26 TD |
| D.Node |
| $\Delta T = $ 729s   Alt. = 0° |
| Gam. = 1.2207   Mag. = 0.5949 |

| **Partial**   **2380 Aug 31** |
| Saros 170   02:45 TD |
| D.Node |
| $\Delta T = $ 730s   Alt. = 0° |
| Gam. = -1.3552   Mag. = 0.3423 |

| **Annular**   **2381 Jan 26** |
| Saros 137   10:47 TD |
| A.Node |
| $\Delta T = $ 731s   Alt. = 36° |
| Gam. = -0.8064   Dur. = 06m57s |

| **Total**   **2381 Jul 22** |
| Saros 142   11:25 TD |
| D.Node |
| $\Delta T = $ 733s   Alt. = 61° |
| Gam. = 0.4748   Dur. = 05m32s |

| **Annular**   **2382 Jan 15** |
| Saros 147   09:53 TD |
| A.Node |
| $\Delta T = $ 734s   Alt. = 83° |
| Gam. = -0.1242   Dur. = 08m40s |

| **Total**   **2382 Jul 12** |
| Saros 152   03:38 TD |
| D.Node |
| $\Delta T = $ 736s   Alt. = 74° |
| Gam. = -0.2743   Dur. = 04m41s |

| **Annular**   **2383 Jan 04** |
| Saros 157   13:46 TD |
| A.Node |
| $\Delta T = $ 737s   Alt. = 55° |
| Gam. = 0.5682   Dur. = 03m26s |

| **Partial**   **2383 Jul 01** |
| Saros 162   14:38 TD |
| D.Node |
| $\Delta T = $ 739s   Alt. = 0° |
| Gam. = -1.0870   Mag. = 0.8276 |

| **Partial**   **2383 Nov 25** |
| Saros 129   14:14 TD |
| A.Node |
| $\Delta T = $ 740s   Alt. = 0° |
| Gam. = -1.4683   Mag. = 0.1260 |

| **Partial**   **2383 Dec 25** |
| Saros 167   00:57 TD |
| A.Node |
| $\Delta T = $ 741s   Alt. = 0° |
| Gam. = 1.2143   Mag. = 0.6034 |

Plate 176

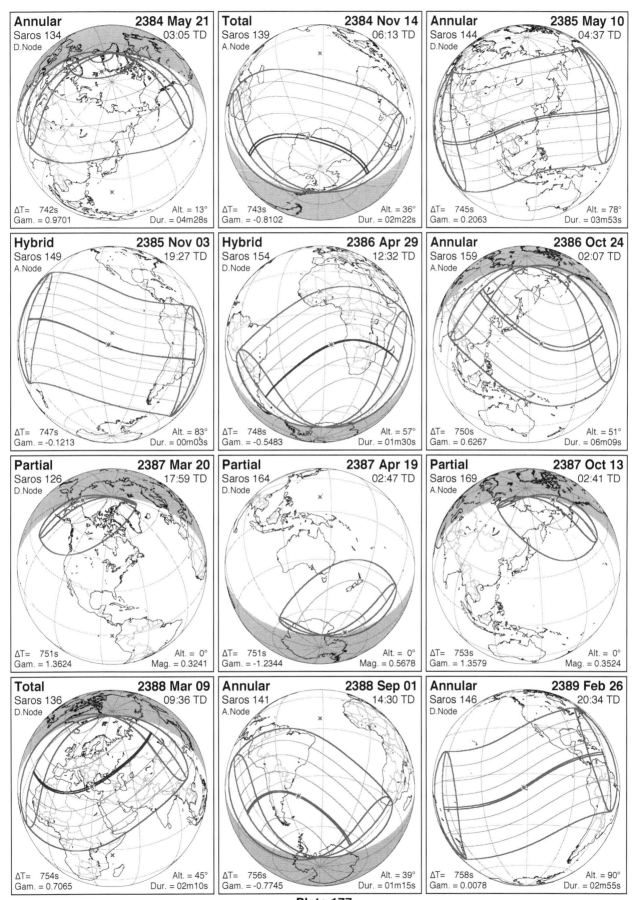

Annular **2384 May 21**	**Total** **2384 Nov 14**	**Annular** **2385 May 10**
Saros 134 03:05 TD	Saros 139 06:13 TD	Saros 144 04:37 TD
D.Node	A.Node	D.Node
ΔT= 742s Alt. = 13°	ΔT= 743s Alt. = 36°	ΔT= 745s Alt. = 78°
Gam. = 0.9701 Dur. = 04m28s	Gam. = -0.8102 Dur. = 02m22s	Gam. = 0.2063 Dur. = 03m53s
Hybrid **2385 Nov 03**	**Hybrid** **2386 Apr 29**	**Annular** **2386 Oct 24**
Saros 149 19:27 TD	Saros 154 12:32 TD	Saros 159 02:07 TD
A.Node	D.Node	A.Node
ΔT= 747s Alt. = 83°	ΔT= 748s Alt. = 57°	ΔT= 750s Alt. = 51°
Gam. = -0.1213 Dur. = 00m03s	Gam. = -0.5483 Dur. = 01m30s	Gam. = 0.6267 Dur. = 06m09s
Partial **2387 Mar 20**	**Partial** **2387 Apr 19**	**Partial** **2387 Oct 13**
Saros 126 17:59 TD	Saros 164 02:47 TD	Saros 169 02:41 TD
D.Node	D.Node	A.Node
ΔT= 751s Alt. = 0°	ΔT= 751s Alt. = 0°	ΔT= 753s Alt. = 0°
Gam. = 1.3624 Mag. = 0.3241	Gam. = -1.2344 Mag. = 0.5678	Gam. = 1.3579 Mag. = 0.3524
Total **2388 Mar 09**	**Annular** **2388 Sep 01**	**Annular** **2389 Feb 26**
Saros 136 09:36 TD	Saros 141 14:30 TD	Saros 146 20:34 TD
D.Node	A.Node	D.Node
ΔT= 754s Alt. = 45°	ΔT= 756s Alt. = 39°	ΔT= 758s Alt. = 90°
Gam. = 0.7065 Dur. = 02m10s	Gam. = -0.7745 Dur. = 01m15s	Gam. = 0.0078 Dur. = 02m55s

Plate 177

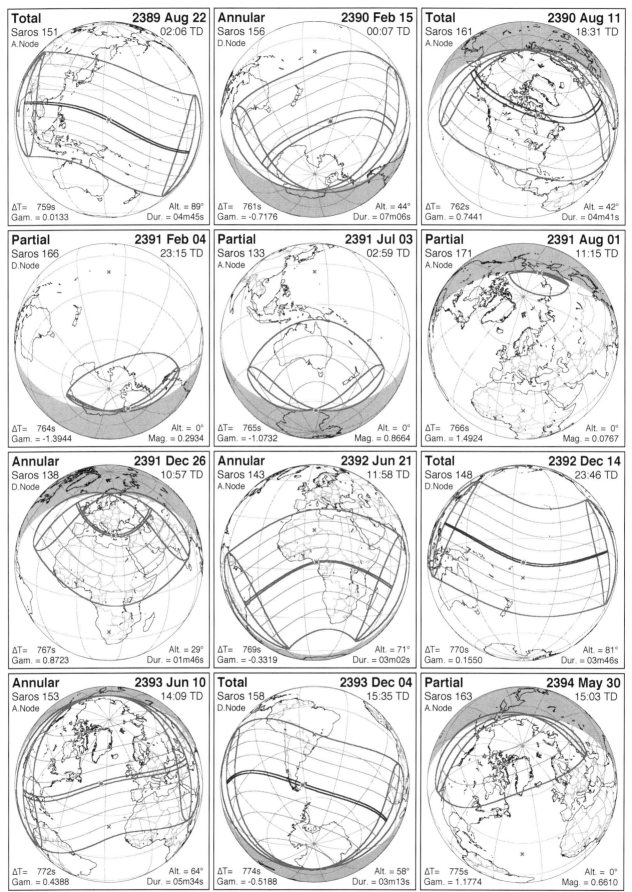

Total **2389 Aug 22** Saros 151 02:06 TD A.Node ΔT= 759s Alt. = 89° Gam. = 0.0133 Dur. = 04m45s	**Annular** **2390 Feb 15** Saros 156 00:07 TD D.Node ΔT= 761s Alt. = 44° Gam. = -0.7176 Dur. = 07m06s	**Total** **2390 Aug 11** Saros 161 18:31 TD A.Node ΔT= 762s Alt. = 42° Gam. = 0.7441 Dur. = 04m41s
Partial **2391 Feb 04** Saros 166 23:15 TD D.Node ΔT= 764s Alt. = 0° Gam. = -1.3944 Mag. = 0.2934	**Partial** **2391 Jul 03** Saros 133 02:59 TD A.Node ΔT= 765s Alt. = 0° Gam. = -1.0732 Mag. = 0.8664	**Partial** **2391 Aug 01** Saros 171 11:15 TD A.Node ΔT= 766s Alt. = 0° Gam. = 1.4924 Mag. = 0.0767
Annular **2391 Dec 26** Saros 138 10:57 TD D.Node ΔT= 767s Alt. = 29° Gam. = 0.8723 Dur. = 01m46s	**Annular** **2392 Jun 21** Saros 143 11:58 TD A.Node ΔT= 769s Alt. = 71° Gam. = -0.3319 Dur. = 03m02s	**Total** **2392 Dec 14** Saros 148 23:46 TD D.Node ΔT= 770s Alt. = 81° Gam. = 0.1550 Dur. = 03m46s
Annular **2393 Jun 10** Saros 153 14:09 TD A.Node ΔT= 772s Alt. = 64° Gam. = 0.4388 Dur. = 05m34s	**Total** **2393 Dec 04** Saros 158 15:35 TD D.Node ΔT= 774s Alt. = 58° Gam. = -0.5188 Dur. = 03m13s	**Partial** **2394 May 30** Saros 163 15:03 TD A.Node ΔT= 775s Alt. = 0° Gam. = 1.1774 Mag. = 0.6610

Plate 178

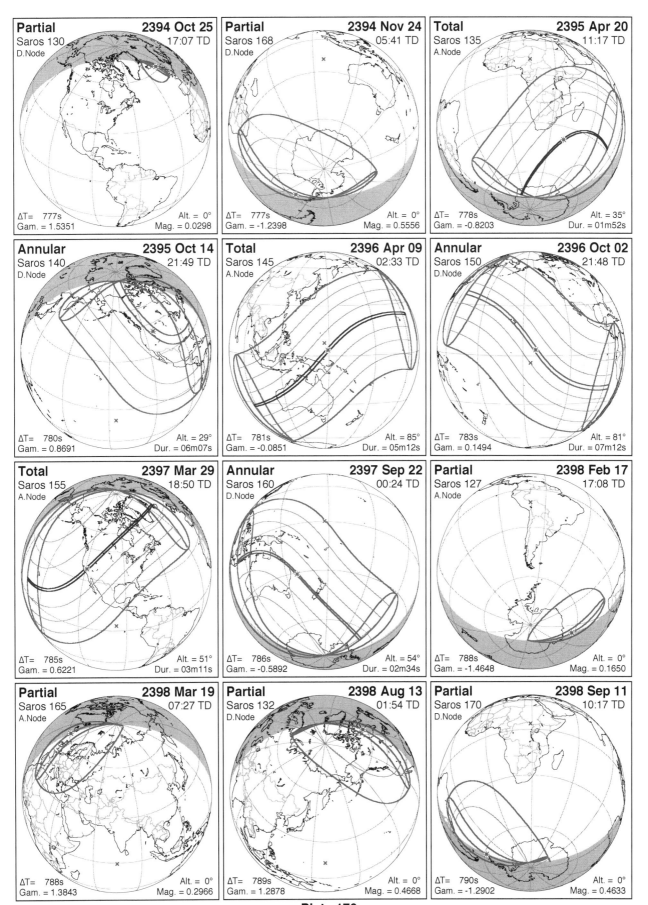

Partial 2394 Oct 25	**Partial** 2394 Nov 24	**Total** 2395 Apr 20
Saros 130 17:07 TD	Saros 168 05:41 TD	Saros 135 11:17 TD
D.Node	D.Node	A.Node
ΔT= 777s Alt. = 0°	ΔT= 777s Alt. = 0°	ΔT= 778s Alt. = 35°
Gam. = 1.5351 Mag. = 0.0298	Gam. = -1.2398 Mag. = 0.5556	Gam. = -0.8203 Dur. = 01m52s
Annular 2395 Oct 14	**Total** 2396 Apr 09	**Annular** 2396 Oct 02
Saros 140 21:49 TD	Saros 145 02:33 TD	Saros 150 21:48 TD
D.Node	A.Node	D.Node
ΔT= 780s Alt. = 29°	ΔT= 781s Alt. = 85°	ΔT= 783s Alt. = 81°
Gam. = 0.8691 Dur. = 06m07s	Gam. = -0.0851 Dur. = 05m12s	Gam. = 0.1494 Dur. = 07m12s
Total 2397 Mar 29	**Annular** 2397 Sep 22	**Partial** 2398 Feb 17
Saros 155 18:50 TD	Saros 160 00:24 TD	Saros 127 17:08 TD
A.Node	D.Node	A.Node
ΔT= 785s Alt. = 51°	ΔT= 786s Alt. = 54°	ΔT= 788s Alt. = 0°
Gam. = 0.6221 Dur. = 03m11s	Gam. = -0.5892 Dur. = 02m34s	Gam. = -1.4648 Mag. = 0.1650
Partial 2398 Mar 19	**Partial** 2398 Aug 13	**Partial** 2398 Sep 11
Saros 165 07:27 TD	Saros 132 01:54 TD	Saros 170 10:17 TD
A.Node	D.Node	D.Node
ΔT= 788s Alt. = 0°	ΔT= 789s Alt. = 0°	ΔT= 790s Alt. = 0°
Gam. = 1.3843 Mag. = 0.2966	Gam. = 1.2878 Mag. = 0.4668	Gam. = -1.2902 Mag. = 0.4633

Plate 179

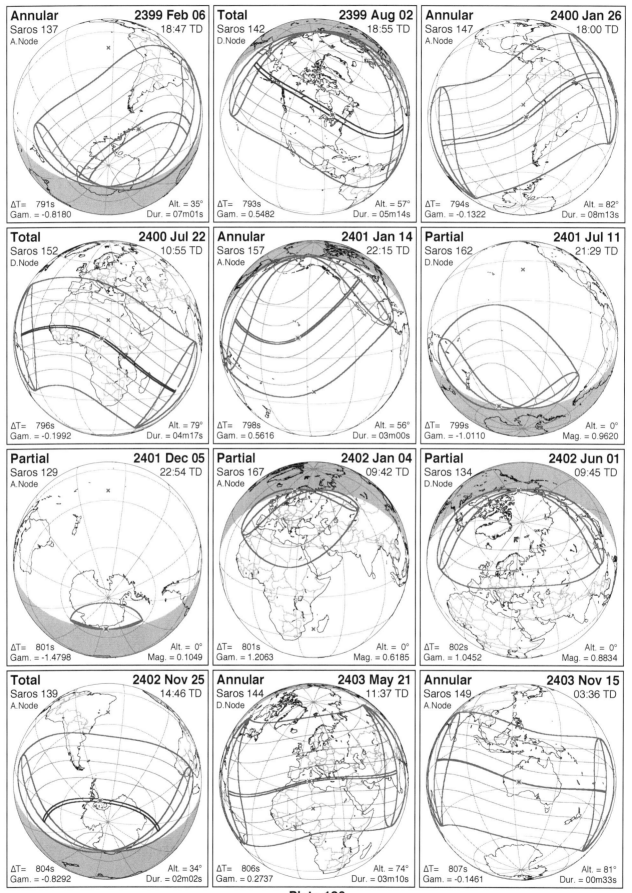

Annular **2399 Feb 06** Saros 137 18:47 TD A.Node ΔT= 791s Alt. = 35° Gam. = -0.8180 Dur. = 07m01s	**Total** **2399 Aug 02** Saros 142 18:55 TD D.Node ΔT= 793s Alt. = 57° Gam. = 0.5482 Dur. = 05m14s	**Annular** **2400 Jan 26** Saros 147 18:00 TD A.Node ΔT= 794s Alt. = 82° Gam. = -0.1322 Dur. = 08m13s
Total **2400 Jul 22** Saros 152 10:55 TD D.Node ΔT= 796s Alt. = 79° Gam. = -0.1992 Dur. = 04m17s	**Annular** **2401 Jan 14** Saros 157 22:15 TD A.Node ΔT= 798s Alt. = 56° Gam. = 0.5616 Dur. = 03m00s	**Partial** **2401 Jul 11** Saros 162 21:29 TD D.Node ΔT= 799s Alt. = 0° Gam. = -1.0110 Mag. = 0.9620
Partial **2401 Dec 05** Saros 129 22:54 TD A.Node ΔT= 801s Alt. = 0° Gam. = -1.4798 Mag. = 0.1049	**Partial** **2402 Jan 04** Saros 167 09:42 TD A.Node ΔT= 801s Alt. = 0° Gam. = 1.2063 Mag. = 0.6185	**Partial** **2402 Jun 01** Saros 134 09:45 TD D.Node ΔT= 802s Alt. = 0° Gam. = 1.0452 Mag. = 0.8834
Total **2402 Nov 25** Saros 139 14:46 TD A.Node ΔT= 804s Alt. = 34° Gam. = -0.8292 Dur. = 02m02s	**Annular** **2403 May 21** Saros 144 11:37 TD D.Node ΔT= 806s Alt. = 74° Gam. = 0.2737 Dur. = 03m10s	**Annular** **2403 Nov 15** Saros 149 03:36 TD A.Node ΔT= 807s Alt. = 81° Gam. = -0.1461 Dur. = 00m33s

Plate 180

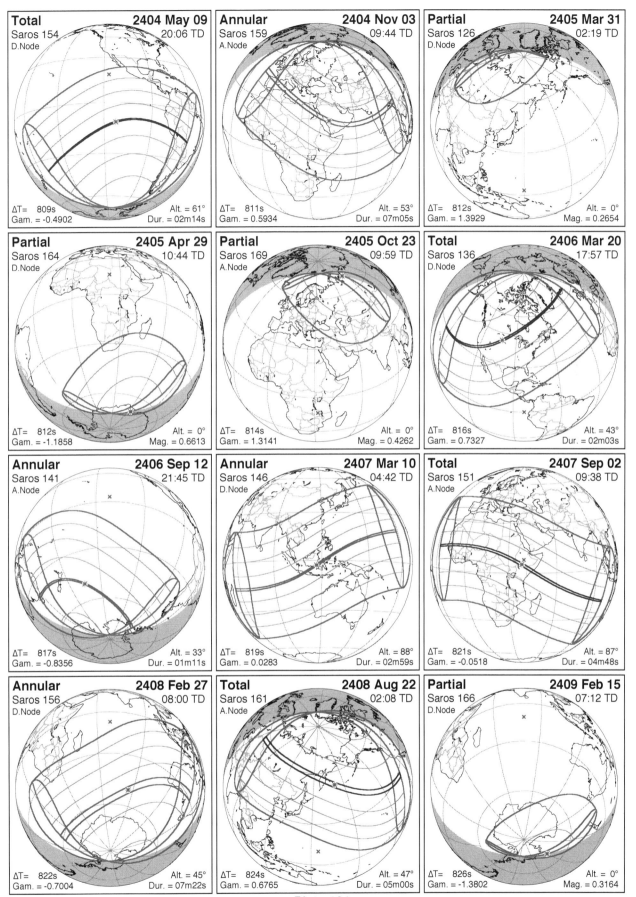

Total 2404 May 09 Saros 154 20:06 TD D.Node ΔT= 809s Alt. = 61° Gam. = -0.4902 Dur. = 02m14s	**Annular** 2404 Nov 03 Saros 159 09:44 TD A.Node ΔT= 811s Alt. = 53° Gam. = 0.5934 Dur. = 07m05s

Plate 181

275

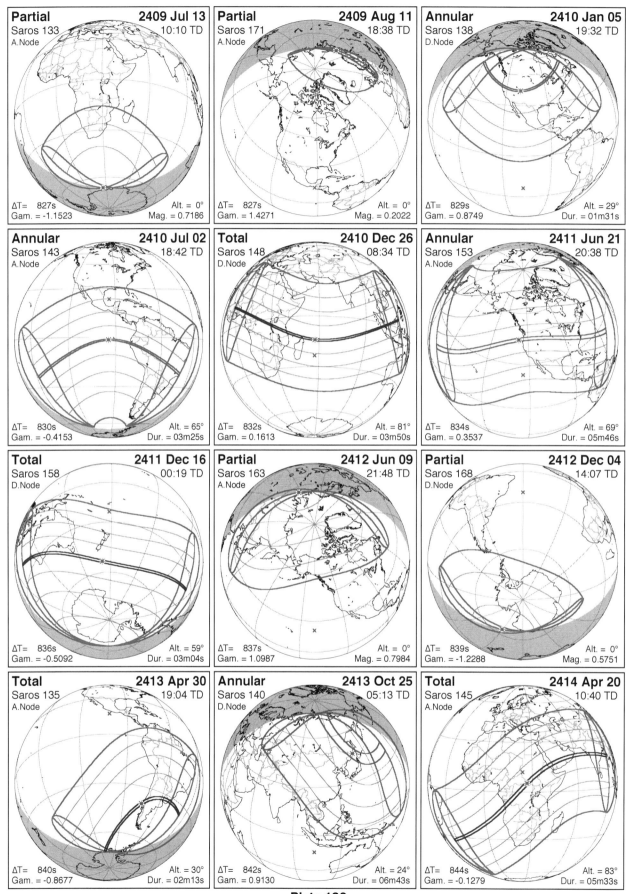

Partial 2409 Jul 13	**Partial** 2409 Aug 11	**Annular** 2410 Jan 05
Saros 133 10:10 TD	Saros 171 18:38 TD	Saros 138 19:32 TD
A.Node	A.Node	D.Node
ΔT= 827s Alt. = 0°	ΔT= 827s Alt. = 0°	ΔT= 829s Alt. = 29°
Gam. = -1.1523 Mag. = 0.7186	Gam. = 1.4271 Mag. = 0.2022	Gam. = 0.8749 Dur. = 01m31s
Annular 2410 Jul 02	**Total** 2410 Dec 26	**Annular** 2411 Jun 21
Saros 143 18:42 TD	Saros 148 08:34 TD	Saros 153 20:38 TD
A.Node	D.Node	A.Node
ΔT= 830s Alt. = 65°	ΔT= 832s Alt. = 81°	ΔT= 834s Alt. = 69°
Gam. = -0.4153 Dur. = 03m25s	Gam. = 0.1613 Dur. = 03m50s	Gam. = 0.3537 Dur. = 05m46s
Total 2411 Dec 16	**Partial** 2412 Jun 09	**Partial** 2412 Dec 04
Saros 158 00:19 TD	Saros 163 21:48 TD	Saros 168 14:07 TD
D.Node	A.Node	D.Node
ΔT= 836s Alt. = 59°	ΔT= 837s Alt. = 0°	ΔT= 839s Alt. = 0°
Gam. = -0.5092 Dur. = 03m04s	Gam. = 1.0987 Mag. = 0.7984	Gam. = -1.2288 Mag. = 0.5751
Total 2413 Apr 30	**Annular** 2413 Oct 25	**Total** 2414 Apr 20
Saros 135 19:04 TD	Saros 140 05:13 TD	Saros 145 10:40 TD
A.Node	D.Node	A.Node
ΔT= 840s Alt. = 30°	ΔT= 842s Alt. = 24°	ΔT= 844s Alt. = 83°
Gam. = -0.8677 Dur. = 02m13s	Gam. = 0.9130 Dur. = 06m43s	Gam. = -0.1279 Dur. = 05m33s

Plate 182

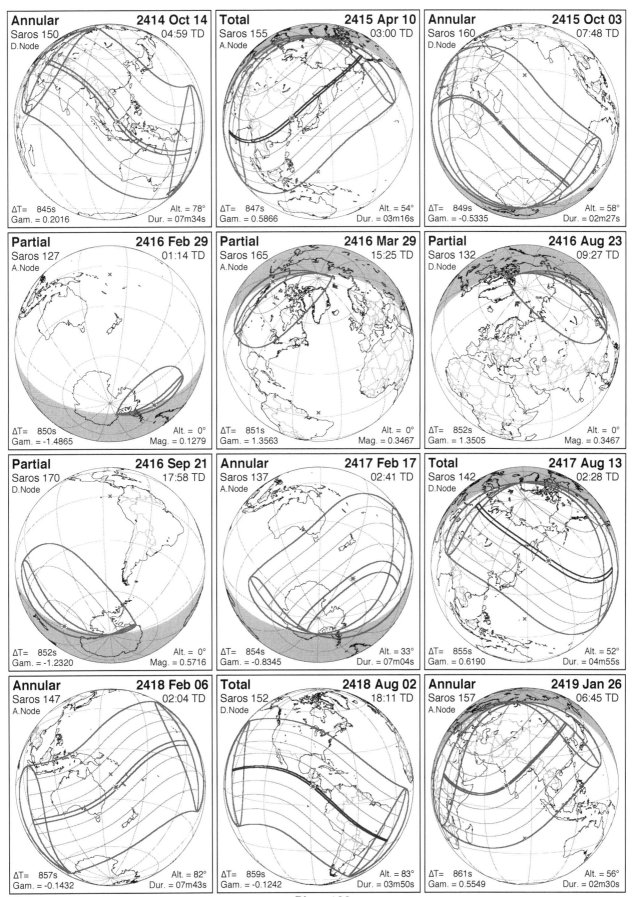

Annular	2414 Oct 14
Saros 150	04:59 TD
D.Node	
ΔT= 845s	Alt. = 78°
Gam. = 0.2016	Dur. = 07m34s

Total	2415 Apr 10
Saros 155	03:00 TD
A.Node	
ΔT= 847s	Alt. = 54°
Gam. = 0.5866	Dur. = 03m16s

Annular	2415 Oct 03
Saros 160	07:48 TD
D.Node	
ΔT= 849s	Alt. = 58°
Gam. = -0.5335	Dur. = 02m27s

Partial	2416 Feb 29
Saros 127	01:14 TD
A.Node	
ΔT= 850s	Alt. = 0°
Gam. = -1.4865	Mag. = 0.1279

Partial	2416 Mar 29
Saros 165	15:25 TD
A.Node	
ΔT= 851s	Alt. = 0°
Gam. = 1.3563	Mag. = 0.3467

Partial	2416 Aug 23
Saros 132	09:27 TD
D.Node	
ΔT= 852s	Alt. = 0°
Gam. = 1.3505	Mag. = 0.3467

Partial	2416 Sep 21
Saros 170	17:58 TD
D.Node	
ΔT= 852s	Alt. = 0°
Gam. = -1.2320	Mag. = 0.5716

Annular	2417 Feb 17
Saros 137	02:41 TD
A.Node	
ΔT= 854s	Alt. = 33°
Gam. = -0.8345	Dur. = 07m04s

Total	2417 Aug 13
Saros 142	02:28 TD
D.Node	
ΔT= 855s	Alt. = 52°
Gam. = 0.6190	Dur. = 04m55s

Annular	2418 Feb 06
Saros 147	02:04 TD
A.Node	
ΔT= 857s	Alt. = 82°
Gam. = -0.1432	Dur. = 07m43s

Total	2418 Aug 02
Saros 152	18:11 TD
D.Node	
ΔT= 859s	Alt. = 83°
Gam. = -0.1242	Dur. = 03m50s

Annular	2419 Jan 26
Saros 157	06:45 TD
A.Node	
ΔT= 861s	Alt. = 56°
Gam. = 0.5549	Dur. = 02m30s

Plate 183

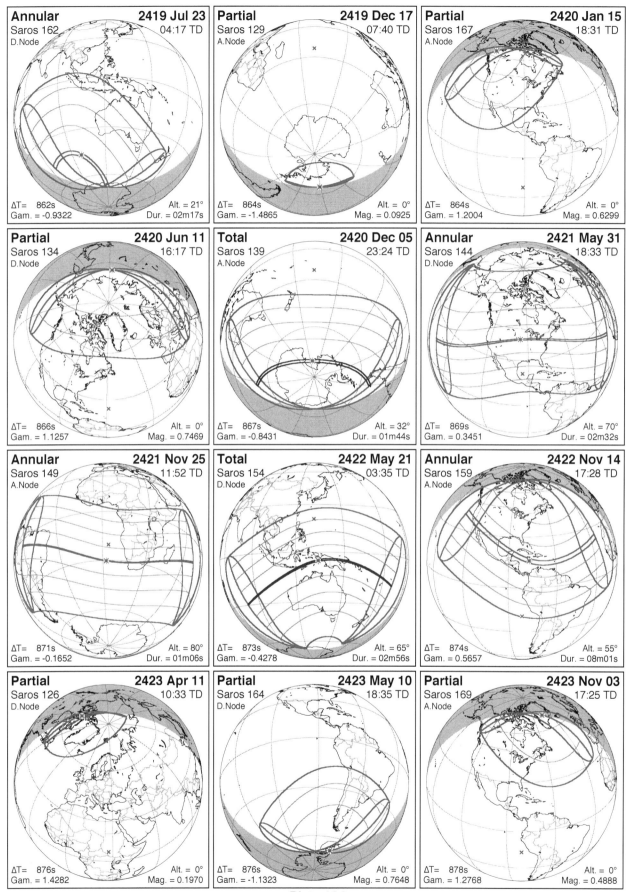

Annular 2419 Jul 23	**Partial** 2419 Dec 17	**Partial** 2420 Jan 15
Saros 162 04:17 TD	Saros 129 07:40 TD	Saros 167 18:31 TD
D.Node	A.Node	A.Node
ΔT= 862s Alt. = 21°	ΔT= 864s Alt. = 0°	ΔT= 864s Alt. = 0°
Gam. = -0.9322 Dur. = 02m17s	Gam. = -1.4865 Mag. = 0.0925	Gam. = 1.2004 Mag. = 0.6299
Partial 2420 Jun 11	**Total** 2420 Dec 05	**Annular** 2421 May 31
Saros 134 16:17 TD	Saros 139 23:24 TD	Saros 144 18:33 TD
D.Node	A.Node	D.Node
ΔT= 866s Alt. = 0°	ΔT= 867s Alt. = 32°	ΔT= 869s Alt. = 70°
Gam. = 1.1257 Mag. = 0.7469	Gam. = -0.8431 Dur. = 01m44s	Gam. = 0.3451 Dur. = 02m32s
Annular 2421 Nov 25	**Total** 2422 May 21	**Annular** 2422 Nov 14
Saros 149 11:52 TD	Saros 154 03:35 TD	Saros 159 17:28 TD
A.Node	D.Node	A.Node
ΔT= 871s Alt. = 80°	ΔT= 873s Alt. = 65°	ΔT= 874s Alt. = 55°
Gam. = -0.1652 Dur. = 01m06s	Gam. = -0.4278 Dur. = 02m56s	Gam. = 0.5657 Dur. = 08m01s
Partial 2423 Apr 11	**Partial** 2423 May 10	**Partial** 2423 Nov 03
Saros 126 10:33 TD	Saros 164 18:35 TD	Saros 169 17:25 TD
D.Node	D.Node	A.Node
ΔT= 876s Alt. = 0°	ΔT= 876s Alt. = 0°	ΔT= 878s Alt. = 0°
Gam. = 1.4282 Mag. = 0.1970	Gam. = -1.1323 Mag. = 0.7648	Gam. = 1.2768 Mag. = 0.4888

Plate 184

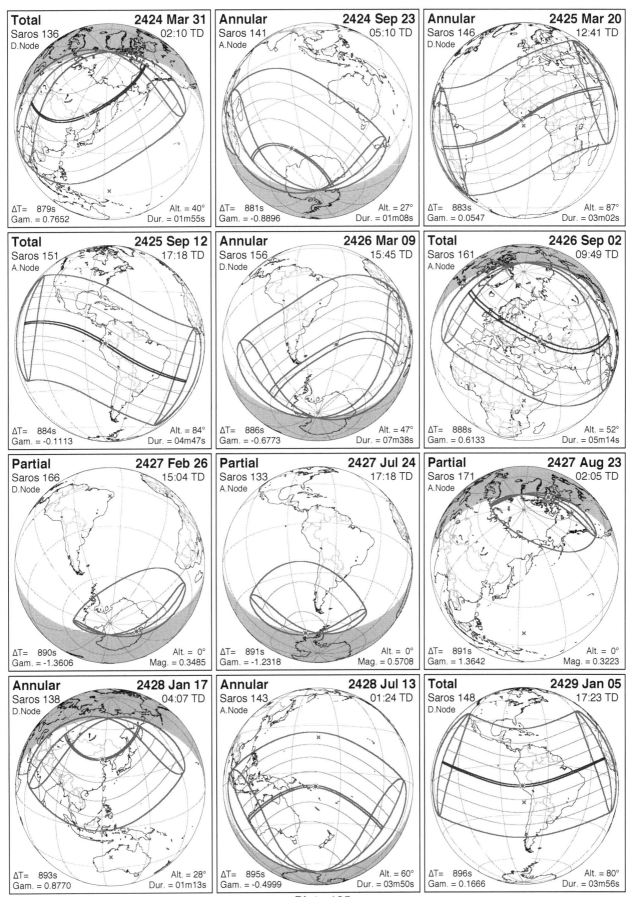

Total	2424 Mar 31
Saros 136	02:10 TD
D.Node	
ΔT= 879s	Alt. = 40°
Gam. = 0.7652	Dur. = 01m55s

Annular	2424 Sep 23
Saros 141	05:10 TD
A.Node	
ΔT= 881s	Alt. = 27°
Gam. = -0.8896	Dur. = 01m08s

Annular	2425 Mar 20
Saros 146	12:41 TD
D.Node	
ΔT= 883s	Alt. = 87°
Gam. = 0.0547	Dur. = 03m02s

Total	2425 Sep 12
Saros 151	17:18 TD
A.Node	
ΔT= 884s	Alt. = 84°
Gam. = -0.1113	Dur. = 04m47s

Annular	2426 Mar 09
Saros 156	15:45 TD
D.Node	
ΔT= 886s	Alt. = 47°
Gam. = -0.6773	Dur. = 07m38s

Total	2426 Sep 02
Saros 161	09:49 TD
A.Node	
ΔT= 888s	Alt. = 52°
Gam. = 0.6133	Dur. = 05m14s

Partial	2427 Feb 26
Saros 166	15:04 TD
D.Node	
ΔT= 890s	Alt. = 0°
Gam. = -1.3606	Mag. = 0.3485

Partial	2427 Jul 24
Saros 133	17:18 TD
A.Node	
ΔT= 891s	Alt. = 0°
Gam. = -1.2318	Mag. = 0.5708

Partial	2427 Aug 23
Saros 171	02:05 TD
A.Node	
ΔT= 891s	Alt. = 0°
Gam. = 1.3642	Mag. = 0.3223

Annular	2428 Jan 17
Saros 138	04:07 TD
D.Node	
ΔT= 893s	Alt. = 28°
Gam. = 0.8770	Dur. = 01m13s

Annular	2428 Jul 13
Saros 143	01:24 TD
A.Node	
ΔT= 895s	Alt. = 60°
Gam. = -0.4999	Dur. = 03m50s

Total	2429 Jan 05
Saros 148	17:23 TD
D.Node	
ΔT= 896s	Alt. = 80°
Gam. = 0.1666	Dur. = 03m56s

Plate 185

279

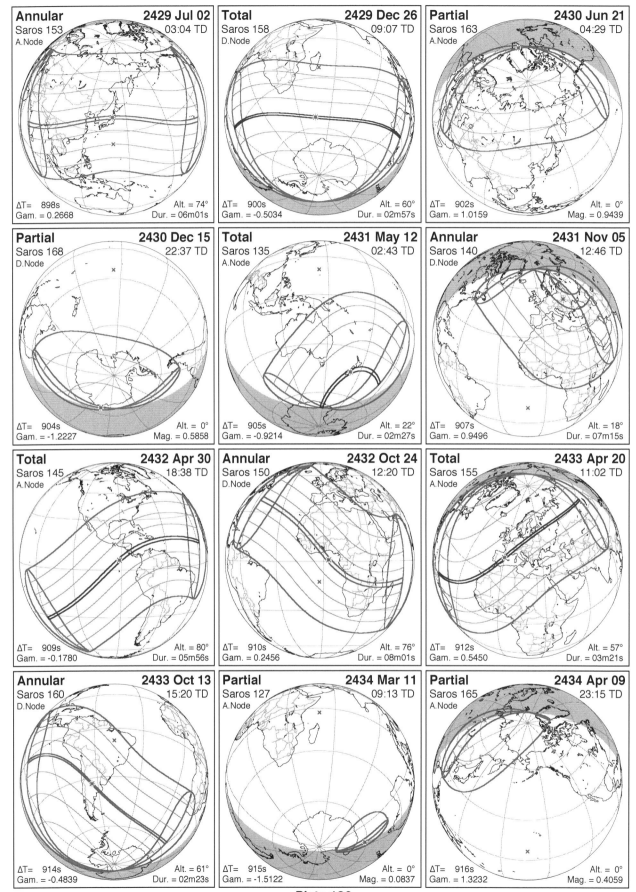

Annular **2429 Jul 02**	**Total** **2429 Dec 26**	**Partial** **2430 Jun 21**
Saros 153 03:04 TD	Saros 158 09:07 TD	Saros 163 04:29 TD
A.Node	D.Node	A.Node
ΔT= 898s Alt. = 74°	ΔT= 900s Alt. = 60°	ΔT= 902s Alt. = 0°
Gam. = 0.2668 Dur. = 06m01s	Gam. = -0.5034 Dur. = 02m57s	Gam. = 1.0159 Mag. = 0.9439
Partial **2430 Dec 15**	**Total** **2431 May 12**	**Annular** **2431 Nov 05**
Saros 168 22:37 TD	Saros 135 02:43 TD	Saros 140 12:46 TD
D.Node	A.Node	D.Node
ΔT= 904s Alt. = 0°	ΔT= 905s Alt. = 22°	ΔT= 907s Alt. = 18°
Gam. = -1.2227 Mag. = 0.5858	Gam. = -0.9214 Dur. = 02m27s	Gam. = 0.9496 Dur. = 07m15s
Total **2432 Apr 30**	**Annular** **2432 Oct 24**	**Total** **2433 Apr 20**
Saros 145 18:38 TD	Saros 150 12:20 TD	Saros 155 11:02 TD
A.Node	D.Node	A.Node
ΔT= 909s Alt. = 80°	ΔT= 910s Alt. = 76°	ΔT= 912s Alt. = 57°
Gam. = -0.1780 Dur. = 05m56s	Gam. = 0.2456 Dur. = 08m01s	Gam. = 0.5450 Dur. = 03m21s
Annular **2433 Oct 13**	**Partial** **2434 Mar 11**	**Partial** **2434 Apr 09**
Saros 160 15:20 TD	Saros 127 09:13 TD	Saros 165 23:15 TD
D.Node	A.Node	A.Node
ΔT= 914s Alt. = 61°	ΔT= 915s Alt. = 0°	ΔT= 916s Alt. = 0°
Gam. = -0.4839 Dur. = 02m23s	Gam. = -1.5122 Mag. = 0.0837	Gam. = 1.3232 Mag. = 0.4059

Plate 186

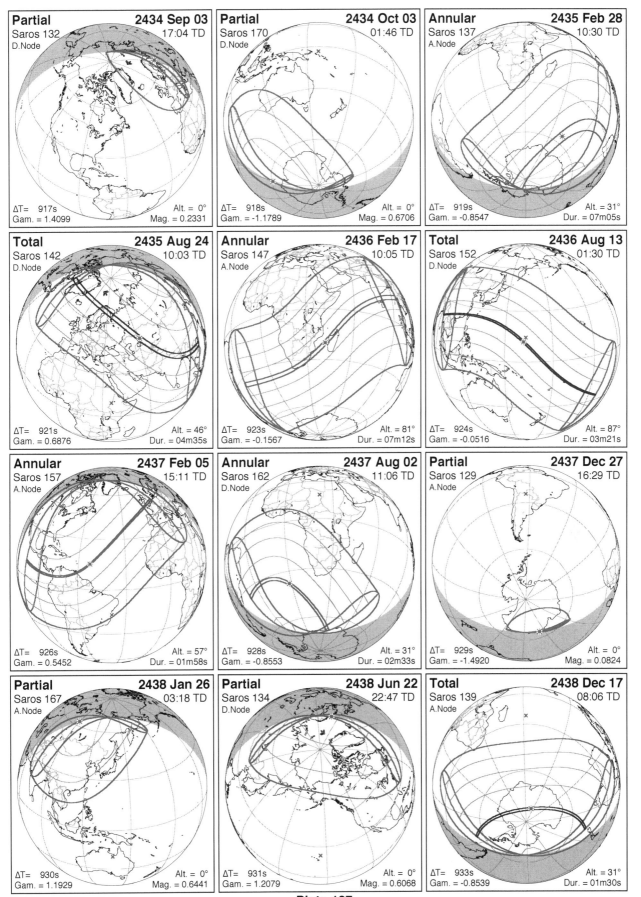

Partial	2434 Sep 03
Saros 132	17:04 TD
D.Node	
ΔT= 917s	Alt. = 0°
Gam. = 1.4099	Mag. = 0.2331

Partial	2434 Oct 03
Saros 170	01:46 TD
D.Node	
ΔT= 918s	Alt. = 0°
Gam. = -1.1789	Mag. = 0.6706

Annular	2435 Feb 28
Saros 137	10:30 TD
A.Node	
ΔT= 919s	Alt. = 31°
Gam. = -0.8547	Dur. = 07m05s

Total	2435 Aug 24
Saros 142	10:03 TD
D.Node	
ΔT= 921s	Alt. = 46°
Gam. = 0.6876	Dur. = 04m35s

Annular	2436 Feb 17
Saros 147	10:05 TD
A.Node	
ΔT= 923s	Alt. = 81°
Gam. = -0.1567	Dur. = 07m12s

Total	2436 Aug 13
Saros 152	01:30 TD
D.Node	
ΔT= 924s	Alt. = 87°
Gam. = -0.0516	Dur. = 03m21s

Annular	2437 Feb 05
Saros 157	15:11 TD
A.Node	
ΔT= 926s	Alt. = 57°
Gam. = 0.5452	Dur. = 01m58s

Annular	2437 Aug 02
Saros 162	11:06 TD
D.Node	
ΔT= 928s	Alt. = 31°
Gam. = -0.8553	Dur. = 02m33s

Partial	2437 Dec 27
Saros 129	16:29 TD
A.Node	
ΔT= 929s	Alt. = 0°
Gam. = -1.4920	Mag. = 0.0824

Partial	2438 Jan 26
Saros 167	03:18 TD
A.Node	
ΔT= 930s	Alt. = 0°
Gam. = 1.1929	Mag. = 0.6441

Partial	2438 Jun 22
Saros 134	22:47 TD
D.Node	
ΔT= 931s	Alt. = 0°
Gam. = 1.2079	Mag. = 0.6068

Total	2438 Dec 17
Saros 139	08:06 TD
A.Node	
ΔT= 933s	Alt. = 31°
Gam. = -0.8539	Dur. = 01m30s

Plate 187

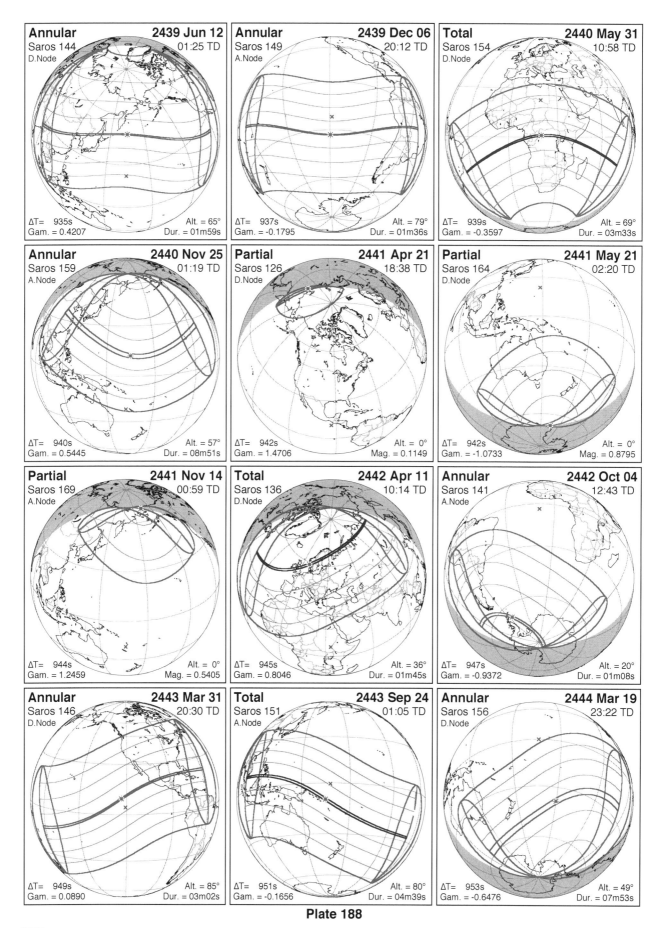

Annular	2439 Jun 12
Saros 144	01:25 TD
D.Node	
ΔT= 935s	Alt. = 65°
Gam. = 0.4207	Dur. = 01m59s

Annular	2439 Dec 06
Saros 149	20:12 TD
A.Node	
ΔT= 937s	Alt. = 79°
Gam. = -0.1795	Dur. = 01m36s

Total	2440 May 31
Saros 154	10:58 TD
D.Node	
ΔT= 939s	Alt. = 69°
Gam. = -0.3597	Dur. = 03m33s

Annular	2440 Nov 25
Saros 159	01:19 TD
A.Node	
ΔT= 940s	Alt. = 57°
Gam. = 0.5445	Dur. = 08m51s

Partial	2441 Apr 21
Saros 126	18:38 TD
D.Node	
ΔT= 942s	Alt. = 0°
Gam. = 1.4706	Mag. = 0.1149

Partial	2441 May 21
Saros 164	02:20 TD
D.Node	
ΔT= 942s	Alt. = 0°
Gam. = -1.0733	Mag. = 0.8795

Partial	2441 Nov 14
Saros 169	00:59 TD
A.Node	
ΔT= 944s	Alt. = 0°
Gam. = 1.2459	Mag. = 0.5405

Total	2442 Apr 11
Saros 136	10:14 TD
D.Node	
ΔT= 945s	Alt. = 36°
Gam. = 0.8046	Dur. = 01m45s

Annular	2442 Oct 04
Saros 141	12:43 TD
A.Node	
ΔT= 947s	Alt. = 20°
Gam. = -0.9372	Dur. = 01m08s

Annular	2443 Mar 31
Saros 146	20:30 TD
D.Node	
ΔT= 949s	Alt. = 85°
Gam. = 0.0890	Dur. = 03m02s

Total	2443 Sep 24
Saros 151	01:05 TD
A.Node	
ΔT= 951s	Alt. = 80°
Gam. = -0.1656	Dur. = 04m39s

Annular	2444 Mar 19
Saros 156	23:22 TD
D.Node	
ΔT= 953s	Alt. = 49°
Gam. = -0.6476	Dur. = 07m53s

Plate 188

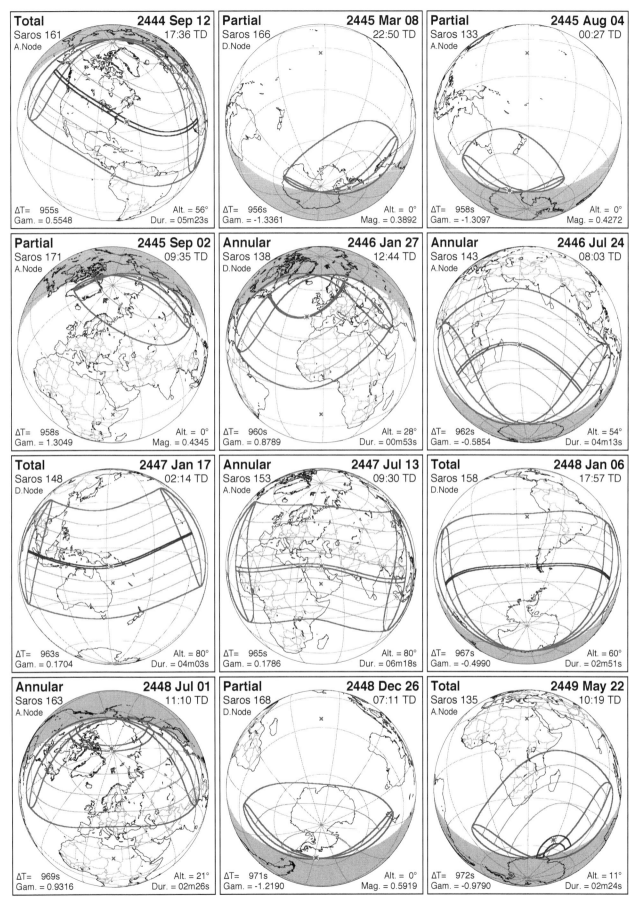

Total — 2444 Sep 12
Saros 161 — 17:36 TD
A.Node
ΔT= 955s — Alt. = 56°
Gam. = 0.5548 — Dur. = 05m23s

Partial — 2445 Mar 08
Saros 166 — 22:50 TD
D.Node
ΔT= 956s — Alt. = 0°
Gam. = -1.3361 — Mag. = 0.3892

Partial — 2445 Aug 04
Saros 133 — 00:27 TD
A.Node
ΔT= 958s — Alt. = 0°
Gam. = -1.3097 — Mag. = 0.4272

Partial — 2445 Sep 02
Saros 171 — 09:35 TD
A.Node
ΔT= 958s — Alt. = 0°
Gam. = 1.3049 — Mag. = 0.4345

Annular — 2446 Jan 27
Saros 138 — 12:44 TD
D.Node
ΔT= 960s — Alt. = 28°
Gam. = 0.8789 — Dur. = 00m53s

Annular — 2446 Jul 24
Saros 143 — 08:03 TD
A.Node
ΔT= 962s — Alt. = 54°
Gam. = -0.5854 — Dur. = 04m13s

Total — 2447 Jan 17
Saros 148 — 02:14 TD
D.Node
ΔT= 963s — Alt. = 80°
Gam. = 0.1704 — Dur. = 04m03s

Annular — 2447 Jul 13
Saros 153 — 09:30 TD
A.Node
ΔT= 965s — Alt. = 80°
Gam. = 0.1786 — Dur. = 06m18s

Total — 2448 Jan 06
Saros 158 — 17:57 TD
D.Node
ΔT= 967s — Alt. = 60°
Gam. = -0.4990 — Dur. = 02m51s

Annular — 2448 Jul 01
Saros 163 — 11:10 TD
A.Node
ΔT= 969s — Alt. = 21°
Gam. = 0.9316 — Dur. = 02m26s

Partial — 2448 Dec 26
Saros 168 — 07:11 TD
D.Node
ΔT= 971s — Alt. = 0°
Gam. = -1.2190 — Mag. = 0.5919

Total — 2449 May 22
Saros 135 — 10:19 TD
A.Node
ΔT= 972s — Alt. = 11°
Gam. = -0.9790 — Dur. = 02m24s

Plate 189

283

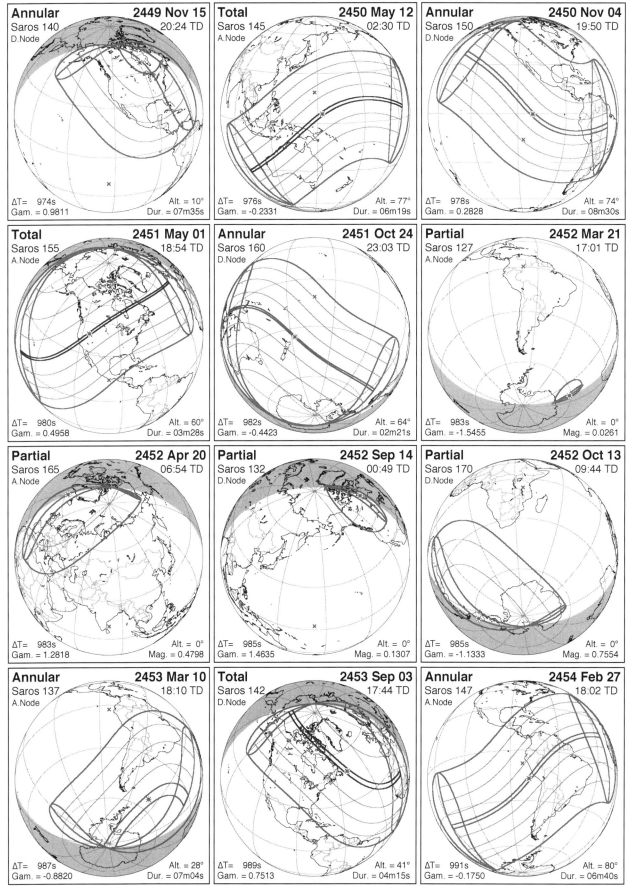

Annular	2449 Nov 15
Saros 140	20:24 TD
D.Node	
ΔT= 974s	Alt. = 10°
Gam. = 0.9811	Dur. = 07m35s

Total	2450 May 12
Saros 145	02:30 TD
A.Node	
ΔT= 976s	Alt. = 77°
Gam. = -0.2331	Dur. = 06m19s

Annular	2450 Nov 04
Saros 150	19:50 TD
D.Node	
ΔT= 978s	Alt. = 74°
Gam. = 0.2828	Dur. = 08m30s

Total	2451 May 01
Saros 155	18:54 TD
A.Node	
ΔT= 980s	Alt. = 60°
Gam. = 0.4958	Dur. = 03m28s

Annular	2451 Oct 24
Saros 160	23:03 TD
D.Node	
ΔT= 982s	Alt. = 64°
Gam. = -0.4423	Dur. = 02m21s

Partial	2452 Mar 21
Saros 127	17:01 TD
A.Node	
ΔT= 983s	Alt. = 0°
Gam. = -1.5455	Mag. = 0.0261

Partial	2452 Apr 20
Saros 165	06:54 TD
A.Node	
ΔT= 983s	Alt. = 0°
Gam. = 1.2818	Mag. = 0.4798

Partial	2452 Sep 14
Saros 132	00:49 TD
D.Node	
ΔT= 985s	Alt. = 0°
Gam. = 1.4635	Mag. = 0.1307

Partial	2452 Oct 13
Saros 170	09:44 TD
D.Node	
ΔT= 985s	Alt. = 0°
Gam. = -1.1333	Mag. = 0.7554

Annular	2453 Mar 10
Saros 137	18:10 TD
A.Node	
ΔT= 987s	Alt. = 28°
Gam. = -0.8820	Dur. = 07m04s

Total	2453 Sep 03
Saros 142	17:44 TD
D.Node	
ΔT= 989s	Alt. = 41°
Gam. = 0.7513	Dur. = 04m15s

Annular	2454 Feb 27
Saros 147	18:02 TD
A.Node	
ΔT= 991s	Alt. = 80°
Gam. = -0.1750	Dur. = 06m40s

Plate 190

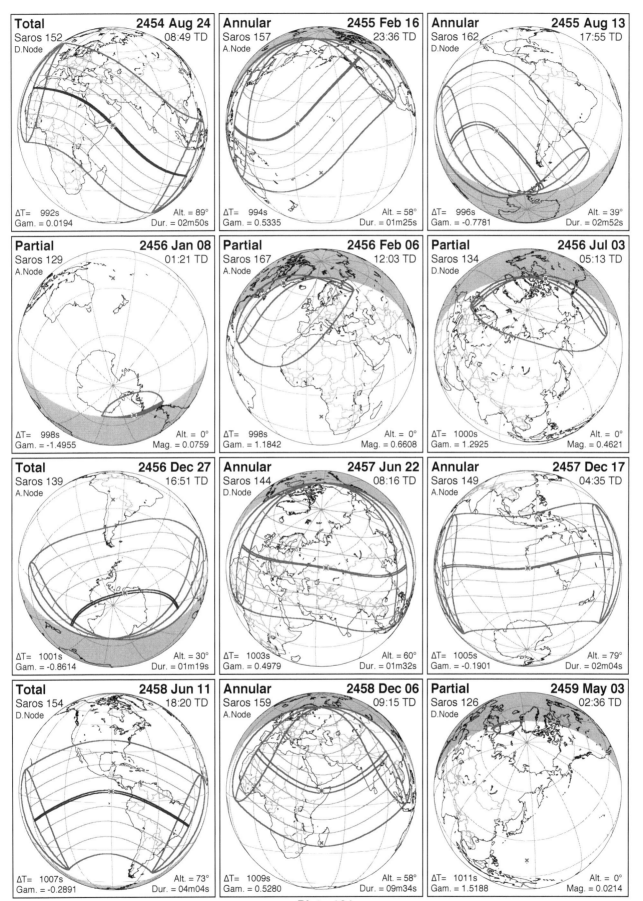

Total 2454 Aug 24	
Saros 152 08:49 TD	
D.Node	
ΔT= 992s Alt. = 89°	
Gam. = 0.0194 Dur. = 02m50s	

Annular 2455 Feb 16
Saros 157 23:36 TD
A.Node
ΔT= 994s Alt. = 58°
Gam. = 0.5335 Dur. = 01m25s

Annular 2455 Aug 13
Saros 162 17:55 TD
D.Node
ΔT= 996s Alt. = 39°
Gam. = -0.7781 Dur. = 02m52s

Partial 2456 Jan 08
Saros 129 01:21 TD
A.Node
ΔT= 998s Alt. = 0°
Gam. = -1.4955 Mag. = 0.0759

Partial 2456 Feb 06
Saros 167 12:03 TD
A.Node
ΔT= 998s Alt. = 0°
Gam. = 1.1842 Mag. = 0.6608

Partial 2456 Jul 03
Saros 134 05:13 TD
D.Node
ΔT= 1000s Alt. = 0°
Gam. = 1.2925 Mag. = 0.4621

Total 2456 Dec 27
Saros 139 16:51 TD
A.Node
ΔT= 1001s Alt. = 30°
Gam. = -0.8614 Dur. = 01m19s

Annular 2457 Jun 22
Saros 144 08:16 TD
D.Node
ΔT= 1003s Alt. = 60°
Gam. = 0.4979 Dur. = 01m32s

Annular 2457 Dec 17
Saros 149 04:35 TD
A.Node
ΔT= 1005s Alt. = 79°
Gam. = -0.1901 Dur. = 02m04s

Total 2458 Jun 11
Saros 154 18:20 TD
D.Node
ΔT= 1007s Alt. = 73°
Gam. = -0.2891 Dur. = 04m04s

Annular 2458 Dec 06
Saros 159 09:15 TD
A.Node
ΔT= 1009s Alt. = 58°
Gam. = 0.5280 Dur. = 09m34s

Partial 2459 May 03
Saros 126 02:36 TD
D.Node
ΔT= 1011s Alt. = 0°
Gam. = 1.5188 Mag. = 0.0214

Plate 191

285

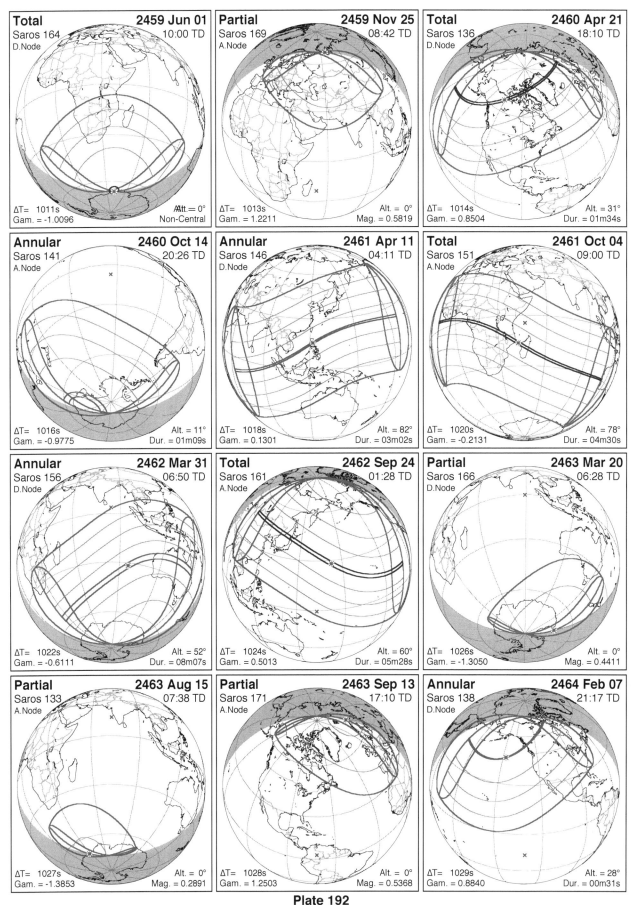

Total 2459 Jun 01 Saros 164 10:00 TD D.Node ΔT= 1011s Alt.= 0° Gam. = -1.0096 Non-Central	**Partial** 2459 Nov 25 Saros 169 08:42 TD A.Node ΔT= 1013s Alt. = 0° Gam. = 1.2211 Mag. = 0.5819	**Total** 2460 Apr 21 Saros 136 18:10 TD D.Node ΔT= 1014s Alt. = 31° Gam. = 0.8504 Dur. = 01m34s
Annular 2460 Oct 14 Saros 141 20:26 TD A.Node ΔT= 1016s Alt. = 11° Gam. = -0.9775 Dur. = 01m09s	**Annular** 2461 Apr 11 Saros 146 04:11 TD D.Node ΔT= 1018s Alt. = 82° Gam. = 0.1301 Dur. = 03m02s	**Total** 2461 Oct 04 Saros 151 09:00 TD A.Node ΔT= 1020s Alt. = 78° Gam. = -0.2131 Dur. = 04m30s
Annular 2462 Mar 31 Saros 156 06:50 TD D.Node ΔT= 1022s Alt. = 52° Gam. = -0.6111 Dur. = 08m07s	**Total** 2462 Sep 24 Saros 161 01:28 TD A.Node ΔT= 1024s Alt. = 60° Gam. = 0.5013 Dur. = 05m28s	**Partial** 2463 Mar 20 Saros 166 06:28 TD D.Node ΔT= 1026s Alt. = 0° Gam. = -1.3050 Mag. = 0.4411
Partial 2463 Aug 15 Saros 133 07:38 TD A.Node ΔT= 1027s Alt. = 0° Gam. = -1.3853 Mag. = 0.2891	**Partial** 2463 Sep 13 Saros 171 17:10 TD A.Node ΔT= 1028s Alt. = 0° Gam. = 1.2503 Mag. = 0.5368	**Annular** 2464 Feb 07 Saros 138 21:17 TD D.Node ΔT= 1029s Alt. = 28° Gam. = 0.8840 Dur. = 00m31s

Plate 192

286

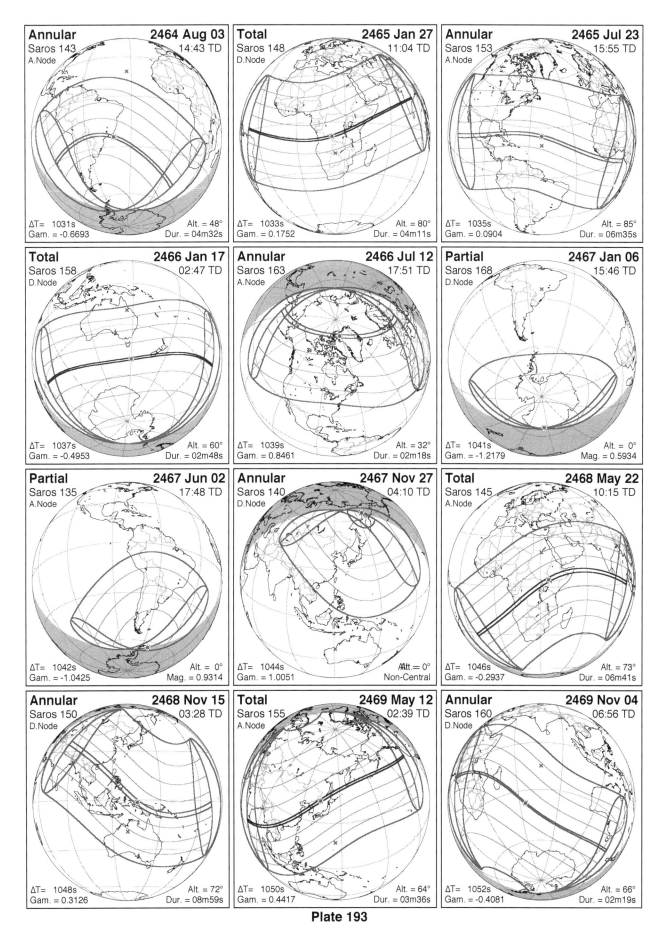

Annular | 2464 Aug 03
Saros 143 | 14:43 TD
A.Node
ΔT= 1031s | Alt. = 48°
Gam. = -0.6693 | Dur. = 04m32s

Total | 2465 Jan 27
Saros 148 | 11:04 TD
D.Node
ΔT= 1033s | Alt. = 80°
Gam. = 0.1752 | Dur. = 04m11s

Annular | 2465 Jul 23
Saros 153 | 15:55 TD
A.Node
ΔT= 1035s | Alt. = 85°
Gam. = 0.0904 | Dur. = 06m35s

Total | 2466 Jan 17
Saros 158 | 02:47 TD
D.Node
ΔT= 1037s | Alt. = 60°
Gam. = -0.4953 | Dur. = 02m48s

Annular | 2466 Jul 12
Saros 163 | 17:51 TD
A.Node
ΔT= 1039s | Alt. = 32°
Gam. = 0.8461 | Dur. = 02m18s

Partial | 2467 Jan 06
Saros 168 | 15:46 TD
D.Node
ΔT= 1041s | Alt. = 0°
Gam. = -1.2179 | Mag. = 0.5934

Partial | 2467 Jun 02
Saros 135 | 17:48 TD
A.Node
ΔT= 1042s | Alt. = 0°
Gam. = -1.0425 | Mag. = 0.9314

Annular | 2467 Nov 27
Saros 140 | 04:10 TD
D.Node
ΔT= 1044s | Alt.= 0°
Gam. = 1.0051 | Non-Central

Total | 2468 May 22
Saros 145 | 10:15 TD
A.Node
ΔT= 1046s | Alt. = 73°
Gam. = -0.2937 | Dur. = 06m41s

Annular | 2468 Nov 15
Saros 150 | 03:28 TD
D.Node
ΔT= 1048s | Alt. = 72°
Gam. = 0.3126 | Dur. = 08m59s

Total | 2469 May 12
Saros 155 | 02:39 TD
A.Node
ΔT= 1050s | Alt. = 64°
Gam. = 0.4417 | Dur. = 03m36s

Annular | 2469 Nov 04
Saros 160 | 06:56 TD
D.Node
ΔT= 1052s | Alt. = 66°
Gam. = -0.4081 | Dur. = 02m19s

Plate 193

287

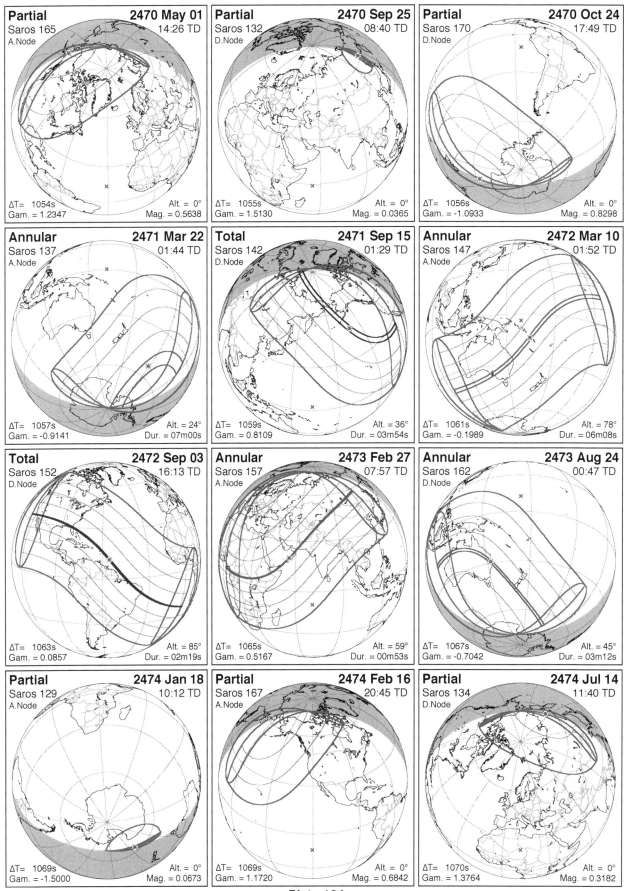

Partial	2470 May 01
Saros 165	14:26 TD
A.Node	
ΔT= 1054s	Alt. = 0°
Gam. = 1.2347	Mag. = 0.5638

Partial	2470 Sep 25
Saros 132	08:40 TD
D.Node	
ΔT= 1055s	Alt. = 0°
Gam. = 1.5130	Mag. = 0.0365

Partial	2470 Oct 24
Saros 170	17:49 TD
D.Node	
ΔT= 1056s	Alt. = 0°
Gam. = -1.0933	Mag. = 0.8298

Annular	2471 Mar 22
Saros 137	01:44 TD
A.Node	
ΔT= 1057s	Alt. = 24°
Gam. = -0.9141	Dur. = 07m00s

Total	2471 Sep 15
Saros 142	01:29 TD
D.Node	
ΔT= 1059s	Alt. = 36°
Gam. = 0.8109	Dur. = 03m54s

Annular	2472 Mar 10
Saros 147	01:52 TD
A.Node	
ΔT= 1061s	Alt. = 78°
Gam. = -0.1989	Dur. = 06m08s

Total	2472 Sep 03
Saros 152	16:13 TD
D.Node	
ΔT= 1063s	Alt. = 85°
Gam. = 0.0857	Dur. = 02m19s

Annular	2473 Feb 27
Saros 157	07:57 TD
A.Node	
ΔT= 1065s	Alt. = 59°
Gam. = 0.5167	Dur. = 00m53s

Annular	2473 Aug 24
Saros 162	00:47 TD
D.Node	
ΔT= 1067s	Alt. = 45°
Gam. = -0.7042	Dur. = 03m12s

Partial	2474 Jan 18
Saros 129	10:12 TD
A.Node	
ΔT= 1069s	Alt. = 0°
Gam. = -1.5000	Mag. = 0.0673

Partial	2474 Feb 16
Saros 167	20:45 TD
A.Node	
ΔT= 1069s	Alt. = 0°
Gam. = 1.1720	Mag. = 0.6842

Partial	2474 Jul 14
Saros 134	11:40 TD
D.Node	
ΔT= 1070s	Alt. = 0°
Gam. = 1.3764	Mag. = 0.3182

Plate 194

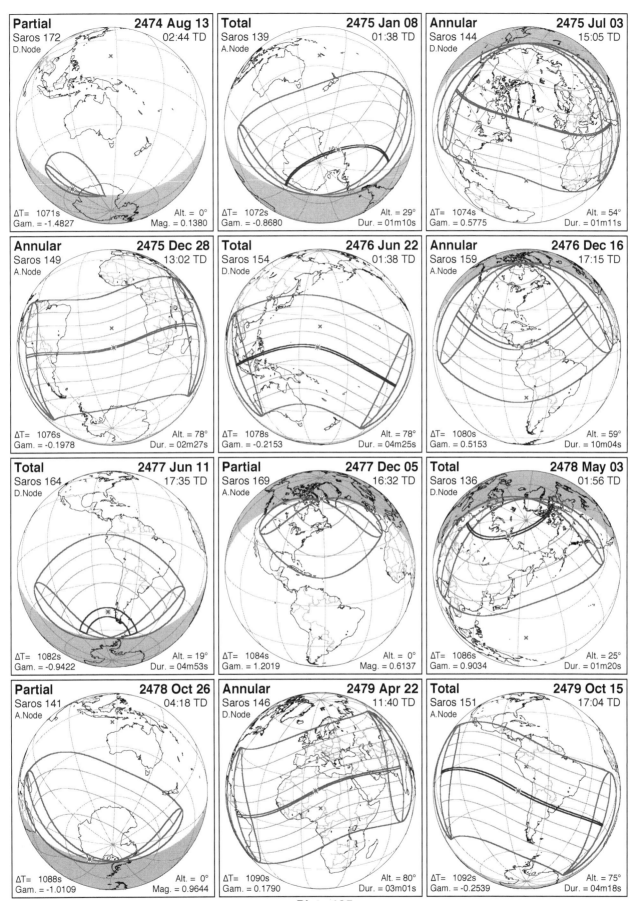

Partial **2474 Aug 13**	**Total** **2475 Jan 08**	**Annular** **2475 Jul 03**
Saros 172 02:44 TD	Saros 139 01:38 TD	Saros 144 15:05 TD
D.Node	A.Node	D.Node
ΔT= 1071s Alt. = 0°	ΔT= 1072s Alt. = 29°	ΔT= 1074s Alt. = 54°
Gam. = -1.4827 Mag. = 0.1380	Gam. = -0.8680 Dur. = 01m10s	Gam. = 0.5775 Dur. = 01m11s
Annular **2475 Dec 28**	**Total** **2476 Jun 22**	**Annular** **2476 Dec 16**
Saros 149 13:02 TD	Saros 154 01:38 TD	Saros 159 17:15 TD
A.Node	D.Node	A.Node
ΔT= 1076s Alt. = 78°	ΔT= 1078s Alt. = 78°	ΔT= 1080s Alt. = 59°
Gam. = -0.1978 Dur. = 02m27s	Gam. = -0.2153 Dur. = 04m25s	Gam. = 0.5153 Dur. = 10m04s
Total **2477 Jun 11**	**Partial** **2477 Dec 05**	**Total** **2478 May 03**
Saros 164 17:35 TD	Saros 169 16:32 TD	Saros 136 01:56 TD
D.Node	A.Node	D.Node
ΔT= 1082s Alt. = 19°	ΔT= 1084s Alt. = 0°	ΔT= 1086s Alt. = 25°
Gam. = -0.9422 Dur. = 04m53s	Gam. = 1.2019 Mag. = 0.6137	Gam. = 0.9034 Dur. = 01m20s
Partial **2478 Oct 26**	**Annular** **2479 Apr 22**	**Total** **2479 Oct 15**
Saros 141 04:18 TD	Saros 146 11:40 TD	Saros 151 17:04 TD
A.Node	D.Node	A.Node
ΔT= 1088s Alt. = 0°	ΔT= 1090s Alt. = 80°	ΔT= 1092s Alt. = 75°
Gam. = -1.0109 Mag. = 0.9644	Gam. = 0.1790 Dur. = 03m01s	Gam. = -0.2539 Dur. = 04m18s

Plate 195

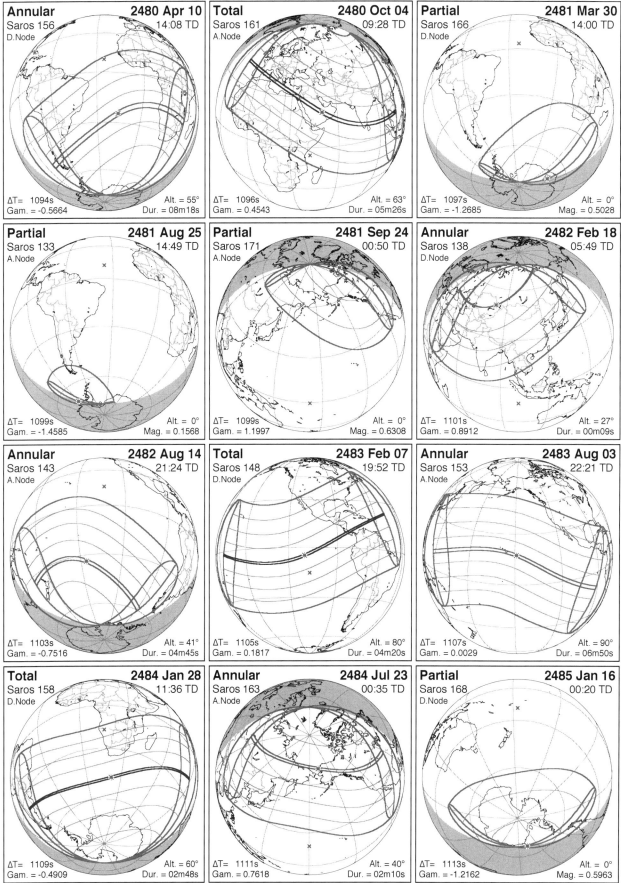

Annular	2480 Apr 10
Saros 156	14:08 TD
D.Node	
ΔT= 1094s	Alt. = 55°
Gam. = -0.5664	Dur. = 08m18s

Total	2480 Oct 04
Saros 161	09:28 TD
A.Node	
ΔT= 1096s	Alt. = 63°
Gam. = 0.4543	Dur. = 05m26s

Partial	2481 Mar 30
Saros 166	14:00 TD
D.Node	
ΔT= 1097s	Alt. = 0°
Gam. = -1.2685	Mag. = 0.5028

Partial	2481 Aug 25
Saros 133	14:49 TD
A.Node	
ΔT= 1099s	Alt. = 0°
Gam. = -1.4585	Mag. = 0.1568

Partial	2481 Sep 24
Saros 171	00:50 TD
A.Node	
ΔT= 1099s	Alt. = 0°
Gam. = 1.1997	Mag. = 0.6308

Annular	2482 Feb 18
Saros 138	05:49 TD
D.Node	
ΔT= 1101s	Alt. = 27°
Gam. = 0.8912	Dur. = 00m09s

Annular	2482 Aug 14
Saros 143	21:24 TD
A.Node	
ΔT= 1103s	Alt. = 41°
Gam. = -0.7516	Dur. = 04m45s

Total	2483 Feb 07
Saros 148	19:52 TD
D.Node	
ΔT= 1105s	Alt. = 80°
Gam. = 0.1817	Dur. = 04m20s

Annular	2483 Aug 03
Saros 153	22:21 TD
A.Node	
ΔT= 1107s	Alt. = 90°
Gam. = 0.0029	Dur. = 06m50s

Total	2484 Jan 28
Saros 158	11:36 TD
D.Node	
ΔT= 1109s	Alt. = 60°
Gam. = -0.4909	Dur. = 02m48s

Annular	2484 Jul 23
Saros 163	00:35 TD
A.Node	
ΔT= 1111s	Alt. = 40°
Gam. = 0.7618	Dur. = 02m10s

Partial	2485 Jan 16
Saros 168	00:20 TD
D.Node	
ΔT= 1113s	Alt. = 0°
Gam. = -1.2162	Mag. = 0.5963

Plate 196

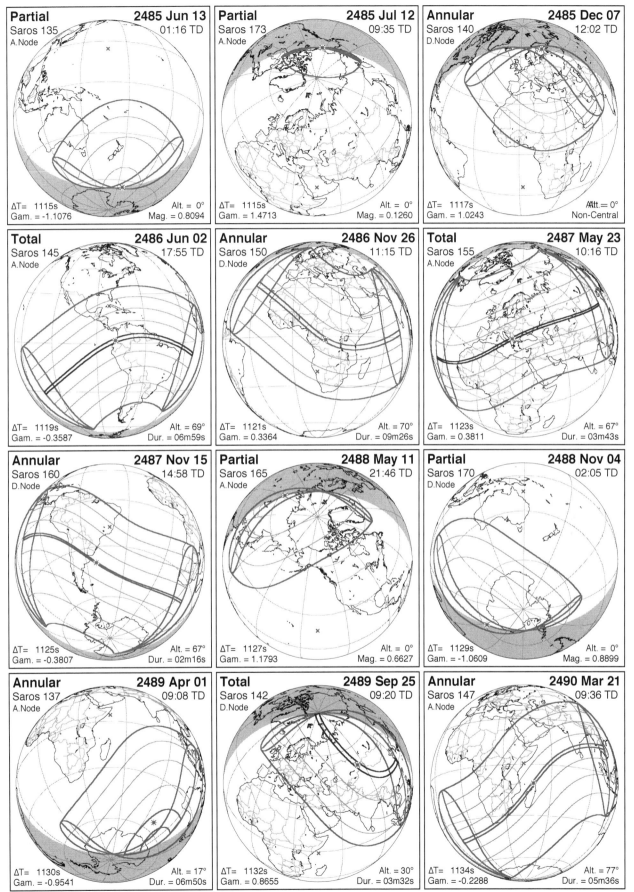

Partial — 2485 Jun 13	**Partial** — 2485 Jul 12	**Annular** — 2485 Dec 07
Saros 135 — 01:16 TD	Saros 173 — 09:35 TD	Saros 140 — 12:02 TD
A.Node	A.Node	D.Node
ΔT= 1115s — Alt. = 0°	ΔT= 1115s — Alt. = 0°	ΔT= 1117s — Alt.= 0°
Gam. = -1.1076 — Mag. = 0.8094	Gam. = 1.4713 — Mag. = 0.1260	Gam. = 1.0243 — Non-Central
Total — 2486 Jun 02	**Annular** — 2486 Nov 26	**Total** — 2487 May 23
Saros 145 — 17:55 TD	Saros 150 — 11:15 TD	Saros 155 — 10:16 TD
A.Node	D.Node	A.Node
ΔT= 1119s — Alt. = 69°	ΔT= 1121s — Alt. = 70°	ΔT= 1123s — Alt. = 67°
Gam. = -0.3587 — Dur. = 06m59s	Gam. = 0.3364 — Dur. = 09m26s	Gam. = 0.3811 — Dur. = 03m43s
Annular — 2487 Nov 15	**Partial** — 2488 May 11	**Partial** — 2488 Nov 04
Saros 160 — 14:58 TD	Saros 165 — 21:46 TD	Saros 170 — 02:05 TD
D.Node	A.Node	D.Node
ΔT= 1125s — Alt. = 67°	ΔT= 1127s — Alt. = 0°	ΔT= 1129s — Alt. = 0°
Gam. = -0.3807 — Dur. = 02m16s	Gam. = 1.1793 — Mag. = 0.6627	Gam. = -1.0609 — Mag. = 0.8899
Annular — 2489 Apr 01	**Total** — 2489 Sep 25	**Annular** — 2490 Mar 21
Saros 137 — 09:08 TD	Saros 142 — 09:20 TD	Saros 147 — 09:36 TD
A.Node	D.Node	A.Node
ΔT= 1130s — Alt. = 17°	ΔT= 1132s — Alt. = 30°	ΔT= 1134s — Alt. = 77°
Gam. = -0.9541 — Dur. = 06m50s	Gam. = 0.8655 — Dur. = 03m32s	Gam. = -0.2288 — Dur. = 05m36s

Plate 197

291

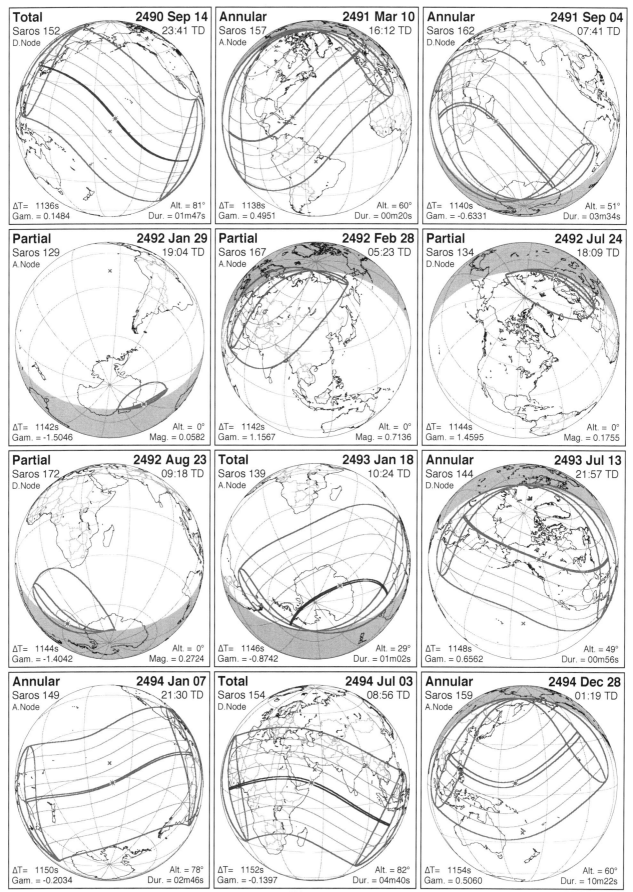

Total   **2490 Sep 14**
Saros 152   23:41 TD
D.Node
ΔT= 1136s   Alt. = 81°
Gam. = 0.1484   Dur. = 01m47s

Annular   **2491 Mar 10**
Saros 157   16:12 TD
A.Node
ΔT= 1138s   Alt. = 60°
Gam. = 0.4951   Dur. = 00m20s

Annular   **2491 Sep 04**
Saros 162   07:41 TD
D.Node
ΔT= 1140s   Alt. = 51°
Gam. = -0.6331   Dur. = 03m34s

Partial   **2492 Jan 29**
Saros 129   19:04 TD
A.Node
ΔT= 1142s   Alt. = 0°
Gam. = -1.5046   Mag. = 0.0582

Partial   **2492 Feb 28**
Saros 167   05:23 TD
A.Node
ΔT= 1142s   Alt. = 0°
Gam. = 1.1567   Mag. = 0.7136

Partial   **2492 Jul 24**
Saros 134   18:09 TD
D.Node
ΔT= 1144s   Alt. = 0°
Gam. = 1.4595   Mag. = 0.1755

Partial   **2492 Aug 23**
Saros 172   09:18 TD
D.Node
ΔT= 1144s   Alt. = 0°
Gam. = -1.4042   Mag. = 0.2724

Total   **2493 Jan 18**
Saros 139   10:24 TD
A.Node
ΔT= 1146s   Alt. = 29°
Gam. = -0.8742   Dur. = 01m02s

Annular   **2493 Jul 13**
Saros 144   21:57 TD
D.Node
ΔT= 1148s   Alt. = 49°
Gam. = 0.6562   Dur. = 00m56s

Annular   **2494 Jan 07**
Saros 149   21:30 TD
A.Node
ΔT= 1150s   Alt. = 78°
Gam. = -0.2034   Dur. = 02m46s

Total   **2494 Jul 03**
Saros 154   08:56 TD
D.Node
ΔT= 1152s   Alt. = 82°
Gam. = -0.1397   Dur. = 04m40s

Annular   **2494 Dec 28**
Saros 159   01:19 TD
A.Node
ΔT= 1154s   Alt. = 60°
Gam. = 0.5060   Dur. = 10m22s

Plate 198

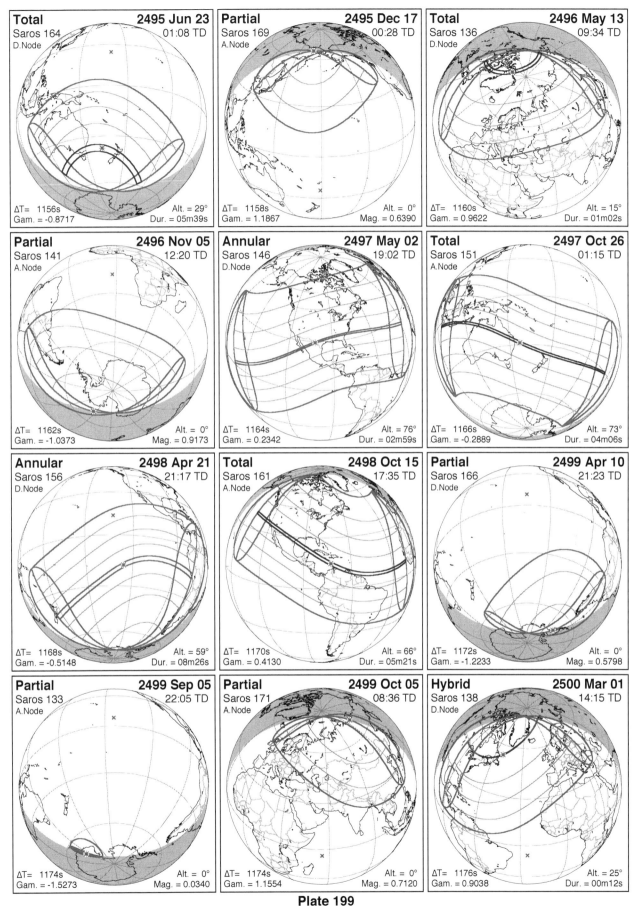

Total	**2495 Jun 23**
Saros 164	01:08 TD
D.Node	
ΔT= 1156s	Alt. = 29°
Gam. = -0.8717	Dur. = 05m39s

Partial	**2495 Dec 17**
Saros 169	00:28 TD
A.Node	
ΔT= 1158s	Alt. = 0°
Gam. = 1.1867	Mag. = 0.6390

Total	**2496 May 13**
Saros 136	09:34 TD
D.Node	
ΔT= 1160s	Alt. = 15°
Gam. = 0.9622	Dur. = 01m02s

Partial	**2496 Nov 05**
Saros 141	12:20 TD
A.Node	
ΔT= 1162s	Alt. = 0°
Gam. = -1.0373	Mag. = 0.9173

Annular	**2497 May 02**
Saros 146	19:02 TD
D.Node	
ΔT= 1164s	Alt. = 76°
Gam. = 0.2342	Dur. = 02m59s

Total	**2497 Oct 26**
Saros 151	01:15 TD
A.Node	
ΔT= 1166s	Alt. = 73°
Gam. = -0.2889	Dur. = 04m06s

Annular	**2498 Apr 21**
Saros 156	21:17 TD
D.Node	
ΔT= 1168s	Alt. = 59°
Gam. = -0.5148	Dur. = 08m26s

Total	**2498 Oct 15**
Saros 161	17:35 TD
A.Node	
ΔT= 1170s	Alt. = 66°
Gam. = 0.4130	Dur. = 05m21s

Partial	**2499 Apr 10**
Saros 166	21:23 TD
D.Node	
ΔT= 1172s	Alt. = 0°
Gam. = -1.2233	Mag. = 0.5798

Partial	**2499 Sep 05**
Saros 133	22:05 TD
A.Node	
ΔT= 1174s	Alt. = 0°
Gam. = -1.5273	Mag. = 0.0340

Partial	**2499 Oct 05**
Saros 171	08:36 TD
A.Node	
ΔT= 1174s	Alt. = 0°
Gam. = 1.1554	Mag. = 0.7120

Hybrid	**2500 Mar 01**
Saros 138	14:15 TD
D.Node	
ΔT= 1176s	Alt. = 25°
Gam. = 0.9038	Dur. = 00m12s

Plate 199

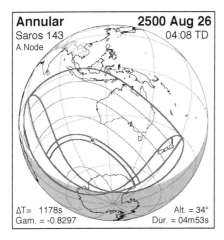

Annular	2500 Aug 26
Saros 143	04:08 TD
A.Node	

ΔT= 1178s	Alt. = 34°
Gam. = -0.8297	Dur. = 04m53s

Plate 200

Printed in Great Britain
by Amazon.co.uk, Ltd.,
Marston Gate.